To Ian and Mary
with love and best wishes from
Peter.

15. VIIj. 97

SO THAT WAS LIFE

A Biography of Sir Geoffrey Jefferson
Kt CBE FRS MS FRCS
(1886–1961)
Master of the Neurosciences and Man of Letters

Peter H Schurr
CBE MA MB BChir FRCS

*'Tis opportune to look back upon old times
and contemplate our Forefathers.
Great examples grow thin,
and to be fetched from the past world'.*

Sir Thomas Browne (1605–1682)

©1997 Royal Society of Medicine Press Limited
1 Wimpole Street, London W1M 8AE, UK
16 East 69th Street, New York NY 10021, USA

British Library Cataloguing in Publication Data
A catalogue record for this book is available from the British Library
ISBN 1-85315-305-2
Typeset by Dobbie Typesetting Limited, Tavistock, Devon
Printed in Great Britain by Ebenezer Baylis, The Trinity Press, Worcester

Contents

Preface

When Antony Jefferson asked me to write a biography of his remarkable father, not only did I feel honoured by the suggestion, for Sir Geoffrey was the founder of my own branch of surgery in Britain after the First World War and pre-eminent in his field, but I also felt an obligation to record his achievements alongside those of the other two pioneer British neurosurgeons in this century, Hugh Cairns and Norman Dott, whose biographies had already been written.

I did not then know that Lady Jefferson had kept almost all the letters that he wrote to her, from the time that they first met; nor did I know, though I could have suspected, that his friends would have done the same. In his turn, Jefferson kept many letters that he received, including a large number from the great American neurosurgeon, Harvey Cushing, none of which had been published. This archive, together with many manuscripts of personal notes, drafts of his lectures, his published writings and what he called his 'meditations', have formed the basis of this book. They have enabled me to allow Sir Geoffrey to tell much of the story in his own words.

Jefferson was considered by Harvey Cushing 'as having one of the most searching and original minds in British medicine'[1]. Furthermore, he had a presence which gave him the centre stage of almost any situation, almost as if he were royalty, and people came from afar to hear what he had to say and then remembered it. His character had many aspects, and in writing about him my aim has been, in his own words, to get the 'dosage of good and imperfect right', avoiding 'too much adulation'[2].

It would not have been possible to complete my task without the kindness and considerable help given to me by Michael Jefferson, whose family recollections were an essential source, and Antony Jefferson who gave me unique archive material and much encouragement; both have filled in details that could have come from no other source, and I cannot thank them enough. There have also been many others who have helped by lending their letters, particularly Dr Harry Botterell of Kingston, Ontario, Dr William H Sweet of Boston, Mass. and Dr Norman Guthkelch of Cambridge, Mass. But they were not alone, and my gratitude is profound to those who spared the time to talk or write about this surgeon-professor-philosopher, who never met anyone without leaving an indelible memory behind him. If I have had to reduce my acknowledgements to them to minimal proportions, it is only because of their number and the impossibility of apportioning the extent of their contributions; my indebtedness and my thanks to them are considerable.

The justification for this book had already been provided by its subject himself. He wrote that: 'The records of the lives of others, whether they fail or succeed, will always have a great appeal and value, and one cannot but enlarge one's outlook and strengthen one's grip on the reins of life by reading of conquest or defeat. So long as a man has accomplished something, it is enough'[3]. Jefferson's accomplishments were magnificent and many still remain as his memorial.

Peter H Schurr
Brook House, Ufford
January 1997

1   Fulton J. *Harvey Cushing, a biography.* Oxford: Blackwell Scientific Publications, 1946: 681.
2   Jefferson G to Fulton J. Letter 12th April 1944.
3   Jefferson G to Flumerfelt G. Letter 14th August 1912.

Acknowledgements

My thanks have already been expressed to Michael and Antony Jefferson and to Drs Botterell, Guthkelch and Sweet for the loan of letters and help in various ways. However there have been many other kind people who have given their time and knowledge, or who have passed on memories which have been invaluable to me. The following list, in alphabetical order, contains the names of most of those who have made such contributions; if there are others whose names I have omitted, may I please be forgiven. To them all I give my sincere gratitude and thanks.

Mair Andrade, Betty and Michael Appleby, the Archivists of Canadian Pacific Ships, Charing Cross Hospital, King's College-London, Lancashire Records Office, Manchester Grammar School, Manchester Medical Society, Manchester Royal Infirmary, Parish of SS. James and Emmanuel in Didsbury, Royal Academy of Arts, Royal Free Hospital and the Tate Gallery. Elizabeth Balmer, Joan Charleton, J S Cookson, The Design and Copyright Artists' Society, Lady Flowers, Michael Harmer, Bernard Harries, Raymond Hierons, Ian Isherwood, Mary Janes, Eirlys Jefferson, (the late) Richard Johnson, W Kuchinsky, (the late) Pauline Leech and Denis Leigh. The Librarians of Hounslow Library, Jefferson Memorial Library, Lambeth Palace Library, National Army Museum Library, Rochdale Library, Royal Army Medical Corps Museum Library, Royal College of Surgeons, Royal Society of Medicine, John Rylands University Library of Manchester University, St Thomas' Hospital Medical Library and York County Library. Pamela Priest, Ruth Martin, Jane Merchant, Pauline Monro, Robert Murray, Dame Kathleen Ollerenshaw, Irina Safronova, Merton Sandler, Anthony Strong, Kenneth Till, Roger Turner and George Udvarhelyi.

My special thanks are due also to Tricia Dixon for seeing the book through all the intricacies of publication.

List of Illustrations

Photographs are from the Jefferson family archive except where otherwise mentioned.

Sir Geoffrey Jefferson
Kt CBE FRS MS FRCS
1886–1961

Chapter 1

An introduction to Sir Geoffrey Jefferson 1886–1961

Sir Geoffrey Jefferson was one of the most famous neurosurgeons of his time yet, in many ways, he did not fit the stereotype of a successful specialist. More than 30 years after his death in 1961, he is still remembered as much for his literary ability and personality as for his surgical achievements. He was essentially a Victorian but one who found himself working in the first half of the twentieth century; in fact he was already 14 years old in 1900, when neurosurgery existed only as a particular interest of a very few surgeons. The great American pioneer, Harvey Cushing, was then touring Europe to gain what experience he could before starting to practise neurosurgery on his own, and he was the first to do so to the exclusion of all other work. As a consequence, by the time Jefferson himself became qualified the specialty was still in its infancy, so he was inevitably at the forefront becoming, on his own admission, a self-taught neurological surgeon, and proud of it. His self-instruction, nevertheless, owed much to the successes and failures of others as well as to his ability to analyse and build on whatever material was available. He was honoured by his country and by universities and societies everywhere; distinctions which he thoroughly deserved and which he thoroughly enjoyed. He was ambitious and, unlike the fortunes of the majority, most of his ambitions were achieved. His humorous, affectionate and kindly qualities were appreciated by all who knew him, as too was his wisdom, born of experience and a considerable amount of reading. It is, however, in the light of his position as the father of the present era of neurosurgery in the United Kingdom that this study has been undertaken.

The very early foundations of British neurosurgery were laid towards the end of the last century by Sir Victor Horsley in England and Sir William Macewen in Scotland. There were others on the continent of Europe who worked in the field, but it was in the United States that neurosurgery became a specialty in its own right. As has been mentioned, this was as a result of the inspiration of Harvey Cushing who established the discipline in Boston, USA, in the years preceding the First World War and in the decade after it. Cushing was the exemplar for a number of surgeons who saw the need for specialist neurosurgery in their own countries, several of whom went to him to learn their skills, either as members of his staff or as observers. Jefferson was in the vanguard of the stream of admirers from Europe who sought experience and learning from Harvey Cushing. He paid him a protracted visit as a privileged observer; it was the first of many meetings, and the two men became friends. Jefferson joined there his contemporary pioneer neurosurgeon from Great Britain, Norman Dott of Edinburgh, and was followed by Hugh Cairns from London, later of Oxford. But it was Jefferson, at Manchester, who initiated neurological surgery as a specialty in mainland Britain, while Adams McConnell developed it in Ireland. In an after-dinner speech that Jefferson made in Dublin in 1952, he himself said 'Neurosurgery in these islands was really founded by Mac and myself'[1]. He was right.

What kind of man was Geoffrey Jefferson? It is perhaps fitting that we should meet him first in his maturity, so that those who did not know him personally can follow the emergence of a character which was undoubtedly complicated and was dominated by a determination to succeed. Not only did he want to be the greatest neurosurgeon of his day but he wished also to be remembered for his writings, on both medical and literary subjects, and for his ability to express his thoughts in words. He objected, however, to any of his work being called 'philosophical', *pace* various obituarists, and he referred to his essays in this vein as meditations or reflections. It has been said that every genius would like also to be remembered for something other than that for which he was most famous: an aphorism which Jefferson supremely exemplifies. He had a determination that became a guiding force and the ability to set aside many of the obstacles that life put in his way. It is not impossible that his desire for recognition and even for fame stemmed from a youthful ambition to show his parents what his capabilities really were. Throughout their lives, his relationship with them was difficult and he stood in awe of a demanding father. This was to some extent understandable in view of a school record that left much to be desired. Yet, even when he had justified himself to a superlative degree, he still felt that his parents did not really appreciate his achievements[2].

Before examining his childhood and parental background let us meet him in his consulting room at 3 Lorne Street, an unpretentious house in an unpretentious row of Victorian buildings behind the Royal Infirmary in Manchester, where he had his 'rooms' during the last years of his life. He preferred to be close to the hospital, within a few yards of his wards, to having a more prestigious address in the city for his private consultations.

It was rather awe-inspiring to be introduced to one who was the doyen of neurosurgery in his day, the founder of the Society of British Neurological Surgeons, and an international surgical neurologist. He would sit with his left arm resting limply on the side of his chair, his pen held in the other hand. As he looked up from his desk and the yellow paper on which he had been writing, an affectation acquired from Cushing, he would gaze over the top of his glasses, but not until he had finished the paragraph that was engaging his attention. When the glasses were removed those blue-grey eyes usually had a slight twinkle and there was a twinkle also in the smile that gave little away, but made one wonder what he was about to say. He was tall and would have been taller were it not for a slight stoop. His high forehead was accentuated by a receding hairline and his grey hair, being somewhat thin, followed the curvature of his head. His small moustache, so neatly trimmed, had been anticipated when he was about twenty-seven years old because he thought he looked 'so poisonously young'; he had then asked his fiancée to allow him to wear one 'if it doesn't look worse than the present state'[2]. However, several years were to elapse before it actually appeared. He usually wore a poorly-fitting grey suit. His waistcoat endeavoured to restrain the pressure on its buttons with mixed success, or if he happened not to have been wearing one, the tension fell upon a single thread or two of the upper fastening of his coat. His tie was a bit awry under his soft collar and fell nonchalantly where it could.

There was an appearance of comfortableness. A grey trilby hat and a mackintosh might be seen lying nearby.

Sir Geoffrey spoke in a slightly high-pitched voice 'in the same calm leisurely way in which he did his work. Everyone listened to his quiet slow pronouncements because he never said anything that wasn't worth hearing and he never said it as anyone else would have said it. He had an extraordinary genius for giving a verbal picture... with the greatest economy'[3].... 'He did not seek to impress his listeners by the use of obscure phrases, but had a superb way of putting together in quite ordinary words a concept of people or affairs that was quite original'[4]. His remarks were often witty for 'he never lost his sense of humour, delighting in the most absurd stories, the creases of his waistcoat rippling up and down with laughter'[3]. Nevertheless there were times when this might be replaced by sarcasm or a terse remark if he wished to express disapproval or dissatisfaction, which could sometimes be hurtful to the recipient. 'If he didn't approve he said so in no uncertain terms, [though] he was equally free with his praise when deserved.... His remarks were always made without malice — in addition they were usually phrased in that peculiarly Jeffersonian way which made them not only valuable but more often than not extremely amusing. He was full of tolerance for human frailty but he never expected [people] to behave badly, and... for that reason most of them didn't, at any rate when they were with him'[5].

Nearly everybody spoke of him as 'Jeff', an affectionate abbreviation of his surname and certainly nothing to do with the name Geoffrey but, of course, never when addressing him directly. He was also referred to as 'GJ'. Work was his ethos and in consequence of this his children saw him more as the commander of their early lives than as a warm and loving father, a pattern which he had inherited from his own background. It was a different matter where his wife was concerned. He held Gertrude in the most tender affection though, as time passed, he may have taken her too much for granted as his career came to take pride of place in his priorities. She responded to this by achievements of her own, for she was herself a very able and unusual person. From their first meeting she decided that he was the only man for her and, in spite of such difficulties as were to come, she remained close to him until his death, she herself dying only a fortnight after her husband. Like everybody else, she had learnt to live with his almost unbelievable lack of punctuality, not to mention his other foibles. Jeff was late for almost everything and always had been; it was a trait that he acquired from his parents. It was something for which most people remember him but for which he was always forgiven, however disconcerting it might have been at the time. This was the price that had to be paid for the pleasure of knowing him. One who suffered from his disregard of time more than most wrote: 'Any peculiarity of behaviour was the outcome of the urge of his creative destiny. This urge allowed of no weakness, no distractions and no concessions'[6].

As a purely technical surgeon Jefferson was not among the greatest of his day, and a colleague wrote: 'He was apt to boast that his writings on operative surgery were minimal; and for a good reason. In the brilliant Manchester school of Arthur Burgess, John Morley, Wilson Hey and Billy Douglas he could be classified as no more than adequate'.... but 'he was meticulous where the welfare of his patients was concerned'[6], and his compendious knowledge of anatomy and physiology ensured safety in his hands and an assurance that he would consider all sides of any question when decisions had to be taken. Surgery was for him an exercise in applied neuro-anatomy and neurophysiology from which there was always something to be discovered. He had no time for the (internal) medicine of his day, which was very often palliative and empirical, at least at the beginning of his career and as far as neurology was concerned. He was strongly attracted by the mysteries of the nervous system, but he wanted to heal and, if not to cure, then at least to alleviate the distress caused by its disorders. Neurology in its medical aspect did not offer sufficient prospect of either, so surgery it had to be.

Jeff also had a passion for literature, which expressed itself in a most catholic taste that spread from poetry to novels and from Aristotle to Descartes and beyond. He was encouraged by his wife, particularly in the early years of their acquaintance, for she had great powers of literary criticism and her comments on the books they read or shared together were a stimulus and an encouragement to Jeff. He loved to discuss books, art or music but found few kindred spirits with whom he could relate in this way. Among them, apart from his wife, were his friends from student days, Harry Platt and John Morley. He desperately wanted to write really well, and there is no doubt that Gertrude Jefferson's remarks and suggestions were welcomed when she read his work. For example, although the pilgrimage they made together when he was collecting material for a lecture on Descartes can now be viewed only from writings in Jeff's hand, he certainly would have owed much to her stimulation; the charming companion always faithfully and devotedly present in the background. Furthermore, 'he spoke as well as he wrote, which is unusual. One of his most engaging skills was the way he used asides or anecdotes as emphasis without tiresomely obscuring his argument or holding up the stream of his story. If you read his compositions carefully enough you may detect a technique of phraseology that was not far removed from that of Wilfred Trotter. He never divulged what that technique was, but it was there'[6]. Writing was both an occupation and a solace to Jeff. He never wasted an opportunity to put his thoughts on paper, whether waiting for several days in the hotel at Paddington Station before flying to America in 1943, or during periods of enforced idleness while in hospital during his relatively frequent periods of illness.

As a scientist, and he was accorded the honour of Fellowship of the Royal Society, a truly rare distinction among surgeons in this century, he wrote a number of papers that will be remembered. His observations on several subjects were quite original and, though much of his later writing was built upon the work of others, this is the usual manner of the evolution of knowledge in which he played an important part. His papers on intracranial pressure, on subarachnoid haemorrhage, on the pituitary gland, the trigeminal ganglion, on consciousness and many others come to mind. Even the titles of some of his 'meditations' are intriguing, such as *On being happy and liking it, The brain as an integrative mechanism, Meditations on sources of knowledge, A postscript to Aristotle* or *The mind of mechanical man*. In all there were about 130 papers or contributions to books; these included many eponymous lectures. It is noticeable that in by far the majority he was the sole author. This may show a slight reluctance to share his thoughts and publications with those who worked with him.

During the years in which he practised neurosurgery in Salford and Manchester, several future neurosurgeons spent part of their long training with Jeff, an experience always remembered with gratitude. But those whom he considered to be his very own trainees could be numbered on one hand. This may have been partly because the neurosurgical unit at the Manchester Royal Infirmary was not formed until late in his career, but it was also a product of his need to continue to practise some general surgery along with his specialty. That need arose partly on financial grounds but also on account of the resistance of most hospital Boards to the creation of specialized units. The aim of the training provided by Medical Schools at that time was to produce competent general practitioners, and it was thought that this could only be achieved if the physicians and surgeons who taught in them were also general exponents of their profession. Jefferson was convinced of the need for accurate clinical observation and meticulous history-taking, which took priority over investigative methods, however important these might be in the ultimate analysis. He was an early advocate of specialized neurosurgical units. Furthermore, Sir Geoffrey 'had all the characteristics of a great teacher, namely: lucidity of expression, freshness of outlook, intense concentration and enthusiasm'. 'His freshness of outlook and freedom from dogmatism was an important factor in his power of moulding the minds of those' whom he taught[7].

This chapter is not intended to be a resumé of Jefferson's life nor a précis of this book. It is simply an introduction to the man whose life and character unfold in the following pages. What has been said cannot convey the magnetism which made people travel many miles to hear him speak or to attend his 'rounds' or lectures; neither can one hear the chuckle and the pause that preceded a remark which could be purely humorous or might be an aphorism, a percipient comment or a statement to be remembered. However, 'there would be something lacking in a picture of Jeff that did not also depict his social glitter.... "As a visitor to one's home his presence permeated the house. Everyone felt the need to please him in some way, to remember some particular fancy—such as his taste for greengages. He assumed in some intangible manner the role of honorary great uncle..."[6].' In a word, he had what used to be called charm and this was a part of his charisma. He was a great man, who may have been a genius, or may possibly have fallen just short of it.

REFERENCES

1 Jefferson, Geoffrey. MS After dinner speech, Dublin, 11th July 1952.
2 Jefferson, Geoffrey. Letter to Gertrude Flumerfelt. ca 21st July 1913.
3 Brockbank W. *The honorary medical staff of the Manchester Royal Infirmary (1830–1948)*. Manchester: Manchester University Press, 1965: 222.
4 Platt R. *Annual address delivered to the Royal College of Physicians*. London: Royal College of Physicians, 1961: 24–5.
5 Bridge E to White JC. Letter 14th March 1961.
6 Rowbotham GF. In Memoriam, Geoffrey Jefferson. *Br J Surg* 1961; **48**: 586–8.
7 Hardman J. *Manchester University Medical Students' Gazette* 1946; **25**: 52–5.

Chapter 2

The family and home

'The trouble is that folk believe they are homogeneous, whilst they are not—we're all a mixture of our forebears in our genes, and goodness knows when that old rogue, great uncle Ned or great aunt Nellie is going to bob up in us!' Geoffrey himself wrote these thoughts in a letter to his friend, the bibliophile and physiologist John Fulton of Yale University[1].

For three generations before Geoffrey, the Jeffersons served in or were connected with the Royal Navy, and this influence extended as far as his own father's schooling. The earliest of these naval ancestors was colourful Francis Jefferson, brave and full of initiative. He was a midshipman on the 64 gun HMS *Greyhound* in 1799 under Captain William Bligh, previously associated with the mutiny on HMS *Bounty* and later to become Governor of New South Wales, an appointment which also ended in a mutiny. Francis served on several other vessels during his career and, notably, in the 1801 expedition to Egypt. In 1809, 3 months after the battle of Corunna, he was 1st Lieutenant on HMS *Cadmus* sailing off the coast of Spain. In an action there, off the northern shores, he captured a French brigantine from under their own batteries. He had taken command of a gun-boat at Vigo, and attacked two French batteries in company with three other boats manned by Spaniards. The latter retreated and Francis Jefferson ordered ball cartridges to be fired over their heads to compel them to return. The fight went on until the British had used all their cartridges, at which point Jefferson ordered the sailors to cut up their jackets, their shirts and their stockings to hold the gunpowder. He was mentioned in despatches after that action and, later in the same year, captured another brigantine in Quiberon Bay, north of the Bay of Biscay. In 1810 he captured five vessels in two actions but, when August came, he was invalided home on account of illness. One wonders what sort of illness it was, since it kept him on half pay for the next 15 years, at the end of which he was posted to Deptford as Agent for Transports Afloat. Finally, in 1836, he commanded Her Majesty's Yachts on Virginia Water near Windsor, an appointment somewhat less dangerous than his earlier service[2].

Geoffrey's grandfather, John Macready Jefferson, who was baptised (and probably born) in 1823, was one of Francis's six children. He wanted to join the Navy as his father had done, but was ineligible for active service because of poor eyesight. With characteristic determination however, he retained the naval connection by serving on land, becoming a Paymaster Captain and working in the Naval Pensions Office in Adam Street, Adelphi, London. In 1854 he married Mary Ann Whiting who had some form of royal duty to Queen Victoria at Windsor Castle. Sadly, he died of typhoid in 1873 in his early 40s, leaving his widow living at Hampton Hill, Middlesex.

Geoffrey Jefferson's own father was Arthur John, the eldest son of John Macready, and was born in London on 8th June 1857. His fair skin and features must have been very marked because, when in his 30s, he described his own 'ultra fair complexion' as having caused the younger native children of Manila in the Philippine Islands, 'to scamper frightened to their mothers'[3]. He had two brothers, Herbert and Frank, and a sister Ada. Ada Jefferson (Aunt Ada or AA) was to play an important part in Jeff's life. She was born in 1863 and married an estate agent named Frederick Parsons who was very deaf and had the military appearance and bearing of Sir Edward Elgar. He was always known as Colonel Parsons on account of his service with the 1st Volunteer Battalion, Royal Sussex Regiment, based in Brighton. He was first commissioned in 1877. He became a Major in 1898 and an Honorary Lieutenant-Colonel in the same year, retiring in 1902. They lived in Hove, which is so near to Brighton, in Sussex, as to be continuous with it. Geoffrey was fond of his aunt Ada and spent many childhood holidays with the Parsons, and the Sussex Downs and countryside were a source of happy memories. Aunt Ada became a warm correspondent of Geoffrey's wife over many years and the two women got on well together. Jeff's aunt and uncle were also very supportive to him when he was working in London and in the early years of his marriage. Ada had a distinguished, old-fashioned appearance, and wore a black ribbon round her neck with a small silver ornament, possibly a charm, attached. She was well educated, having been at a school with a naval connection, thus continuing the family tradition, even in the female line.

Without any doubt, however, the one person who had the most powerful formative influence on Geoffrey until he reached university was his father, Arthur John Jefferson. Arthur was educated at the Royal Naval School at New Cross, in London. Arthur Jefferson's career dictated the expectations he had of his sons and became a determining influence on both of their early lives, not the least for his decision not to follow his father and grandfather into the Royal Navy but to become a doctor.

Arthur Jefferson qualified from St Thomas' Hospital, London in 1880 as a Licentiate of the Society of Apothecaries (LSA) and of the Royal College of Physicians (LRCP). He also obtained the diploma of Membership of the Royal College of Surgeons (MRCS). It is not clear what his first appointments were, or what he did between 1880 and 1882, but we do know that he was never on the junior staff of St Thomas's. His address at that time was 4 Clarence Terrace, New Hampton, Middlesex (now in Hounslow).

Two years after he qualified Arthur Jefferson obtained a post at the York County Hospital, a move to the north of the country that was to have far reaching consequences on the future of the family. This hospital was founded in 1851 and was closed in 1976. Arthur was appointed house surgeon there in 1881, as recorded in the Annual Report for that year. His salary was £100 per annum with an allowance of eight guineas for wine. He was the only junior doctor on the staff, and therefore the only resident doctor, with responsibility for 150 beds. The visiting consultants consisted of two honorary physicians, one consulting surgeon and three honorary surgeons. The tremendous burden of work that he carried was reduced in 1884 when the House Committee appointed an additional assistant or Junior House Surgeon. This was in response to pressure from the physicians and surgeons and as a result of the expansion of the hospital. Arthur Jefferson was then called Senior House Surgeon. While he was there he published

Figure 1   *Dr Arthur Jefferson, Geoffrey Jefferson's father.*

at least three papers and continued to study for his doctorate of medicine. He was also very involved with a scheme for improvement of the drainage in the buildings, a subject that may have attracted him because of its association with the death of his father, apart from the obvious impact it would have had on at least one of the senses. On the 5th September 1882, he read a 'long and interesting report' on the hospital drainage system to the House Committee 'who asked him to join with a Mr Styan [possibly an engineer] in making recommendations'. In November the principles of the joint report were accepted and the improvements were carried out by a sanitary engineer 'with the advice and assistance of Mr Jefferson'[4].

On 19th August 1884, Arthur Jefferson was granted 6 weeks' leave of absence beginning in the first week of October, which he asked to be extended for a further week 'for exam purposes'; this was granted. He may have used time purely for study or he may have failed the examination at his first attempt, for he applied for a further 3 weeks' leave in June 1885, after which he passed the examination for the degree of Bachelor of Surgery of London University. There is no mention of the Bachelor of Medicine degree in the Medical Register of that time, though he later obtained a doctorate[4].

At York County Hospital he met Cecilia James, a nurse, whom he married in Stockton at the beginning of 1886. Arthur Jefferson gave the necessary 3 months' notice of his intention to resign from his appointment on 30th June 1885. On 6th October the Committee sent him the following testimonial:- 'That this Committee has great pleasure in testifying to the very able and satisfactory manner in which Mr Arthur Jefferson has performed his duties as House Surgeon during the four years in which he has held that appointment. The Committee exceedingly regret the loss of his services and wish him every success in his future career'. The Annual Report for 1885 noted that... 'he had laboured most assiduously for the Institution, and enjoyed the confidence and appreciation both of the Committee and Medical Staff'. According to Dr Katherine Webb, the present archivist of the York Health Authority, 'Such glowing references were not given to all House Surgeons as a matter of course, so they must reflect the fact that Jefferson was one of the more outstanding holders of this post'[4].

Cecilia James, now Cecilia Jefferson was half Welsh for her father had come to County Durham from the iron-rolling trade in South Wales. He was remembered by his grand-daughter, Geoffrey's sister Joyce, as a silver-haired old man who was very deaf. He spoke Welsh and occasional expressions rubbed off onto his children. When Arthur Jefferson met Cecilia her parents were living just outside Stockton-on-Tees. Her brothers had already left home and owned a corn-chandler's mill, and Joyce recalled them as being white with flour from carrying the huge sacks. They spoke a fairly broad Yorkshire dialect which they could, and often did, exaggerate. Apparently they were full of fun and great leg-pullers[5]. Cecilia also had two living sisters, Edie, of whom Geoffrey was to become very fond and Cilla, who did not figure very much in the life of her nephew.

For his part, Geoffrey Jefferson always liked to be regarded as a Yorkshireman, but in fact he was born at 27 Barrett Street, Stockton-on-Tees, in County Durham on 10th April 1886. From a letter written by Geoffrey in 1956, it is apparent that this was where the James family lived[6]. Having resigned his hospital appointment, Arthur had no finances to fall back on and no practice to provide money, so that he gratefully accepted the opportunity of a temporary home with his in-laws. Geoffrey never mentioned his birthplace in conversation, though many years later, GF Rowbotham came near to discovering about it when he and Jeff were travelling by rail 'from the north-east to the midlands. [He] had contrived to miss the direct train and we made our way south by the more circuitous coastal route. He was unusually silent and obviously preoccupied. As we passed through Stockton he became agitated, walked into the corridor, and beckoned me to follow. In the distance, away from the sea, he pointed to what looked like a small village and insistently asked where it was and what it was and what it did and why it was there. I didn't know the answers and in fact I am quite sure he didn't want them. He knew them. This was the first time that I realised that he had any personal associations with the County of Durham. When

Figure 2   *Dr Arthur Jefferson in Manila (ca. 1893).*

the penny dropped I quizzed him but nothing came of it'[7], and Rowbotham made no further enquiries.

In 1887 a second son, John Cecil (Jack) Jefferson was born to Arthur and Cecilia, also in Stockton. Later in the year the family moved to Liscard in Cheshire where it seems that Arthur may have had an appointment, possibly with the army. He also obtained his London MD, which shows his continuing application to study and the improvement of his qualifications.

Inevitably, Arthur Jefferson was troubled about his future. He was now responsible for a growing family that was likely to grow further and for whom he had high ambitions. He wished to become a partner in a general practice somewhere in England, but the problem was one of finance. In the last century and the first half of the twentieth the only way to a partnership was by purchase of the 'Good-will', which could be very costly. One might be a paid assistant for a time, but this did not produce much reward and did not automatically lead to a permanent relationship with the practice. If a partnership was available and an applicant, in answer to an advertisement, was approved by the 'Principal', it might be possible to come to an arrangement whereby the cost of the 'Good-will' could be paid over a number of years, with appropriate interest — rather like a mortgage, but this could be a tremendous burden on a young man. Arthur decided that the solution was to go abroad and earn sufficient money to be able to purchase a partnership outright, even if this took several years to achieve.

With this in mind, he responded to an advertisement for a medical officer to go to Manila in the Philippines (then still under Spanish rule), where a British company was building a narrow-gauge railway system. Cecilia and the two boys, Geoffrey aged three and Jack aged two, were left with his mother at Hampton Hill, Middlesex[9], and Arthur sailed for the far east where, in 1889, his next address was care of Messrs Hett Maylot & Co, Calle Auslage 17, Manila. This changed in the following year to Malcañon 15, Manila. Although it was a time of increasing nationalism in the Philippines, and that must have been apparent to Arthur Jefferson, insurrection did not break out until 1896 and he had returned home safely by 1895. He had spent 'five year's residence in Manila'[3] during which time he saved a very useful fortune and was able to consider the purchase of a partnership in a general practice.

Jeff recorded a few very early memories in 1956, which include a description of the James family home. If his estimate of time is correct, Cecilia must have taken her boys on a visit to 27 Barrett Street, Stockton, while her husband was in Manila. Geoffrey wrote:- '...Funny how vivid memories can be but few continuous strings of films as it were. Barrett St.—the kitchen and front room with Aunt Edie's collecting box for the Missions to Seamen with a ship on it on the piano against the wall on the left as you went in—the back room used as a sitting out room for (I think) Uncle Henry getting engaged to Aunt Cilla—a dark room and not used for anything else that I recollect except Aunt Cilla getting engaged to Uncle Harry! Then a wonderful Xmas cake and Wensleydale cheese in Aunt Edie's house in the road that led to Norton Green, that was in the back room—dining room I suppose. There was more light there than at Barrett St, where the only things that I remember besides were the kitchen where Grandpa James and the Uncles used to come a lot—a bed upstairs with me in and Grandma James passing the foot, I can't remember her except as a figure and nothing that she ever did or said. Yes and a loose brick or two in the yard that used to squelch water deliciously if you trod on them the right way after rain. I must have been very young, that's probably 65 years ago, maybe more'[6].

On 31st January 1896 Dr Arthur Jefferson gave a long lecture to the Rochdale Literary and Scientific Society, entitled *Men and manners in Manila*. In it he not only described the history and geography of the Philippine Islands but also gave a detailed account of their inhabitants. Remarkably, though almost inadvertently, Arthur Jefferson revealed his continuing opposition to Darwin's theory of evolution by such phrases as 'we must not contradict the sacred Scriptures, which clearly teach that all men are descended from Adam' and 'we are bound to trace the origin of all living things from Mount Ararat'[3]. Yet, on the other hand, he had interesting and advanced views on the spread of man and animals etc. across the earth, concluding that there was at one time a continuous landmass across which 'the first population passed to these new Indies...not so much by vessels or by swimming, but simply on their feet'[3] and he quoted others in support of his assertion that the Malay Archipelago was once part of a continent. It is noteworthy that he told of the streets of Manila, even in 1895, being illuminated by electricity, and that there was a telephone service 'with several hundreds of subscribers' in 1894. The railway 'under English direction', with which he was associated, was 'about 120 miles long'[3].

Arthur Jefferson had heard of a single-handed practice that was for sale in Lancashire in Rochdale, near Manchester, which belonged to Dr H Colley March. In 1896 he moved to 3 Roche Place, Rochdale, in order to work temporarily as an assistant to the doctor. He liked the practice and when Dr March sold it to him in 1897, he moved with his family into the doctor's commodious gas-lit house at 2 West Street, Rochdale, which also accommodated the surgery. It was where Jeff grew up and the house was 'home' for him until he was 27 years old. The year they moved to West Street was that of Queen Victoria's Diamond Jubilee and Geoffrey, who was 11 years old at the time, remembered 'Rochdale's wonderful procession of fire engines and such military as it could muster'[8]. Arthur Jefferson ran his practice single-handedly until his death in 1915.

Geoffrey's eldest sister, Joyce, vividly recalled her childhood[5]. Arthur, their father, 'was very tall, six feet, fair-haired, blue-eyed with a red-gold moustache. He had beautiful hands. I remember him as a cheerful man...I think he had a quick temper though I never remember him venting it on mother or us girls. In later years the boys said he could be pretty fierce with them'[5]. There is no doubt that there was relatively little understanding between the two sons and their father. Arthur Jefferson had a passion for education and was also later described by Jeff as a feminist. Geoffrey went on to say that his father 'never quite reconciled himself to the fact that one could be at one time a gentleman and also a non-conformist and a Liberal. Of the two non-conformity was more forgivable than Liberalism. Rochdale must have been a little upsetting to him', for their house faced the 'Baptist Chapel attended by the famous Kemp family and others of Rochdale's upper class. Not only were the Kemps Baptists but the other dominant family, the Brights—whose daughters were not only numerous but beautiful and extremely intelligent, an almost impossible combination—were Quakers. Social stratification was pronounced and more rigid than it is today [1956] but it would be wrong to remember it as water-tight. As "the doctor's sons" we were asked to all sorts of parties'[9].

Geoffrey's mother, Cecilia, was 'a dignified little lady'. Joyce described her as a 'pretty round person. Blue-eyed and brown-haired and altogether comfortable and comforting', yet it seems that she lacked real warmth of affection for her children, whom she did not kiss or cuddle and whom she always referred to as her Chicks or Chickens. In later years, she became something of a tyrant. She made considerable demands on the boys, though she may have treated her girls rather differently. According to her daughter, Joyce, her almost total disregard for time was the special trait that she handed on to Geoffrey. It was apparently so extreme with Cecilia that it was seldom discovered. She was always at least 24 hours in arrears, so she had little difficulty in passing her lateness off as a mere careless misunderstanding; for her she was therefore absolutely punctual. However, there is a suspicion that this amusing little tale may have been manufactured in the first place by Geoffrey himself, making his mother the scapegoat for his own shortcoming! She idolized her husband and, when he died, even took over the management of his medical practice—and of those who worked in it. In middle age Jeff wrote that she was 'a woman of stern common sense, an extremely able manager with a sound sense of values, especially the virtues of success. She was not a clever woman in an intellectual sense but she was a mighty solid and well integrated personality'[9].

Number Two West Street was a large Georgian building on a corner formed by West Street and a cul-de-sac leading down to the door of the surgery; this lane, which was to the right of the house, also provided access to the coachhouse and stables and was therefore sufficiently broad to allow a carriage to traverse it. The house was painted cream and abutted on to the pavement from which it was separated by green railings. 'A shallow flight of steps led to a very solid mahogany front door flanked by windows on either side. These were cleaned by Robert, the coachman, by the simple method of hurling bucketfuls of water at them and then sweeping it down with a brush on the end of a long pole.' The first floor windows had flower boxes which were always filled with hyacinths in the spring, and scarlet geraniums, white marguerites and dark blue lobelia in the summer. This was Mrs Jefferson's domain, for she was 'a gardener at heart and always liked to have some kind of growing things to look after'[5].

Down the twitten or side road and beyond the surgery door, there was a high wall enclosing the cobbled yard. Further along was the entrance to the stables and coachhouse, where a landau was kept for fine days and a brougham for wet weather. 'The first of father's horses to live in the stables was "Billy", a bay. Later there was "Robin", a chestnut.' The stables were Robert's territory of course, until it was discovered that he had been swindling Dr Jefferson over the corn and hay account and he was summarily dismissed. This came as a great shock to the Doctor who was not money-minded and, being utterly honest himself, expected others to be the same. Joyce remembers him saying that 'one should never put temptation in people's way,'[5] although it is difficult to see how it could have been avoided in these circumstances.

Inside the solid front door of the house there was a vestibule with glass-panelled doors that led to a long hall off which the various ground floor rooms opened. The hall floor was stone-flagged and partly covered with rugs. There stood a big oak chest on which was a silver salver and half of a gourd that held the calling cards left by visitors. 'If the caller happened to be a lady she would leave three cards, one from herself and two from her husband.' If she called and the family was out, she would turn down the corner of her card. 'Also on the chest, among the gloves and other oddments, there was a Swiss cow-bell which was used to summon the children to meals. Mother used to say that it was the signal for us all to scatter'[5].

On one wall of the hall there were large portraits of two of Dr Arthur Jefferson's grandparents. Whether one of these was the gallant Francis Jefferson we do not know, but Joyce would probably have said so if it had been. At the end of the hall on the left, was the staircase with its 'good mahogany baluster that had excellent qualities for sliding'. At the foot of the stairs, which were covered with a green patterned carpet that had replaced an earlier red one, there was an iron fixture that held an aspidistra, lovingly cared for by Cecilia Jefferson of course. The telephone was also there and was one of the most important items in the house. It had a central mouthpiece in the middle of a brown wooden box, and a hook on the side which held the receiver. To use it, the receiver was lifted off the hook and a handle below it was turned rapidly in order to make contact with the exchange who then asked for the number required and made the connection. Arthur Jefferson became a visiting physician at the Rochdale Infirmary and this was a frequent source of telephone calls. It has been recorded that he was particularly popular with the children in the hospital, who called him 'father'; this is in interesting contrast to his relationship with his sons[5].

The drawing room and dining room looked out on to the street. The drawing room was to the right of the front door. 'It was a pretty room with a blue Persian carpet, a piano and—a never ceasing source of wonder—a cabinet lined with blue plush on the glass shelves of which stood curios that father had brought back from the east. There was a gorgeous ivory crayfish, with long antennae and an articulated tail, and an ivory egg with the head of a chicken peering out of it'[5].

The dining room door was opposite the drawing room door and led to a big room with painted walls that had a red patterned dado below, and which were coloured Chinese yellow above. The floor was covered with a vast Turkish carpet. Joyce wrote: 'There was a large sideboard that smelled of biscuits and which held, among other things, a jar of the olives which father loved. There was a big dining table seating nine or ten people, and in addition to the accompanying chairs there were velvet-covered armchairs on either side of the hearth. In the window stood a writing table and, to one side, was a glass-fronted bookcase.' There was a door next to the sideboard that opened into a big store cupboard, like a little room, which smelled of groceries. There was an even bigger one on the other side, known as the silver cupboard because it contained the lead-lined chest where Mrs Jefferson kept the silver cutlery, entrée dishes, sauce boats and silver vases. Cecilia counted out the items to be used whenever there was a dinner party. Beyond this cupboard a door led into the kitchen[5].

The consulting room doubled as a study and lay beyond the drawing room on that side of the hall. 'It was book-lined and dark' and overlooked the cul-de-sac leading to the surgery door. In the middle of the room there was a large desk at which Arthur Jefferson saw his 'higher class patients who always came to the front door'. Hanging over the fireplace was a print of a well-known painting entitled *The Doctor* by (Sir) Luke Fildes*. This depicts a benevolent physician sitting beside a sick child. Geoffrey and Jack used the room to study in when there were no private patients and would be likely to throw a book at one of the girls if they had the temerity to try to enter[5].

The surgery was next to the consulting room and had an inner sanctum where Dr Jefferson did his dispensing. His wife often helped him, and she also insisted that when the boys returned from school in the afternoon they lent a hand with wrapping the medicines in clean white paper and sealing the packages with red sealing-wax. 'There was a hatch in the dispensary wall where the bottles, addressed in the doctor's Greek script, waited to be called for. The patients themselves waited on a long bench or on chairs and were examined in a little room off the main surgery[5].'

The kitchen, scullery and wash-house completed the ground floor rooms. From the latter clouds of steam produced by the 'copper' issued on Monday mornings

---

*Fildes. Sir Luke Fildes RA (1843–1927) painted *The Doctor* in 1891 on a commission of £3000 from Sir Henry Tate, who gave it to the Tate Gallery where it now hangs. The engraving was published by Agnews of London. It was reproduced on USA and Dominican Republic stamps in 1947 and 1970 respectively. Rinsler A. *J Med Biog* 1993; **1**: 165–70.

while a visiting washerwoman worked vigorously with a wooden 'dolly' on a scrubbing board[5].

Upstairs were the nursery and family bedrooms and, on the top floor where dormer windows protruded through the roof, there was a large playroom where Geoffrey and Jack carried out chemistry experiments. Jeff himself wrote: 'And there in a cubby-hole we found one early day a mummified arm left by my father's predecessor, Dr March, a horror to a boy that I still recall with no pleasure'[8].

We have a picture of life in the period when road transport meant horse-drawn carriages or carts; when gas lighting was almost universal in the towns but paraffin lamps were still the usual source of artificial light in the country and when cooking was on a coal-fired 'range'; a time before the petrol engine had introduced speed into daily living and when leisure activities were mainly self-created. Reading and writing had not been supplanted by more passive entertainment and society was divided into distinct and clearly defined classes who, mostly, respected each other and the word of God as interpreted by the Church of England. It was a somewhat complicated family that inhabited the house in Rochdale, where the Doctor was the undisputed head and autocrat, but where there were undercurrents of protest and dissent that only became apparent as the children grew up; and where a staff of servants was under the command of the Doctor's wife, who also busied herself among the patients and their prescriptions.

REFERENCES

1   Jefferson, Geoffrey to Fulton, John. Letter 12th April 1944.
2   O'Byrne W. *A naval biographical dictionary comprising the life and services of every living officer in Her Majesty's Navy.* London: Murray, 1849.
3   Jefferson A. Men and manners in Manila. *Transactions of the Rochdale Literary and Scientific Society* 1896–97; **5**: 6–38.
4   Webb, Katherine. Personal Communication, 11th October 1993. Also House Committee Minutes of the York County Hospital 1883–89 and the Annual Reports for 1882 and 1885.
5   Jefferson, Joyce. MS. Recollections of her family.
6   Jefferson, Geoffrey to Petch, Joan. Letter 12th December 1956.
7   Rowbotham GF. In Memoriam, Geoffrey Jefferson. *Br J Surg* 1961; **48**: 586–8.
8   Jefferson, Geoffrey. *Rochdale Observer*, Centenary Supplement. 18th February 1956.
9   Jefferson, Geoffrey. MS. Personal Notes for Fellowship of the Royal Society.

Chapter 3

The Rochdale years
1895–1909

By 1895, in practice and comfortably at home at 2 West Street, Rochdale, the family life of Cecilia and Arthur Jefferson became established. More children arrived and the ambitions the parents had for them were to be justified even if their efforts were not fully appreciated. Jack, who was 2 years younger than Geoffrey, and was the boon companion of his youth, attended Manchester Grammar School and then graduated in medicine from Manchester University in 1911, having taken several prizes on the way and obtaining honours in the London MB. He became house surgeon to Mr AH Burgess at the Manchester Royal Infirmary, as did his elder brother, but then moved on to become the surgical registrar. In 1914 he obtained the FRCS Eng. and he joined the Royal Army Medical Corps on the outbreak of World War I. However, his plans were completely changed by the death of his father in 1915. Jack had to leave the army and took over the general practice in Rochdale, although he was able to combine that work with some surgery at the Rochdale Infirmary. Had it not been for his father's death and his family responsibilities he would undoubtedly have made a distinguished career for himself as a surgeon. Eventually, he did give up family medicine in order to concentrate on surgery alone, and he rapidly built up a large practice in the locality. Jack also gave much of his time to various administrative duties. The Town Council marked their appreciation of his services to the community by the award of an Honorary Freedom of Rochdale but, sadly, not until the day before his death in 1954 at the age of 66.

Soon after the family moved to Rochdale in 1895, Margery (Madge), the first of four daughters was born. She lived to be 85 years old. She read either English or History at Oxford and was considered to be very intelligent. On the death of her father, however, she decided to make a career in medicine and to achieve this she left Oxford and transferred to Manchester University. She began with the preliminary sciences and, with supreme determination, she qualified as a doctor in 1920 when she passed the Conjoint examination (MRCS.LRCP). Following this she obtained the Manchester degree of Bachelor of Medicine and Surgery (MB BS) in 1921 and the Fellowship of the Royal College of Surgeons of Edinburgh (FRCS Ed.) in the following year. However, it is unlikely that she ever contemplated a career devoted to surgery, due to the demands of the family practice. General practice in those days included the possibility of surgery within its scope and she had taken the decision, undoubtedly influenced by the persuasions of her mother, to join her brother in a partnership as soon as she qualified. They worked together for about 7 years, until her marriage to a Rochdale solicitor.

Another daughter Joyce Ada was born in 1897, and it is her vivid recollections that form an invaluable record of this part of Geoffrey Jefferson's life. She

16

married an Australian singer named Hawkins. Her husband gave up the idea of a musical career, however, and instead he became a clergyman and vicar of Langport in Somerset. This may have been just as well, for Madge said 'Of course he had a wonderful voice but he could not keep the pitch right'. He died, rather dramatically, as a consequence of taking part in a hundred yards race in the Langport village sports[1].

Jeff's third sister, Charlotte Cicely, was born in 1904. She became a dentist and had an appointment at the Eastman Dental Hospital in Gray's Inn Road, London. She never married and lived a lonely, rather discontented life, until she died at over 80 years of age, almost blind from the effects of a pituitary tumour and crippled by Parkinsonism[1].

Finally, Helen Margaret (Peg) was born in 1906 when her mother was 44 years old. She married a mill-owner and also lived to be over 80. Like her sister Cicely, she too eventually suffered from Parkinsonism. She was the prettiest of the Jefferson daughters, and clever too, but 'never trained for any profession except marriage'[1].

There were virtually two families, Geoffrey was 20 years older than his youngest sister. Nevertheless, the boys sometimes invited the older girls to join in their games of cricket in the yard behind the house in Rochdale. This was probably mainly for the purpose of providing fielders and one wonders if they were given a chance to bat. In the winter the family went skating on the local sewage farm, where Geoffrey and Jack helped to support the 'tottering forms' of their young sisters. The girls were also allowed to join in games of rounders. Geoffrey professed a lasting love of cricket and, in their games in the backyard 'of no dimensions', they acted out their fantasies, he and Jack impersonating their various heroes in imaginary matches. They would also visit Old Trafford to watch 'the great cricketers of the Golden Age, Maclaren, Spooner, Jackson, Rhodes, Hirst, Fry and Ranji ... '[2]. 'Cricket mad we certainly all were, and on the Castleton Club's ground ... we used to play endlessly when we were not constrained by our private Test Matches at home'[3]. Mixed hockey was also a game in which he participated. 'Rochdale was a holiday place meant for games, climbing about in Peter's woodyard or the Shaw's wool warehouse, sailing boats on Syke or making boats to sail there, walking on Blackstone Edge with the Leaches [sic] of South Street'[3].

Mrs Jefferson had her own hobbies and 'classes were held in her house for drawn-thread work, church embroidery and marquetry. Above all she was mother-confessor to the patients' and many of the humbler ones were as pleased with her advice as with the doctor's. She was in her element where childish ailments were concerned[4].

Although church played an important part in the lives of the children and the Sabbath was observed by the family according to Church of England precepts, 'there was nothing puritan' about the household and the children were not restricted in their choice of books and toys on that day. It seems that Dr Jefferson went to the hospital on Sunday mornings for he is not mentioned as a regular attender at church, and Joyce records that they nearly always went to Matins with their mother. Treats were simple and few and far between. A great excitement for the girls was to be taken on their father's visits to his patients, but Geoffrey may have been too old or too busy to have participated in this. Joyce also remembered how Robert, the coachman, would chew tobacco while waiting for the doctor outside a house or would simply fold his newspaper into a tight wad and cogitate[4].

In addition to an unknown number of servants, the household included a governess for the girls called Miss Knott. Arthur Jefferson treated a number of wealthy private patients, and among these was a family who lent the children their governess-cart and pony while they were away on holiday. This vehicle was a very light trap with high sides, inside which there were seats; it was entered by a door at the rear. This treat especially pleased Madge, whom Joyce describes as 'practically a horse herself'. The girls would set out for expeditions in the cart, driven by a rather apprehensive Miss Knott in a prim straw hat, while they wore their floppy broderie anglaise hats[4] and undoubtedly enjoyed both the ride and the picture they presented. Jeff's comment deserves to be recorded: The girls were '...much too young to be of any importance: also, bless their hearts, they had a governess'[3]. What scorn!

Yet for all the difference in their ages, the girls on their side felt that their brothers were very much part of their lives. The reverse was not entirely true, though Jack was very fond of children. Joyce said that her brothers often teased them such as when Jack made the skull from an articulated skeleton in the consulting room peer around the nursery door. Their mother thought Geoffrey was very extravagant because, being very fond of chocolates, he would actually pay ninepence a quarter for them[4]. This fondness did not diminish with the years.

Geoffrey Jefferson's formal education must have started in London, for he was 9 years old by the time the family moved to Lancashire. When they arrived there in 1895 he was sent to the Rochdale Collegiate School, a private institution where he was regarded as 'a very bright boy'. The headmaster was Mr Looker, whose 'wife was, or had been an actress who, so the boys said (no doubt incorrectly) appeared in current melodramas at the Theatre Royal'. This theatre had opened as the Prince of Wales Theatre in 1867, becoming the Theatre Royal in 1883; it was unfortunately destroyed by fire in 1954. The melodramas were those 'such as *The face at the window, The grip of iron, Her luck in London*, and *The daughter of the regiment*, the last with this delightful couplet printed on the picture posters that advertised the show:-

> "Take this sword and kill him rather
> Than bring dishonour on my father"[3].

To Dr Arthur Jefferson with his interest in education, one of the attractions of his Rochdale practice was the nearby presence of the famous Manchester Grammar School and Owen's College, which had become the Victoria University of Manchester in 1880. He realized that it would be possible for the boys to travel to either establishment daily by train from home, and so avoid the need for boarding. Accordingly Geoffrey entered Manchester Grammar School at the beginning of the Michaelmas term 1899, to be joined 3 years later by Jack. The school had been founded by a bishop of Exeter in the sixteenth century. Thomas De Quincey, who entered its doors in 1800, was at pains to point out that the word *Grammar* referred to *the subject matter of literature*, being derived from the Latin word *grammatica*, and that it did not originally have the meaning which it has acquired today[5]. Joyce, was clearly much impressed by the school uniform and recalled that the boys wore blue and white strapped caps with an owl badge on the front[4]. At that time Manchester Grammar School was in the centre of the city between the cathedral and Victoria Station. In addition to formal schooling, Arthur Jefferson arranged for Geoffrey to have conversations with Thomas Henry Huxley's daughter, presumably with a view to developing an ability to assemble his thoughts and express them clearly; this must have been a formidable undertaking for a small boy[1].

Jeff wrote: 'I never went in for scholarships, it was never suggested that I should. I didn't know any boys who did until my last year at school, when the Classical Sixth boys were the only ones that seemed to be thought much of. I am a Victorian and when I was young science wasn't much thought of in my circle.' Arthur Jefferson controlled the education of his boys and determined that Geoffrey should be a classicist, for he believed in the virtue of work for its own sake. Geoffrey was accordingly placed in the Classical Upper Fourth Form. Despite his later undoubted passion for literature, especially Milton, Shakespeare and Keats, there is not much evidence that he was similarly attracted by the classical past or its writings. Furthermore, Rochdale Collegiate School may also have been a great deal less demanding than Manchester Grammar, for their 'very bright boy' was bottom of the class of 25 at the end of his first term at the new school. In fact his highest placing during the 5 years that he spent at Manchester Grammar School was 13th out of 21 and he was as often as not in the lowest five places[6]. Geoffrey detested his *alma mater* 'with as keen a loathing as any boy ever had for his school', and he 'disliked the famous High Master, J L Paton most cordially'[2].

Some 11 years after leaving the Grammar School, Geoffrey wrote an article for the Manchester Medical Students' Gazette, of which he was then the editor[7]. Its title was simply *School* and, even if some literary licence is allowed, it cannot be anything but a cry from the heart and an endeavour to expiate the profound misery he suffered during his time there. It ran as follows:-

'I well remember the first afternoon at school in my regular form. After the entrance exam I had been placed in the upper fourth on the classical side — a position far too high for me as my school record subsequently quite conclusively proved. It was a dark, muggy, foggy afternoon in late September and the gas jets were flaring above us, throwing grotesque and flickering shadows of our heads on to the whittled desks in front of us. The rest of the class were struggling with the opening passages of the new Latin "book" which we were going to do that term. But my own thoughts were far from Roman authors that depressing day. Fogs always gave me severe neuralgic pains in the eye, and these, coupled with an intense longing for home and for some show of kindness or gentleness from somebody, were a torment to me almost too great. At that moment my eyes fell on my satchel which was lying on the floor. Its flap was undone and plainly to be seen inside was my own name boldly written in my mother's handwriting. This was too much for me; I began to cry softly to myself. I think we must have been

*It is interesting to compare De Quincey's experience in a similar situation almost a hundred years earlier, but in the senior common room of the same school. 'Everything had combined to depress me .... One of the young men noticing my state of dejection, brought out some brandy — a form of alcohol which I, for my part, tasted for the first time, having previously taken only wine, and never once in quantities to affect my spirits. So much the greater was my astonishment at the rapid change worked in my state of feeling — a change which at once reinstalled me in my natural advantages of conversation[5].'

trying to learn some of the lines off by heart or perhaps to prepare a few lines to construe in turn. Anyhow a fat boy soon got up from his place and went up to the master's desk, ostensibly to ask his opinion on a construction. The advice given, the boy with a well meant blundering kindness which I never afterwards forgave, said "Please Sir, the new boy's crying"*'.

'That was the beginning of a life of torture to me. I was naturally a very highly strung and neurotic child, and the least show of sternness or lack of sympathy was enough to let loose the flood gates of my emotion. I don't remember, looking back on it now, just how often I wept—and often very bitterly, even tears of blood at some flaring injustice, and these are not few in the wear of ordinary school life, but it seems to me as if scarcely a day passed without a few small tears coming to my eyes.... This grew to such a pass that no sooner would I be called upon to stand up to translate or read, but most of the handkerchiefs in the class would be surreptitiously offered to me beneath the cover of the desks. Up to the time of going to the great school from the small local teacher's, I had enjoyed no little reputation as a classical scholar.... In English literature I was not very well versed for my age but what I had read I remembered very well. In mathematics I was weak then, am weaker now, and shall no doubt be weaker still. I hated it with a deadly hatred that would have withered ordinary paper.... I was just thirteen years old at this time, very weakly and small and very easily tired. The first week at my new school had finished me. All ease of learning, all facility of working had gone. What it was that had happened to me I don't know even now. But for three solid years at least from this time on, I sunk lower and lower in the scale.... It is curious that I was only punished by detention four times in five years.... I got on fairly well with the other boys when all is said; a few bullied me, more took little notice of me.... I was said to be inattentive in my school report. I could have told many a tale about that inattention. Part of it was no doubt innate. I dreamed then as I have loved to dream since. I lived in a small way in a world of dreams of my own making.... Virtually, for school classification purposes, I was a silly little boy'[7].

Jeff went on to recall his failure to understand Xenophon and, in a speech entitled *Postscript to Aristotle* which he made to Old Mancunians in October 1949[8], he complained how his teachers failed to make the text come alive. 'I cannot recall that anyone ever related to us any of the homely anecdotes, real or imaginary, that would have made us understand that those authors [Virgil, Cicero, Xenophon etc.] had once been men with something exciting to say.... Why were not extracts from their letters...read to us...to give us a different glimpse into their minds. The idea that any of those men had personal histories, had ever been so normal as to write a letter, would indeed have surprised us— and the admission that they must have enjoyed the same trivial things that we enjoyed would, I now feel, have been regarded as too damaging to scholastic prestige to be permissible information.' He also considered that the ideas expressed in most of the texts were 'beyond boyhood's conception', and continued:- 'When do we become able to interpret the structure of human motives and the words and events that these motives cause? Very rarely, I should answer, before the end of school age.... Childhood, boyhood, has no insight into other people, whence arises not only its crudities but its undoubted cruelties.... In the early years Masters have been struggling with the mind as an imperfect organ, not with a perfection that the child naughtily will not use.... Attention and memory depend on interest, and on it alone, and where interest is not aroused attention flags and fails until we fall to looking about for any triviality that will provide an escape from the intolerable drone of the voices of our Masters and the too familiar antics of our contemporaries'[8].

This attempt at self-vindication, when placed in the honorific but awkward position of a speech to be delivered to the very institution which he professed to have so detested, blames almost everything on the school including his poor record there. There will undoubtedly be those who disagree with his arguments—which is the reason that they have been quoted at length. He concluded by saying: 'It seems more likely that the explanation why boys manage to learn anything at all comes chiefly from something different—from the same sort of herd instinct as makes the individuals of the herd uncomfortable, not merely if their dress or behaviour differs from those of the mass, but if their scholastic performance is dissonant—they learn because the herd is learning. Thus mimicry, the wish to conform, is a potent factor when learning is for a few years the object of the herd's movement.... From the herd will emerge the leaders whose pace is faster than that of the majority because it was their good fortune to be born with brains in which better use could be made early of the connections to which I referred, the few with better memories and more facilitation than the majority'[8]. Jeff does not seem to have recalled that, nearer the time of his schooling, he commented on his ability to remember, and he manifestly was not a member of any herd. That he was very soon to achieve academic distinction was not detected by his teachers, and late cerebral 'connections' are not very likely to have been the reason that he did not blossom earlier.

It is not clear when Jeff, or his father on his behalf, decided on a medical career. At the turn of the century and for the next 50 years the majority of doctors' sons slipped into medicine almost without considering any alternative possibility; it was assumed that they would quite naturally take over the practice or at least follow in their father's profession. Arthur Jefferson insisted that Geoffrey took his medical degrees as an external student of London University. He himself had a London degree and it was obvious to him that his sons should have the same even if they studied locally. Madge, however, was later to graduate from Manchester, but her father had died by then and her guide during her higher education was her brother Jack. To take a London degree, Jeff was to write, 'meant doing the London Matriculation, a very unpopular examination with Paton [the High Master] at the Manchester Grammar School. He held me back on the classical side to do more mathematics, which was bad. [Though, according to Jeff's own admission, it would seem to have been necessary in order to get through the examination.] But my feebleness there seemed to be as much due to bad teaching as to anything else, for in my last year under Bruton mathematics suddenly became both easy and interesting'[2]. However undistinguished Jeff's career at Manchester Grammar School may have been, he became a school prefect during his final year though, according to the school records, 'he never reached the status of a sixth-former'[6].

During the time that he was working for the London Matriculation, which he passed at the first attempt, he said: 'I learnt more in my last year or perhaps two years than in the whole of the weary time before then. Under cover of my new found weapon of sarcasm I could hide all my longings and dreams of my early days. A new era was come upon me. I was proof from the boys' attacks because I had a sharper weapon in my tongue than they in their muscles. So that a period of peace came to me in the end of all .... But I was hardened. I don't believe any boy or master in the school could have made me weep .... The first years were bitter enough to taint the latter closing ones .... To sleep and dream, was my desire as a little boy, to do a little and to dream a little is my ambition now. Do dreams pass as years go by and leave us naked to the world? I wonder this too sometimes.

> "Eheu, fugaces Postume!*
> An old quotation out of mode,
> My cloak of dreams is fall'n away
> My youth is passing down the road'''.
>   [H. Belloc][7]

In September 1904, at the age of 18, Geoffrey Jefferson entered Manchester University to begin his medical training and take the London University degree of Bachelor of Medicine and Surgery as an external student.

There had been courses of medical lectures in Manchester since 1783, when they were held under the auspices of the College of Arts and Sciences in the rooms of the Literary and Philosophical Society. In those days an apprenticeship in medicine in Manchester lasted about 5 years and cost between 300 and 500 Guineas; it cost double that in London. After the Apothecaries Act of 1815 a doctor could not dispense his own medicines without the diploma of the Society of Apothecaries, which limited the scope of provincial medical schools. However, in 1817, Dr Joseph Jordan arranged for students to be able to undertake their clinical studies in Manchester and sit for their diploma in London, which is what Geoffrey did. Jordan gave the first course of systematic lectures in Manchester in 1815. It is interesting to note in passing that he had problems concerning the 'resurrectionists' which resulted in him being fined £20. A purpose-built medical school was opened in 1826 but closed after 8 years. However, a second school was already in being when this happened. This latter school was particularly well endowed with pathological specimens and, in 1834, the Royal College of Surgeons of England recognised the clinical teaching in Manchester. Two more schools opened and all three were absorbed by Owen's College in 1871. In 1873 the very poor examination results led to the foundation of a chair of Anatomy, following which the numbers of students steadily increased. When Owen's College became the Victoria University of Manchester in 1880 it still lacked the power to give medical degrees. This ability was granted in 1883. Women were admitted to the medical school in 1899 and the first Manchester degree given to a woman was in 1905[9].

*'Eheu fugaces, Postume, Postume,
labuntur anni nec pietas moram
rugis instanti senectae
adferet indomitaeque morti'.

This is the first verse of Horace's Ode XIV, Liber II. 'Ah, how they glide by, Postumus, Postumus, The years, the swift years! Wrinkles and imminent old age and death, which no one conquers — piety cannot delay their onward march.' *The Odes of Horace.* Translated by James Michie. London: The Folio Society, 1987: 120–1.

Geoffrey Jefferson had not made significant contact with any of the sciences when at school, and it was necessary for him to pass the Preliminary Sciences Examination of London University before he could begin the study of Anatomy and Physiology. Accordingly he worked at Chemistry, Botany, Zoology and Physics during his first 2 years at Manchester University and passed the London Preliminary Sciences examination in October 1906.

It was at this point in his career that he first met Harry Platt, later to become a famous orthopaedic surgeon, to be knighted and to be the president of the Royal College of Surgeons. He became one of Jeff's closest friends throughout the rest of his life. Joyce remembered that shortly after term began 'Geoffrey announced that he was going to bring a fellow medical student home for the weekend. He caught me on the stairs and said that he would give me sixpence if I washed my neck every day that Harry was at West Street'[4]. When he opened the Jefferson Memorial Library at the Manchester Royal Infirmary in 1971, Sir Harry Platt recalled the first time he met Geoffrey Jefferson. 'It was in the Inorganic Chemistry Laboratory in the University — a somewhat bewildering experience for both of us, for neither of us had seen a test-tube before.... In a few weeks Geoffrey and I found each other, and the long friendship took root'[10].

One of the bonds between Geoffrey and Harry Platt was that of music. Platt was a very competent pianist and Jeff, though he did not play any instrument, developed an abiding love of music. Together they were also constant attenders at 'the Wednesday matinées at the Prince's Theatre, the Gaiety or sometimes the Palace to see George Robey, Little Titch, Marie Lloyd, Wilkie Bard and the wonderful George Formby senior.... We went in the Pit, entrance 1/-, and queued outside'[11]. With the unhappiness of school now left well behind, the maturing Jeff was discovering a full and expanding world of interest that was becoming available to him.

Geoffrey next studied Anatomy and Physiology for the second part of the MB examination. He found that both subjects fascinated him. But more important even than this, was the good fortune that Sir Grafton Elliot Smith (1871–1937) was his Professor of Anatomy, and later his guide and a fresh source of inspiration. He it was who directed Jeff's interest towards the nervous system. Harry Platt regarded the Professor as perhaps having the greatest intellect he had ever encountered. Elliot Smith came to Manchester from Cairo where he had not only been Professor of Anatomy but was also an anthropologist of repute. In an address to the Royal College of Surgeons in 1967, Platt said:- 'It did not take long for Geoffrey and myself to fall under the spell of Elliot Smith. Despite the profundity of his knowledge and the brilliance of his intellect, we found him to be rather a simple man, kindly, tolerant and quite humble-minded.... He had a penchant for "licking into shape" articles written by his own staff... and he was, like many anatomists, an accomplished draughtsman'[12]. Jefferson came gradually to appreciate the genius of his teacher, but the appreciation was on both sides and several years later Elliot Smith was to appoint both Jeff and Harry Platt to be his demonstrators.

After a year the time came to sit the second MB examination, following which clinical studies would begin in the wards of the Manchester Royal Infirmary where, eventually, both Jefferson and Platt would become Professors. They had the advantage of doing their clinical work in a brand new hospital, for the Royal Infirmary had been relocated in Oxford Road from its former site in Piccadilly, Manchester. The new building was formally opened on 6th July 1909 by King Edward VII and Queen Alexandra, accompanied by Princess Victoria[13].

At last Jefferson was able to prove himself. He had obtained a London University Scholarship in Anatomy in October 1907, and in 1908 was awarded the Renshaw Exhibition in Physiology by Manchester University, both as a result of his success in the Second MB examination.

For any aspiring surgeon south of the Scottish border the Fellowship of the Royal College of Surgeons of England was an essential diploma. The examination consists of two parts, the first being mainly anatomy and physiology. It was therefore not unusual to take the first part, or Primary, soon after passing the Second MB, while one's knowledge of these subjects was still clear. It was necessary to delve more deeply into detail than was required for the University examination. The Primary examination for the FRCS became Jeff's next goal and he passed it also in 1908. Joyce Jefferson remembered their father's fury when, during these student days, Geoffrey 'tried the effect of morphia on himself out of interest. He said that he had no intention of becoming a drug addict but father said that even one dose could lead to addiction. So that was the end of that . . .'[4].

In addition to Medicine, Surgery, Therapeutics, and the various 'specials' such as Ophthalmology, the clinical course being followed by these students included lectures and demonstrations in Obstetrics and Gynaecology. In order to fulfil the requirements for adequate medical training, which were laid down by the General Medical Council, it is also necessary for the student to deliver a given number of babies under supervision. Groups of students enter a medical course at least once a year, and the supply of babies at the right time and in the right locality is never sufficient for all of the deliveries needed by them. It is therefore necessary for some students, or even the majority, to look elsewhere for this experience. The hospital they select has, of course, to be recognised and approved for the purpose. The most popular choice at that time was undoubtedly the Rotunda Lying-in Hospital in Dublin. The whole of Ireland was then under the British Crown, and the teaching and practical experience obtained at the Rotunda was second to none. It was patronised by students from all over the British Isles and the opportunity to travel to Ireland and live there for a week or two was, in itself, attractive. Geoffrey Jefferson and his friend Harry Platt signed on, took the ferry from Liverpool and delivered their quota of babies. Jefferson recalled the time in an after-dinner speech in Dublin in 1952. It survives in manuscript, and is a good example of his later style of writing, though the notes were not fully edited as they would have been before presentation; the quotation is given *verbatim*.

'Forty and more years ago I did my student midwifery at the Rotunda. I had passed my Primary Fellowship as a student and was treated with surprising respect on that account, not only by the Master, Dr Tweedy, but by a young man who was a clinical assistant named Bethel Solomon, and a remarkably vivid and cheery American, the other assistant, Dr Freeman of Pittsburgh who most tragically died of pneumonia before he had time to make the mark he would have done. I loved those Dublin days in the reign of Edward VII; that hey-day of social life. Not that poor students could enter into it. I remember how Harry Platt and I clubbed together to buy a ticket for the only good-looking girl amongst the "midder" students, to take her to see Seymour Hicks and Ellaline Terriss in, I think, *The Gay Gordons*. It will soon be forty-five years ago — so the calendar says — but it seems no more than fifteen. Dublin so enchanted us that I recollect that Harry Platt and I were near to tears as we went homeward bound on the Holyhead boat. Somehow since then Dublin has been a part of me because it wore itself into my being'[14].

This is followed by a long paragraph in parenthesis which was not to be included in the speech. Typically, in these notes which he called a 'meditation', he continued by talking to himself about Irish plays:-

'I ought, except that it would have made my speech too long, to have referred to my devotion to the Irish plays, of how I sat entranced at the...Gaiety Theatre in Manchester, to watch Marie O'Neil and Fred O'Donovan, Sarah Allgood and Arthur Sinclair in the Irish plays of Synge and Lady Gregory, of the lasting impression that the works of those writers and of Yeats made on me. I might have told them how, when I told Archibald MacLeish, the American poet, about it he had glowed with delight and put out a finger, saying: "May I touch you?"'[14].

Jeff had already decided by this time that he would be a surgeon, not just an ordinary surgeon, but one of the greatest — a conscious conclusion, as he was later to assert more than once when writing to his fiancée. Medical practice as a physician did not then appear to him to offer sufficient satisfaction, either for the doctor or the patient. It was the custom to qualify with a diploma before taking a University degree, partly because the diploma examinations could be taken in several parts and also because the MB BS was more difficult and failure more likely. Geoffrey obtained the MRCS LRCP on 29th July 1909. On 3rd August he was registered with the General Medical Council and so qualified to practise medicine. The next important event in his career was not for 4 months. Therefore, unless he helped his father in the practice at Rochdale which is very likely, he would have spent the intervening period revising for the next examination. This was the London MB BS which he took in December and passed with honours. He obtained a distinction in surgery, thus making clear his devotion to the subject and marking out the pattern of his career. His friend Harry Platt obtained the gold medal, a matter which Geoffrey envied and considered he had evened out when he too obtained a different gold medal a few years later.

In December 1909 Geoffrey Jefferson was appointed to the post of House Surgeon at the Manchester Royal Infirmary, and his medical career began in earnest.

REFERENCES

1   Jefferson, Michael. Personal communication.
2   Jefferson, Geoffrey. MS. Personal notes for Fellowship of the Royal Society.
3   Jefferson, Geoffrey. *Rochdale Observer* Centenary Supplement. 18th February 1956.
4   Jefferson, Joyce. MS. Recollections of her family.
5   De Quincey T. *The confessions of an English opium eater*. London: Folio Society, 1948: 31, 35.
6   Bailey, Ian. (Manchester Grammar School). Personal communication. 11th July 1993.

7   Jefferson, Geoffrey under the pseudonym of JNM. School. *Manchester University Medical Students' Gazette* 1912; **12**: 22–5.

8   Jefferson Geoffrey. *A postscript to Aristotle.* Manchester: Old Mancunian Association, 1949.

9   Brockbank, W. The early history of the Manchester Medical School. *Manchester University Medical Students' Gazette,* 1968; **47**.

10 Platt, Harry. MS. Speech at the opening of the Jefferson Memorial Library. 9th June 1971.

11 Jefferson, Geoffrey. MS. *Notes on Sir Harry Platt for Sir Wilfred Fish.* 27th September 1958.

12 Platt, Harry. MS. *Great men.* After dinner speech at the Royal College of Surgeons of England. 12th April 1967.

13 Brockbank, William. The MRI story. *Manchester University Medical Student's Gazette,* 1969; **48**.

14 Jefferson, Geoffrey. MS. After dinner 'meditation', Dublin. 11th July 1952.

Chapter 4

House surgeon and
anatomy demonstrator in Manchester
1909–1911

The personality, which medical men present in their role as *doctor*, often reflects the profound and lasting influence which their teachers have had upon them. This may show itself in their behaviour towards patients, in their attitudes to their profession and to research, in the way they apportion time between work and family, and in their mannerisms. It can even affect the way they speak. This observation can readily be verified by a study of the lives of those who are, or were, sufficiently well-known to be adequately documented; indeed most medical readers will almost certainly be able to think of examples from their own experience. Such an influence is not exerted by every teacher of course, but sooner or later one or two will be encountered who are considered, consciously or subconsciously, to be worthy of admiration and emulation. Therefore, the first appointments of a newly qualified doctor as house surgeon or physician, and the ensuing ones as a junior hospital doctor or in similar training posts, are of paramount importance. This used not to be sufficiently realised by many of those who were in the privileged position of mentor, for some consultants regarded their juniors as little more than an essential aid to their practices, both public and private. It is worth noting that an obligation, not only to instruct but to train well, is embodied in the Hippocratic Oath and in the main this obligation has been honoured. So it was to be with Geoffrey Jefferson. He, in due time, was to have an enormous and beneficial influence on the lives of most of those who worked with him or with whom he came into contact, while in his turn, Jeff was most fortunate in those men for whom he worked during these early formative years and who undoubtedly left their mark.

Jefferson's first appointments at the Manchester Royal Infirmary were as House Surgeon to the 'firm' of Professor George Arthur Wright (1851–1920) and Arthur Henry Burgess (1874–1948). Jeff was Junior House Surgeon to GA Wright from 1st December 1909, and Senior House Surgeon to Arthur Burgess from 1st June 1910 for 6 months.

GA Wright was an Oxford graduate, who had his clinical training at Guy's Hospital, London, where he won a Gold Medal in surgery in 1877. Three years later he went to Manchester as Resident Surgical Officer to the Royal Infirmary and joined the Honorary Surgical staff 2 years after that. Known as an excellent teacher, he became the Professor of Surgery in 1900 until his retirement in 1911. Wright was devoted to children and was the joint author, with Henry Ashby, of a textbook called *The diseases of children: medical and surgical*[1]. This may have been significant since Jefferson subsequently worked at the Victoria Children's Hospital in London. William Brockbank, the author of a book about the

Medical Staff of the Manchester Royal Infirmary, makes the comment that 'G A Wright was even more a patrician [than Sir William Thorburn] and kind only to the few who passed his rather enigmatic tests of likeableness'[2]. It seems that Jeff was probably one of these, and benefited accordingly.

Arthur Henry Burgess was a Lancastrian who introduced modern methods of surgery into Manchester. He worked at Crumpsall at first and then joined the staff of the Royal Infirmary in 1905, becoming the Professor of Surgery in 1921. He, too, had an interest in Paediatric surgery and was Honorary Consultant Surgeon to the Children's Hospital and to the Christie Cancer Hospital, Manchester, the two surgical specialties in which Jefferson worked when he went to London in 1912. Urology was one of Arthur Burgess's main interests, and an early paper by Jefferson was in this field[3]. William Brockbank wrote: 'To be his house surgeon was in itself a surgical education. The example of a man so eminent in his profession, constantly endeavouring to improve his art was inspiring to all associated with him [and] his energy was inexhaustible.... The students and housemen idolised him for he was a superb technician, one of the best abdominal surgeons of his generation, [but his] outstanding characteristic was his intellectual and moral integrity. He was as conspicuously upright in character as he was in carriage'[4]. During the 1914–18 war he was to find himself working with the RAMC but yet still in Manchester, attached to the 2nd Western General Hospital there, as were others on the staff of the Royal Infirmary.

There is one other member of the Manchester Royal Infirmary consultant staff who should be mentioned here. Although Jefferson does not appear to have worked under Professor (Sir) William Thorburn (1861–1923), he watched him operate and attended his lectures. Geoffrey's great friend Harry Platt was his House Surgeon. This eminent professor may well have unwittingly helped to stimulate Geoffrey's initial interest in the nervous system for, as a Surgical Registrar, Thorburn had studied the problem of spinal localization and the correlation of paralysis with segmental levels. He also described the significant posture of the arms in lesions of the cord at the seventh cervical level, having assembled a considerable number of cases with verified pathology on many of whom he carried out the autopsy himself. These had been published in 1889 in a monograph entitled *A contribution to the surgery of the spinal cord*[5]. Of the 82 papers eventually written by Thorburn no less than 46 were on neurological or neurosurgical subjects. Jeff may have become vaguely aware, even at this period in his career, of the possibility of making neurological surgery his main aim. Later, during World War I, Thorburn was given charge of the surgical division of the 2nd Western General Hospital, and there Jeff will have worked under him as a civilian for the short time that he was with the unit in 1918[6].

We are fortunate that Geoffrey Jefferson himself has given us a description of some of the feelings and emotions which he experienced as he took his first steps into clinical medicine. Between 1910 and 1912, while he was at the Royal Infirmary, he became the editor of the Manchester Medical Students' Gazette. With his strongly developing interest in writing as a means of self-expression, he must have delighted in this opportunity to be involved in a literary task. On account of the usual difficulty that editors of student journals have in obtaining copy for their publications, he wrote a number of articles himself under the interesting, and even enlightening, pseudonym (among other *noms de plume*) of JNM. This stood for *Junius natus minimus*—the youngest of the Junius family. The Junius clan were Roman aristocrats, but the name was also taken as a pseudonym by the writer of the *Letters of Junius* in the London *Public Advertiser* from 1769 to 1772. Not only were these 'letters' of political importance since they were written in an attempt to discredit the government, but there was a mystery as to their authorship. Jeff would have had little hesitation in associating himself with the famous Roman family whom he would have come across during his classical studies, and this seems the more likely attribution of the two. As a result of this editorial responsibility, the galley proofs of one or two of these articles have survived. The paper is brittle and torn, and so fragile and discoloured that it is difficult to handle but it is, nevertheless, completely legible. One of these proofs has already been quoted in connection with Geoffrey's school years, but there is another which provides a moving insight into the time when he was 'walking the wards' of the Royal Infirmary. It was published in 1910, and the article is ambiguously entitled *Nunc Dimittis*—Now let us go forth. He looks back with nostalgic affection on his time as a medical student and junior House Surgeon:

'It cannot after all be so very long ago and yet it seems to have been away back in the mists of time when we first came here—to our Home. And a great home it has proved to be to many of us and in it we will have found affection and some even more'[7].

'It will all look just the same to our followers if they have eyes to see and ears to hear, and so learn the lesson that is daily being read and taught. And we for our part shall be forgotten. For have we not seen many pass in our own short time and now hear no whisper of their name. Into that same oblivion shall we surely go too, though we may seem ourselves to be different from other men. Yet though we be in our time very old we will remember though others forget. In those days all will look much the same to our eyes—the corridors a little more smooth and worn with countless steps, and the birches a little darker and more mellow in their tinge, and the stone, maybe, will be black with a city's soot. Yet as we shall look along these corridors at night we shall see the lights along their roofs like the same bright string of beads that we have seen just now. And those whom we meet we shall recognise as being as we were once in that long ago—the present'[7].

'The wards will surely always look the same. At night the blinds were down and each white bed glimmered in the half light—white oblongs, all the same and yet all different by reason of the varying attitudes of the almost happy men upon them. Not sufferers these'[7].

'The face old and worn with pain, the muffled cries of agony delighted in by writers who pander to popular superstitions, are the exceptions. They mostly sleep; occasionally one of them, as we watch, turns with a sigh and sleeps again. In front of us is a green-shaded lamp hung low towards the table by the door. It sheds its soft light over the nearest beds, and burns like a little beacon of safety, like the night-light of our childhood days, watching over us and guarding us from the goblins and elves that *we knew* lurked in the shadows by the curtained window and scampered across the floor from behind the ward-robe to hide beneath the bed. And though the grown-ups might prove to us beyond a doubt with confident voice and blaze of light that we were alone, we knew full well that as the footsteps died away one by one down the stairs and the door shut with a dull boom far below, that the fairy folk would be back once more scratching on the mattress beneath our head or tugging, a little wistfully sometimes, at the clothes. So must this light be to them, made little children by disease. And at the far end comes the sound of the roar of the fire in the chimney, and the shadows and blaze dance on the walls and flash like little signals of delight from the occasional brass plates above the bed'[7].

And then the scene changes and it is a Sunday morning in winter, with the nip of cheerful frost in the air and bright white snow on the ground beneath the verandah. Nature has decked her world anew. And the snow falls and the wind blows the snow into the open windows, and darkens them by piling its soft white canopy upon their glass roofs. And as we walk along to the Accident Room the flakes nestle on our white jackets and make our human attempts at whiteness poor and mean, and settle on our dark trousers and each becomes a gem of pure delight. And at the entrance we meet our Chief, and as he enters he brings with him eddying gusts of flakes that dance and nestle and dissolve in all nature's carelessness and prodigality. He looks an old man, surely, wrapped up in his big coat and muffler, but there is the light of youth and kindliness about his wrinkled eyes, which having, no man can be old even though his face be furrowed and his hair be white with many winters. A man who carries on him the absolute majesty of personality — a glance suffices to teach us that he has won renown in many fields. And later on that same morning there is left to me an impression only of some small but rather difficult operation in the ward. I see almost in a haze the blue of the hangings of the screen around me and the fierce white light of that winter's morning reflected through the windows in front of me and on my left — for we are in the corner. I recall all this most faintly and indistinctly, yet very happily because perhaps of others who were there. And spring and summer came and went with their sun and lengthy days and their deep blue evening skies, or often with the cumuli of great white cloud or grey of rain. And autumn passed and winter has come again. And all looks the same except that everything that I used to see and wonder at, I have now learnt to love. She has been a gentle Mother to many, this great Infirmary of ours, teaching to the sick the lesson of patience and serenity — and to us, who have been her ministers she has unfolded the first page of the Book of Life, and points us along the Road of Duty'[7].

'It all seems just the same as it did in that not very long ago, and though the faces around us are most of them new — She changes not'[7].

There was an earnestness among the youth of the early twentieth century; let us admire them for it. Let us judge their writing in the context of its time and remember what lay in store for both young and old in only a few years time, and how they responded to a nightmare unmatched by any dream. The style of the essay-article is immature and Jeff might have been a little hesitant if he had been asked if it could be quoted; however, it tells us almost as much about its author as about the hospital which he was describing.

The appointment as House Surgeon lasted for a year and, in January 1911, instead of applying for the post of House Physician which might have been regarded as the next step towards the completion of a rounded training (at that period there was no pre-registration year, for full registration was obtained on qualification), Geoffrey Jefferson became one of the Demonstrators in Anatomy under Professor (Sir) Grafton Elliot Smith. It is more than likely that he and Harry Platt were invited to apply for their appointments, for posts were usually filled by the choice of the Professor rather than by open competition and the two friends were only too happy to work together once more. Knowing of Jeff's antipathy to medicine as opposed to surgery and his love of anatomy, he would have had absolutely no hesitation in accepting such an offer as soon as it came his way. It was to have a much greater effect on his career than he or anybody else could have possibly realised.

Sir Harry Platt's opinion of Elliot Smith has been quoted and their Professor was no less the idol and mentor of Geoffrey Jefferson. In addition to routine demonstrations of anatomical dissections there was now, for the first time, an opportunity for them to carry out original work under his supervision. The two young men joined forces in a study of the surface anatomy of the parotid gland, which resulted in a paper published in a German journal in 1912, but written in English[8]. Six parotid glands were examined. Among the more original observations were the facts that the gland was grooved by the digastric and sternomastoid muscles and that it was not wrapped around the styloid process; also that there were changes in shape during mastication and in old age. They verified their findings by the ingenious method of pressing modelling clay into the bed of the gland after its removal. In this way they reproduced the impressions which they had seen on their specimens.

The first few months of 1911, while Jefferson was involved in the parotid study, were still partly occupied by revision for the final examination for the Fellowship of the Royal College of Surgeons of England. Jefferson passed it in May and received his diploma on the 25th of that month. He then spent a few days in Hove with his relatives, Aunt Ada and her husband Frederick Parsons, and while there received congratulations from his brother Jack. 'You must be feeling like a Grand Turk, a regular Sea-Side Sultan as you stroll along the front'[9]. It was during these and subsequent visits to Sussex that Jeff developed a love for the South Downs.

Having overcome the hurdle of the FRCS, Geoffrey now began to carry out his first studies on the nervous system at the instigation of Professor Elliot Smith, who not only provided the research material but also made suggestions and gave help in the preparation of the subsequent papers. This was to prove an invaluable training in the art of scientific communication, and it showed itself in all Jefferson's future writing. The first of these studies was a morphological exercise in which he described the variations in the 'furrows of the parietal region' and enquired into their significance. Two papers were to be published on this work, one in 1912[10] and the other in 1914[11]. Jefferson examined 86 brain specimens and concluded that each element in the interparietal sulcus had a separate and distinct phylogenetic and ontogenetic history, being made up of a confluence of sulci whose 'various limbs' outlined areas of great importance. He proposed names for three of these 'limbs' of the interparietal sulcus, thus raising their status from being mere rami to that of sulci in their own right.

In order to maintain some contact with clinical medicine and also to supplement his meagre income, Geoffrey applied for the post of Junior Visiting Anaesthetist at the Manchester Royal Infirmary, which carried a salary of £50 per annum and to which he was appointed in January 1911. This was renewed for a further period of 12 months in July. The experience he gained turned out to be very useful in his future jobs in London, where he frequently had to administer the anaesthetic for his 'chief' in the absence of a specialist anaesthetist. He also helped out in a locum capacity when one of the house-staff was absent or if additional assistance was required for any other reason, particularly in the outpatient clinics.

Jefferson found lodgings at 86 Acomb Street, Whitworth Park, Manchester, and, in response to a request from one of the medical students, he agreed to give tutorials in Surgery and Anatomy in order to supplement the normal course of instruction. This student was a Canadian girl named Gertrude Flumerfelt, who had previously been at the Royal Free Hospital Medical School in London but had transferred to Manchester University. The coaching would have been expected to have taken place in Jefferson's rooms, but it seems that, at least sometimes, he may have preferred to visit her more comfortable lodgings. In fact she had a small house at 82 Cecil Street, Manchester, and even the luxury of a maid. It appears, however, that she did not wish to be seen to have entertained a man there after dark or to be seen leaving 86 Acomb Street in any circumstance that might possibly be construed as compromising. In consequence of this Jefferson wrote her the following letter. It was undated but postmarked 20th October 1911:

'Dear Miss Flumerfelt

Very many thanks for your long, if somewhat cryptic, letter. As to the staying-late part, I fear I must agree with you as to possibilities of opinion. Would coming earlier and going earlier meet the difficulty, do you think? The main objection would be that it cut into your general work. I think the whole crux lies in leaving well before the school classes. It was very stupid of me not to have realised it before. Of course I thought of it, but men rarely recognise how much it means all at once'[12].

'As to any indebtedness to me, if you really feel bad about it you shall pay my book-bill. This will more than adjust the balance. It is on the other hand only a veiled way of receiving money from you, and it is a question whether it would not be more honest to take it openly. You see of course my difficulty. We have on the one hand a person, very kind and hospitable, keeping open house to a number of very desirable males (i.e. me). One of these persons is requested to coach the "kind and hospitable" one who desires to increase her credit by paying him huge sums of gold dust and precious stones for the probably quite erroneous and absurd information which he imparts on surgery and anatomy. So far as I can see the debt is all on one side. For when you had more than paid me for any trouble taken in preparing matter for coaching, there is still a great debt to be wiped out in some manner or another for somatic and mental food, music and the arts and all the "extras" that help to make a life in "digs" like home'[12].

'I don't seem to have got much further after all this. If you really would <u>very</u> much prefer to pay me in coin of the realm, do. I cannot however accept any hospitality from you that arises directly out of coaching. Mr Jefferson MB, the coach, cannot come in to lunch on Saturdays, say after a séance. Whilst Mr Geoffrey Jefferson, the youth, would be only too pleased to come to supper on Sundays'[12].

'I am more than relieved to find from Todd (just entered) that no paid coaching is allowed within the precincts of the University. Therefore you will come as before and pay me the usual fee for Surgery. If I accept nothing for Anatomy therefore I am not coaching in the technical sense. I am afraid as you did not take out your anatomy here you will have to pay $2\frac{1}{2}$ Guineas to the University for the year for Anatomy observation & Dems. That entitles you to everything except the Professor's lectures which you don't want of course'[12].

'This is a fearfully straggling and long-winded letter but I am sending it just as it is. The psychology of it is rather absurd'[12].

'Final Position:

1) Surgery; usual fee.
2) Anat., no fee allowed, so this releases us from obligation to one
    another.
Thurs. & Sat. (4.15–5.30) & (12.15–1.30).
Please agree to this Ultimatum & final appeal.

Yours very truly
Geoffrey Jefferson

P.S. See the Dean about Anat. Observation fee'[12].

It is quite obvious that surgery and anatomy were not the only topics of conversation. Geoffrey was always seeking kindred spirits with whom he could talk about music and literature. This was one of the bonds between him and Harry Platt, and in the years to come when he was thrown into unselected company by the war, he complained of the lack of such a person. Gertrude Flumerfelt filled the role to perfection. She was highly intelligent, well-read and musical, shared Geoffrey's taste for poetry and novels as well as classical literature and was adept at commenting upon and forming an opinion about whatever she had read. The fact that she kept this letter is significant. There was undoubtedly a mutual attraction that showed itself by her invitation for him to dine and in the confusion of the writer of the letter, who was only too anxious to accept; so different from Jefferson's usual fluency. It was the first letter to pass between them, the first of a correspondence that was to continue intermittently for many years.

Geoffrey wrote again a fortnight later to thank her for the loan of a book and for a note. He told her he had bought tickets for *The tales of Hoffmann* and managed to get 'the last seat in the Upper Balcony (300 ft. up about) at 7 o'clock, so I think we ought to be there about $\frac{3}{4}$ hour before.... It is very kind of you to ask me to supper (I mean dinner), I shall be very pleased to come'[13].

On the 18th November 1911 they became engaged; Geoffrey was 25 years old and Gertrude admitted to 26, but was older. The events of that important and memorable day were recalled by Jeff in letters written 2 years later. In the morning Jeff went up to the Pathological Laboratory to help her with some slides and jokingly called her 'Miss <u>Gertrude</u> Flum'. He had tea with her; her mother was also there. He then went to supper with his family in Rochdale — presumably quite early. In the evening the two of them met at the theatre for a 'concert with Irene Scharrer and others' at which Gertrude wore her 'nice dark evening cloak'. When it was over they returned to her house at 82 Cecil Street and to the comfort of armchairs and a bright fire burning. Jeff 'sat by the fire' and, as he remembered, 'you lay on the sofa and told me about Rex and came weeping to me, and we just went into one another's arms...'[14].

REFERENCES

1   Ashby H, Wright GA. *Disease of children: medical and surgical*. London: Longmans Green, 1889.

2   Brockbank W. *The Honorary Medical Staff of the Manchester Royal Infirmary (1830–1948)*. Manchester: Manchester University Press, 1965: 165.

3   Jefferson G. The peripenic muscle; some observations on the anatomy of phimosis. *Surg Gynecol Obstet* 1916; **23**: 171–81.

4   Brockbank W. *The Honorary Medical Staff of the Manchester Royal Infirmary (1830–1948)*. Manchester: Manchester University Press, 1965: 138–41.

5   Thorburn W. *A contribution to the surgery of the spinal cord*. London: Charles Griffin & Co, 1889.

6   Brockbank W. *The Honorary Medical Staff of the Manchester Royal Infirmary (1830–1948)*. Manchester: Manchester University Press, 1965: 103–106.

7   Jefferson G (under the pseudonym of JNM). Nunc dimittis. *Manchester University Medical Students' Gazette* 1910; **10**: 104–105.

8   Jefferson G, Platt H. The parotid gland. *Anatomische Anzeige Jena* 1912; **41**: 81–9.

9   Jefferson, Jack to Jefferson, Geoffrey. Letter 26th May 1911.

10 Jefferson G. The morphology of the sulcus interparietalis (BNA). *J Anat Physiol Lond*. 1912–1913; **47**: 365–80.

11 Jefferson G. The parietal area. *Revue Neurol Psychiat* 1914; **12**: 54–8.

12 Jefferson, Geoffrey to Flumerfelt, Gertrude. Letter 20th October 1911.

13 Jefferson, Geoffrey to Flumerfelt, Gertrude. Letter 3rd November 1911.

14 Jefferson, Geoffrey to Flumerfelt, Gertrude. Letters 18th and 20th November 1913.

Chapter 5

Engagement to Gertrude Flumerfelt
1911–1912

Gertrude May Flumerfelt was 'fair-haired, blue-eyed and fragile-looking to a degree'[1], her voice was 'ever so kind and soothing and full of sympathy, and so low and quiet'[2]. Joyce Jefferson, who was to be her future sister-in-law, remembered 'particularly well her small hands and delicately boned wrists, but inside that frail body was a determination and strength which could surmount anything that life would bring her.... We others got an immense amount of amusement from Trude's management or non-management of her affairs. She was not a practical woman and had not much sense of humour, but I can say this about her, that she would have given you her bed or the coat off her back if you needed it. She was truly "good"'[1]. 'She had beauty ... intelligence and a wide education. These were combined with a deep love of humanity and a strong religious sense'[3]. She also had strong views about the place of women in society. She was in favour of equal opportunity and fair competition between the sexes. Once asked if she was a supporter of Mrs Pankhurst's suffragettes, she replied that she did not go that far and disapproved of their methods, but it should be pointed out that the question had been posed after women had obtained enfranchisement. Her strong moral principles demanded that a bride should come as a virgin to her marriage, and she strongly objected to the double standards of the time whereby the same was not demanded of the bridegroom. Injustice, wherever she might see, it was abhorrent to her.

She had been born in Winnipeg, Manitoba, Canada, on 1st May 1882[*], her father, Alfred Cornelius Flumerfelt, being a third or fourth generation Canadian who was said to have been of Dutch, though possibly German, extraction. He was born on 29th September 1856 and had lost his father when he was just 10 years old; when his mother died he was still only 17. Consequently, he was very young when he became responsible for the care of himself and his sisters. This he did by starting a boot and shoe manufacturing concern. By the time he had reached the age of 21 this business was firmly established, and he later added other interests, including an open-cast coal mine, with the result that he eventually acquired considerable wealth. He married Ada Kilvington, the youngest daughter of a Yorkshire immigrant who, though she had little education, fulfilled the rôle of wife and mother to perfection. Gertrude was

---

[*]1882. Gertrude gave her true age (as shown by her application to the Royal Free Hospital Medical School when she was 24) until she met Geoffrey, after which she wished to conceal the fact that she was older than he was, and assumed the year of birth of her sister Norma. The dates in various obituaries were therefore incorrectly given as 1884 or 1885. It is worth noting that at the time of her engagement she was approaching 30.

Figure 3   *Ruhebühne, the Flumerfelt family home in Victoria, British Columbia.*

extremely fond of her mother and they had a very close relationship. Towards the end of the nineteenth century the family moved from Winnipeg, Manitoba, to Victoria, British Columbia, where they lived in a large house with its own grounds called by the name of Ruhebühne*. This had been built for them in 1895 by a well-known Canadian architect but it has since been demolished. It was in Pemberton Road in the affluent part of town, and they also had a small frame house in the country. The Flumerfelt household included a housekeeper, a cook, Chinese kitchen boys, a personal maid, a coachman, a gardener and quite possibly other helping hands. By 1911 Gertrude's father was a man of considerable influence and importance. His wealth came mainly from the coal mine and from his interests in the Granby Smelting Company of Grand Yorks BC. During World War I he was to become Minister of Finance in the Provincial government of British Columbia and he held other civil appointments. Sadly, however, the 'slump' which followed that war brought about his financial ruin.

The affection which Gertrude felt for her mother was almost extreme; she appears to have regarded her as a kind of saint. So that when her mother died in

***Ruhebühne**. Literally *'Peaceful Stage'* (*Theatrical*). However it is difficult to find a suitable English house name that is equivalent. Even as a German name it is unusual. A peaceful retreat is the meaning.

Figure 4 *The Flumerfelt mine, British Columbia.*

1924 her death caused her elder daughter very deep distress. Trude was a firm believer in extrasensory perception and that she could divine the actions and thoughts of others who were close to her; she was particularly interested in various experiments on the subject. Her belief in her ability to sense events applied in the case of her mother's death, which was quite unexpected and followed soon after a routine gall bladder operation. Gertrude said that she had awakened in the night and knew immediately that her mother had died. It is interesting to note that, at a much later date, she was appointed to a committee, one of whose remits concerned spiritual healing. Her father later remarried, much to Gertrude's disapproval. He never regained his fortune and when he died in 1930, though he left everything to his second wife and a small amount to each of his two daughters, these bequests amounted to nothing once the liabilities had been settled. He was a kind and generous man. 'Whatever mistakes he may have made were only those of judgement.... [One was] forced to the conclusion that it was just this kindly trait in his character that brought about some of his worst troubles'[4].

Gertrude had been educated privately until she was 16 years old when she was sent to a finishing school in Switzerland, at Vevey on Lake Geneva, for about 2 years. Following this she travelled extensively in France, Italy and Germany with her mother and sister, Norma. She studied pianoforte at the Brussels Conservatoire but she does not seem to have maintained her skill after her marriage. The time she spent in Europe enabled her to become an accomplished linguist and engendered in her a love for its classical literature which she studied avidly, though she showed somewhat less appreciation of the English classics. Gertrude's nature was naturally rather serious and shy but, even in her teens, she

Figure 5   *Mrs AC Flumerfelt, Gertrude's mother.*

became interested in the human mind and was fascinated by Max Müller's theories of the origins and modulations of language[3]. 'She was conscious of being both more intelligent and better educated than most of her contemporaries, and desperately eager to make use of her talents.' Indeed, any young man who showed an interest in her was hard put to make any headway unless he could satisfy her stringent intellectual demands. She was 'almost the model of a Henry James heroine (but by no means a suffragette) with a distinct tang of the New World's liberty of spirit and disregard for established custom and privilege'[1].

When Trude was about 20 she returned to Canada. Although she did not make friends easily, several life-long relationships were formed at this time, one being a friendship with Gillian Scaife, an actress who became well-known on both sides of the Atlantic and whom she was later to meet again in England. Gertrude had a strong sense of purpose, founded on a religious conviction which was often her motivation in both thought and deed. She 'was eager to use her talents in the service of the things she loved', so that it was not surprising that 'she was drawn to medicine and, after some initial difficulty, persuaded her parents to allow her to come to England'[3].

Having eventually won a battle against parental and social opposition, the aspiring medical student landed in Britain in 1905. In view of her disregard for custom and privilege, it was predictable that soon after her arrival here she turned down an offer of presentation at Court. At 23 she was unusually old to begin to study the preliminary sciences, which was the first step in the long process of obtaining a medical qualification.

Nevertheless, undaunted, she began a medical career at the so-called Women's Department of King's College London, which was then located at 13 Kensington Square, London W, and she lived in nearby lodgings. A little later she moved to Cambridge Terrace, Paddington, a photograph of which shows that Lizzie Aldridge was then her maid, a very faithful cockney girl who, in due course, followed Gertrude to Manchester. Gertrude was also befriended by a lady named Miss Eyre, who mothered her and with whom she kept in contact for many years. Trude spent just over a year at King's before going to the Royal Free Hospital Medical School at the beginning of 1907. This was then known as the London (Royal Free Hospital) School of Medicine for Women, and was at 8 Hunter Street, London WC1, nearer, in fact, to University College Hospital than to the Royal Free Hospital itself, which was in Gray's Inn Road. She did not pass the Preliminary Sciences examination until 1908, so she must have continued the study of at least some of these subjects after her move from King's College, and the records show that her certificate in biology was awarded by the Royal Free. During this period she lived in lodgings at 69 Ridgemount Gardens, Gower Street, which was very near Hunter Street. By July 1910 the work which she had done on Anatomy and Physiology enabled her to pass the appropriate preliminary examinations of the Conjoint Board and for the London MB in those subjects.

At about this time Gertrude began a lasting friendship with (Sir) William Osler (1849–1919), the famous Canadian physician who had been Professor of Medicine at the Johns Hopkins University in Baltimore, USA. By then he had come to England and was now the Regius Professor of Medicine at Oxford. When she first met him he had not received his baronetcy, which came in 1911. The presence in England of a young and attractive fellow countrywoman, who was also one of the few women studying medicine at that time, immediately endeared her to the great doctor. 'I was at that time working for the second MB', she wrote later to Dr Harvey Cushing, the neurosurgeon who was to be Osler's biographer, 'and had been introduced through two mutual friends, the one a medical student, the other an aspiring lawyer who had recently left Oxford. To them Dr and Mrs Osler stood for the ideal man and woman, to them No 13 Norham Gardens was a place of rest and delight known as the "Open Arms".... In every stage of my medical life, from the day of my first meeting, Sir William stood by me, a very present help in all days of need. The rare week-ends I spent with them stand out as the most delicious moments of rest in strenuous student days'[5]. Geoffrey had not yet met him, but there are some undated manuscript fragments written some years later, in which he has given us a description of the doctor—for he is always remembered as 'the doctor' or the 'great physician' rather than as the Professor. 'Osler's claims to remembrance are so numerous that no short answer is possible, but the greatest fall under three heads. First that he was deeply interested in demonstrating the way in which pathological processes caused the symptoms and signs of disease. Second that he re-organized the instruction at the bed-side of medical students in the United States and, third, that he brought to medicine a depth of historical learning that has not been surpassed. His achievements in these fields were made possible by his unusual sweetness of disposition, joined to great modesty and approachability, whilst beneath all were the most prodigious industry and economy of effort'[6].

Osler had the habit of providing nicknames for his friends and acquaintances, and Gertrude was dubbed "Trotula" at her first meeting with him. 'His delight was great at the general mystification of all my friends, including my medical friends, as to who or what Trotula was', Gertrude wrote to Harvey Cushing some years later, 'and it was months before a friend managed to unearth her history for me. It turned out that she was a female surgeon of Salerno who lived about the middle of the eleventh century, who was suspended for quackery, but later emerged triumphant and wrote several books'[5]. Many of Gertrude's close friends, including Geoffrey, delighted in also referring to her by this nickname.

Osler sent her a fictitious physiology paper, illustrated in Cushing's biography of Osler[5], in which he wrote a number of impossible questions. It was dated 'The Hilary Term 1660' and signed 'Thomas Willis ex Aede Christi'. She was to remark later, in mock self-deprecation, that she thought it was provided in order to demonstrate the impossibility of her passing the physiology examination she was then about to sit. This interpretation seems unlikely; rather it was the kind of academic joke which always delighted the professor.

Towards the end of 1911, Osler invited Gertrude to spend Christmas in Oxford, and wrote to her:

'Dear Trotula,

I am delighted to hear from you. I thought you were dead, and for months have had your memory enclosed in a melanotic border. What are you doing for Christmas? We should be delighted to have you here, & you could work hard, and I would guard your heart!'

When she did pass the examinations in physiology he commented:

'I am glad to hear — though not surprised — that the examiners were deceived. Considering how little you know of the higher physiology illustrated by my paper, you must have had shocking duffers as examiners in that subject. I still have hopes that you may be rejected at the University Examination.... I will come and see you before long'[5].

Gertrude could have continued her studies at the Royal Free Hospital, but she decided to attend an institution in which the sexes were mixed. In her typically thorough way, she sent a questionnaire to the main European and provincial medical schools before making her choice. Her application was

Figure 6 *Geoffrey Jefferson (ca. 1912).*

turned down by the Dean of St Thomas' Hospital, who was said to have just been jilted and in no mood to accept a woman, and by University College Hospital. However, she was offered a place by the medical school of Manchester University, possibly with some help from Osler. The records show that she began clinical studies there in the winter term of 1910, 5 years after her arrival in England. And it was there, in the Manchester Medical School, that she met Geoffrey Jefferson, Demonstrator of Anatomy, to whom she applied for extra tuition in Anatomy and Surgery. The request for anatomical coaching is surprising in view of the fact that she had already passed the examinations in that subject! The consequences have already been related; were they not in fact hoped for by her?

Geoffrey Jefferson was passionately in love and there is no doubt that it was reciprocated. However, the mores of the time demanded parental approval before an engagement could be announced and, having already met Mrs

Flumerfelt, Jeff was more confident of receiving a welcome from his fiancée's relatives than a congratulation from his own. Christmas was going to present a problem for him because it would obviously be tactful to make sure of his acceptance by the Canadian family before entering the possibly stormy waters of Rochdale. Shortly before Christmas Gertrude went to Oxford, in response to the invitation from the Oslers, and Geoffrey moved temporarily from the relative discomfort of his lodgings at 86 Acomb Street into her house at 82 Cecil Street. Here he had the luxury of the attendance of Lizzie Aldridge, Gertrude's devoted maid: 'Lizzie has just given me tea ... I feel so much better here than I did at 86, because here amongst all your belongings that have become so very sweet to me you seem to be so near to me'[7].

Jeff spent his Christmas in Rochdale but did not immediately mention the matter of his engagement to anyone. On Christmas morning 1911 he wrote to Gertrude in Oxford, who had certainly not yet divulged her secret to the Oslers. He did so in order, as he said, to relieve his feelings. He admitted that he had removed two pictures from her photograph album while he was staying in her home: 'All I have of you here is but memory, a faint scent, and a small picture of you in the trap with Norma ... which I stole from your album'. He then related the following somewhat characteristic episode: 'I went to early Communion this morning with Madge and Jack, but was late of course and missing the 10 Commandments (much to my relief), had to sit alone at the back of the church. This was fortunate because I could now have you [the photograph] out ... and you and I went through the greater part of the service together.... I kissed you twice in Church which was against the rules but very enchanting.' After another page there follows a remarkable sentence: 'I'm sure if anybody ever thought of publishing "letters of Geoffrey Jefferson to Gertrude Flumerfelt" he'd get (no it would probably be she, it always is) she'd get a frightful shock'[8]. Even if it was subconscious, the thought that his biography might one day be written was in his mind.

The letter continues: 'I want to tell the Mater about you really but am waiting to hear if anything is said by GMF's people first'[8]. There is no mention of breaking the news to his father and perhaps he thought that he might leave that task for his mother to perform. Fate then intervened in the shape of a telegram emanating from Oxford that morning and delivered to No 2 West Street at six p.m. on Christmas day. It arrived before he had finished the letter which he had started in the morning after church. The telegram was from Gertrude and indicated that the Flumerfelt parents gave their approval to the engagement. Geoffrey added a postscript to his letter, written down the side of the notepaper. After thanking her for the telegram he said:- '...I shall probably spend some time in explaining to the family who it was from. I shall tell the truth, Bravo G!!'[8]. The 'G' stood for Geoffrey, not for Gertrude.

We do not know exactly how the news of the engagement was received by the Jefferson household in Rochdale but, from Joyce's recollections, we can be sure that there were considerable reservations, to say the least. She remembered that 'naturally father and mother thought that he ought to have taken more time to establish himself. Here was a brilliant young man, with all the honours he had earned, rushing straight into marriage, and this without a bean. Or if there was a bean it was a very small one'. She continued: 'The strange thing about mother was, I think, that she was inclined to believe that marriage in general was rather a mistake and that if people did marry then children were almost a disaster...but father and mother were fighting a losing battle.... Still poor mother and father were deeply distressed by the whole affair.... When love flies in at the window, often common-sense flies out at the door'[1]. Jeff probably hurried back to Acomb Street soon after this.

Geoffrey and Gertrude must have seen much of each other again quite soon after Christmas and subsequently, for there was no further occasion to write for over 2 months. The next letter, dated 4th March 1912[9] was written when Gertrude was staying briefly with Professor George Murray in Bowdon (now in Greater Manchester), and tells us something of the routine of Jeff's life. It seems that he had telephoned her early in the day which he had spent abstracting an article for a journal, doing some German and preparing for her next period of coaching. This routine, in addition to his duties as Demonstrator of Anatomy, filled his time quite fully.

On 5th June 1912 'Trotula' received a letter from Sir William Osler to whom she had by now mentioned the news of her engagement:

'Dear Trotula,

Twas as I thought & hoped, and knew! Hearty congratulations—only having known ME, to decide on a Surgeon is a bit hard. You must bring him over here & talk about your plans. Would you like to be married here? Why bother about that exam? [The qualifying examination of the Conjoint Boards of the colleges of physicians and surgeons.] Silly thing! Chuck your head— you will never need it again...[10].'

Osler had not only underestimated 'Trotula' but, in common with many of his generation, he clearly did not see any future for a married woman in a medical career. She sent him a present of a rug, and on 10th June he wrote to thank her:- 'I am sure the rug for the "elderly gentleman" will be much appreciated. I am very anxious to to see the "Light of your Life" so after all the worry of examinations is over we shall expect you both for a week-end. I think it would be a very good arrangement to have a nice quiet wedding at Christ Church'[11]. This delightful plan was not to be fulfilled, for their engagement had yet to last for just over 18 more months before they were married.

By the second half of June, Gertrude was back in London again working for the final MRCS LRCP examination, which would last for several days at the beginning of July, and staying at 25 Gordon Mansions, Gower Street, where she was accompanied by Mrs Flumerfelt. This time her mother's visit to England was occasioned by the need to consult Dr Hunter Todd, in whose advice she had much faith, about some abdominal problem which does not appear to have been too serious.

Meanwhile Geoffrey, clearly under instruction from 'Trude', had been 'to the best tailor I could hear of (Verity) and have been most extravagant to wit:- 1 Morning coat and trousers £7:10:0. 1 Covert coat [light overcoat] £5:15:0. 1 Lounge suit—blue £6:6:0—Isn't it awful!'

He told Gertrude that he had decided to get a second lounge suit 'in a pretty grey' and postpone buying evening clothes for a few months[12].

Jeff had also written to enquire about the possibility of a house appointment at the Victoria Children's Hospital in Tite Street, Chelsea. It is likely that this choice was prompted by a suggestion from his chief, George Wright, who had himself made paediatric surgery his specialty for 18 years, until his appointment to the staff of the Royal Infirmary. 'Tite Street' had an excellent reputation as did its Honorary Staff. In a letter to Gertrude, Jeff remarked that if he did not get the job he would be bankrupt or have to take locums in order to earn some money; this in spite of the fact that, at that time, the appointment had not even been advertised[12].

There were, however, other reasons for Geoffrey to wish to make a move from Manchester to London. Foremost was the need, as he would have seen it, for a surgeon with his ambitions to leave the provinces and try to make his mark in the metropolis, then regarded as the centre of medical excellence. Even if he did not finally establish himself in London, the training and contacts he would make there would stand him in good stead thereafter. He had now completed his first house appointments in surgery and had research projects that were about to be published. Together with his impressive record at the medical school, these made him a very strong candidate for a surgical post in London in spite of having to compete with graduates from the London teaching hospitals.

A possible second reason may have been the knowledge that Gertrude, herself, would probably not stay in Manchester. She was about to sit for her final qualifying examinations and, unlike Jeff, she had no particular allegiance to Lancashire. She would, therefore, be free to apply for 'house' appointments anywhere and preferably in London, where she had begun her medical training. Finally, Geoffrey would not have been blind to the advantages of being further away from Rochdale, where the atmosphere had become too tense for them to feel at ease, thus escaping from his family and allowing himself greater freedom to spread his wings in whatever way he wished.

REFERENCES

GJ=Geoffrey Jefferson; GMF=Gertrude Flumerfelt

1. Jefferson, Joyce. MS. Recollections of her family.
2. GJ to GMF. Letter 21st September 1912.
3. *Manchester Guardian* 13th February 1961. Obituary of Gertrude Jefferson.
4. Davis, Harry (Solicitor) to Jefferson, Gertrude. Letter 10th February 1939.
5. Cushing H. *Life of Sir William Osler*. Oxford: Clarendon Press 1925; 2: 202–204.
6. GJ. MS. *Sir William Osler*. Undated.
7. GJ to GMF. Letter 'Christmas Time' 1911.
8. GJ to GMF. Letter 25th December 1911.
9. GJ to GMF. Letter 4th March 1912.
10. Cushing H. *Life of Sir William Osler*. Oxford: Clarendon Press, 1925; 2: 317–318.
11. Osler W to GMF. Letter 10th June 1912.
12. GJ to GMF. Letter 25th June 1912.

Chapter 6

House surgeon at the
Victoria Children's Hospital, Chelsea
1912–1913

Geoffrey was disappointed that there was no immediate sign of an advertisement for the post of house surgeon at the Victoria Children's Hospital, Chelsea. In his letters to Gertrude early in July 1912 he wished her good luck for her forthcoming examination for the diploma of MRCS LRCP and advised her not to be put off by the looks of the examiners who 'are usually very nice in the vivas'. He also reminded Gertrude that she had 'a power of expression and a command of language far above the ordinary . . . . It is the ordinary who are in for the exam so I am confident of your success'[1]. In another letter he had quoted part of a poem by Francis Thompson. ' . . . And who read, may read the sweet/Direction in his lady's face'; an expression of his thoughts about her that he could not suppress, even when he was giving her encouragement for the ordeal of an examination[2]. The third of four very loving letters that Geoffrey wrote to her, all on 3rd July, is very creased and folded four times; did she take it with her into the examination?[3].

Gertrude successfully passed the 'Conjoint' (MRCS LRCP) at the end of July. She sent a note to Geoffrey with the news, and he returned many congratulations. We have a rare insight into his attitude towards religion from these excited communications, for he had remarked after she got through the pathology exam: 'We must not forget to thank God dear for helping you to pass'[4], and again: ' . . . I do pray God that he may keep us both in the fullness of His grace and love'[5]. Gertrude, herself, had strong religious feelings and they probably influenced Jeff in these early years. Later in his life, however, his faith was to lose much of its strength. During that summer, also, his letters convey morbid fears that she might die[6] and, in the coming months, he often worried about her health.

Following the examination, Gertrude and her mother went on holiday to Cornwall for a week or two and Geoffrey was able to accompany them; it was probably the first holiday the engaged couple had been able to have together. Jeff had written that he would come up to London to meet them at the flat near Gower Street, which they continued to occupy until the beginning of August[7].

Writing again after their holiday, he addressed his letter of 2nd August, for the time, to 'Miss G M Flumerfelt MRCS'; this was c/o The Cheyne Club, 11 Oakley Street, Chelsea. She had moved there for a few days in order to be nearer the Victoria Hospital and before going to Preston, Lancashire, to take up a locum appointment on 4th August. She had applied for a post at the West London Hospital but that had not materialized, to their mutual disappointment[5].

Geoffrey was very sad about her move to the north Midlands: 'I cannot express well my sorrow at parting from you after so many days and months of absolute oneness with you!'[5]. In the next letter he gave her some quite lengthy instructions for the treatment of 'diarrhoea (summer) in kiddies' which he thought she might find was a common complaint. After mentioning the physical signs, he recommended water only for 24–48 hours, an electric light beneath a cradle in the child's bed, a rectal washout and 'No medicine'[8]. This advice suggests that her locum post was in a general practice rather than in a hospital, a probability that is supported by her address, which was 9 Fishergate Hill, Preston.

The advertisement for the job at the Children's Hospital in Chelsea that Geoffrey was so anxious to have, had appeared at last and he had been given the appointment. He actually took it up on 8th August 1912, although he wrote from the hospital in the previous week to say that he was already working in the Casualty Department, the post of House Surgeon to Mr Waterhouse having been awarded to him but not yet officially confirmed by the Hospital Board. This explains Gertrude's brief stay at the Cheyne Club. In due course, Geoffrey appeared before the Board of Governors who 'asked me if I was punctual and down early in the morning. I gave a vague *yes* in answer — but really I haven't been bad so far dear. I manage 9.15 brekker pretty well'[9]. The irony of this would not have been lost on Gertrude. Incidentally, he had been extremely embarrassed on discovering one day that he had left her photograph under his pillow where it was found by one of the maids. He wrote self-consciously, 'I disregarded the presence of that maid again when I met her'[9].

Gertrude now wrote to Osler to tell him of her examination success for, on 3rd August 1912, she had been officially placed on the Medical Register as a fully qualified medical practitioner. On the 14th Osler replied to her letter as follows:-

'Dear Trotula

Heavens! How sorry I am for you & your patients! and such a slump! after those happy weeks in Cornwall with the L of your L. But it will be happy — no I mean good — experience for you. Do let me help you about a hospital appointment — let me know of anything likely & I will write one of my most mendacious letters. When are you going to be married? Do not wait too long — please. No man is worth waiting for more than six months.... Come & see us soon'[10].

The Honorary Consultant Surgeon to whom Geoffrey was now appointed as House Surgeon was Herbert Waterhouse, who was to be knighted in 1917 and was later to play a vital part in Jeff's experiences during World War I. Waterhouse (1854–1931) was an Edinburgh graduate who had worked under Sir William Macewen at the Glasgow Royal Infirmary. Macewen was one of the first British surgeons to operate succesfully on the brain, and the young doctor must have been impressed by his achievements. Waterhouse had moved to London in 1890 as Demonstrator in Anatomy at Charing Cross Hospital, and eventually became an Honorary Surgeon and then Dean of the Medical School. He joined the staff of the Children's Hospital in Tite Street in 1893. He was described as 'rapid and dexterous as a surgeon, impatient of delay, quick to distinguish the useful from the valueless, somewhat too enthusiastic, and with little capacity for sustained interest or tedious hack-work. He excelled as a teacher'[11]. His particular interest was in peritonitis, which was the subject of his MD thesis and of several papers. Once again Geoffrey was to have the good fortune to work for a man of stature.

When starting a new job, the full extent of a young house surgeon's commitments is not always immediately apparent and at first there may seem to be time that could be spared for recreation. Geoffrey filled these ephemeral minutes by reading Oscar Wilde's *Poet critic* and an Edgar Alan Poe anthology, one of whose poems he had quoted in an earlier letter. As had been customary for many decades, and it was to persist until the advent of radio and television, those who enjoyed literature read almost as much poetry as prose, and Jeff was no exception. This is well illustrated by *October and other poems*, a volume of verse by Robert Bridges, which went through no less than 14 impressions and editions during its first year of publication in 1914[12]. On his second day at Chelsea Jeff bought a book of poems; this was by Francis Thompson, a fellow Mancunian, and another collection by William Henley. His friend Harry Platt had a copy of the Henley poems which he had once, earlier, asked Jeff to give to the future Lady Platt when she was nursing on night duty at the Manchester Royal Infirmary. Geoffrey remarked later: '...and that was how he broke the news to me of his engagement'. During his browsing of the bookshops, Jeff had come across 'a gorgeous edition of Shakespeare's Sonnets (£2:2:0), Dove Press, which we simply must have some day soon'[13]. He always had difficulty in resisting the attraction of books, even when he was desperately worried financially, and he usually succumbed. Books, according to Geoffrey, just made their way into his company. 'How often do we resolve that we shall limit our purchases to this subject or that, to such and such a period, or to a few writers in whom we are particularly interested. And how vainly!'[14]. In a letter to a friend, written many years later, Jeff makes the illuminating remark which will be quoted again, '...because you had not got any money...seems to me to be a very inadequate reason for not buying [the books] straight off'[15].

The medical care of children is very different from that of adults and it took Geoffrey a few days to regain his confidence; he was still not 'at home' at the end of his first week in the new job. Nevertheless, within a few days of his appointment as House Surgeon, he performed a circumcision and four tonsillectomies under supervision. Waterhouse also showed that he had faith in his new House Surgeon for, on 9th August, he let Geoffrey operate on one side of an inguinal hernia after doing the other himself, and in the evening invited him to join his wife and family at dinner, followed by a visit to the theatre. He pleased the young Jefferson by saying that he thought the clinical teaching in Manchester was far ahead of London in its opportunities. For his part, and on first acquaintance, Geoffrey was not uncritical of his new chief whom he categorized as 'v. insincere I should imagine, but quite unintentionally so'; Geoffrey's first impressions were not always right. There was also some criticism of the daughters, one of whom was 'quite nice but colourless' and the other 'rather pert and v. objectionable', but we must allow that Geoffrey's opinion might have been affected by his recent association with his own fair ideal with whom no other could then compare. However, Mrs Waterhouse was considered to be 'very nice indeed', which undoubtedly saved the evening. Geoffrey was justifiably offended by a remark that 'Northerners' were 'rather crude' and 'unpolished', but his final assessment of the occasion was that he and Waterhouse 'got on splendidly together' and 'talked for 2 hours on morals and philosophy'[16].

Geoffrey's next letter to Gertrude, written on 14th August, was essentially a commentary on his current reading. He mentioned his sadness on reading Yeats: 'I think the *Twisting of the Rope* and the *Death of Hanrahan* with perhaps the 1st tale are the most beautiful in the volume. We can picture so well the wet ground, and the rocks faintly gleaming with water, and the mist just hiding in the distance and giving an air of unreality to the near things. All these things you will find even more beautifully in Synge's *Aran Isles* [sic. *The Arran Islands*], because in these the appeal is to nature herself and the whole volume depends simply upon the perfection of the descriptions and atmosphere thus created and not at all on the adventitious interest of a tale'. Other favourites were the studies of *The boy Prince* and *The fisherman* by Oscar Wilde. He goes on to comment on the sadness of Edgar Alan Poe's life. 'However, records of the lives of others whether they fail or succeed will always have a great appeal and value, and one cannot but enlarge ones outlook and strengthen ones grip on the reins of life by reading of conquest or defeat. So long as a man had accomplished something, it is enough.' In strange contrast to this literary diversion and with a peculiar mixture of subjects in one sentence, Geoffrey goes on to tell his fiancée that 'Waterhouse has just done a difficult appendix, he brought a pair of beautiful squirrels along to show me today'. He also wrote that when he could spare a little time he would cross the river and go for a walk in Battersea Park, where he enjoyed 'a happy loneliness'[17].

Geoffrey managed to go to Manchester for a brief reunion with Gertrude and returned on 19th August. She was still applying for hospital appointments which, he hoped, would not be too far away from London. Following one of his walks in Battersea Park, which had now become a daily affair, he 'strolled up to 36 Park Mansions and was just on the point of leaving when I ran straight into Gillian'. This was Gillian Scaife, Gertrude's actress friend from her home town in Canada. 'We stared at one another for a moment and then recognised one another. As a matter of fact I only had her photo to go on as she was so heavily veiled when I saw her in mufti before. However she took me into her flat. They are rehearsing* very hard just now — she is Rose Sibley — later Rose Rhead, (afterwards old Lady Rhead) and not Gertrude as we had imagined. Charlie, Gillian Scaife's husband, [Charles Gamble] is to be Sam Sibley and not v. pleased with it I think. Gillian took me over to her mother's flat but her mother was too deshabillée so I couldn't stay for their "tea" '[18]. Geoffrey was offered a drink of 'whiskey' by Charlie and caused some consternation by announcing that he did not drink spirits. 'It really is extraordinary, the state of intelligence that assumes that a man must have a drink with another just as it were for friendships sake'[18]. In later life Geoffrey drank an occasional cocktail but never liked spirits. He kept little or no wine in the house and for many years would only occasionally share a bottle of lager with Gertrude and give the boys ginger beer as a treat.

Three days later Jeff wrote: 'I have got all my old confidence back now sweetheart in dealing with cases and feel ready to start on anything...the reason for my confidence in the future and of my own success is largely due to my knowledge of

*Rehearsing.** The play was *Milestones* by Arnold Bennett and Edward Knoblauch. It was to be performed in 1912 at the Liberty Theatre in London and was subsequently taken to Broadway, in New York. Gillian Scaife was the 'star'. She was to have another success in *The melting pot* by Israel Zangwill at the Queen's Theatre, London, 1914.

my own powers as an operator . . . the 2 yrs inactivity during which I have performed nothing but learnt a lot has materially enhanced my capabilities and finish'[19]. Geoffrey constantly found it necessary to reassure himself at this stage of his career. However, a strong confidence in his own abilities was later to become a hallmark of his character; it sustained him and was one of the reasons for his eventual success in the neurosurgical career that he was to carve out. He had an intense desire to 'cut a surgical figure in life. Not . . . for the sake of fame, but to prove himself'[20].

Work as a house surgeon then, as now, was extremely onerous. He had to be available night and day, and tiredness was never an excuse. That Geoffrey suffered in the same way as the majority of young doctors is clear, both from a letter written at 12.15 am which he wrongly addressed to Dr *Graham* Flumerfelt, and by his failure to go to a concert for which he had tickets, simply because he felt too tired. In the evenings Jeff usually went to bed after midnight when he had completed his round of the wards and attended to emergencies, so that he did have a slight excuse for beginning his day tardily, 'at 9.45 in the wards'. However, this would not have been appreciated by the staff. In order to get exercise and to correct a tendency to round-shoulders, he set about 'Sandow's new exercises' which he felt were doing him good. Sandow was the 'strong man' of the day and the embodiment of masculine prowess.

Often there were operating lists which lasted most of the morning and prevented the house surgeon from carrying out his other duties. In addition to Herbert Waterhouse, Geoffrey worked for Walter Fedden (1878–1952) who was also an assistant surgeon at St George's Hospital, becoming a full surgeon there in 1914. Fedden was to be responsible for the chapter on applied anatomy in the 19th and 20th editions (1916 and 1918) of *Gray's anatomy*, and the subject would have been a source of common interest with Jeff[21].

As was usual at a children's hospital at that time, some patients who would now receive treatment by a specialist were operated upon or treated by general surgeons and physicians. On 26th August 1912, a typical day, Jeff assisted Fedden in performing an operation on a child with torticollis, and further procedures followed that were for an acute mastoid with a cerebellar abscess and a radical mastoidectomy. Jeff then went to the outpatient theatre and did two circumcisions, put carbon dioxide snow on two lesions, and ended with three tonsillectomy and adenoidectomies (Ts & As). He next went to the out-patient clinic where he 'saw 20–30 O.Ps until 2.30. Lunch. An O.P or two, swabbed a throat for Dip., redressed a mastoid that was bleeding, and just now tea . . . before going up to anaesthetise an empyema which I have presented to the H.P. [House Physician] as a treat'[22]. This was a good example of the hard work done by house surgeons then, as now, and without mentioning the inevitable calls to the wards during the evening and night.

It is sad that, for the most part, only one side of the correspondence between these two young people is available, for occasional remarks leave one wishing to know the reason for them. On 26th August 1912 (often more than one letter was sent during the day in both directions) Geoffrey wrote: 'Since I have loved you darling I have approached all women in quite a different way . . . even the prettiest has absolutely no attraction at all for me now'[23]. It is a confession that pretty girls were attractive to him, and in the future he continued to be affected to some degree by almost every comely young woman, though neither was to know this then. But the remark shows that he had assessed the ladies or he would not have known that those who he said no longer attracted him were in fact pretty! This protestation was probably prompted by a slightly guilty feeling on Geoffrey's part, however innocent his analyses may have been, and to fulfil a need to reassure Gertrude that she was alone in his affections despite the obvious vulnerability of a young and attractive hospital doctor separated by many miles from his fiancée. In fact the letters written at this time of separation are full of the tenderest endearments, in the expression of which he went to the limit of his not inconsiderable capability with the use of mere words.

On 29th August Jeff wrote to congratulate Gertrude on having obtained a house surgeon appointment at the Victoria Hospital, Burnley, which is about 20 miles north of Manchester, but was disappointed that it would prevent her from visiting him for week-ends in London. However, he remarked that 'it puts us so much nearer getting married'[24]. This may seem a surprising observation but it could mean that they had already formulated an idea that would emerge later, of a joint surgical practice or partnership, and he pointed out that the experience she would get in Burnley would stand her in good stead when she went up for the Manchester MB degree. In Jeff's mind, her acquisition of this was very important and, at that time, he regarded it as an essential requirement before setting up in practice, since it demanded a higher standard than did the normal qualifying diplomas that she already held.

A letter written at the beginning of September adds to the picture of the illnesses that were being commonly treated at the Tite Street hospital before World War I, and there is comment on an observation, made by Geoffrey himself, which shows his continued interest in applied anatomy. Arthur Ralph Thompson (1876–1955), was the Surgeon in charge of outpatients at the Children's Hospital and had an interest in Orthopaedics. Geoffrey reported to Gertrude that Thompson was 'fearfully bucked over an observation of mine on Torticollis...that the clavicle is raised on the contracted side and the configuration of the bone altered also at its inner end by the pull of the muscle.... He proposes showing it to the Anat. Society.... My out-patients are various sorts of things. There is not a wonderful variety in children's stuff, but I work hard to keep it interesting. The vast majority are the 3 great child's complaints, Ts and As, Phimosis & otorrhoea. The rest are various tuberculous things, naevuses, hernia etc. The ear things are my bugbear...'[25].

In another letter of similar date[26] he wrote that he found his colleagues were uninteresting. 'They are good at their work but are not of our way of thinking which I like to believe is one of philosophy and capable of deep if not extensive development.' Then there follows a note on open anaesthesia. Before the advent of intravenous anaesthetics, it was usual to drip the volatile agents, such as ether or chloroform or a mixture of both, on to a piece of lint or gauze stretched over a wire mask placed over the patient's nose and mouth. This alcohol, chloroform and ether mixture was always abbreviated to ACE, and the anaesthetist inhaled almost as much as the patient. 'ACE is never used here, we just mix our CE as we want it 1/2+1/4 or 2E to 1C. The A does no good and is a bit deceptive by keeping the lint wet when all the C and E has evaporated'[26]. Throughout his correspondence with Gertrude, Geoffrey used his letters as an outlet for his thoughts and opinions, and as an opportunity to speculate and to remind them both that, where medicine was concerned, nothing less than the best was to be good enough for them or from them.

Jeff was always anxious to protect Gertrude from harm and he continued to instruct her, as he had done when she was a student: 'One of the most important things and one that one rarely pays enough attention to at first is to keep one's fingers out of pus ... septic fingers are so easy to get'. There is then an aside on his own work: 'I am taking such infinite pains with all my work however minor the things are, to do them well and thoroughly. I take a great time over my O.P., sometimes till the other men have even done theirs and had lunch, but I do want so much not only to learn to treat things which any man can do, but also to *heal* them'. He ended by saying that he hoped they would get married soon, for he feared that the difference in their ages could be a source of anxiety to the Rochdale family. 'I expect my people will be horrified at the idea [of an early marriage], they are so conventional, but the few months difference of age makes it better that we should without too great delay'[26]. The difference in their ages was actually 4 years, as he was to discover much later. Was his anxiety in reality, that Gertrude would be bearing children in her thirties, a greater hazard then than now, and did he already suspect that she was older than she admitted?

On 7th September he visited St George's Hospital to watch Mr Fedden operate on what may have been the first surgical procedure on the brain that Jeff had seen. It was on a patient who had a 'gangrenous encephalitis as a result of bronchiectasis' and 'today he opened up the wound and fluid gangrenous brain simply ran out when he stuck a director in'[27]. An inauspicious introduction to neurosurgery, but Jeff drew the right conclusion nevertheless when he wrote: 'It's aseptic and gentle manipulation that counts'[27].

In a letter written on the following day there is the first clear indication that Geoffrey and Gertrude had been making firm plans to emigrate to Canada and work together in Victoria in a joint practice near her parental home. This idea had not been received enthusiastically by Ralph Thompson, and he had asked if there were not good prospects in Salford. It is interesting to read Jeff's reply since, fortuitously, this was the very town in which he was later to practise surgery for many years. 'I told him Salford was no good for money, but he said that he thought that personality could make a man anywhere. I was rather pleased at the inference.' Despite Jeff's ambitious nature he showed a surprising degree of self-doubt and vulnerability in this letter: 'I am more concerned than ever about my prospects anywhere [in Britain] .... The thought of staying anywhere in England is a little distasteful to me. Particularly because I cannot visualise our home ... anywhere but in a New Country.' Or he may have been trying to justify to himself the possibility that he might emigrate, concerning which decision he was undoubtedly under pressure from Gertrude. 'I feel very much older in many ways .... In my dealings with honoraries [consultants] etc. I think I am older and more dignified, and so also perhaps with the nurses. I certainly never descend as I used to ingratiate myself with them, tho' again my sense of humour and weakness for a joke puts no wall between us.' As if to reassure himself further before making a final commitment to the concept of emigration, he asked her if she had any second thoughts about marrying him; was she completely satisfied or did he fall short of her ideals? He was only too aware of the considerable difference in their financial resources and asked: 'Ought we not to wait until I am in some position to support you?'[28]. Gillian Scaife and her husband had apparently also been urging them towards an early marriage[26], which Jeff seemed still to favour in spite of the above remark, and so he asked Gertrude whether she felt she had acquired enough experience in England to return home and practise very soon. He assumed that she would pass the MB examination without difficulty[28]. It is sad that we do not know how she replied.

However, after another fortnight, Geoffrey's confidence had returned and any doubts about money matters were suppressed. 'Not long ago my only and very great amibition was to be a great surgeon — one with a reputation greater than any now living.... Now my ambition is to live happily in *our* own home and just be quiet and happy. The other ambition is still there but it has to take rather a back seat'[29].

As house surgeons do, he had long conversations with the night sister, who was 'a funny old person, *v.* fussy and old-maidy but a very good sort at bottom'. She was 'remarkably tolerant on religion... if necessary every man [may have] his own religion, but he must have some. She also does not want to know the new scientific stuff because she says it might weaken her faith and make her a less good woman. She admits of her own accord that it is narrow, but the best for her'[29]. In that 'funny old person' he had found someone in the hospital who was prepared to discuss things with him at a slightly deeper level than usual.

During the next week Geoffrey had an encouraging chat with some Canadian visitors, but there followed a conversation with the 'pretty theatre sister', which was less satisfactory. She talked about 'surgeons who are good and those who think they are — meaning me... she has absolutely no idea of a high surgical ideal'[30]. Taking a more dispassionate view, it is possible that she may have been rather perspicacious. He now, wisely, and somewhat belatedly, decided to give up the editorship of the Manchester Medical Student's Gazette which he had continued to run from London.

The paper by Platt and Jefferson on the parotid gland, which had been published in English in a German journal, had come to the attention of the editor of *Cunningham's practical anatomy*, who presented Geoffrey with a copy of the new edition of this standard textbook'[31]. 'Arthur Thomson [*sic*] the editor', in fact the editor was Arthur Robinson, 'has adopted the description of the parotid gland worked out by Platt and me and his pictures of it are almost identical or rather absolutely identical with those that Platt and I did, only Cunningham's are coloured and shaded a lot. I am so glad aren't you dear, esp. as one of the pictures shows the Sterno-Mast. & Digastric grooves which I spotted first & then showed to Platt'[32]. There is no acknowledgement to Jefferson and Platt in this edition, but that does not seem to have upset Jeff.

He now thought of obtaining another surgical post, at the Cancer Hospital in the Fulham Road in London, in order to extend his experience in this surgical field without spending time obtaining further medical knowledge as a house physician. He made a wild statement in his letter of 26th October concerning eye surgery, which he thought they might be faced with in practise in Victoria. He told Gertrude that if there was no 'special eye man... we'd have a shot at it wouldn't we', for 'you can always get sheep's eyes to practice on'[32].

Further opposition to the idea of emigrating to Canada now came from Walter Fedden who, according to Geoffrey, thought that 'it is a great rolling savage country full of bears with ac. appendicitis or lions with strangulated herniae and that when you have finished these there aren't more than a dozen humans for patients.... No one seems to realise that it is much like England, certainly like the English provinces if not like London & the great cities'[32]. Nevertheless, Fedden must have realised the ability and worth of his House Surgeon and probably tried to discourage him in order that he would not be lost to British medicine.

Geoffrey's anxiety about his shortage of money surfaced again. He was very disturbed that his question concerning Gertrude's desire to marry him had upset her, and explained that 'I feel rather depressed and cramped by not having more money and the *right* to ask you to marry me at any time without the possibility of my being weak enough to be humiliated by you having more money than I have. And also dear at those times I get a little disheartened by thinking and realising how very little money I can earn by any means that will be of future value to us; the small sums one gets as resident goes such a very small way.... My own idea lovie dear is that we had both better do another 6 mos. somewhere, and if you could get your M.B. in May at the same time it would be lovely'[33].

On the anniversary of their engagement, Gertrude sent Geoffrey with one of her letters, a large lock of her fair golden-brown hair, enclosed in a small envelope. It was secured with two red sealing-wax seals, now broken beyond recognition. The envelope is inscribed 'To my own darling Geoffrey. 18 Nov 1912. A year ago today — From G.'[34].

It seems that some reservations had been raised concerning Geoffrey's concentration on surgery at the expense of medical experience. Gertrude suggested that they should ask Professor Osler's advice about this and also about emigrating to Canada. Her advocacy of that idea was not entirely based on their medical prospects but was heavily weighted by her desire to be near her mother, and how much this came into the open we cannot know. However, Geoffrey thought that nothing that the great man could say would affect their plans and he wrote, 'I mean I am sure that we are right...I'm sure I don't need HP [House Physician] work. I feel very strongly just now as if I'd like to write a book on surgery, making everything very clear and plain & logical for the student, with lots of little rough drawings to make the meaning clear. I hope we'll be able to do it together some day'[35].

When Geoffrey had completed 5 of the 6 months of his appointment at the Children's Hospital he was not only confident but enthusiastic. 'All my old love for my work has returned to me after the lapse into anatomy, from which I really believe that much of my best work & ideas spring. I am just as fond as ever of literature and all that is really beautiful, of course, dearest, just as we both are....' 'I came to the conclusion that I have never been so much at peace or more really and truly happy than I am now.... I do want so awfully [for] people to like me'[36]. He was full of ideas for the future. Many of them were far more theoretical than practical; his account of his personal attitudes and self-analysis was much more critical than the analysis he made of his projects.

At the beginning of December 1912, Geoffrey seems to have had some kind of minor illness, and on the 8th of the month he went to stay for the weekend with his Uncle Fred and Aunt Ada at 25 Dyke Road, in Hove. In a letter finished in pencil in the train when returning from there, he wrote to Gertrude about her ability to write well and continued: 'None of the family, except Jack, know that I can write or speak at all. I have never shown father or mother any of the things that I have written as they are not interested at all and I don't think they w^d ever understand'. Finally, he remarked: 'when I get back I will send the ring to you dearest tonight in a pill box'[37]. Was this her engagement ring? Gertrude must have left it in London on her last visit, for they had been engaged for over a year and it would be surprising if he had only recently given it to her; perhaps the size had been altered, or she may have just forgotten to put it on.

Geoffrey could not get home for Christmas this year but Gertrude, very tactfully, planned to spend it with the Jeffersons in Rochdale. Among the few letters written by her to Jeff that are still extant, is one in which she tells him about the Christmas presents she had bought, and she suggests that he should send a telegram of good wishes to Lady Osler. Then she refers to his anxiety about money 'I know just how unsettled you feel about the money, but don't worry sweetheart. We will just enjoy the pleasure of giving for once and I shall have to be very economical for a long time in the future'. In another she says that she is trying to sell 82 Cecil Street, Manchester and make arrangements for those things that she did not immediately require to be shipped back to Canada. 'We shall start our new home quite fresh but with sweet memories of the old little house in Cecil Street. Perhaps after all it will be better to have all new things with no subtle influences of our few difficulties and struggles of the early days lingering about the furniture'[38]. There was now no doubt whatever about their commitment to the move to Canada, although it had obviously been the subject of intense discussion for many weeks. They appear to have been looking forward to a future viewed by her as one of affluence, and by him as one of immediate success, both of them having scant regard for reality.

We do not know how she got on in Rochdale that Christmas, for Geoffrey does not refer to it. In his next letter, dated the 30th December, he says that he is applying for a post at the Cancer Hospital (now the Royal Marsden Hospital, London), which would prevent any possibility of an early marriage. But '...we are really able to wait aren't we lovie if it is for the best'[39]. On the following day he described a familiar problem for conscientious research workers. 'I often wonder whether I am keen enough on writing things but I do so very much want to reach the truths on things and speak from experience that I hesitate so much to rush into print with anything'[32]. These were the observations of a man, wise beyond his years in this direction, whatever may have been his misjudgements elsewhere. He congratulated Gertrude on her decisiveness, particularly in the disposal of her possessions.

On New Year's Day 1913 Gertrude enclosed some flowers from a bouquet given to her by a patient and said that she had written home to tell her 'Father about our wished for plans & that we want to be quite independent'[40]. Now, as if two letters in one day was not a frequent enough correspondence, there were telegrams and occasional telephone calls between letters as well. Also, on this day Geoffrey was fetched from a play at the Hospital for Sick Children, Great Ormond Street, due to the admission to the hospital in Chelsea of a child who had been diagnosed as suffering from acute appendicitis. It is rather surprising that Jeff had gone so far away if he was on call. However, all was apparently well and he was given the case to operate upon. It turned out to be a pneumococcal peritonitis, but Geoffrey was delighted with what may have been one of his first solo explorations even if, after all, there was no appendicectomy. However, he thought he had not done the operation very neatly and wrote: 'It is splendid practice...fishing out the appendix and groping around the coelom [an anatomical term for the body cavity of an embryo, not usually used as a clinical expression meaning the peritoneal cavity]. I didn't remove the appendix as the little girl was very bad.... I have got her on horse serum 10 cc which gives them a splendid start off by supplying complement; continuous saline & pituit[rin]. I'm giving up using brandy [then regarded as an all-purpose stimulant] at all as it *is* a depressant. I did it in about 20–25 mins'[41].

According to the practice of the time, Geoffrey spent the morning of the 3rd January 1913 calling on the Honorary staff of the Cancer Hospital and met two of the various surgeons for whom he hoped he would work, Jocelyn Swan and Cecil Rowntree, in their consulting rooms. He had intended to call on William Miles as well but went to Harley Street instead of Wimpole Street as a result of a message from 'a silly maidservant', and so had to go back again later. The interviews appeared to have gone smoothly. 'I had a long long talk with Miles on abd. perin. [abdomino-perineal] excision of the rectum which he practically invented & he gave me a copy of the paper.... They think I'll get on, tho' there were 11 men up for the job a month ago.... It is so *beautiful* to think it will be my last post'[42].

In the afternoon Waterhouse gave him another appendicectomy to do 'and he said I did it splendidly! He told me he thought my testimonial was the best he had ever given!'[42] After the operation Waterhouse took him to dinner at Pagani's restaurant. Geoffrey remarked that he was looking forward to operating together with Gertrude, 'though I sometimes wonder if you will be *quite* happy in surgery', but he promised to make it 'awfully scientific...and get great interest and joy out of it'[42]. It may have been at this dinner, when there was an opportunity for quiet discussion, that Waterhouse urged Geoffrey to take the London Master of Surgery (MS) examination. Jeff then told Gertrude that the £20 entrance fee was awful and that he did not feel 'ready for the exam', although 'I think I have such a very big grip of surgery in most of its branches — of the foundations at least'[43]. After which rather conflicting observations he queried whether he was being a bit swollen-headed.

On 11th January Geoffrey carried out his first tracheotomy on a $2\frac{1}{2}$ year old child suffering from airway obstruction as a result of diphtheria. In this letter he also expressed his opinion that tonsils should be enucleated by dissection rather than removed with a guillotine, an observation that was ahead of current thought. In fact the guillotine continued to be used by some surgeons for the next 30 years[44]. Later on that month, and not for the first or last time, he remarked 'I do detest medical cases, chests & hearts and so on'[45].

As he had confidently expected, for Geoffrey always had faith in his ability to impress those who might select him for a post, he was given the appointment at the Cancer Hospital for which he had been applying and he began work there on the 1st February 1913. His feet were now firmly planted in the surgical field.

REFERENCES

GJ=Geoffrey Jefferson; GMF=Gertrude Jefferson
1   GJ to GMF. Letters 3rd July 1912 (a) 11.30 am and 5.30 pm.

2   GJ to GMF. Letter 1st July 1912.
3   GJ to GMF. Letter 3rd July 1912. (b) 11 pm.
4   GJ to GMF. Letter 7th July 1912.
5   GJ to GMF. Letter 2nd August 1912.
6   GJ to GMF. Letter 3rd July 1912 (c) 11.30 pm.
7   GJ to GMF. Letter 9th July 1912.
8   GJ to GMF. Letter 4th August 1912.
9   GJ to GMF. Letter 7th August 1912.
10   Cushing H. *The life of Sir William Osler.* Oxford: Oxford University Press, 1925; **2**: 329 (Osler to GMF 14th August 1912).
11   Power d'A, Le Fanu WR, eds. *The lives of the fellows of the Royal College of Surgeons of England, 1930–1951.* London: Royal College of Surgeons, 1953: 821–3.
12   James T. Robert Seymour Bridges. *J Roy Soc Med* 1994; **87**: 286–9.
13   GJ to GMF. Letter 8th August 1912.
14   GJ Harvey Cushing and his books. *J Hist Med Allied Sci* 1945; **1**: 246–53.
15   GJ to Botterell EH. Letter 7th October 1944.
16   GJ to GMF. Letters 10th/11th August 1912.
17   GJ to GMF. Letter 14th August 1912.
18   GJ to GMF. Letter 19th August 1912.
19   GJ to GMF. Letter 22nd August 1912.
20   Jefferson, Antony. Personal Communication, 27th July 1993.
21   Robinson RH, Le Fanu WR, eds. *The lives of the fellows of the Royal College of Surgeons of England. 1952–1964.* London: Livingstone, 1970: 128–9.
22   GJ to GMF. Letter 26th August 1912 (a).
23   GJ to GMF. Letter 26th August 1912 (b).
24   GJ to GMF. Letter 29th August 1912.
25   GJ to GMF. Letter 3rd September 1912.
26   GJ to GMF. Letter 4th September 1912.
27   GJ to GMF. Letter 7th September 1912.
28   GJ to GMF. Letter 8th September 1912.
29   GJ to GMF. Letter 21st September 1912.
30   GJ to GMF. Letters 23/29th September 1912.
31   Robinson A, *Cunningham's manual of practical anatomy.* 5th ed. Glasgow: Henry Doude and Hodder and Stoughton, 1912.
32   GJ to GMF. Letter 26th October 1912.
33   GJ to GMF. Letter 28th October 1912.
34   GMF to GJ. Letter 18th November 1912.
35   GJ to GMF. Letter 25th November 1912.
36   GJ to GMF. Letter 24th November 1912.
37   GJ to GMF. Letter 8th December 1912.
38   GMF to GJ. Letters 23/30th December 1912.
39   GJ to GMF. Letters 30/31st December 1912.
40   GMF to GJ. Letter 1st January 1913.
41   GJ to GMF. Letter 1st January 1913.
42   GJ to GMF. Letter 3rd January 1913.
43   GJ to GMF. Letter 5th January 1913.
44   GJ to GMF. Letter 11th January 1913.
45   GJ to GMF. Letter 21st January 1913.

Chapter 7

House surgeon at the Cancer Hospital
Emigration to Canada
1913

The Cancer Hospital in Fulham Road, London, where Jeff was next to work, was founded in 1851 by the philanthropist, W Marsden, for the treatment of all forms of malignant disease, and now bears the name of the Royal Marsden Hospital after its founder who was, incidentally, also the founder of the Royal Free Hospital. Its considerable scope provided the junior medical staff with wide experience. Of course only a limited number of malignant conditions were treatable then, even palliatively. Apparently Geoffrey's father and brother were both strongly against him working at the Cancer Hospital instead of in a general medical appointment, that would balance the exclusively surgical training posts which he had held so far. He would not accept their reasons for this and his, not very convincing, comment on the new job was: 'The fact of there being 15 applicants for the post shows there must be something in it'[1].

When Jefferson went to the Cancer Hospital in February 1913 for a 6 month appointment as house surgeon, it was to work for several Honorary Surgeons and for the Radiologist, Robert Knox. X-Rays were only identified by Röntgen in 1895 and it is noteworthy that Knox was appointed to the hospital as early as 1897. The x-ray department impressed Geoffrey very much, and he wrote that it was the most expensive in England. The sister in charge apparently took all the 'skiagrams' (x-rays) herself, and he reported to Gertrude that he was looking forward to learning a lot about the stomach from the radiology there. This he certainly did, the result being an important early paper, *The contraction forms of the human stomach*[2], together with two other papers on the stomach, mentioned later, and three papers on the duodenum, one of which was written in collaboration with Gertrude.

The most senior of the surgeons at the Cancer Hospital was William Miles (1869–1947). He was particularly interested in cancer of the bowel and his operation for abdomino-perineal removal of the rectum and sigmoid colon, which he introduced in 1907, has been a standard procedure ever since. Miles also made advances in the pathology of rectal carcinoma and numbered many famous surgeons among his trainees[3]. Jocelyn Swan (RHJ Swan, 1876–1943) was especially interested in genito-urinary surgery and also worked at St Peter's Hospital for Stone. However, he was an all-round surgeon and included peripheral nerve injuries and breast operations among his other concerns. Another surgeon for whom Geoffrey worked was Joseph Cunning (1872–1948) who came from Australia. He was also on the staff of the Victoria Children's Hospital, where Jeff had just been House Surgeon, and he was at the same time an 'Honorary' at St Bartholomew's Hospital. His interest lay in the upper abdomen and the stomach in particular[3]. Cecil Rowntree (1880–1943) was an enthusiastic and friendly man with high principles. He was relatively junior in 1913 but developed an international reputation as a cancer surgeon after World War I. His experience was largely gained at the Cancer Hospital under William Miles[3]. Finally, there was Charles Ryall (1870–1922) who was a genial Irishman with a reputation for operating for cancer of the breast, uterus, tongue and abdomen. He had been House Surgeon at the Cancer Hospital and had made such an impression that he was elected surgeon from that post on obtaining his FRCS. He was knighted in 1921[4]. These men together constituted a strong staff, providing a varied experience for their house officers.

Geoffrey had managed a short visit to Burnley to see Gertrude before starting work at the Cancer Hospital and while there he stayed with Dr Watson, the physician for whom she was working at the time. On arriving back in London on 4th February to take up his new job Jeff said he hoped to see her in 3 weeks, by which time she would have finished her appointment. He had mislaid a small 'G' tie brooch with a nugget on it, and asked Gertrude to make enquiries in case one of the maids at the Watsons had 'put it in a draw' [sic]. This was not to be by any means the last thing that he would mislay! It was the custom for a house surgeon to pay a locum to cover his duties if he was away on leave. In this case, whoever he had asked to cover this last weekend at the Victoria Children's Hospital 'was satisfied with a guinea, and our lovely time was worth it wasn't it darling'[5].

Jeff's report to Gertrude of his first day in the new appointment is interesting for its account of the work. Jocelyn Swan's afternoon operating list began with the exploration of an abdominal tumour which proved to be irremoveable on account of aortic glands. That was followed by a partial gastrectomy accompanied by the removal of a piece of abdominal wall 3" × 4" (7.5 × 10 cms) to which the cancer was adherent. This took $2\frac{1}{4}$ hours and there was difficulty in closing the wound. The patient was a 72 year old woman and Geoffrey expressed doubt about the wisdom of carrying out an operation which could only be justified on the grounds of doing anything that seemed to be possible. The list for the following day included a gastrectomy, removal of gall-stones, an operation for cancer of the jaw and a gland biopsy. Geoffrey commented: 'The theatre work here is good and the operative technique is also rather excellent. They have a magnificent table.... We use dry gloves and they have 3 nurses in the theatre all specially trained so everything goes like clockwork'[5]. The reference to dry gloves indicates that they had been sterilized in an autoclave. Wet gloves were boiled after use and put on when still wet — a risky method which was sometimes reverted to, as a result of necessity, during World War II. When wet gloves had been put on they were then scrubbed like hands. This reference suggests that 'wet gloves' had been used by Jeff elsewhere, and possibly in his last post in Chelsea. However, there is a most interesting remark on the subject of gloves in a footnote in one of the three papers he wrote later on the subject of Harvey Cushing. In it he said: 'In the writer's own time here [Manchester Royal Infirmary] as a house surgeon, 1909–1910, the two senior surgeons rarely wore rubber gloves, G A Wright (logically) when operating on a septic case, W Thorburn (illogically) when opening a knee joint'[6]. One would agree with his first comment but surely not with the second!

Jeff was responsible for about 52 beds at the Cancer Hospital, most of which were occupied by women. Nearly all the time that he spent in the operating theatre was in the rôle of an assistant to the surgeon, and he did not have much operating to do by himself.

It will be recalled that shortly before Jefferson left the Victoria Children's Hospital Herbert Waterhouse had urged him to sit for the London University degree of Master of Surgery (MS). But Geoffrey was hesitant. He certainly grudged the examination fee but, in the end, he did decide to attempt it. So he began to work for the examination due to be held in the summer, as soon as he was settled into the new appointment[7].

Before the Clean Air Act of 1956, and in the days when heating was almost universally by means of coal fires, fog was a familiar event in London. Not just a pale mist, but a dense yellow-black fog that prevented any vision further than a yard or two, and which brought a spate of respiratory diseases and deaths in its wake. The only sure way to travel at all rapidly in London on these occasions was by the Underground. In the middle of February 1913 Geoffrey wrote that, on one of these unpleasant days, he had been unable to go out on account of fog and rain and that the lights had been on in the hospital all day. He described it as being 'perfectly dreadful'.

Gertrude's job had finished by the weekend of 15/16th February and she was due to come to London on Thursday 20th. They were greatly looking forward to the opportunity of seeing each other more frequently than had been the case. However, Geoffrey thought that the separation of the last 6 months had been good for them, partly because their reunions had been 'so very sweet and splendid' but also on account of the clinical experience which they had both gained. Nevertheless he wondered if by coming into her life he might have upset her opportunities for advancement in her profession. 'If it hadn't been for me you would be going on to other posts and fresh appointments and taking more degrees and perhaps doing research for a few years either here or abroad before you settled down'[8]. But then, as if to justify their plans for an early marriage, which he must have realised would curb his own training and also curtail his experience, he commented that he felt that the compensation of their future partnership would in the end be a great gain to them both. 'We will share all our experience lovie when we are married and I have great visions of experimental work together at Vancouver — and the founding of perhaps a very great hospital there'[8]. He was thinking, no doubt, of the professorial appointment he aspired to at the then non-existent university in Vancouver, all of which lay entirely in the realms of fantasy. He wrote of himself, '...G has such dreams of success and of *Fame* for both of Us'. Coming down to earth again, he said that when Gertrude arrived in London he wanted to take her to a theatre or two, to see *Rosalind* at the Coliseum and to go to the Russian ballet[8].

Jeff wrote further that he had given two intravenous arsphenamine (Salvarsan) injections, which used to be prescribed for the treatment of syphilis, and had assisted with a gastro-enterostomy and the removal of a tongue. The injections were carried out in the operating theatre and in the ward. 'Of course I failed to get into the vein with the intravenous needle before the crowd, which was again fatal to G's self-conceit, but I got in finally.' He said he was writing up his work on the superior parietal sulcus of the brain prior to publication and thought that he would have it ready for Trude's criticism in a day or two[9].

Their reunion, however, was postponed because Gertrude also took the opportunity to visit the Jefferson parents again in Rochdale. From there, on 20th February, she wrote 'I grudged coming here just as much as you did my coming but felt it was in a way my duty. I am quite ready for Brighton on Sunday if you think best to go'[10]. She went by train from Burnley to Rochdale and then south to Oxford for one night before taking another train to London where she met Geoffrey. They then travelled together to meet his uncle and aunt in Hove. After the weekend she returned to Oxford, probably in a state of exhaustion, to stay with friends at 6 Park Crescent, Park Town, a pleasant part of the city.

In his letter of 25th February Jeff recalled how unsettled he was when she went back to Oxford after their short time together. He remarked that he had assisted with a laminectomy at which several posterior nerve roots were cut for the relief of chronic intractable pain. '...I hope it relieves her pain, but it is a curious fact that many cases have had just as severe pain after root section as before it, so cases in the literature show'[11]. He would be less surprised at this when he was older, but it indicates that, when he could spare it, he spent time reading 'the literature'. He had been given a tiny fibro-adenoma of the breast to remove, which he regarded as hardly worth doing, and had hinted to Mr Ryall that he hoped for something bigger to operate on. The letter concluded with a long quotation from *The shepherdess* by Alice Meynell, a poet and essayist whose work was then highly regarded[11].

Gertrude was still in Oxford when Geoffrey wrote to her on 25th March. One presumes that she had paid several visits to London in the meantime, as she continued to see him frequently during April. Geoffrey had written letters to various people with Easter greetings and was still revising the 'sulcus' paper. 'I really never can look at it without tinkering at it and altering and adding sentences. I've added a good bit tonight. Fortunately I'm sending it off tonight to be typed by Miss Green in M'ster or I'm sure I'd have crossed out tomorrow what I've written tonight and so on ad inf.... I am pretty confident in the truth of what I have written though it is largely theory.' He then told her about a number of urological cases before saying that he had bought a suitcase for 46/- and a small attaché case for 17/- '...a thing which I fear was very silly and selfish'[12].

Geoffrey was now being given a small amount of operating to do himself. Charles Ryall allowed him to dissect out some neck glands from the patient whose tongue had been removed for a carcinomatous tumour and Jocelyn Swan let him explore a tuberculous sinus. Jeff, at the same time, was making a study of the gastric mucosa as seen in x-rays, work which was to culminate in papers published in the next 2 years[13,14]. He received strong encouragement from Dr Knox and also from the Oxford radiologist, Dr AE Barclay*. He wrote on 7th

---

*Barclay, Alfred E. (1876–1949). Appointed medical officer in charge of radiography and electricity at Manchester Royal Infirmary in 1909. Pioneered the use of bismuth and barium to visualize the stomach and intestinal tract. Appointed to the Honorary staff 1918. Went to Cambridge and established a Diploma in Medical Radiology. In 1937 joined the MRC research team in Oxford and produced dramatic discoveries concerning the foetal circulation and that of the kidney and stomach. (Elwood WJ, Tuxford AF. *A biographical collection to mark the 150th anniversary of the Manchester Medical Society. 1834–1984.* Manchester: Manchester University Press, 1984).

April that he had shown his x-rays 'of bismuths' to Dr Knox who 'was extremely interested in them and proposes to use one or two of them for a book he is writing. He said he would refer to me in it.... I've been so excited ever since, thinking out possible ways of taking photographs.... I've written to Barclay telling him I am working at bismuths.... I seem to know a good deal more about it than the X-ray men here'. 'Knox is going to take me to Barclay's paper. It would be nice if I was asked to speak'[15].

It is not clear what happened during the next two months but, unfortunately, Gertrude did not pass the MB examination. She and Geoffrey were obviously able to see a lot of each other as she had now returned to London. Her address was 10 Zetland House, presumably in or near Fulham, so there was no need for letters. She clearly missed the company of her mother very much, and arrangements were made for her to return to Canada for a short visit to see her parents, leaving from Liverpool on 6th June and returning to England at the end of July. Geoffrey had recently visited a tailor to be measured for some new suits, for which Trude had chosen the cloth. He helped her to pack and, after a sad farewell, wrote a letter in time to reach Liverpool before she sailed[16]. On 14th June he received a telegram to say that she had arrived safely in Quebec. Geoffrey, in the meanwhile, had spent an enjoyable week-end at 'Uncle Frank's', in Hove and reported that 'Aunt Ada was very struck with Gertrude and thought she was awfully nice'[17].

Jefferson was due to sit the examination for the London University MS degree in the second week of July and had written: 'I am beginning to get a little panic stricken about the exam. Its awful really, I haven't looked at so many things and must put in some good work the next 3 weeks'[17]. But he managed to meet his old friend Harry Platt, who was working at the Royal National Orthopaedic Hospital in Great Portland Street, for a walk during one afternoon; they had some tea and enjoyed each others company very much. On the eve of the examination, he wrote that he had 'slaved all day long.... I don't know how I shall do, but feel fairly confident'[18].

There must have been a letter, now missing, in which he discussed the possibility of taking a holiday while Gertrude was away, and which he then regretted having written. Several of the letters kept by Gertrude are incomplete, with a page missing at the beginning or elsewhere. She disliked anything that she regarded as unpleasant in any way, and this would account for the absence of a page or more that had caused her distress; other missing pieces may have contained things she could have regarded as of too personal a nature to keep. The very preservation of such a large collection of letters for so many years, and the fact of Gertrude having slightly edited them, shows that she had the remote possibility of a biography at the back of her mind. It is unlikely that any other censorship took place.

Geoffrey wrote further on the subject of his projected holiday: 'It wouldn't be bad if the J [Jefferson] family were going away somewhere & would let me accompany them but that would hardly be possible, as if I was free they would expect me to be doing the locum [in the Rochdale practice] & reproach me for being with them when I might be doing the locum. That's just what has ruined my home life dear.' He told her to enjoy her holiday in Canada and contrasted her willingness to fulfil her duty to her parents with his situation. 'I can't help thinking what a different duty my parents expect of me and it makes me jealous'[18]. This outburst confirms the strained relationships that then existed within the Jefferson family.

The written part of the MS Examination was held on 7th July and was followed by *viva voce* sessions. The Operative Surgery examination was due to begin on 11th July at 1.30 pm but Jeff was angered to find out on the previous day that he had been put on the list to anaesthetise at 9.30 am for Cecil Rowntree, when he had planned to spend the morning doing some last minute revision. In the event he 'struck after the first case at a quarter to eleven' and got someone else to take over from him. He was nervous: 'I simply couldn't swallow any food. When I got to the Exam. Hall we had to wait nearly 45 minutes and then went in...'. Mr Raymond Johnson, from University College Hospital, asked him to perform an extraperitoneal ligation of the External Iliac artery 'Which I got all right but the patient [corpse] was a very difficult one and it took a long time. R.J. said it was a very difficult operation, which was comforting. My hand shook so when I was trying to incise the fascia transversalis I made a ragged sort of tear, but all my nervousness disappeared when I found I had *not* opened the peritoneal cavity...'. Wilfred Trotter*, a famous surgeon from the same hospital whose skill as an author has already been mentioned, gave him an excision of the lower jaw to perform. Trotter himself was renowned for his expertise in operating on maxillary and facial growths. 'I got it all right. It was a tremendous relief tho' it took an hour to do the two. I am so very thankful it is over'[19].

In the same letter, but continuing on the following day, he added: 'I am so very relieved as the operative which I feared so much is over. It was awful really, I was almost paralysed with funk.... I went down to Univ. College for the clinical and had these cases again with Raymond Johnson. 1) Case of fract. scapula with great effusion 4 weeks old ?growth. 2) Naevoid stainings (grey coloured).... This fairly had me as I thought it was a skin disease, but I blurted out something about naevus in the end.... 3) Carcinoma of the tongue, with suppurating glands in neck. 4) Curious case with abdominal sinuses which I said was probably actinomycotic (he agreed).' The co-examiner with Raymond Johnson on this occasion was Professor William Thorburn from Manchester, 'who never winked an eye-lid to show that he knew me, which rather upset me'. Jeff was examined on '1) A nodule in the v. fat breast of a woman which I said was a carcinoma or a cyst. I believe it was tuberculous as a matter of fact. 2) A case of traumatic coxa vara in a little girl. W.T. left an x-ray cover lying by her with cong. discloc. of Hip on it! 3) A scrotum case, testicle disorganised with abscess formation — I failed to diagnose it. 4) A neuropathic shoulder joint — due to syringomyelia. I suggested Tabes at first, & later Syringo. So tho' I wasn't bad with Johnson, I did worse with W.T. a good bit. I think on the whole though I ought to be through, as I felt I was doing pretty well. I came home quite pleased with myself but very tired'[19]. That evening he dined with several fellow Mancunians, including Harry Platt and the neurologist Fergus Ferguson, another life-time friend, both also members of the London-based 'MRI Club', which had been formed by a number of colleagues

---

*Trotter WR. (1872–1939). Though an FRS, famous in his day and revered at University College Hospital, Trotter is now remembered most for his book, *Herd instincts in peace and war*, published in 1916. In it he considered human behaviour and the self-destructive effects of man's aggression.

from the Manchester Royal Infirmary. After dinner they went to the Hippodrome to see a revue called *Hello Ragtime*.

There was a pathology *viva* the next day in which he got '3 or perhaps 4 out of 5 slides right, 2 quite right and the others in rather a scratchy manner. I spotted the culture (Actinomyces on potato) and 1 x-ray, periostitis of fibula. I suppose I got pass marks without undue brilliancy'[20].

On the afternoon following the examination Jefferson travelled by train to Stoke Poges, in Buckinghamshire, and spent the weekend there with the Swan family at their country cottage. He found the place 'more beautiful I think than anything I have ever seen'. The golf club was in a building 'which had been Charles II's pleasure house. Wonderful old lawns with very big and perfect trees, and splendid terraces and gardens.... This cottage is set amongst trees on the edge of the links'. Geoffrey played golf and tennis but felt very tired. 'Graham White flew over the links in his biplane twice. It was the first flight that I have ever seen.' By the same post he sent Gertrude a reprint of an article he had had published and remarked that all his papers so far (three or four) had been written after they were engaged[20].

He had to get up at 7.30 am on the Monday in order to catch the London train, but managed to do so and arrived back at the hospital around 9.45 am, feeling so relieved that the examination was over that he could even feign indifference as to whether he was 'either entirely below or altogether above the pass line'[21].

Geoffrey's delight can hardly be imagined when, on Thursday 17th July, he was able to write that 'Waterhouse rang me up to tell me I had got the gold-medal in the MS. He said Thorburn had told him secretly and I am not to tell anyone. I am very happy and pleased as it is a splending ending to my examination career and really fulfils my last and highest ambition.... It also balances Platt's getting the medal in the final M.B. and not in the M.S. I don't believe a M'ster man has ever won the M.S. medal before'[22]. Geoffrey 'borrowed 10 shillings from a night nurse, via night sister and rushed down to Charing X,' to send a telegram to Gertrude with the news. He arrived there 10 minutes before the telegraph office closed at midnight. He had celebrated the end of the examination with Harry Platt that evening by going out to dinner and visiting the Coliseum theatre.

The following day Geoffrey was faced with a difficult situation. 'Thorburn asked me via Higgins to go to see him at the R.C.S. [Royal College of Surgeons] where he was examining today. He told me I had the medal and he wanted to be the first to congratulate me. I had just seen Waterhouse in the hall & he told me not to let on that I knew. W.T's message from Higgins was that if I went to see him today I should hear something greatly to my advantage. It was nice of W.T. wasn't it. He told me I had done very well, esp. in anatomy in which I had got a very big mark indeed'[23]. Jeff must have now forgiven Thorburn for not showing any sign of recognition during the examination! His faithful brother Jack wrote to congratulate him: 'The people at home will dance with glee, especially the old Dad as he has been rather gloomy lately. He has got into the habit, while he is playing patience of saying "Now we'll see whether Geoff is through" & he has not succeded in getting "Patience" more than about once in twenty times when consulting fate about the result of the M.S. So he had become quite resigned to your failure'[24].

There are several undated pages, written on different days, which follow the news about the MS examination and it is difficult to be sure of their order.

However, one of these contains some telling thoughts, and expresses Jeff and Gertrude's clear and firm intention to emigrate soon to Canada. As was frequently the case, the discrepancy between their financial situations emerged again as a great source of worry: 'I am not very favourably disposed towards settling in Vict. dear, [he wrote to her at her family's home] as I'm sure we should not be able to call our souls our own thro' your parents' solicitude and generosity. And what with their Pride dear, there would be no room for Ours. I feel most militant and wish we could just fight our way and live on very little regardless of what they want. I am prepared to do it myself now dear if I could get a small opening on a staff somewhere. That's what makes me feel my ignorance of the country so keenly. I wonder what the qualifying exam is like, I hope you are bringing some books of questions they set over [with you] as it would be interesting to see them. Is there a clinical exam as well?'. These remarks did not mean that he had second thoughts about emigrating to Canada but merely with regard to living in the relatively small town of Victoria. His real ambition was for a Professorial Chair in either surgery or anatomy in a future University in Vancouver, and he may have thought, but not said, that the chances of such recognition were more likely in the capital of the Province than in a less important neighbourhood. 'I should like to have a teaching post so much, as I fear we should degenerate unless we were connected with a medical school'[25].

Geoffrey was looking forward to her return and wondered if they might manage to stay with his maternal Uncle John (John James — who was later knighted and moved to Ollerton Grange, near Knutsford) and his Aunt Gracie at Coulby Manor, Ormesby, Near Marton, North Yorkshire, where they were then living, 'and have his motor to ourselves.... Then if you will come to R'dale for a few days we can hold a solemn conclave, and thrash matters out a bit. I do wish I did not look so poisonously young dearie and think you must allow me to wear a moustache if it doesn't look worse than the present state'. Again his anxiety about money came to the surface. 'I do so wish that I had an assured position so that I could ask you to marry me dear without delay. All the uncertainty springs from my being a money-earning nonentity'[23]. In the event Geoffrey visited Coulby Manor on his own.

On 23rd July Jeff operated on an ectopic gestation 'with Ryall's help'. His appointment at the Cancer Hospital was running out and it was necessary to begin to make final preparations for the journey to Canada. He went to see Jocelyn Swan who 'showed me all his instruments and told me the best pattern of cystoscope & urethroscope'. Afterwards Swan and he dined alone and then went to see a revue at the Alhambra (*Eightpence a mile*), which Jeff had seen previously. 'We had stalls and could hear better — also see better; the girls had awfully little on.' Next day he dashed up to Oxford 'by the 3.18 and caught the 7.35 back'[26]. In the short time that he was there he made arrangements for Gertrude's bicycle to be sent to Rochdale and saw Lady Osler.

Many years later, on 1st April 1942, when Jocelyn Swan was in the Private Wing of University College Hospital dying of carcinoma of the lung, he received a letter from Geoffrey Jefferson. In his reply Swan wrote: '...I too vividly recall the days when you were my H.S. at the Cancer Hospital, when you set a standard that I never saw equalled & only once approached. How well you summed up the staff then at work — with the exception of myself. I always felt I owed much to the surgery and techniques of Ryall & Miles & that I was fortunate to work under them. Miles improved greatly as he matured. Cunning did not remain with us long & soon after bought a lovely estate in Surrey to which he retired as a country squire. Wilson resigned when he was appointed to Bart's.... Rowntree was really good provided one broke through his Kitcheneresque pose.... We had a good team in those days'[27].

On 24th July 1913, the day on which Gertrude began her long journey back to England, Geoffrey played tennis but acquired a sore elbow as a result and probably a painful knee, since this achieved prominent mention in a subsequent letter. He was elated at having beaten his first opponent '6 sets to none', [since it was underlined by Jeff one presumes that it really was 6 Sets and not 6 games]. He was then beaten 5–7 and won 6–1 against someone else. If he really did play eight sets in an afternoon it shows grim determination if nothing else and, in his physical state, subsequent discomfort or disability would have been inevitable.

The next day Jeff went to the Holloway Instrument Company to buy some of the instruments that he would need to take to Canada — financed by Gertrude on the understanding that they would be used in partnership. These included an abdominal retractor, Moynihan's tissue forceps, Miles' suture forceps, Cushing's needle holder, Lane's tissue forceps, O'Malley's tonsil guillotine [despite his earlier remarks about its inefficiency], St Clair Thompson's adenoid curette, towel clips and Lane's stomach clamps. He played some more tennis too, this time against one of the Sisters whom he beat 6–0. '...but I am terribly pleased with myself as I discovered I could do a new stroke, esp. practised by Wilding [the author of a second-hand book on tennis which Geoffrey had purchased]. It is the lifting drive and it came off every time at great speed. I am delighted. I'm beginning to get conceited about tennis as I have improved a great deal this summer all round'[28].

The MRI Club was going for a day trip to Boulogne on Sunday 27th July, and Geoffrey had written to Trude that he hoped that she would not mind him accompanying them. However, he changed his plans and instead, on Saturday 26th July, he completed his packing and the hand-over of his patients, and took the Scottish Express to Ormesby, in Yorkshire, in order to spend a few days with his Uncle John. The train was 'simply bursting with people so considered it best to travel 1st Class as my knee was hardly fit to sit 6 aside and have people falling over it.... I was so nervous of getting it twisted at all'. On Sunday he went for a 'very pretty motor drive inland to a village called Helmesley'. Geoffrey 'went out with Uncle J. in the car and he let me drive it about 8 miles, I did fairly well but not altogether marvellously. Another 3 or 4 times and I shall be all right. Its the gear changing, starting and stopping which need experience'[29]. Such was the hazardous process by which drivers learnt their skills before the days of driving tests. He enjoyed talking to his uncle and was tempted to stay up late to do so. He continued to stay in Ormesby but did no more motoring 'as the top gear is being overhauled'[29]. One wonders why!

On that eventful day at the College of Surgeons, when Sir William Thorburn had told Geoffrey of his success in the MS examination, he had also given him some information about Gertrude's failure in the MB. This he now passed on to her in a letter written from Yorkshire. She was apparently only one mark below the pass in Forensic Medicine, and that would have been overlooked if she had not also done poorly in Midwifery. Also in the same letter, but written on a different day, he told her more about his own situation and his expectation of how the family would have reacted to his news. 'I don't think Father quite realises what it means [to have got the MS gold medal] and thinks it is like the M.D., which is a general practitioners exam. Whilst the M.S. is considered in London the hall-mark of the consulting surgeon'[30]. Our reaction to this scornful dismissal of the London doctorate has to be tempered by an appreciation of Geoffrey's elation at the time and the expectation he would have had that his father, who held a <u>Doctorate</u> in Medicine, would not be as impressed by a <u>Master's</u> degree as Jeff would have liked. It is even possible that Arthur Jefferson might have been unaware that there was no such London degree as a doctorate in surgery. His thoughts then turned to their future together in Canada. 'What does make me glad is that it ought to be the sure means of getting a Univ. appointment in Canada. I wonder what you have heard about the Vancouver Univ. and what openings there will be there'[30]. Alas, the University remained no more than a dream which would not become reality for many years*.

In his conclusion, to the letter just quoted, Geoffrey said that he felt that he ought to be working and not just enjoying himself in Yorkshire. He was without employment and was just waiting for the day when he would sail for Canada. He even passed the thought on to Gertrude that he might go on a voyage as a ship's doctor while she was preparing to resit the MB, or precede her to Victoria while she delayed her departure until after the examination in November. 'I'm <u>quite quite quite</u> sure you'll get thro' the M.B. in Nov. with all sails set and flags flying'[30]. She, on her part, undoubtedly felt the pressure that he was exerting upon her. However, at the beginning of October his anxiety about her health and strength led him to write, 'Don't hesitate to only take half the exam, as I am terrified of the strain being too much for you'[31].

Geoffrey met Gertrude when she arrived at the Liverpool docks from Canada and for the next month, as a consequence of their being together, we have no precise information as to events and where they were. However, during this time plans were made for Geoffrey to go out to Canada, ahead of Gertrude, on the Cunarder RMS *Megantic*. At the beginning of September, whilst staying with his parents, he wrote that he ought to spend a few days in Manchester dissecting stomachs, after which he thought 12 more days at home in Rochdale 'ought to satisfy them but I really don't see that much good will come of it as I just laze away the time here, do the dispensing, pay odd visits and so on — all of which is more trying than exciting'[32]. Gertrude was in Manchester at this time and Jeff arranged to meet her on 4th September, at the corner of Market Street and Cross Street at 1.45 pm. There was obviously much that they had to discuss.

The next day, Geoffrey went up to London and stayed in an hotel in Pembridge Gardens, Notting Hill Gate. He then spent almost the whole of the following day purchasing more instruments of various kinds for their joint practice. These included a urethro-broncho-oesophagoscope, which extraordinary instrument cost £12.17.9! He said that he had endeavoured to keep the prices down and in

---

*University of British Columbia. Forty years were to elapse before the first class graduated in British Columbia. The university was eventually located in Vancouver but did not open until 1950, the year before Jefferson retired.

some cases purchased at half the cost of comparable instruments elsewhere. 'However, it is a simply magnificent outfit and I shall be so proud of it for our sakes.... I don't think it would be any pleasure to me to feel that it was entirely my own.... At the present I am worth £336.10.5., far far far the most money that I have ever had before. It is so very very sweet of you to lend it to me'[33].

Geoffrey did not, after all, go out to Canada on the *Megantic* and a passage was booked on the SS *Virginian* of the Allen Line. He sailed on the 24th September 1913, taking his instruments with him, to be followed by Gertrude a few months later. On 30th September he wrote from the ship to report that he was nearing Quebec[34].

REFERENCES

GJ=Geoffrey Jefferson; GMF=Gertrude Flumerfelt
1   GJ to GMF. Letter 13th February 1913.
2   Jefferson G. The contraction forms of the human stomach. *Arch Radiol Electrotherapy* 1917/18; **22**: 161–73.
3   Power d'A, Le Fanu WR, eds. *The lives of the fellows of the Royal College of Surgeons of England. 1930–1951*. London: Royal College of Surgeons, 1953: 190, 692–3, 750–1.
4   Power d'A, ed. *Plarr's lives of the fellows of the Royal College of Surgeons of England*. London: Royal College of Surgeons, 1930; **2**: 257.
5   GJ to GMF. Letter 4th February 1913.
6   Jefferson G. Harvey Cushing. *Manchester University Medical Students' Gazette* 1943; **22**: 2–16.
7   GJ to GMF. Letter 5th January 1913.
8   GJ to GMF. Letter 18th February 1913.
9   GJ to GMF. Letter 19th February 1913.
10   GJ to GMF. Letter 20th February 1913.
11   GJ to GMF. Letter 25th February 1913.
12   GJ to GMF. Letter 25th March 1913.
13   Jefferson G. The human stomach and the canalis gastricus (Lewis). *J Anat Physiol* 1914; **44**: 165–81.
14   Jefferson G. A note on the passage of fluid through the body of the human stomach. *Arch Roentgen Ray* 1915; **14**: 414–6.
15   GJ to GMF. Letter 7th April 1913.
16   GJ to GMF. Letter 5th June 1913.
17   GJ to GMF. Letter 14th June 1913.
18   GJ to GMF. Letter 6th July 1913.
19   GJ to GMF. Letter 10th/11th July 1913.
20   GJ to GMF. Letter 12th July 1913.
21   GJ to GMF. Letter 14th July 1913.
22   GJ to GMF. Letter 17th July 1913.
23   GJ to GMF. Letter 18th July 1913.
24   Jefferson, Jack to GJ. Letter undated 1913.
25   GJ to GMF. Letter undated 1913.
26   GJ to GMF. Letters undated sequence July 1913.
27   Swan J to GJ. Letter 1st April 1942.
28   GJ to GMF. Letter 25th July 1913.
29   GJ to GMF. Letters undated sequence. ?26th–30th July 1913.
30   GJ to GMF. Letter undated ?1st August 1913.
31   GJ to GMF. Letter undated October 1913.
32   GJ to GMF. Letter 3rd September 1913.
33   GJ to GMF. Letter 5th September 1913.
34   GJ to GMF. Letter 30th September 1913.

Chapter 8

Canada
1913–1916

In his letter of 30th September, written while on board ship, Geoffrey Jefferson gave Gertrude his impressions of the voyage to Canada on the steamship *Virginian*. He remarked on the incomparable beauty of an iceberg that the ship had passed; 'its marvellous whiteness and semi-transparent green-ness and then a marvellous band of blue across it where there was a crack in it. I have really enjoyed the voyage.... I am in love with Canada already.... I feel so glad and free dear—to be away from England and all the little worries. Of course I expect fresh worries in the New Country and new bonds, but they will at least be my own.... I shall not be feeling torn between family & my future'[1].

Jefferson met Gertrude's father for the first time at the Windsor Hotel in Montreal. 'Well is this Geoffrey' was his cordial greeting, and they appear to have got on well together from the start. Jeff wrote: 'He was quite charming', but 'he has a restless mind tho' dear & that keeps him rather uncomfortable I think—v. little repose'. Mr Flumerfelt showed Geoffrey round the city, made him a temporary member of the Mount Royal Club and introduced him to a Governor of McGill University who took him all over the campus. He also met the curator of the university's pathological museum who impressed him. Finally, Gertrude's father suggested that they should go to New York together as he had business to attend to there[1].

Accordingly they travelled south on the night sleeper train and were ensconced in the Waldorf Astoria Hotel in New York next day, during which Jeff visited the American College of Surgeons. On the following morning he went to the College of Physicians and 'walked 26 blocks+1 mile' to the Columbia Medical Center, where he had an introduction to the famous pathologist, Professor Macallum, but, as he was away, they unfortunately failed to meet. Professor Huntington in the Pathological Anatomy Department created particular excitement for Geoffrey on account of his investigations of the neural tube. He 'had many very very elaborate and difficult reconstructions. It was all most fascinating'. He was also interested to see preparations made by the corrosive method, using wax injections to preserve the anatomy of cavities or vessels before digesting the soft tissues by various means. As quite often seems to have been the case in London, the day ended with a visit to a theatrical revue. The next day Jefferson spent sightseeing. In the evening he invited Mr Flumerfelt to dinner at the Ritz-Carlton, which cost $6.80 'but we didn't have much & its terrible anyway'. Geoffrey felt he was getting to know his future father-in-law and his conclusion was that Mr Flumerfelt had neglected 'the softer side of life' and that he would like him 'better when I have done something to make him respect me—not I mean that he doesn't but I feel how he has accomplished great things himself & I'm only a beginner at it'[2].

On 5th October we find Geoffrey writing in pencil on the train travelling from New York back to Montreal. He was alone since Mr Flumerfelt had remained in Manhattan on business. Gertrude, meanwhile, was staying at Camp End, Malvern, in Worcestershire. Jeff had been reading Gerhardt Hauptmann's *Coming of peace* (presumably in English, judging by the title) and also a play called *The necessary evil*, the script of which he had bought in New York. The subject of the play was prostitution and its evils. Jeff thought it 'should have a very wide scope, as it will inform women who know nothing of the existence of unfortunates. (I must plead guilty to being attracted by the title in buying it—but I'm very glad I did as it will be a good book to hand to people to get them interested too)'. He then went on to praise Gertrude's capabilities. 'You know dear you are a remarkable girl, as I find all your arguments used in these plays and books, just as I found your religion in Ibsen and Shaw*. And yet I know you evolved it all yourself.' He begged her not to work too hard or to 'feel too deeply about social problems...as you simply wear yourself away. I haven't forgotten that day at Beechwood when you trembled from head to foot'[3].

On arrival at Montreal, Jeff returned to the Windsor Hotel and visited various medical institutions in the city, about which he wrote rather scathingly after a very brief acquaintance. Characteristically, he had left his Gladstone bag at the Allen Line shipping office when he disembarked from the *Virginian* but did not discover its loss for 5 to 6 days. One hopes that it did not contain any of the precious new instruments.

Geoffrey began his letter of 6th October with a description of how he had met a girl named Q– on the *Virginian*, who was going out to Canada with her father and elder sister to be married. Geoffrey had shared their table in the ship's dining room. Her father turned up at the hotel and gave Jeff the news that the engagement had been broken by Q–'s fiancé who had decided to marry someone else; as a consequence, the wedding was no longer going to take place. Apparently she had written to Geoffrey to give him the news, but the letter never arrived. Jeff in turn told Gertrude: 'It has been an awful blow to me, a real grief as she is such a nice girl—indeed darling I have quite an affection for her and her sister...it hurts me to see her suffer. I've written to her but it is difficult not to rush in where angels fear to tread.... I was glad I had expounded [our] religion to her (she thought it lovely), so that I was able to say in my letter how I thought it was Destiny working for the best and saving her from who knows what sorrows. She showed me his photo'. Geoffrey was careful to explain that it was 'a very real "affection" that he felt for the girl—not <u>love</u> dear', such as he and Gertrude felt for each other, and in writing to Q– he had explained how happy and secure he and Gertrude were. 'My motive was to let her be quite sure that my

---

*Ibsen and Shaw. Ibsen persistently attacked orthodox Christianity, not on the grounds of reason but in the name of more intense Christianity. He believed that the greatest wrong one can commit is to deny love. In 1898 Shaw defended Ibsen strongly against his critics, who did not appreciate that he stood for his own interpretation of Christianity, which was based on a greater degree of love than the church evinced and on a broader interpretation of the word, rather than against Christianity itself.

Shaw, on the other hand, identified God with a Life Force; he saw the Universe as the evolution of deity from the lowest forms of life, eventually to become God Himself. He also believed that Man, as an expression of God, must be responsible for his own destiny.

writing to her was entirely platonic and due to the friendliness I bore her and nothing more'[4]. Nevertheless, this innocent "affection" was a manifestation of the tenderness, not to say attraction, that Geoffrey always felt for women, and it needed to be explained rather carefully. Almost 40 years later Sir George Pickering, then Regius Professor of Medicine at Oxford, wrote concerning a train journey that Jeff had made; he realised 'that the journey had not been unbearable. As the Scots say "The de'il taks care of his ain"', but he usually seems to manifest himself to you as a charming young lady'[5].

In Montreal he also met a friend of Gertrude's named Beryl and they had a long talk. Beryl 'thinks you spoil me and just do whatever I say ... but I think I do pretty well what you say in return.... I do so hope I give too darling, and don't do all the talking'. After their talk 'I walked in the twilight (what there is of it here) back to the Hosp. with her [where Beryl worked]'. In an endeavour to retrieve his Gladstone bag, he 'spent nearly 2 hours trying to find the Allen Coy's wharf by the riverside. I got in a hopeless tangle and ended 2 miles too high up the river in a horrible looking French quarter where I was eyed suspiciously. I got into such a muddle with the trams in the dark, as I don't know the streets at all — in fact have no idea of the geography of M. The result was I got back here at 8.0 (I left Beryl at 6.20) but I found my bag all right'[4].

By 9th October, en route for British Columbia, Geoffrey had reached Winnipeg where he broke the journey again. The city was of some interest to him since Gertrude had been born there. 'In the streets here ... I saw many people I had only seen on the cinematograph — rough riders etc.... all sorts of men, mostly very rough and poor-looking, but all looked well and healthy. It was interesting to see how many fire-arm shops there were, for hunting etc; canoe shops and all the funny rough fur-lined boots and coats were for sale. It is bitterly cold here.' As a postcript he added 'I went into an Art Gallery and saw some beautiful water colours by Russell Flint'[6].

Geoffrey had an introduction to the Superintendent of the Winnipeg General Hospital, which he soon put to good use. After being shown over the buildings, he wrote that he was impressed by the small wards of four to six beds and by the arrangements for private and semi-private patients. 'I'm sure there will be a great opening in time for the man who will dare to stand or fall by surgery alone.... The only thing is, it will need money to wait. But of that later. Your Father I think is so generous, and I hate to be dependent, as I hate to feel anyone has a special call on me to direct my actions as I am in his debt.' He concluded that money rather than original work was the goal of most of the doctors in Winnipeg. 'A good man would electrify the place, but probably have to face severe discouragement. I should not at all like to live here ... I don't like the atmosphere a bit — it is quite different from Montreal which I liked.... I'm sure we'll beat Winnipeg easily if we can only lay our hands on the money, as we have the ideals'[6]. He apparently ignored the fact that the General Hospital in Winnipeg had a total of no less than 600 beds. It was strong competition! Jefferson was 27 when he produced these somewhat fanciful and arrogant remarks. However, it must be remembered that they were written over 80 years ago, when the state of medicine was hardly comparable with the present situation, especially in the more remote towns in Canada. It was also a time when Jeff needed all the enthusiasm and hope that he could muster in order to justify his move from England to a distant, as yet unknown to him, part of the New World.

The first page of the letter of the 13/14th October is missing but, from the next, one is aware that Gertrude had had some sort of accident and had damaged a skirt of which she was obviously very fond. Geoffrey was extremely upset and told her, as he had on many occasions, to take care of herself for both their sakes. He hoped that she would put on weight after her next attempt at the MB examination, and that when the worry of this was over she would be less tired[7]. Geoffrey himself had complained of tiredness several times during the year but, possibly more significantly, he seems to have had frequent headaches which were quite incapacitating and may have been migrainous or related to tension and anxiety. These continued to occur in Canada.

By mid-October 1913 Geoffrey had arrived in British Columbia, and was staying in the Flumerfelt home, Ruhebühne, in Pemberton Road, Victoria. Gertrude's mother, whom Geoffrey had come to know quite well in England, was ready to talk confidentially with him. She discussed the marriage of her younger daughter Norma and her English husband Herbert Ritchie. No doubt this was more than a conversation piece and was intended to be advice for Geoffrey and Gertrude's benefit. Mrs Flumerfelt entertained Jeff well, and even gave him breakfast in bed for at least the first 2 days after he arrived.

A family friend, Dr Wasson, came to visit them and was most kind to Jeff. He provided him with various books that he needed, and advised him to stick to surgery rather than start with a general practice, but this did not fit in with Geoffrey's plans. After he had told Gertrude about Dr Wasson's advice, he wrote: 'I fear I shall have to spend a lot of money on periodicals, tho' I should like to get a library going here and think it might be done, as Dr Wasson and Dr Fagan both thought it high time there was one. I went in to see Dr Fagan after, he is Sec. for the exam [the Provincial qualifying examination]. He is a nice old chap with a dry sense of humour. I thought it as well to make a good impression on him, and I told him what I had done as he is one of the examiners'. Jeff said he was going to work up various subjects for the examination 'and invent the rest. I daresay they'll push me thro' all right even if I don't do well in the lesser subjects. I think the idea of the exam as far as Dr Fagan could conscientiously tell us is simply so that they can keep undesirables out when they come along'. He was sorry that Gertrude would also have to take it and took the opportunity to wish her luck with the MB, '...I know [you'll] do very well and get through with flying colours. It would be nice to get Honours, but Oh what a joy a simple pass will be'. Geoffrey must have realised that, once again, he was putting on too much pressure, for he continued: 'I shan't be disappointed except for your sake if you don't get thro' in part or all dear, tho' I have no fear of that at all and don't quite know why I say it'[7]. Gertrude must have read all this with some apprehension.

It was too cold to go into the countryside, so Geoffrey was driven in the car around the town and neighbourhood. He was especially attracted by an area which was being developed and, half teasingly, said how nice it would be to build a house there. Mrs Flumerfelt had a long talk with him in the evening about his prospects, for Gertrude's father was still away on business. 'I have decided dear to start doing surgery and medicine as well but not midder. Then perhaps when you really start out here, I could hand the medicine over to you and then finally you'd emerge from it and we'd stand together'[7]. This was a somewhat different proposal from the plans that were made in England, but Gertude was probably too concerned about the forthcoming MB examination to contest them.

No letters have been preserved from the next month; presumably they were mislaid or not kept for some reason, for letters there must have been. By 12th November 1913 Geoffrey was visiting Seattle which, though in the United States, is not far from Victoria if the strait between Washington State and Vancouver is crossed by ferry. There he was the guest of Norma and Herbert Ritchie. Herbert, who was a professional musician, entertained him by playing the violin, but Geoffrey did not appreciate the music which he thought was 'too abstract and technically difficult'. He told Trude: 'Norma says that Herbert is rather given to playing very modern technical pieces that haven't much tune in them.... I was very lame in my congratulations'. As to Norma herself, Geoffrey thought she could be 'a great musician if she could be a little more <u>abandoned</u>.... She needs someone to draw her out and make her realise her great beauty and power'. There is no doubt that Jeff was quite struck by Norma, who was more sensitive and aesthetic than Gertrude, yet also more practical, and he might even have wished that he could cast himself in the role of her redeemer. 'Poor soul, I am so fond of her dearie. I have quite fallen in love with my sweetheart's sister. We had a little talk about books etc. on Mon, and each day since'[8].

While he was in Seattle Geoffrey bought an examination couch for $47. 'I think I shall buy the big steriliser too as it will do for you too. It will be $72. I have thought it over carefully and think it will be wisest to pay this and get the best article. This will have an instrument steriliser, dressing towel steriliser (wet & dry heat), sterile water receptacle & hot water receptacle.' During the previous weeks a suitable flat for use as consulting rooms had been found in Fort Street, Victoria, and this was being redecorated. Geoffrey described their new offices and drew a plan for Trude to show how their equipment could be fitted in. He said that he was currently using the larger front room, but would be willing to let her have it when she arrived[8]. Later he wrote that her parents 'have spent a lot of money in having those offices made nice. They persuaded me the Western Lands [owners of the building] had done it but today the cat escaped from the bag...it makes me feel sad how they <u>insist</u> on undermining ones independence'. In this letter he also said: 'I think I can see a field of activity ahead of me and success and am quite happy about my own future here. I shall do as little med. as possible and emphasise surgery as being my *forte* (midder I feel is barred)'. He could not, however, resist saying 'I should love you to have the M.B.'[9].

Norma drove Geoffrey over to Victoria on 17th November to say goodbye to Mr Flumerfelt who had returned from New York and was about to leave for Vancouver on his way to England to meet Gertrude. As if in answer to Jeff's earlier misgivings about having pressed too hard concerning her next attempt at the MB examination, he now heard that she had decided not to sit for it after all. He wrote that he was happy that she was relieved of the strain and worry. 'And yet how complex our feelings are...for what will be best and most perfect. I should love you to have the M.B. dear really as I know you would too.' Even now he could not stop trying to persuade her to take it, for it seems to have become almost an obsession that she should have the degree. However, Gertrude's father had other ideas and wanted her to have golf lessons! He had put Geoffrey up for the Oak Bay Club and had made him a temporary member of the Union Club in Victoria, probably with the idea that by meeting people socially at both places Jeff might find it easier to establish their medical practice. Nevertheless this well-meant gesture was not altogether appreciated, for Geoffrey wrote that he had 'no particular desire for club life'[9].

When Gertrude's father arrived in England, he proposed that they should take a trip around Europe which would incidentally, give her the opportunity to visit one or two clinics there. Geoffrey advised her that '... the main thing is to catch the atmosphere of the clinic and type of work without trying to enter too deeply into its work.... That as you know is my own method'. Almost unbelievably, his obsession for her to have a degree surfaced yet again: 'If when you have done this for a bit you feel as if you could take the M.B. without too much change of thought, I certainly should', and he begged her not to make a final decision until she had compared her position with foreign standards. Finally, he said that it was as well that she was not going to join him immediately because the painters would not be out of the offices until the next day. He hoped that they would marry in the summer, which would entail a further delay of at least 6 or 7 months[9].

Gertrude and her father travelled to London and stayed at the Ritz Hotel in Piccadilly. On 21st November Geoffrey wrote to her, actually penning the letter in the new office in Fort Street for the first time, and said he had ordered some headed notepaper. He must also, by now, have made himself available for consultation and perhaps even ordered a brass plate engraved with their names. 'Mother thinks they are the nicest offices in town,' he proudly reported. Geoffrey was most impressed and described the furnishing and layout of the rooms in more detail, including the pictures he proposed to hang on the walls — one of

Figure 7 *Geoffrey Jefferson at his desk in Victoria, BC (ca. 1915).*

which was *Sir Galahad* by Isaac Watts. He asked Gertrude to buy reproductions of one or two more similar paintings by Watts and a catalogue of the Medici Society publications, because pictures of that quality could not be obtained locally. But then he felt he had over-stepped the mark: 'I don't suppose you have any spare money at all any more than I have, so on 2nd thoughts, don't buy anything'[10].

Remorse was yet again the subject of much of the letter that he wrote on 26th November, pleading for her forgiveness for having hurt her by his continued harping on the need for the MB degree. His contrition and self-reproach almost exceeded his power of expression. 'I was <u>glad</u> to have you ask couldn't I be happy without wanting to make a name, be a professor or write papers. I often have longed for nothing but peace and obscurity in my home with you but never dared to tell you so. I honestly don't value anything beside you...'[11]. This was not true. It was a statement that came from the loneliness and insecurity of their circumstances and the frustration of their separation; it was quite contrary to Geoffrey's nature and frequently expressed ambitions, as the future was eventually to prove. It does, nevertheless, give a glimpse of Gertrude's innermost thoughts, and shows how her devotion to Jeff was to be called on to sustain her in the years to come.

The address of the new offices was Western Lands Building, $725\frac{1}{2}$ Fort Street, Victoria B.C., and his letter to Gertrude of 28th November was the first to be written on the new headed notepaper. Their boxes and belongings had just arrived from England and most of them were stored in the billiard room at Ruhebühne, waiting until the Jeffersons had a home of their own. He asked Gertrude to send him French's '*Lab methods*' and 'I must tell you that Doris Somerville's book "*Green chalk*" is out.... Send it to me after you have read it, if you think I am old enough and that it is fit for me. I fear it may not be'[12]. This remark shows that they both still managed to keep up their non-medical reading. In another letter, he commented on an 'interesting article on Masefield'. This letter also contained quite a long piece on Geoffrey's disbelief in spiritualism and his arguments against it[13]. In view of Gertrude's belief in thought-transference and extra-sensory perception, it may have been a contentious subject.

The situation, as far as Geoffrey was concerned, was not, in fact, altogether satisfactory. His true motives for going to Canada were not exclusively those which he acknowledged in his letters to Gertrude. Perhaps he did wish to escape the worries that beset him in England in relation to his family, his future in surgery and his financial situation, but there can be little doubt that some of the attractions of Canada were also those of pleasing Gertrude and being able to establish himself with the aid of her financial resources, but on the clear understanding that the use of them was shared for their mutual benefit.

Looked at dispassionately, however, we are presented with a young doctor who had worked for not more than 2 years as a House Surgeon (equivalent to posts of junior and senior House Officer today). His indepedent operating and decision-making was minimal. However, he was extremely well qualified academically and had strong support from influential people to whom he had proved his worth in London and Manchester. There can be little doubt that if he had remained in England he would have been a very strong candidate for a position on the staff of a hospital in either city or in some other important situation. Jeff does not appear to have openly acknowledged these possibilities nor to have taken them seriously into consideration. The fact that war was coming and might have intervened in his career cannot be included as a factor, for its imminence was not understood.

In Britain, Gertrude would still have been able to give him the financial help that he would have needed to set himself up in practice, under a similar arrangement to the unwritten agreement that they had worked out for their practice in Canada and which was mainly a salve for Jeff's conscience. The original plan of a shared medical practice had been modified even before it was put into action, for he proposed to confine his own activities mainly to surgery, leaving the medicine and obstetrics to Gertrude in what would be, in effect, a general practice. It would seem that his high ideals had been set aside, for though he had connections with two hospitals in Victoria, he had no opportunity to teach or carry out any significant research, which was a condition that he had so strongly emphasised in the recent past. His idea of doing general surgery more or less exclusively was largely a fantasy in the absence of a well-established practice. Furthermore, the limitations imposed by working in Victoria were considerable and, however much he might deplore the generosity of the Flumerfelt family, he was almost entirely dependent upon them. The possibility of neurosurgical specialization did not arise at this stage of his career; even supposing that it was then at the back of his mind, he could not have dared to think of it.

At the very end of 1913 Gertrude left England for Canada to rejoin her fiancé, get married and start their work together. Her father was still in Europe and would return later. In the meanwhile she had corresponded with Geoffrey on the question of the form of their marriage ceremony and the date and location of their wedding. The reference to 'fearful tension' in the following quotation becomes clear from a draft of a letter to Jack[16], which is quoted later and relates to the wishes of the couple to have a form of service and a choice of vows that was compatible with their own personal beliefs. In consequence of their specific wishes, there had been stress in the Flumerfelt household because Mrs Flumerfelt had had to concede the loss of a society church wedding, which she would undoubtedly have preferred. She was also very concerned that the marriage was going to take place at short notice, for Gertrude was unwilling to accept the suggested delay until summer. Geoffrey wrote: 'It will be well for us to recuperate, apart from the fearful tension of the last few days. I don't of course mean that you were the cause of this. It had to be, and now it seems to be practically over. Mother is cabling Father today from here saying that the event to which he gave his consent is fixed for 17th, that she isn't in favour of it (or words to that effect) is sorry he is away but thinks it best that it should take place'[14]. As will be seen, it had been inevitable that the marriage ceremony should be held at the Flumerfelt house instead of in a church, and for this arrangement a special licence was needed. Geoffrey soon set about obtaining this and thought he would suggest to Mrs Flumerfelt that she should get some catalogues so that their friends could choose the wedding presents[14].

Mr Flumerfelt cabled from Europe giving his consent to this wedding plan and his wife gradually came to approve of the arrangements. On 6th January 1914 Geoffrey was preparing to send a cable to his own mother to tell her what was about to happen, when he received one himself from Gertrude to say that she had arrived safely in Canada. In it, even at this late date, she raised the option of postponing the marriage a little longer — perhaps until her father returned home, but Jeff wrote to say that no good would come of waiting. 'Mother apparently never expected that you would desire a "nice" (from the ordinary point of view) wedding, and is really quite content with things as they are. She would not like anyone to come to church to see you married in a coat and skirt that wasn't white, and as she can't have that she is quite content that no one should come. As for any little advt. that it might have been for the practice, I think the practice will get that anyway by a few lines in the paper and a little reception perhaps.... If there is one thing that I think your health demands, it is an early marriage — very early in fact, certainly not later than 17th. My own mind is quite made up.... I feel quite medieval about it and am quite capable of carrying you off on 17th against your will! Mother is quite happy for it to be then.... I will get the licence on Monday'[15]. By the second week of the New Year Gertrude had arrived in Seattle and was staying with her sister Norma. From there she went home to Victoria.

The wedding took place in the drawing room at Ruhebühne on 17th January 1914 as planned. A description is contained in the draft of a letter by Geoffrey to his brother Jack[16] which, though dated 2nd February, was not addressed or signed; it is not even possible to confirm that it was ever sent. Jeff was very close to his brother at that time, although in later years they grew apart, and he would not ordinarily have written to him with such attention to detail, neither would he have drafted the letter first. It is therefore probable that he intended that his careful explanations were to be passed on by Jack to their father and mother.

My dear old man,   February 2nd. '14

I can't tell you how much I appreciated your really Stevensonian* letter. It has brought me great happiness and pleasure, so much so that I feel impelled to answer it, or rather thank you for it immediately. We were both sorry not to have you present at our wedding, but your place as best man was not usurped by any alien as you shall hear. You know how deeply an advanced girl like G. feels any implied or actual slight on her sex. You will understand just how much she would be grieved by the Anglican marriage service with its obey, the giving and pledging of the ring by one person only, the presenting of the girl's self by one man to another (glossed over by the euphemism "giving away"), and the homily of St. Paul on the woman's submission to her husband and her obedience to him. Well, that wouldn't do at all and the established Ch. of E. found itself unable to adapt itself to new thoughts and ideas. The old vicar of St. Johns, an old friend of the family, said he was under oath not to change a word of the service. He would not leave out the word "obey" even, which I thought was a really common omission. We appealed to the Bishop of B.C., also a friend of the family, and though he was kind enough to say afterwards that he was both charmed with us and in complete sympathy with our views, he found himself still more unable to make a precedent. We had a long argument with him about it, and he tried to give way to us, but was too full of Oxford and the true Ch. of E. conservatism (if he had not he assuredly would not have been Bishop) to make himself allow a change. His Lordship having

*Stevensonian. Possibly a reference to RL Stevenson's *Virginibus puerisque*.

failed us, we were forced to turn to other denominations and found a service to our liking—indeed one of perfect equality—in the Presbyterian Ch. of Scotland. Hence the Reverend Dr Clay D.D. performed the deed. We felt that as we were not married in the English Ch., we would rather be married at home, instead of going to a strange church. This was accordingly done. We were married in the drawing room of Ruhebühne on the 17th at 2.45 p.m. in the presence of our Mother, Sister and Brother-in-law and one Aggie Renny niece of Richard Angus of Montreal and Gertrude's greatest friend here. This will no doubt come as much of a suprise to you, and I fear you may have some difficulty in understanding—or if not in understanding, at least in fully sympathising with—our deep feeling of resentment at the unfairness of the Ch. of E. service, and also the really strong desire to do what our consciences told us was right, that prompted the change. You may imagine that it needed more courage to be true to one's principles than it would have done to give in—that is a platitude of universal application. I fear personally I would too often give in about something that I felt was wrong rather than run counter to public opinion. G. is however cast in a finer and more indomitable mould. Public opinion has however been very kind to us, and we have been more often praised for our courage than blamed for eccentricity. I hope I haven't worried you with this, but it is difficult to set down in a few words an account of the emotions and the events produced by them, which in all covered a space of many days. Our wedding was therefore about as quiet as could be imagined; we exchanged rings, I am wearing mine at present as a wedding ring on the usual finger, but later on it is understood that we are to wear them how or when we like or not at all'[16].

'We had a quiet week in Seattle, spent largely in shopping and going to Cinemas! It is a noisy city... very new and very prosperous. The University of Washington is there, and I rather covet a position there some day. I doubt just how desirable the Univ. of B.C. is going to be, the Univ. of Manitoba (Winnipeg) is frankly undesirable—largely because of the horrible climate. G. and I both covet the hopes of retiring from active medical life before we get too old and plunging ourselves in literature and art.... Of course these are all dreams.... Here before our eyes nearly every day are the great snow-capped mountains. No one with eyes can be an utter clod here. The Olympic mountains, just short of 10,000 feet high, rise out of the sea 80 miles away, look about as near as Brown Winde or Blackstone Edge used to look from home. The only thing that makes one believe in their distance is the extraordinary variety of the appearance of them.... I have never seen pink or red mountains before but you get all here, orange, red yellow, depending on the light.... Mt. Adams & Mt. Rainier 12,000 and 14,000 feet are also visible but not quite so constantly'[16].

On the day of the wedding, Jack had written to his brother Geoffrey from the Infirmary at Greenwich to congratulate him on having made a start in Canada. Concerning the news from their home in Rochdale he reported: 'I only spent about four days there at Christmas time & to tell the truth I was jolly glad to get away. The governor, though a splendid fellow to work with or even correspond with, is almost impossible in any other capacity. One would have thought when I went home this time, that I was the biggest slacker & rotter on the face of the globe & all because I returned from a four weeks holiday one day & left the next to spend a weekend with Radley. God knows what he would have one do! Though amusing for a time, a very little goes a long way. I know he thinks that he has not been successful with his sons. Can he wonder at it?'[17].

So, 2 years and 4 months after meeting each other, Geoffrey and Gertrude were finally able to begin their new life together.

William Osler wrote to 'Trotula' on 21st July 1914 from Oxford in reply to a letter from her. The meaning of the reference to his portrait is not clear, it was possibly a caricature.

Dear Trotula,

That letter was beautifully type-written, but I preferred the familiar script at the bottom. Thanks for that beautiful portrait of me. How all the quacks and particularly the osteopaths, have enjoyed exploiting my therapeutic nihilism.

I wish I could look in and see you both. I hope you are making a clean cut cleavage in your departments of practice. Otherwise the 'L. of your L.' will have no chance whatever; and it really is very mortifying to a man, even in the practice of medicine, to play second fiddle to a mere woman!

Grace and the boy leave next week for Canada. I sail September 5th on the Aquitania.

With greetings and best wishes to you both.

Sincerely yours,

W[m] Osler[18].

At some time in 1914 the Jeffersons established themselves in a very agreeable home of their own at 18, Hampton Court, Victoria, BC, Canada. Their daughter Monica was born prematurely on 14th January 1915. She 'was so tiny that her first cradle was her grandmother's work basket, in which she reposed wrapped in cotton wool'[19].

His few private patients were very worrying to Jeff. Jack appreciated this and in his letters he congratulated his brother on having had 'another operation' and on 'doing a bit with vaccines'. This was the era of vaccines and complement, long before the arrival of antibiotics, which Almroth Wright thought would be the answer to almost all infections. The practice in Victoria was beginning to get established thanks to recommendations by friends of the family and others. The Jeffersons even acquired a Ford motor car. Gertrude worked under her maiden name, which was of course well-known in the town, but we have almost no information as to what went on, how they shared the patients or what kinds of cases they treated.

Geoffrey joined the Victoria Medical Society, which had only 14 members at that time, and during 1914 he attended all the meetings. Gertrude accompanied him to two or more of them and was possibly also a member, as she is recorded as having worked the projector on at least one occasion. On 5th March 1915

Jefferson presented a paper on cerebral localization and furrow formation, based on his superior parietal sulcus work[20]. In April 1915 he demonstrated the pathological specimen of a carcinoma that had started in the duodenum, a gastro-enterostomy having been performed 2 years before the patient died[21]. Geoffrey gave another paper in October, the subject of which is not recorded in the minutes of the Society, and this was followed by one on osteitis deformans in November[22]. In addition to these activities, he was also made a member of a committee of two charged with arranging the programme for the coming winter[23], and he found time to continue the dissections of the stomach wall that he had begun in London and Manchester.

There must have been some difficulty in getting papers for presentation to the society for Geoffrey himself spoke again in December on duodenal carcinoma, and, on 7th January 1916, he 'gave a short talk on the shape of the stomach and arrangement of muscle fibres in the stomach'[23]. Publication of this work, which dated from his time at the Cancer Hospital, did not take place until 1918[24]. However, other papers on the stomach and duodenum came out in the years 1915 to 1918, one of which was written with Gertrude as co-author[25]. An article, the importance of which has not been recognised until recently, concerned a description of the peripenic muscle and some observations on the anatomy of phimosis, published in 1916[26]. That year there were also two neuro-anatomical papers on cortical localization and furrow formation[20,27] based on work done when he was in Manchester.

In fact, and of necessity, during the 2 years that Geoffrey was to spend in Canada, virtually all of his writing and presentations were based on his Manchester and London material. He went out there fired with academic enthusiasm; he was going to be head of a university department, to teach and, eventually, to be a great surgeon. However, it had turned out differently. He was running a general practice with little surgery to do and no teaching, though the medical society gave him an opportunity to present papers. Nevertheless, he did manage some original research, though it never came out in print. Its very existence did not emerge until Geoffrey mentioned it in a letter to his great friend of World War II and after, Harry Botterell, who was then head of the neurosurgical department of the Toronto General Hospital. In 1951 he wrote that he regretted not having published his work on the muscle layers of the stomach, on which he had spent so much time[28]. The fact that it was never written up is a measure of the frustration he was feeling, and his isolation from the stimulus of enthusiastic colleagues.

When World War I had broken out on 4th August 1914 Geoffrey, like most people, initially considered that it would be over in 6 months. Sadly, we have no record of the thoughts of either of the Jeffersons on the subject of the war. Canada was automatically at war with Germany from the moment that it was declared by Britain, and Canadian forces were heavily involved from the beginning, especially during the battle of Ypres in 1915. Perhaps surprisingly, the war gradually made a considerable impact on daily life in Canada, even though it was so far from the fighting and conscription was not introduced until 1917. The cost of living rose steadily at this time and it would have been impossible for Geoffrey and Gertrude to have ignored world events. Then appalling reports from France and Belgium began to fill the newspapers.

At home Jack had joined the Royal Army Medical Corps (Territorial) on the outbreak of war and began training with a Field Ambulance unit. He wrote to Geoffrey on 7th of August 1914 that 'The country is in an uproar. The streets are flooded with soldiers and about everyone one ever knew is in khaki'[29]. By 9th October Jack had arrived in Egypt, which he described in a letter to Jeff written 10 days later from the Turf Club in Cairo. After giving his impressions of the dusty, noisy, bustling Middle East capital he said: 'I hope that this [war] has not been much of a set-back for you. The financial panic must to a certain extent have interfered with progress, but I hope not too much so. I heard that you had been forced to invest in a Ford. Of course most of the world's research work will have stopped & the workers will be in the trenches'[30].

Then, quite unexpectedly, on 4th May 1915 Dr Arthur Jefferson died of pernicious anaemia. His final illness must have been short-lived, for his Will was signed with a cross instead of his usual signature. Joyce Jefferson recalls that 'Somehow with the help of influential people [Jack] was got out of the army to take over the practice. One will never know what this sacrifice must have meant to him or how his life would have developed if he had been free. He was a brilliant doctor, and there is no doubt that we four sisters [for whom Jack became responsible] were "the terrible incubus" that one of his patients described'[19]. Mrs Cecilia Jefferson now controlled most of the family affairs, as her husband had done when he was alive, and she 'ran' the practice from the time of his death. All this must have been very disturbing to Geoffrey, thousands of miles away, as he endeavoured to establish a viable surgical practice in Victoria and a direction for his career. Further distress was caused, too, because Gertrude was blamed by her mother-in-law for the failure of Jeff, her elder son, to return to Rochdale on the death of his father. Cecilia felt that he should have taken over the practice instead of Jack, who would then have been free to pursue a surgical career in the army and after the end of the war.

Jeff spent part of October 1915 in Seattle, staying with his sister-in-law Norma Ritchie and her husband. He wrote to Gertrude from there to say that he would be returning home on the following day and was looking forward to seeing Monica again. The purpose of his visit had been to use the Seattle library to look up references in various journals which were not available in Victoria. He also thanked Gertrude for looking after the medical work while he was away: 'I hope there have been no special emergencies'[31]. This is almost the only reference in the existing letters to Gertrude's active participation in the practice although one assumes that she had worked there regularly, subject to the demands of her pregnancy and then of her daughter, which must have interfered over a period of several months.

The Jeffersons were kept busy establishing their practice, and looking after Monica who was now thriving normally, but they came to believe that it was their duty to contribute to the war effort in Europe in some capacity or other. So Geoffrey wrote to his former chief Herbert Waterhouse, who had been very helpful in the past. It so happened that Waterhouse had become involved with the organization of an Anglo-Russian Hospital which was already being set up in Petrograd in conjunction with the British and Russian Red Cross. He was later to become the senior surgeon there and, in response to Geoffrey's request for advice as to what to do, he suggested that Jeff should come to England and join the hospital, the staff for which was being recruited. This advice must have provoked several serious discussions, but it led to the decision that Geoffrey and Gertrude should return to Britain leaving little Monica in Victoria with her grandmother, assisted by a nanny who may have been with the family for years and may even have cared for Gertrude herself or for Norma's daughter. The evidence for this was found among Trude's papers in a number of letters, which were signed 'Nana', but which unfortunately no longer exist. Their contents were couched in terms of affectionate familiarity that pointed to a long-standing relationship. The letters ceased about 1930, which may have been when Nana died[32].

The plan was for Geoffrey to go to Russia and for Gertrude to obtain a post in a hospital in Britain where, since junior doctors were in very short supply, her help would be greatly appreciated. During the years of the Empire it was not unusual for parents to leave a child or children with relatives while they were abroad. Gertrude did not have a strong maternal instinct and would have been confident that her mother, whom she idolized, with Nana whom she also loved, would care for Monica almost better than she would herself. Further, she had two strong motives for leaving Canada. The first was to be near Geoffrey and, if possible, share in whatever he was going to do. The second was a genuine desire to relieve suffering, and she could do this better in Europe than in Victoria. Accordingly the Jeffersons returned to Liverpool on 25th February 1916, sailing from New York in First Class accommodation on the USMS *Finland*. The *Lusitania* had been sunk on the 7th May 1915 with the loss of 193 American lives, but the United States did not *not* declare war on Germany until 6th April 1917, so that Geoffrey and Gertrude were able to cross the Atlantic in relative safety on board an American ship.

Yet the truth was, 'In a strange sort of way the Great War saved them'[19]. It gave Geoffrey the opportunity to escape from his obligations to his parents-in-law, and a chance to begin his career all over again and correct what had turned out to be a serious mistake. He must have realised that his prospects in the small town of Victoria were sterile to say the least, and that he would never have been able to fulfil his true ambition there.

One cannot help feeling great sympathy towards the Flumerfelt family. They had poured money into the Jefferson's home and office, not to mention purchasing all their equipment and furniture. Then, after exactly two years, all their investment and their aspirations for the couple were thrown aside, even though for very good and understandable reasons. Finally, the grandparents were left with responsibility for a one year old baby, which was no small undertaking. It was the end of an ill-conceived idea, the end of a dream.

REFERENCES

GJ=Geoffrey Jefferson; GM(F)J=Gertrude (Flumerfelt) Jefferson
1   GJ to GMF. Letter 30th September 1913.
2   GJ to GMF. Letters 30th September to 4th October 1913.
3   GJ to GMF. Letter 5th October 1913.
4   GJ to GMF. Letter 6th October 1913.
5   Pickering, George to GJ. Letter 9th January 1951.
6   GJ to GMF. Letter 9th October 1913.

7   GJ to GMF. Letter 13/14th October 1913.
8   GJ to GMF. Letter 12th November 1913.
9   GJ to GMF. Letter 17th November 1913.
10 GJ to GMF. Letter 21st November 1913.
11 GJ to GMF. Letter 26th November 1913.
12 GJ to GMF. Letter 28th November 1913.
13 GJ to GMF. Loose page with letter of 28th November 1913.
14 GJ to GMF. Letter 6th January 1914.
15 GJ to GMF. Letter 9th January 1914.
16 GJ to Jefferson, Jack. Letter 2nd February 1914.
17 Jefferson, Jack to GJ. Letter 17th January 1914.
18 Osler W to GMJ. Letter 21st July 1914.
19 Jefferson, Joyce. MS. Recollections of her family.
20 Jefferson G. Cerebral localization and furrow formation. *J Comparative Neurol* 1915; **25**: 291–300
21 Jefferson G. Carcinoma of the supra-papillary duodenum. Causally associated with a pre-existing simple ulcer. *Br J Surg* 1916–1917; **4**: 209–26.
22 Jefferson G. A case of a Paget's disease (osteitis deformans) with a note upon the pathology. *Br J Surg* 1915–1916; **3**: 219–33.
23 Harvey JE to Jefferson A. Letter 25th August 1985 and the Minutes of the Victoria Medical Society.
24 Jefferson G. The contraction forms of the human stomach, illustrated from plasticine models. *Arch Radiol Electrother* 1917–18; **22**: 161–73.
25 Jefferson G, Flumerfelt G. The anatomical and physiological subdivision of the duodenum, with a note on the pathogenesis of ulcer. *Annal Surg* 1916; **63**: 318–27.
26 Jefferson G. The peripenic muscle, some observations on the anatomy of phimosis. *Surg Gynecol Obstet* 1916; **23**: 177–81.
27 Jefferson G. Notes on cortical localization. *Can Med Assoc J* 1916; **6**: 30–8.
28 GJ to Botterell EH. Letter 14th October 1951.
29 Jefferson, Jack to GJ. Letter 7th August 1914.
30 Jefferson, Jack to GJ. Letter 19th October 1914.
31 GJ to GMJ. Letter 13th October 1915.
32 Jefferson, Michael. Personal communication 2nd March 1994.

Chapter 9

Russia
1916–1917

In March 1916 Geoffrey Jefferson visited Herbert Waterhouse to get further information about the hospital in Russia and accepted the suggestion that he should join its staff, having already virtually decided while yet in Canada. Accordingly it was necessary to obtain various documents and to make contact with the representatives of the Anglo-Russian Hospital Committee in London. Gertrude accepted an appointment as Senior Resident at the Royal Hospital for Sick Children in Edinburgh, where she worked for a paediatrician named Dr Leonard Findlay, probably from March to August 1916.

There followed a unique and quite extraordinary experience for Geoffrey, that of working as a surgeon in the Anglo-Russian Hospital in Petrograd* and then with the Russian army on the Eastern Front of the conflict in Europe. After it was over, he collaborated with a senior colleague in writing part of the official report on the work of the hospital and its achievements. Thereafter little was written about it until Michael Harmer, whose father was at one time the senior surgeon on the staff, carried out careful research into its history and published a very informative book which he appropriately entitled *The forgotten hospital*†[1].

The Anglo-Russian Hospital had been established in Petrograd in November 1915 as a gesture of assistance towards the Russians, who had declared war on Germany and the Austro-Hungarian Empire on 2nd August 1914, 2 days before Britain, and had suffered severe casualties during the great retreat during 1915 when they were severely attacked by the Germans and Austrians. In the hope of easing some of the pressure on their troops, Russia had called on its allies for the opening of a new offensive elsewhere, a request which Britain and France could not possibly meet in view of the serious situation on the Western Front. However, the idea of providing a hospital was put forward by Lady Muriel Paget who had been approached by Bernard Pares, Professor of Russian at Liverpool University and the secretary of the Anglo-Russian Committee — an unofficial body created some years before the war with the aim of furthering good relations between the two countries. The Foreign Office gave strong moral support to the project which was, nevertheless, to be funded by public subscription and a large donation from the British Red Cross and the Order of St John of Jerusalem; the Canadian Government also provided help. Further local support was to come later from the

---

*Petrograd. The city of St Petersburg was renamed Petrograd in August 1914. In August 1927 it became Leningrad, but reverted to St Petersburg in June 1991.
†The forgotten hospital. Except where reference is made to letters or other sources, most of the following information was obtained from a report to the Committee of the Anglo-Russian Hospital by Andrew Fleming and Geoffrey Jefferson, (*The work of the Anglo-Russian Hospital, September 1915 to June 1917*. London: Published by the Committee, 1917.), and from Michael Harmer's book, *The forgotten hospital*. Chichester: Springwood Books, 1982.

Russian Red Cross and the British Colony in Petrograd. The chief organizer, answerable to a Committee, was Lady Muriel Paget herself, who was only 39 when she began the project. She was the daughter of the Earl of Winchelsea. Her deputy was Lady Sybil Grey, who was 33 and the daughter of Earl Grey a former Governor General of Canada. Although the hospital was supported by the Red Cross, it was neither run nor owned by them. Consequently it was not an official Red Cross establishment, so it therefore lacked the safeguards which that organization would have provided if, for instance, when established, it or any of its detachments had been over-run. Fortunately this did not happen.

It has to be remembered that in 1915, Poland and Finland were Russian provinces and that they, and the Baltic States, were the border areas between Russia and the German and Austro-Hungarian Empires. Fighting was very severe in what is now Lithuania, and especially in the region further south, of the Pripyat (Pripet) Marshes on the border between northern Ukraine and the south of Byelorussia, near the Pripyat River which flows into the Dnieper. Germany had advanced successfully in the direction of Warsaw, but the Russians struck back by invading East Prussia. However, no less than 150,000 troops were lost or taken prisoner. In the south, Russian troops advanced far into Austrian territory in the area known as Bukovina. During the spring of 1915 there was a massive German attack across Poland in which the Russians lost over a million men; Warsaw fell in the summer and the Russians also lost ground in the south. This was the serious situation at the time when the Anglo-Russian Hospital was being established.

In England, in August and September 1915, the Anglo-Russian Hospital Committee were recruiting staff and buying equipment, which was initially for 180–200 beds, though the number of patients was to rise above this figure at times later on. The medical staff was to consist of two surgeons and a physician, two assistant surgeons and an anaesthetist, a radiologist and a dispenser. The matron was Miss Irvine Robertson who headed a staff of 30 trained nurses and volunteer assistants (VADs). In addition there were two medical students who acted as dressers, an electrician and a mechanic. When the hospital was set up in Russia about 30 Russian soldiers acted as orderlies and some Russian-speaking English ladies served as interpreters. Herbert Waterhouse was to be the Surgeon-in-Chief but, as he did not travel with the early groups, this role was at first filled by another surgeon, William Douglas Harmer. He was 9 years younger than Waterhouse and had been appointed to the Honorary Staff of St Bartholomew's Hospital when he was only 30.

It was planned that the base hospital should be set up first, and that detachments would then go wherever they were needed. Most of the suitable buildings in Petrograd had already been commandeered but, thanks to the forethought of Sir George Buchanan, the British Ambassador, the hospital secured a home in the palace of the Grand Duke Dmitri Pavlovich on the Nevsky Prospekt (now known as the Beloselsky-Belozersky Palace). This imposing red-coloured building with pale cream pilasters and surrounds to the windows, is situated on one of the city's main streets adjacent to the Anitchkov Bridge. It subsequently became the headquarters of the then Leningrad Soviet, and it survived the siege of the city during World War II. From here Geoffrey was later to have a front-window view of the Kerensky revolution of February 1917. It was outside the Dmitri Palace that the first shots were to be fired at the crowds which had gathered in the streets, and the first casualties of that revolution were in fact admitted to the Anglo-Russian Hospital.

In mid-October 1915, however, an advance party planning to make preparations for the establishment of the hospital in Petrograd had departed from Newcastle on the way to Norway. They completed the journey to Petrograd by train via Sweden and Finland. The main party sailed from London on 30th October to Archangel in the *Calypso* and arrived in Petrograd on 14th November. However, the arctic port froze early in what was to be the coldest winter for 100 years, with the result that the *Abaris*, the ship carrying supplies and equipment for the hospital, was frozen into the ice. The consequence of this was that its cargo was inaccessible and did not reach Petrograd for a further 5 months. This meant that the whole establishment had to be re-equipped locally from resources that were already severely depleted. There were more than 500,000 refugees in the city at the time, and the British demands for supplies were in competition with those of the Russian army and the civilian population[1].

Conversion of the Dmitri Palace into a hospital was no easy task. In the first place the building had no plumbing and only primitive drainage. There was no staff accommodation so the Russian Red Cross took over two floors of a near-by commercial club for this purpose. Water was laid on in the Palace and lavatories and bathrooms were created. The three main wards were on the first floor and were converted out of the concert hall and two large reception rooms. On the same floor an operating theatre, anaesthetic room, sterilizing room, x-ray department and a laboratory were built, together with a small area for the dispensary and a dentist. The kitchen, carpenter's shop and a storeroom were in the basement. The heavily gilded decorations on walls adorned with damask silk, and the many priceless paintings in the rooms now to be used as wards were covered by a lining of three-ply wood painted white. Additional temporary buildings were also erected in the courtyard. The Grand Duke and his entourage continued to live on the ground floor of the Palace and in the attics.

There was a long delay before the hospital was ready to receive patients and the staff became restless and felt that they could have been more useful elsewhere. In an effort to fill the time profitably, the nurses were given tuition in French and Russian. However, the hospital was eventually opened on the 1st February 1916* and blessed by the Russian Orthodox Church. The first convoy of wounded soldiers arrived on 11th February and by 17th February 110 beds were occupied. 'Within a few days of the opening patients came in rapidly in convoys of twenty to thirty — sometimes even forty — at a time, till from 150 to 170 beds were occupied. More than once every available bed was occupied, but the average number from month to month kept fairly steadily between the 150 and 170 mark'[2]. For the first few months after opening they were, at the same time, severely understaffed, recruitment in England not having then been completed.

As was inevitable, given the circumstances of the first aid treatment at the front and of the subsequent evacuation, as soon as the hospital opened it was filled

---

*Dates. It is not easy to be accurate about dates, since the Russian calendar was at this time 13 days behind that of the United Kingdom and it is not always clear which calendar was being used. Where dates have been given they are according to the British calendar.

Figure 8   *Geoffrey Jefferson's Red Cross identification card and Passport to Russia, 1916.*

with patients whose wounds were septic, and nearly all of which discharged pus copiously at some time or another. Douglas Harmer wrote home to his wife that the temperature was 'between 20° and 30° below zero'† so that 'you simply can't open windows for more than a few minutes at a time. Result, the wounds all smell and before we know what has happened we get temperatures flying about and all kinds of indefinite fevers. I only hope we shan't get erysipelas or something worse'[1]. The terrible infection and smell of many of the wounds was due to gas gangrene. This scourge of the Russian, or Eastern, front was in contrast to the Franco-Belgian or Western front, where tetanus was rife.

Back in London, in April 1916, Geoffrey was appointed assistant surgeon to the hospital. He obtained a passport on 4th April in which he is described as 5'11" in height, with grey-blue eyes and light brown hair. He was recorded as having a scar on the right side of his neck, the legacy of an operation for

---

†**Temperature.** The Réaumur scale was in use in Russia at this time but the value of −20° to −30°Celsius is not significantly different.

Figure 9   *Geoffrey Jefferson in Red Cross uniform, 1916.*

tuberculous glands, a common event among young people of all walks of life at this time. On 11th April he received an 'Army Certificate of Identity for Civilians wearing a Red Cross Brassard', in which his status was described as Medical Officer to the Anglo-Russian Hospital.

Then he had to sign an agreement with the Hospital Committee, the terms of which were such that they enabled both Lady Muriel and Lady Sybil, in the months to come, and on their own authority, to replace several doctors whom they considered to be unable to carry out their duties satisfactorily. The initial period of the contract was for 6 months from the date of departure from England, to be 'continued from month to month for the duration of the war', and terminable by one month's notice on either side. The salary was £400 per annum, plus uniform, passage to and from Russia and accommodation; there is no mention of subsistence, which was certainly included. 'Should the Surgeon object to perform any duties for which the Representative of the Committee for the time being in Russia may think the Surgeon qualified or should the

Representative...for any reason whatever consider the Surgeon unsuitable owing to ill-health or any other cause, then it shall be competent for the said Representative...to forthwith terminate this Agreement and thereupon this Agreement shall become absolutely void and the Surgeon shall not be entitled to any claim against the Committee or any members thereof in respect of salary, board and lodging or otherwise'[1]. These were harsh terms indeed.

During the next few days Geoffrey obtained his Red Cross uniform and brassard. He sailed from Newcastle on 22nd April for Bergen, where he docked at about 7.00 am on the following morning. There was a scramble to catch the 8.30 train to Stockholm, where his passport was stamped on 26th April. He wrote to Gertrude from the Hotel Continental in Stockholm, saying that there were 13 people in the party, including Lady Muriel herself and her secretary[3]. From there they took a train through Finland to Petrograd, where Jeff should have arrived in the evening of 1st May if everything went to schedule, and he makes no comment to suggest that it did not. His Russian adventure had begun.

In a letter to Gertrude dated 3rd May, Geoffrey described the hospital in the Dmitri Palace in Petrograd. 'The rooms are very large, bright and high. One or two must contain about 70 beds each arranged in double rows. We have 165 beds full now but there is not much work to be done'[4]. One of the reasons for this slow pace in the midst of active conflict was that the Russians insisted that all wounds should be absolutely healed before a patient could be discharged from hospital, at which time he had to be assessed by a medical board who decided on his disposal. This rule blocked beds severely until arrangements were made to send convalescent patients to another hospital that was run by the Countess Tolstoi, or for them to work on the land during the summer. 'I saw my first war cases today — very septic, granulating things, more like poor law work in civil practice' — a telling comment on the state of affairs among the indigent at home. 'There are often many quite interesting amputations to be done, arteries to be ligated etc., although these are all for sepsis and secondary haemorrhage. The cases are 4–5 days old when they arrive here, mainly from the Dvinski region so we get no primary amputations and some cases have already had something done when they arrive'[4]. Dvinsk (Daugavpils) and the River Dvina are both now in Latvia.

There then took place a considerable change in the letters received by Gertrude compared with those of previous separations. Their earlier correspondence had been largely concerned with the problems of examinations and the way their future should be shaped, coupled with Geoffrey's constant anxiety over his own financial position. There were also the difficult decisions connected with their marriage. That was now over 3 years ago and they had a daughter; difficult decisions had been made and action taken. They were starting afresh but moving into the unknown. It was impossible any more to make plans, they had to live in the present and take whatever came their way. The letters do not mention a future joint surgical practice in Canada or elsewhere and there was too much happening for comments on poetry or literature. The contrast between the situation in Russia, where the armies were falling back and where poverty and food shortages were evident, and the luxury Geoffrey had so recently experienced in Canada only a month or two earlier, was abrupt and stark. This may account for his difficulty in responding immediately to the privations of a poor nation in dire straits, and why he showed a certain amount of insensitivity

Figure 10   *The Dmitri (Beloselsky-Belozersky) Palace, when occupied by the Anglo-Russian Hospital, 1915–1918.*
Courtesy of Dr Pauline Monro, and Michael Harmer.

to the conditions he was shortly to discover. His view of the horrors of multitudes of wounded and dying men is almost self-centred, and mostly expressed in immature terms concerned with his own particular requirements as a young surgeon, the need to develop his skill as an operator and the strain the demands put on such expertise as he possessed when faced with situations for which he had had no proper preparation. The letters at times express excitement rather than the earlier endearments, the calm intellectual exchanges or contemplative musings.

Geoffrey gave a rather unsympathetic picture of Petrograd in a letter written shortly after he arrived there. 'All the snow has gone, the sun shines brightly but there is a very cold wind. Petrograd is frankly a most disappointing place. The streets and houses are shabby and the nice shops few. It cannot compare with Edinburgh, let alone London. The outstanding features are the large Palaces, and the many Churches, one or two of which are beautiful, the rest merely picturesque or interesting, all very big. The streets are badly paved with cobbles and in the less important streets the shops have large paintings of their goods on the outside as many of the shoppers are illiterate'[4].

However, after a week in the hospital Jeff was able to remark that 'Petrograd grows on you and I am much more in love with it'. When he had become even more familiar with the city he wrote: 'At the top of the Nevski is the Admiralty Building which has a very beautiful spire. It is very high and very slender rather like the spire of St. Peter and St. Paul. I saw it last night by moonlight and it is wonderful, just one long facet of silver. In the daytime I do not care for it much, but at night it is divine. One of the great charms of Petrograd just now is the long

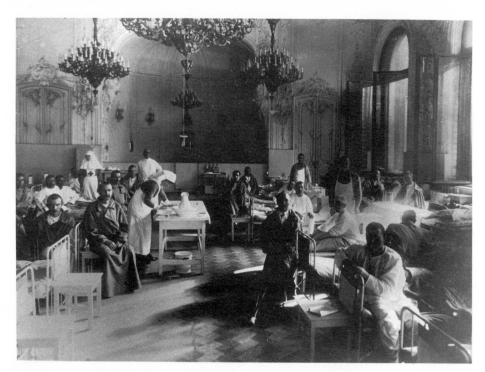

Figure 11   *A ward in the Anglo-Russian Hospital, 1915–1918.*
Courtesy of Dr Pauline Monro.

Figure 12   *The staff of the Anglo-Russian Hospital, with the Tsarina and her daughters, Grand Duchesses Marie, Olga, Tatiana and Anastasia in 1916. Jefferson is second from the right in the back row. Courtesy of Michael Harmer, FRCS.*

long twilight'[5]. He took a boat trip to the islands and saw where the Neva opened into the sea, and one evening he went for a walk with Waterhouse and visited a Cathedral, where the service impressed him and particularly the richness of the vestments. The long evenings, however, lent a special charm, and when revisiting Petrograd 40 years later, Jeff wrote, with more understanding than before: 'Dull red, orange-yellow and blue or green had been the dominant colours of the plaster-faced brick buildings.... How charming they had looked, their imperfections softened in the tender light of the "white nights" of Petrograd's spring and summer. To walk late along the Fontanka or Moika canals that cut across the city from one limit to the other of the arc made by the Neva River was to experience something unique, a glimpse through the western window of an essentially Eastern country.... The river front is one of the loveliest in the world... it cannot fail to move the watcher however grey the sky'[6].

A week after he arrived Geoffrey had not yet been able to assess the situation properly with regard to his work, and he thought he would die of boredom unless he was saved by some tennis. Little did he guess what lay ahead. On 7th May he had extracted his 'first bullet and was naturally very pleased. It had gone in at the side of the thigh and was lodged in an abscess cavity in front. On incising the abscess I quickly found the bullet and abstracted [sic] it. It was a perfect specimen, quite undented but unfortunately the trophies all go to the patients'[7].

It was apparent to everyone on the medical staff that the Base Hospital needed to form one or more detachments that would work on the Eastern Front close to the fighting. 'After much discussion with the senior medical staff and with the head officials of the Russian Red Cross it was decided that the most useful unit we could furnish would be a lazaret or field hospital with its own tents and equipment, plus a limited number of horse ambulances, with three, to be increased to six, motor ambulances.... The collection of material and equipment was pushed on as fast as possible.... No word had yet been received as to the whereabouts of the original equipment sent off from England in the preceding October, so all hospital equipment, drugs, dressings instruments, &c., had to be selected and purchased in Russia'[2]. It had become obvious, even to Jeff in the short time that he had been with the hospital, that a detachment nearer to the fighting was essential.

In his letters Geoffrey described some of the cases he had operated upon, all of which were of a fairly minor nature. On 8th May, however, he wrote that 'the Women's Suffrage* is sending out 4 lady doctors. The Suffrage are going to keep no doctor here as none is needed. They show more sense than our people since we ought to be much nearer the front, perhaps at Kiev for example'[8].

*Women's Suffrage. Few women had medical qualifications in 1915, and no rôle for them had been considered by those in charge of the Allied war effort. They therefore took matters into their own hands and a voluntary Women's Hospital Corps was formed and operated a hospital in Paris under the Red Cross. Later they opened one in Boulogne and another in London. After a year or two the value of women doctors to the army was recognised, and they became graded in rank from Lieutenant to Lieutenant-Colonel but received no pay or badges. The War Office recruited 40 female doctors to serve in Malta in 1917 and by 1918 they were working in Army hospitals in the Middle East. However, they were only employed in a junior capacity, without recognition of their ages or experience (Lehman L. Medical women in the First World War BMJ 1993; 307: 1592–4.).

On or about 11th May the Anglo-Russian Hospital was reviewed by no less a person than the Empress of Russia, the Tsarina herself, accompanied by her four daughters and several other dignitaries. Later, on a similar occasion, Jeff said: 'These functions are an awful bore. We had 2 Princesses and a Grand Duchess as V.A.D.'s but only 1 Princess remains (in one of my wards) the other has left to have her appendix out. We are visited also by another Princess who is a great friend of mine, but what her name is I can never remember'[9]. However, he did preserve a photograph of the review in which he featured in the back row.

Geoffrey continued to dress wounds, assist with the operations and perform some on his own, including the re-amputation of a leg, trephining for osteomyelitis of the skull and drainage of a perinephric abscess. On 21st May he wrote: 'We met some Russian soldiers on the march. They rarely have bands but sing as they go, very well and impressively, evidently stuff much more serious than Tipperary. They march very slowly, swinging their arms a great deal, and a soloist, usually a magnificent baritone, sings and they all join in. It is a fine thing to hear and see'[10]. He had also written previously: 'Our soldiers in hospital (those who have been able to get up) sing their Grace before their dinner and supper to an icon in the corner of their dining room high up on the wall'[11].

The Field Hospital, which was to be almost as big as the Base Hospital when set up, was ready to depart by the end of May and, as was customary, it was blessed by the Church. Geoffrey found this 'an extraordinarily beautiful and impressive scene'. The ceremony was held in the courtyard of a training school for the Emperor's pages. 'It was a beautiful afternoon, very bright and sunshiny but very cold again. In the midst of the trees an altar had been erected, and here stood the chief priest and his attendants and the choir. The priests wear the most wonderful robes, the sort of rich cloth of gold, very rich and magnificent. On their heads they wear hats studded with small jewels also of gold. This and their long hair gives them a most venerable appearance. The long hair and beards evidently need a lot of attention as they are always combing their heads and beards. Sitting down to tea for example they will draw out a long comb and pass it through their hair a few times before really starting. The choir wear a sort of uniform, usually of purple with yellow straps and facings, no surplices. As I have told you before, they sing most magnificently. They do not sing in unison and the chord effect they produce is very strange and beautiful, further it is very high pitched. Well, to continue with today, the scene made by the priests in their robes with the sun shining through the trees on to them was most exquisite. After prayers were over the priests took a bowl of Holy water and went round all the carts, horses, orderlies and motor ambulances spraying water over them with a brush which [they] constantly rewetted in the bowl. The service ends with the congregation kissing the cross which the priest holds — a small bronze cross about a foot long. He also blessed an icon and gave it to Lady Muriel after she, Sir George Buchanan, and the Grand Duchess Marie had kissed it.... I enjoyed this afternoon greatly for its beauty'[12].

A few days later we find Geoffrey assessing the two ladies who were in charge of the administration of the hospital. He did not spare his opinions in writing to Gertrude. 'Lady Sybil Grey is a very charming and sensible woman, worth 17 Lady Muriels. They are all very fed up with Lady M here, as she has such silly ideas and is always wanting some fresh scheme. She talks about sending out 5

Field Hospitals and they can't even get one off; it is 2 months overdue now. Then she wants a hospital train, as if it were possible to buy a train here. They are short of rolling stock already and it isn't likely that we could get one made'[13]. Perhaps Geoffrey had forgotten that Lady Muriel had been the prime mover in setting up the whole Anglo-Russian Hospital project, and the suggestion of an Ambulance Train was far from extreme, since this form of transport had already given great service on the Western Front and was also being used by the Russians. However, it was generally acknowledged that her ideas were inclined to outstrip reality. He continued: 'We had three French generals round here yesterday . . . they say the war will last 2–3 years yet. Meanwhile France is being bled white . . . '[13]. And not France alone.

The Field Hospital eventually left Petrograd for the Eastern Front on 8th June 1916. The train carrying it had 53 assorted trucks and carriages. There were 19 medical, nursing and administrative staff, including Lady Sybil, three doctors, a dispenser and 11 sisters and nurses. Three Russian Red Cross officials accompanied them. There were 125 Russian orderlies, 44 ambulance carts, 105 horses with their attendant grooms and two mobile field kitchens. To acquire all this and move the unit to the front in the time that was taken, even if it appeared too slow for Geoffrey, was no small achievement on the part of Lady Muriel. Jeff himself remained in Petrograd.

It took 5 days for the Field Hospital to cover the 395 miles to Voropayevo, midway between Minsk and Pinsk in the south of what is now Byelorussia, where they arrived at midnight in pouring rain and bitterly cold weather. On 18th June, the hospital having moved forward to Drolzumolv, near Molodechno, Lady Sybil was standing in a bunker about 50 yards behind some trenches watching hand grenade practice by the Russian soldiers, when a splinter, by very ill chance, came through the narrow slit out of which she had been looking and struck her in the face just above the mouth. The fragment penetrated about 2½ inches, to lie 'just below the sphenoid and apex of orbit'[1]. Douglas Harmer accompanied her back to Petrograd where he removed the missile. She then returned to England on sick leave. However, she made a good recovery and was back in Russia after 3 months.

The Field Hospital next established itself at Molodechno, a few miles north-west of Minsk. However, there was still little activity in that area so a further move was made to Rozhische, north of Lutsk, which lies south-west of the Pripyat Marshes in Northern Ukraine. Here they were subjected to attack by air and shells, so that 80 people were killed in the camp on one day, but none of the doctors or nurses are mentioned as having been among them. On 5th July they moved nearer to Lutsk prior to the 'battle of the River Stokhod', which lasted from July 28th to 30th. Here the hospital was kept busy treating 538 wounded, and they carried out 74 operations with 21 deaths'[1].

To return to Geoffrey in Petrograd. In one of his letters he made a few slightly caustic remarks to Gertrude about the Field Hospital. They were to 'go off tomorrow — at long last. They have been ages getting ready and are the joke of the mess. Exactly where they are off to is not known but it is 50 miles behind the front well out of range of everything — including patients I should think'[14]. How wrong he was. He then wrote further of a Memorial Service for Lord Kitchener, who had been drowned when HMS *Hampshire* was sunk by a mine on her way to

Russia. It was held in the English Church in Petrograd on 14th June. 'It was a very fine affair, spectacular as all the Ambassadors were there in their best bibs and tuckers, as well as a host of Russian Military men and our own Russian staff. The sermon was the worst I have ever heard and that is saying a good deal. We all hoped the Russians did not listen to it or understand it'[15].

Then a convoy arrived from the fierce fighting at Bukhovina which kept him busy. With the departure of the First Field Hospital, Geoffrey and another medical officer named Charles Jennings Marshall had each been left in charge of a surgical ward, but this arrangement was not to last for long. Lady Muriel had gone to Bukhovina to assess the situation there at first hand. It is an area to the east of the Carpathian Mountains that had been part of Austro-Hungary until the Russian advance into that territory. She 'found them terribly in need of doctors', so she organized what she called an 'emergency hospital', though it was no more than a Field Ambulance in size. 'It was about this time', Fleming wrote, 'that the Russian Armies under General Brusiloff had broken the Austrian line, captured the town of Lutsk and forced the passage of the Styr.... A small detachment...with Mr Jefferson as operating surgeon...was designed to be attached to a field hospital as an additional operating unit, wherever it might be required'[2]. As Herbert Waterhouse and his colleagues were to describe afterwards, in fact it developed into 'a hospital in a large barracks at Lutsk, under the care of Mr Geoffrey Jefferson, M.S.Lond., F.R.C.S.Eng. In this hospital a vast amount of surgical work was most efficiently performed'[16]. Two of the surgeons from the First Field Hospital visited Geoffrey's unit occasionally for consultation only, and he had no other outside help.

'I am asked to go down with 4 sisters and Lady Muriel to some place in the Rovno region', Geoffrey wrote from Petrograd on 28th June 1916 before he left. 'We shall be under canvas and will help with the 200,000 wounded that are struggling down there. It isn't a field dressing station or regimental M.O. that I am going to be. I shall be surgeon and have a little tent operating theatre with nurses to run it for me. We go first to Kiev'[17]. He assembled the equipment, six tents, and three motor ambulances with drivers. Jeff enjoyed the views of the countryside seen from the train and found Kiev to his liking, before going on to Rovno. Here they dressed 51 cases before moving to Rozshische[18], where they were 'on Prince Galitzin's estate on rolling farm land, studded with poppy and scabious, with copses of poplar and birch — the graceful birch tree, which like the wild cherry is almost an emblem of Russia'[6]. It will be remembered that the First Field Hospital was also in this vicinity.

'After a spell under canvas, the casualties became too heavy and the unit was moved into an officers' barracks outside Lutsk...a grim square building three stories high'[1]. Geoffrey was not impressed. 'I don't care very much for Lutsk. It is a large village with one main street, the houses straggling out to the station about a mile away. The roads are rough pavé and bad going in wet or fine. When it is raining the road is glutinous and deep, when it is fine the dust is terrible. We thought when we left Petrograd that we were going to the country and would have all sorts of good fresh things to eat. We have had a rude awakening. I have [had] more concentrated discomfort since I arrived in this region than I have ever experienced before. The food is very poor. I sleep on a thin straw mattress with a straw pillow. The wards are very dirty but the patients are only supposed to stay

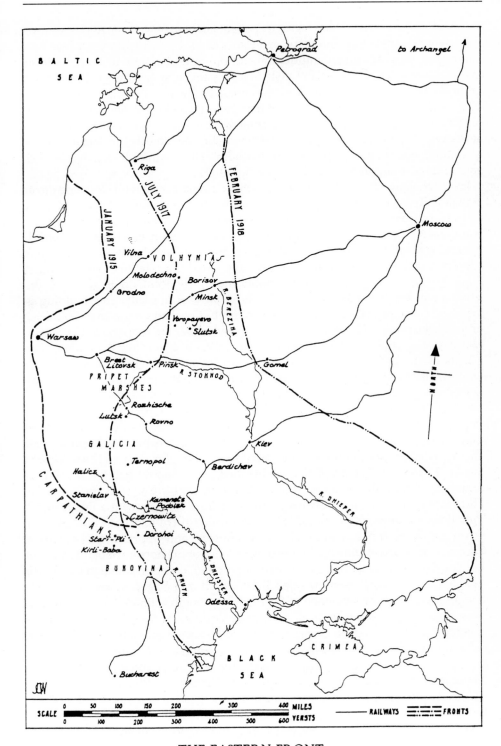

THE EASTERN FRONT

Figure 13   *The Eastern Front, 1915–1917. Courtesy of Michael Harmer, FRCS.*

in them for a day or two. I have seen 60 patients in here now, some new ones, two head wounds and two abdomens came in just as I left for dinner. I had two operations tonight, a finger amputation and removal of a piece of shrapnel from the ischiorectal fossa'[19]. Here in Lutsk, in a very touching gesture of appreciation of the work he was doing, Geoffrey was presented with a Fabergé cigarette case by Alexei Khomiakov, whose father had been president of the second Duma (parliament). He had come to the detachment, with Prince Lobanov Rostovski, to act as a liaison officer. The case was inscribed: 'En souvenir de Lutsk et de tout ce que c'est passé de gai, de triste et de macabre'. How extraordinary that he was able to have it engraved so close to the fighting[6].

For a whole week Geoffrey, who was still communicating with Gertrude on an almost daily basis, did not write 'because of the terrific amount of work we have had. In the past 7 days I have dressed 340 major wounds and it has been wonderful experience. I have done 33 operations...so it has been well worth it.... Our army must have lost 15,000 men and the Guards the same, only our army has succeeded whilst the Guards have failed. The sights of the wounded lying about in heaps have been astounding'[20]. He went on to describe the situation in the barracks in which the hospital was housed: 'This building is intended for some 700 patients, originally 200, but we had no less than 1500 for 2 or 3 days last week. The extra cases were stored under the roof and in the cellars, lying in every conceivable attitude, and seen at night it was like the inferno. The groans of the patients, the shadows thrown by the swinging lanterns on the whitewashed walls, the straw on the floor on which the unfortunate fellows lay with their blood-splashed bandages, and the heavy atmosphere, heavy with the smell of blood, dirty wounds, and bodies, was most extraordinary. The wounded came in by rail — on a narrow gauge railway in trucks drawn by horses, and here they all lay, dead and dying mixed together. It was terrible. I will tell you all about it later and when I have had time to get my thoughts clearer. The work was terrific. I had breakfast at 9.30 and we lunched at 4.00 to 5.00, had tea at 9.00 and dined at 2.00 am. It was an experience I would not have missed for anything. Fortunately there is a lull now owing to our failure. We are with a fine army'[20]. This description reminds one of the situation that there had been at Scutari 62 years earlier. It conveys the excitement, bravado and apprehension felt by a young surgeon describing his first real experience of the horrors of battle, and yet he remains a somewhat dispassionate observer. Jeff also found time to pay a visit to the Field Hospital, accompanied by Lady Muriel Paget, to see one of his drivers who had been wounded in the thigh by a bomb splinter. 'They have been very busy there too but with all their huge equipment they have not done as much as my little band, so we are very proud'[20]. Forty years later Dr AB Rosher, who was pathologist to the Anglo-Russian Hospital and came from Charing Cross Hospital, where he returned after the war to become Director of the Laboratory, wrote to Geoffrey to congratulate him on his FRS and reminded him of the hospital at Lutsk. 'Do you remember the gas gangrene at Lutsk and the bugs in the beds at night and how we killed them with ether?'[21]. This was just before Jeff revisited the country which was coming to mean so much to him in these his younger days.

'During the late summer and autumn of 1916 the fighting on the Stokhod [river] was of a particularly fierce character'[2]. Geoffrey wrote a report to the

Committee of the Anglo-Russian Hospital as follows: 'We have had further rushes of work. These have been casualties (always grands blessés, stretcher cases) resulting from the activities of the Eighth Army in the Lutsk salient...I have not pressed the forward move of my own detachment owing to our unique position at the terminus of three railway lines. Two of them are light railways from the front; these bring us most of our patients to the very door of the hospital, the third is a branch of the main line to Kiev, rendering easy evacuation of the wounded. Since the last report the detachment has dealt with 472 new cases and performed 1069 dressings. 50 operations were performed. We have encountered a great deal of gas gangrene. We have had two bad aeroplane bombardments. On September 6th [19th Western calendar] some 100 bombs being thrown on the station and railway a few yards from us...an ammunition depot was blown up.... Most of the windows in the hospital were blown in but nobody was injured. In the face of these raids I thought it advisable to withdraw our detachment from its tents and put them in an officers' barrack building where we are all now safely housed.' The move into the building actually took place some time before September 19th, after the first 'bad bombardment'[2].

Suddenly, at about the end of August, no more letters from Geoffrey to Gertrude appear for some time. The explanation is given by Jeff: '...My wife eventually got herself to Lutsk by her own Canadian determination'[6]. A remarkable feat in the midst of a terrible war. She had finished her appointment in Edinburgh at the end of July and went to stay briefly with the Jameses in Yorkshire; Coulby Manor was not far from Newcastle, which was the port of embarkation for Russia. She knew the Canadian High Commissioner and through his influence managed to obtain a laisser passer to Russia; she also joined the Russian Red Cross in London. Having learnt a little Russian and speaking French and German, she was accepted for service in Russia. After crossing the North Sea on a posting from London, she arrived at the Hotel D'Angleterre, Petrograd, in the middle of August. Her motive in undertaking the journey was chiefly a desire not to be parted from Geoffrey, backed up by a wish to be of service to whoever could benefit from her expertise. Unknown to anyone concerned, according to Joyce Jefferson, she arrived at the Anglo-Russian Hospital only to find that Geoffrey was in the Ukraine. At this point fate seemed against her for the Russian Red Cross posted her to Kazan, a long way east of Moscow and 36 hours away from Petrograd by express train, followed then by a day or two or more journeying across country[22].

However, her resourcefulness was not exhausted and, bringing Lady Muriel Paget to her aid, Geoffrey was given leave to meet her in Kiev, in spite of innumerable difficulties. She travelled there by train 'and it was so lovely to be with him again for 4 days'[23]. On Gertrude's return to Petrograd Lady Muriel got the Kazan posting cancelled and it was arranged that she should go to the Angelski Hospital in Lutsk, not far from Geoffrey's unit, well within range of the sound of the guns and subject to occasional air attack.

A letter written to Geoffrey by Gertrude in June, shortly before she left her job at the Children's Hospital in Edinburgh, though concerned with reports from Victoria of Monica's ill health, gives rise to a suspicion that Geoffrey may have known about her intention to try to join him. Yet it is almost as though she had censored the information. She referred first to Monica, who had gained only 2 lbs since the Jeffersons had left Canada in February, 4 months previously. 'I do wish we could be with the dear one to watch over her ourselves' she wrote, 'It will be lovely when the war is over and we can be together again with another little babch too .... I want to stay well and yet I don't want to slack; it is so hard to know what is right and best. I keep saying to myself — only till Oct. and then my darling husband — '[24]. Was October the month in which she meant to arrive in Petrograd? Geoffrey must have begged her to sit for the MB examination once more, for she wrote 'I wish I knew what I had better do when I leave here [Edinburgh]. I often feel tired and lazy.... I must be well and happy, plenty of energy for work in order to succeed with the exam. Miss Eyre wants me to go to Braemar for a month'[24]. She chose not to sit again for the examination, enabling her to arrive in Russia during August.

She had reached Lutsk about 3rd September. The Angelski hospital was 'in an old monastery and is said to have the thickest walls' in the town, she wrote to her mother reassuringly. 'The aeroplanes come over nearly every day but don't drop anything very often. I feel quite safe from bombs if one is sensible and stays inside buildings. I have a small ward of 8 beds but I see a lot of other cases. I have 2 male nurses (orderlies really I suppose you'd call them) who speak a little German, and a female nurse called Vanda who is supposed to understand German too.... My room is a very big one with double shutters and my bed is a long way from the window in an alcove. I have a straw mattress, a little table, a wardrobe, a primitive washstand and there is a stove. Sometimes in the evening I feel so homesick.... The food is good once one gets accustomed to the Russian dishes.... About 18 people sit down at a long table. The chief surgeon is at the head of the table who talks German and a little French, and I sit next to him on his right. Opposite me is the only other doctor, a girl, who only speaks Russian, so conversation is limited. Unfortunately, next to me on my right is a priest, quite kindly I suppose but bearded and filthy and ignorant-looking, with most unpleasant table manners'[23].

Gertrude remained working in that hospital throughout September. There was clearly no difficulty in making contact with Geoffrey, who referred to her presence there in a letter written to her from France in 1918: 'We do not hear the artillery as clearly as we used to at Lutsk, saving the other evening. Of course we are much further behind the lines than we were there. Do you remember how the guns used to thunder and rumble every night?'[25].

By now Gertrude must have told Geoffrey, not having told anybody else, that she was pregnant — a fact which could not be concealed indefinitely. She mentioned it in a letter to her mother dated 5th October; it has been assumed that, for her mother's benefit, Gertrude would have used the Western calendar rather than the Russian one.

Whatever may have been the circumstances in which the news of her pregnancy was imparted, the result was that she returned by herself to Petrograd on the instructions of Lady Muriel Paget. She left Lutsk on 3rd November, after about 7 weeks at the Angelski Hospital, and had an unpleasant return to Petrograd which began with a rail journey from Lutsk to Kiev. Here 'hoards of Russian soldiers surrounded her, pushing and shoving at the carriage door to board the train'. An expensive light dustcoat she was wearing was ripped down the back and practically torn in two. It had been given to her by her mother, and consequently had a sentimental value[26]. The Russian Red Cross said that they had no medical work for her to do but, fortunately, and not ungenerously, they continued to give her a salary. So she installed herself in the recently built Astoria Hotel in Petrograd where Geoffrey was able to join her early in November.

Geoffrey's sister, Joyce, gave the reaction of their mother, Mrs Cecilia Jefferson, to these events: 'This amazing person was pregnant again but had decided to follow Geoffrey to Russia. Imagine the horror of mother, father having died, and her sisters. It was virtually unknown for a woman to go out to Russia at that time, but after tremendous string-pulling she managed it and departed amidst the gloomiest prognostications. Mother was really wild...'[22].

Geoffrey had been recalled to the Base Hospital in order to be with Gertude, October having arrived and, with it, a lull in the fighting as winter set in. His replacement was a pathologist, and so it seems likely that the detachment was absorbed by the Field Hospital after Jeff left, though this is conjecture. Jennings Marshall had accompanied Jeff from Petrograd when the detachment was formed, but he worked with the Field Hospital as is apparent from their report[16]. Geoffrey asked for assistance during the time when the work was heaviest but, apart from the two consultative visits that have been mentioned, this did not come and he had no additional help in Lutsk. He appears to have been solely responsible for the unit and for the treatment it carried out. His efforts were praised in all the reports, and he was awarded the Medal of the Order of St George by the Russians for his achievements there.

Despite decreased activity on the various fronts, a steady number of patients continued to be admitted to the Base Hospital in the Dmitri Palace, although 'the difficulty in obtaining food made the Government anxious to keep wounded out of Petrograd...'[2]. In a letter to Lady Muriel, Lady Sybil wrote from Petrograd: 'I expect Jefferson will remain. He is better up here than at the Field, because he is a very good operator but *very* slow, which is quite a disadvantage in a Field Hospital'[1].

At the beginning of December Gertrude was moved to a Russian hospital when she showed signs of going into labour prematurely (she was not due until January), and Michael Jefferson was born there on 9th December 1916. The conditions in the hospital were 'primitive and Geoffrey was afraid to leave her there for more than a day or two, so had her moved back by ambulance to the Dmitri Palace'[22].

During 1916, throughout Russia there was an impression of the 'failing competence of the government and that it was only a matter of time before the whole country collapsed in revolution'[1]. The complete history of Rasputin does not belong in this narrative, but it is well-known how he influenced the Tsarina and claimed curative powers, particularly in relation to her haemophiliac son. This led to a great hatred of Rasputin in certain quarters, and he was assassinated on the night of 29th December 1916. Among the small number of aristocratic conspirators was the Grand Duke Dmitri Pavlovich, the owner of the palace in which the Anglo-Russian base hospital was accommodated. The murder of Rasputin took place at Prince Yusupov's palace, following an ineffectual attempt to poison him during dinner. He was finally shot while attempting to escape, after which his corpse was put into the frozen River Neva. The body was recovered, embalmed by order of the Tsarina and buried at the royal palace of Tsarkoe Salo. Eventually revolutionary soldiers dug it up and burnt it.

Immediately after the assassination, Prince Yusupov and the Grand Duke Dmitri took refuge in the Grand Duke's home, quickly followed there by supporters of Rasputin who made an attempt to find them on the pretext of visiting some patients. Lady Sybil refused permission to enter! The royal conspirators hid in the Grand Duke's private apartments for some days, during which a fish-bone became stuck in the Prince's throat, and was removed by Geoffrey Jefferson, adding another bizarre note to an already remarkable story. The key to the apartments where the two were hiding was even held by Lady Sybil, but there was a secret staircase leading to an upper floor which was used by the Grand Duke. The Prince tried to escape to the Crimea but was arrested at the railway station, and Dmitri Pavlovich was ordered not to leave his Palace. However, the Tsar, who had by now assumed personal command of the armies, somewhat cheerfully ordered Dmitri to be posted to the Persian front and he departed thence into exile by train'[1].

As anticipated, Russia did collapse internally, and the events of the beginning of the 1917 Revolution in Petrograd were described by Jefferson in a report to the Anglo-Russian Hospital Committee. Once again, the palace turned hospital was to be closely involved in Russia's political problems. This time, being situated at the very heart of the March revolution, it admitted the first civilian casualties. During December and January there had been 'enough operative work to keep us employed waiting for the spring when we could again move out to the front'. However, 'this serene state of affairs was rudely interrupted on the 10th March 1917 (25th February Russian System) by the shooting on the Nevski Prospekt which heralded the Revolution'. There had been an uprising in Petrograd on 8th March and on the following day the 'hospital was given a guard of 30 soldiers.... First and last we admitted some sixty to seventy cases, the majority of whom had no idea as to which side had shot them. On the first two days, the Saturday and Sunday [10th and 11th March], the casualties were the result of the police firing upon the crowds in the Nevski, and the wounded were naturally civilians'[2]. That night the nurses, escorted by two doctors, dashed for the doorway of their accommodation across the street, 'the bullets throwing up a little shower of snow as they hit the pavement, but we all arrived safely'[1]. 'On the Monday when the soldiers and civilians ceased to hold the bridges over the Neva and threw in their lot with the workmen who crossed from the Petersburg and Viborg sides, we had mixed casualties of soldiers and civilians'[1]. An angry crowd demanded that the building should be searched for hidden police and machine guns but the orderlies held them off, and the mob were finally convinced that it was an English hospital for Russian soldiers, and that there were no officers, so they departed[1]. 'Owing to our position in the Dmitri Palace, one of the most important buildings on the Nevski Prospekt commanding a fine view of that great street, we had opportunities of seeing quite as much of the fighting as anyone could have wished for, and indeed a great deal more than was pleasant'[2].

Of course the Revolutionaries did not pass the hospital by. Jeff's sister Joyce wrote later that they would come to Jeff 'for treatment of some wound or injury. They would look him squarely in the eye and say "if this does not heal, we will come back and shoot you". On several occasions the Anglo-Russian team of doctors was threatened with execution'[22]. These were the signs of anarchy.

'Everywhere people were busy tearing down Imperial emblems.... Our Palace Eagle met its end, a heap of plaster on the road it had proudly gazed on for many years'[1]. For three days the rattle of machine gun and rifle fire was practically unceasing night and day, and many times the courtyard of the palace was invaded by a stampeding mob seeking cover. The night of 13th March was very disturbed, as were the three which followed. 'The tragic thing about all such fighting is the large number of innocent people who are hit through no fault of their own, who are shot accidentally in the wild folly of the moment.... The behaviour of our patients during the Revolution was really very commendable. They united in thinking that the Revolution was a good and necessary thing, a most undeniable sentiment, but they also thought that the wildness of those few days was "ne Kharosho" [not good]. Whilst discipline amongst the troops had utterly gone, largely as a result of the proclamation from the Council of Soldiers' and Workmen's Deputies declaring all men equal and abolishing saluting, discipline within the hospital remained fairly good. The food shortage caused a certain amount of discontent and this was fermented by a few born agitators who revealed themselves among the patients. However, ... within a fortnight all was quiet again. Our sanitars (orderlies) were loyal to us— barring their decision to control their own work.... But the old feeling of security...had passed away. One must experience a revolution, an experience I would not recommend to anyone in the world, to realise the absolute impotence of the individual'[2].

'Following on the proclamation of universal brotherhood, fighting at the front ceased...and we were forced to admit large numbers of medical cases to fill our beds...mainly scurvy from the Northern front', Geoffrey had written in his report, and he concluded it by praising the Russian soldiers and sympathising with the 'Russians of the upper classes' who despaired for the future of their country and were ashamed for having reneged on the Allies[2]. In almost 2 years '...we had established a base hospital in the capital second to none, we had organised in the field two most useful units, and had running a large fleet of motor ambulances, which was of immense value at the Russian front with its great distances and absence of railway facilities. We had, moreover, established good relations with our allies, and had been to them a sign manual of British appreciation and sympathy'[2]. Not to mention that it was a remarkable memorial to the astonishing achievements of Lady Muriel Paget and Lady Sybil Grey.

Gertrude was never apt at any household task, and this included caring for young babies. Soon after Michael was born she tried, without success, to find a nursemaid to look after him, though the hotel chambermaid had acted as a stand-in for half an hour a few times. Nevertheless, about 5 weeks later, she was able to tell her mother triumphantly 'I have been able to get a very nice Russian woman who comes every day for as long as I want and does the diapers and woollens and does my mending'[27]. Of course this came to a sudden end when the revolution broke out, for the 'Russian woman' had immediately disappeared and Gertrude was left to her own devices from then on.

On 15th March 1917 Gertrude wrote a hurried note to her mother in which she said: 'We left the hotel on 12th March suddenly as it was thought it would be safer if we were all together. I'd been a prisoner in the hotel for 2 or 3 days, but the A-R H managed to find a room in it for us. We had some thrilling experiences but it is marvellous how quickly and quietly the Revolution has been resolved. Many of the shops are open again and the banks and telegraph office, and the railways running again too'[28].

The Jeffersons even managed to spend some time together in the city, for the ballet, opera and concerts still continued to function and, of course, the Church. Geoffrey, when he revisited Petrograd in 1956, recalled passing the Kazan Cathedral: 'Looking at its fine elevation my mind went back to the night of Easter Saturday in 1917. My wife and I had stood there in the great crowd waiting for midnight when the Cathedral's great doors would be opened. Everyone was carrying a candle shaded against the wind as they had done on Easter Eve for generations. Present at this scene was the miracle-working eikon of the Virgin of Kazan. On the stroke of midnight the great doors were swung open and the Archbishop emerged to bless the people and to declare that "Christ is risen". Those words, the reply to which was, "He is risen indeed!" were for a day the traditional Easter greeting and conferred, even on strangers it was said, the right to kiss at random or by choice. The Easter scene outside Kazan Cathedral must have been impressive always but this time in 1917 the occasion was enlivened by occasional rifle shots and a short burst of machine-gun fire in some nearby street. True, this was more or less of a commonplace of those immediately post-revolution nights; no one ever knew whether anyone was hit—the motivation was perhaps revolutionary high spirits. None the less the unecclesiastical noises suggested that it was time to walk home'[6].

The time when Geoffrey and Gertrude were together at the Anglo-Russian Hospital during this, the Kerensky, revolution gave them plenty of opportunity to discuss the future. The first decision was not difficult to take, and it was that Gertrude and the baby had to leave Russia as soon as possible. However, their destination was not so straightforward. Gertrude was desperate to return to Canada, to her mother and her beautiful parental home. She begged Geoffrey to let her go, not to England, but via the Trans-Siberian Railway to Vladivostock and then across the ocean to Vancouver. 'This would assuage her dreadful home-sickness, allow her to see her parents and Monica, and let Michael grow up, even for a short while, in the peace and beauty of the Victoria which she loved so much. However, Geoffrey absolutely refused to let her do this'[22]. His reasons were clearly that he did not want again to run the risk of coming under the influence of his parents-in-law or being trapped into settling for the second time in Canada, as Gertrude patently would have wished. Geoffrey's mind was clear on one point, which was that his future lay in Britain. Whereabouts in Britain was another matter but, in the uncertainty of the moment, and war still being waged terribly in Europe, that could wait. Gertrude dutifully gave way though the prospect of life in England made her miserable. However, she was not one to complain for long and she resolved to make the best of any situation she might find herself in, so long as she and Geoffrey were together.

Somehow Gertrude and Michael had to be sent home and they travelled back to England in April 1917, her last letter to her mother from Russia being dated 16th of that month. However, Geoffrey could not leave until he had a replacement. So this intrepid woman undertook the journey back to England alone with her baby via Finland, Sweden and Norway. They were held up for a fortnight at a hotel in Bergen waiting for a ship to transport them, a wait made worse by the fact that Michael was a very small baby, 'barely 6 months old, had measles with a high temperature, and Gertrude's jewel case was stolen which contained amongst other valuables the medal — the Cross of St George — which Geoffrey had been awarded in recognition of his services at Lutsk'[22]. The ship taking them across the North Sea sailed about 17th May 1917, and they disembarked at Aberdeen[29]. On account of the danger of submarine attack, all personnel were ordered to wear life-jackets throughout the crossing of the North Sea, which did not please Trude. However, she told her mother that they were quite safe since they were escorted all the way by two torpedo-boat destroyers[29].

On arrival in Scotland Gertrude telegraphed Uncle John James at Coulby Manor and asked him and his wife Gracie for refuge at their home near Marton, then in the North Riding of Yorkshire. She changed trains at Edinburgh and was met by them at Darlington in due course. Joyce Jefferson recalled that: 'Aunt Gracie burst into tears on seeing the baby.... She said that Michael was just a collection of bones covered in skin'[22]. John James' account to Michael was that 'We'd never seen such a wretched thin undernourished little scrap...but Gracie soon put that right so that you looked like a proper baby. But Trude, well she just hopped it after two or three days. She didn't say where she was going, though we guessed it was London, or what for or when she'd be back. She was gone for three or four weeks, and we heard nothing. But when she came back she brought Miss Feury with her as a nurse and then all three of you vanished'[29].

One can infer that during this period of absence from Marton, Gertrude had left the baby behind and been down to Hove for a short visit, as it was through Aunt Ada Parsons that she was introduced to Miss Mabel Feury who was first nurse and then nanny to Michael. He came to love her dearly and called her 'Pan' (a childish interpretation of Nan). She remained with the family for the next five years, apart from a break in 1919 while Gertrude and Michael visited Canada[29].

In Russia the first revolution of 1917 was suppressed and things quietened down for a few months. It has to be remembered that Lenin had not come to the fore at this point and the Bolsheviks were not yet in marked evidence. On 16th March, the Emperor had abdicated and a provisional government had been formed. Written presumably in April, there is an incomplete and undated letter from Geoffrey to Gertrude which had probably been intended to greet her on her arrival back in England, part of which reads: 'All is quiet here now. Lots of silly rumours. There is a Socialist fanatic called Lenin at large. Came from Switzerland via Germany (mark you), and is preaching "Stop the War" and doing a lot of harm. Today many of our wounded went in procession to the Duma and voted for a continuation of the war and the arrest of Lenin, which I hope will be a *fait accompli* in a few days. We have closed C [ward] and will then be ready for lots of work...'[30]. Lenin and the other Bolshevik leaders arrived in Petrograd on 16th April 1917.

A letter, dated 17th (4th) May, had been interrupted in the middle. Geoffrey wrote: 'At this point I have been called to see a man shot in the ankle by one of Lenin's "Stop the War" gang. However I don't anticipate very much trouble from them, they are very much outnumbered and even if they got the upper hand in Petrograd the rest of Russia wouldn't put up with it as they do want to win.... I have no doubt whatever that there will be but little trouble here, so don't worry darling'[31]. How difficult it is to assess a situation in which one is personally involved and when all the necessary information is not available.

By now Geoffrey must have applied for permission to return to England and have given the required month's notice, for he had completed the time for which he had contracted to serve the Anglo-Russian Hospital. Late in May his mood was depressed: 'Russia is now hesitating and I shouldn't be surprised if the war dragged on for another year.... Of course the people at large have no idea why they are fighting.... Food is becoming scarce again, the queues are enormous. People have to get up at 4.00 am and by 2.00 pm sometimes they have obtained no white bread. It's like the old times again. As a matter of fact they talk, and talk, and talk and don't do anything. Only 70% of the crops this year have been sown and elsewhere they are destroying wide-cast'[32].

Geoffrey's replacement had actually arrived in March, which had left him free to leave for home, though he did not begin to do so for another 3 months. Writing at the end of May, he remarked that he had regrets at the prospect of leaving Russia. His initial, rather harsh, impressions had been replaced by a better understanding of the country and, having shared so closely in its hardships, had shifted his concern from himself to the nation he had served. On 23rd May, ignoring the dramatic events that had been taking place around him, Geoffrey read a paper to the Russian Society of Surgeons of Pirogov at the Mariinski Hospital in Petrograd, on the case of an 18 year old Tartar soldier patient from whom he had successfully removed a bullet lodged in the cerebellum. Jeff 'had a very interesting evening. They were most kind, talked of the Anglo-Russian *entente* and ended by making me a life-member of the Society. Rather nice, isn't it? All is quiet here now. No processions, no meetings in the street, but so far no fighting at the front'[1,33]. This was the first paper of a purely neurosurgical nature that Jeff had prepared, and the report was published in the *British Journal of Surgery* in 1918[34]. It was also the first of many honorary memberships of foreign Medical Societies.

A lull in work at the hospital and diminished responsibility owing to his resignation, allowed Geoffrey to take the opportunity to pay visits to the opera and the ballet, as well as to a few local places of medical interest. He went to the laboratories where antisera were being made, and to Pavlov's laboratory 'where they are working on conditioned reflexes. That was very interesting and the machinery and so on for excluding errors the most remarkable and ingenious that I have ever seen. I did not see Pavlov himself'[35]. A few days later he visited the Neurological Institute of Professor Poussep and we can see, almost for the first time since working for Elliot Smith, how his interest in neurology was beginning to be rekindled.

On the 16th June 1917 Geoffrey obtained a visa from the British Consulate in Petrograd and 2 days later, on 18th June, his passport was stamped at Tornio, Finland; he had left Russia. He continued the journey across Sweden to

Norway and arrived in Bergen by the 26th June. From there he wrote: 'I haven't had any word yet as to when we are to leave. Until the war is over I am sure I couldn't rest unless doing war work and I do want to join the R.A.M.C. or the C.A.M.S.'[36]. He sailed from Bergen on the 28th June and arrived in Britain on the following day. The months spent in Russia proved to have been very formative. Not only had he found a new direction and purpose for his life, but he had matured considerably and had obtained experience of responsibility in difficult situations. He was no longer critical of Russia and its people; on the contrary, he had formed a lasting affection for both, yet preserving an intense distaste for their radical politics, still later to be transferred to communism in general, and this never left him.

The further history of the Anglo-Russian Hospital and of the Russian Revolution is not part of Geoffrey Jefferson's story, but a short summary of the former may be of interest. The Field Hospital had moved from the Lutsk area to Bukovina on the Carpathian Front in October 1916, where fighting became intense during the summer of 1917. However, on 12th January 1918 the hospital equipment, stores and transport were handed to the Russian Red Cross, since all fighting on the Eastern Front had ceased with the signing of an Armistice between Russia and the Central Powers, Germany and Austria, on 17th December 1917. For the same reason there was no longer a need for the base hospital to continue working in Petrograd, quite apart from the dangerous situation they were in as representatives of pre-revolution institutions. The hospital closed on 18th January 1918 and the British staff were evacuated to safety over the Finnish border. Lady Muriel had been suffering from typhoid, but she had recovered, and was now in Kiev. At the end of February she went from there to Odessa to join the Field Hospital and rescue the rest of the Anglo-Russian Hospital personnel who had become isolated there and had not been able to move to Finland. The Bolsheviks were in control in Odessa but, with her unflagging drive, she organized a passage for the group by fourth class railway carriage to Moscow. There she hired two coaches on the Trans-Siberian Express. Included in their small amount of baggage were eight sucking pigs and a large quantity of black bread. Among the party were five Red Guards, provided to protect them from deserting soldiers and who accompanied them as far as Irkutsk in Siberia, which was about 1000 miles from their Russian journey's end in Vladivostok. From Vladivostock the party made their way by sea to Canada, landing at Vancouver, and eventually proceeding home to England. A truly remarkable world tour during wartime. Equally remarkable was the presence among them of a person travelling under the name of 'Thomas Marsden'. He was Thomask Masaryk, the Czech patriot who became the first president of Czechoslovakia in November 1918. His sister had been a friend of Lady Muriel Paget, and it was through this connection that Masaryk managed to escape from Russia to make his own most significant mark on post-war world history[1].

REFERENCES

GJ=Geoffrey Jefferson; GMJ=Gertrude Jefferson;
1   Harmer M. *The forgotten hospital* Chichester: Springwood Books, 1982.

2   Fleming A, Jefferson G. *The work of the Anglo-Russian Hospital, September 1915 to June 1917*. London: The Committee of the Anglo-Russian Hospital, 1917.
3   GJ to GMJ. Letter 26th April 1916.
4   GJ to GMJ. Letter 3rd May 1916.
5   GJ to GMJ. Letter 2nd June 1916.
6   Jefferson G. Return to Russia. In: *Selected Papers*. London: Pitman Medical, 1960: 541–9.
7   GJ to GMJ. Letter 15th May 1916.
8   GJ to GMJ. Letter 8th May 1916.
9   GJ to GMJ. Letter 24th May 1916.
10   GJ to GMJ. Letter 21st May 1916.
11   GJ to GMJ. Letter 2nd May 1916.
12   GJ to GMJ. Letter 28th May 1916.
13   GJ to GMJ. Letter 1st June 1916.
14   GJ to GMJ. Letter 7th June 1916.
15   GJ to GMJ. Letter 14th June 1916.
16   Waterhouse H, Harmer WD, Marshall CJ. Notes from the Anglo-Russian hospitals. *BMJ* 1917; **2**: 441–5.
17   GJ to GMJ. Letter 28th June 1916.
18   GJ to GMJ. Letter 25/26th July 1916.
19   GJ to GMJ. Letter 26th July 1916.
20   GJ to GMJ. Letter 7th August 1916.
21   Rosher AB to GJ. Letter 29th July 1956.
22   Jefferson, Joyce. MS Recollections of her family.
23   GMJ to Mrs A Flumerfelt. Letter 10th September 1916.
24   GMJ to GJ. Letter 13th June 1916.
25   GJ to GMJ. Letter 6th May 1918.
26   GMJ to Mrs A Flumerfelt. Letter undated 1916 and quoted by Michael Jefferson, personal communication.
27   GMJ to Mrs A Flumerfelt. Letter 29th December 1916.
28   GMJ to Mrs A Flumerfelt. Letter 15th March 1917.
29   Jefferson, Michael. Personal communication.
30   GJ to GMJ. Letter undated 1917.
31   GJ to GMJ. Letter 17(4)th May 1917.
32   GJ to GMJ. Letter 21(8)st May 1917.
33   GJ to GMJ. Letter 24th May 1917.
34   Jefferson G. Removal of a rifle bullet from the right lobe of the cerebellum. Illustrating the spontaneous movement of a bullet in the brain. *Br J Surg* 1917–1918; **5**: 422–4.
35   GJ to GMJ. Letter 31st May 1917.
36   GJ to GMJ. Letter 26th June 1917.

Chapter 10

France
1918–1919

On his return from Russia at the end of June 1917, Geoffrey was in very poor health and his family was split up, for Monica was still in Canada and Gertrude and Michael were in England. However, he had had his first experience of concentrated surgical responsibility, he had performed operations entirely on his own initiative and, at least while at Lutsk, with nobody on the spot acting as his superior. Furthermore, his interest in neurosurgery had been aroused once more by the case of the cerebellar bullet.

The next few months are not well documented. Geoffrey tried to enlist in the Royal Army Medical Corps, but was turned down on medical grounds and ordered to serve in a Ministry of Pensions post until his health had sufficiently recovered. This he did at the 2nd Western General Hospital, which was located in Manchester, but in a civilian capacity. Had he not been instructed where he was to go he would probably have been drawn into the practice at Rochdale, at least on a temporary basis, for Jack was now working there alone, his sister Madge being still in the early days of her medical training.

The 2nd Western was a 'Territorial Force General Hospital' housed originally in the Manchester Municipal Central School, but as the numbers of wounded continued to pour in from France, it had extended into many other school premises, the Town Hall and the Poor Law Infirmary. When Jefferson was there in 1917 the original 520 beds had expanded 'from one public building to another in Manchester and its suburbs until, at one time, in August 1917, it consisted of a hospital of 6700 beds scattered over 34 different premises, the majority being schools, each with accommodation for 100 to 200 beds or more'. In 1918, an additional 1200 beds were set up under canvas in the University Athletic Grounds[1]. One of his former chiefs, Arthur Burgess, was a surgeon there and William Thorburn was in charge of the Surgical Division. Other honorary consultants and staff from the Manchester Royal Infirmary also took their share of the work.

Gertrude and Michael were now living at 2 Langdale Road, Victoria Park, Manchester, so Geoffrey, not being in the army, was almost certainly able to stay with them rather than live in a hospital mess. During the next 9 months Geoffrey's health improved sufficiently for him to be able to join the Royal Army Medical Corps, which he did in April 1918, and he was posted to the British Expeditionary Force with the allied armies in France.

This posting, on 1st May 1918, was to the Surgical Division of the 14th General Hospital at Wimereux, about 4 miles north of Boulogne, as a General Duty Medical Officer or GDO. Gertrude had accompanied him to London the day before and was able to see him off from Victoria station. Geoffrey described to her what happened after he arrived in France. 'I was driven out here with my baggage. Our quarters here are quite comfortable, we have beds, sheets etc., and are supposed to be the best mess around here, altogether rather a swagger hospital so I believe. However, it is rather lonely being dumped down among a lot of strangers.... I am quite happy to be in a safe place.... I am to have a ward in the Casino', which had been commandeered to form part of the hospital[2]. His billet was in an old hotel about a quarter of a mile away, 'Pas de drainage, tu sais, but the smells nothing like Lutsk. Comme ils étaient terrible'[3].

On the Western Front in May 1918 the German and Allied armies had been entrenched for years, and terrible slaughter had been taking place during the major offensives of both sides. The German commander, General Ludendorff, had recently made various assaults on different parts of the Allied line without any significant success, until he directed his main force against Amiens. This brought about an Allied retreat, and British casualties that were numbered at more than 300,000 men. Reinforcements were sent urgently to the British lines and the German advance was contained. This was the state of affairs when Geoffrey arrived at Wimereux. There was a brief pause in the tide of battle before Ludendorff launched another attack, on 27th May 1918, which reached the Marne. He now had two huge forward 'bulges' in his line but had used up all his reserves, and American troops were pouring in to reinforce the Allied resistance to German pressure. The French repulsed the enemy advance to the Marne in July, and early in August the Germans were dealt a severe blow south of the Somme. Ludendorff was driven to say: 'August 8th was the black day of the German army.... It put the decline of fighting power beyond doubt.... The war must be ended'[4]. The Bulgarians capitulated in September and the Turks in October, causing the Germans to appeal for an armistice on 3rd October. This appeal was ignored; instead the Allies made a final advance on the Hindenburg Line and penetrated the defences. Austria capitulated on 30th October and signed a separate armistice, adding to Ludendorff's problems. Furthermore, revolution had broken out in Germany and was spreading, but the Kaiser refused to abdicate. The German navy mutinied; this, and the collapse of the home front, were yet other factors which led Germany to send delegates to the armistice conference and then to accept the severe terms imposed by the Allied armies. A further Allied attack intended for 14th November never took place for World War I came to an end at 11 am on 11th November 1918.

However, the course of history could not be apparent to Geoffrey, who wrote home 6 months before this, on 4th May: 'My present job looks like being a rotten one as no one knows anything about me.... I don't suppose the present lull will last long and I shall be busy with lots to do. I have 42 beds at present with the likelihood of an increase at any time and [as] I shall do all the operative work arising out of this the possibilities are therefore fairly bright.... I do miss Michael. Give him a big hug from his Dad'[5]. Next day Geoffrey commented in his letter on the achievements which had taken place in aircraft design and capability during the years that had passed since he saw his first biplane at Gerrards Cross. He had just seen a display of aerobatics, looping the loop and rolling, and 'the manner in which they can climb now is extraordinary; they bank up quite vertically. I did wish you were with me to see the fun, you would have liked it.... Nose diving must be great fun, like going down in an enormously express lift, you know, feeling as if you had left your tummy on the top floor and want to go back for it'[5].

The mail had not yet caught up with Geoffrey's move and he was anxious to know how things were at home. On 6th May he went for a walk to a pretty little village where an auction was taking place and was amused by the rapid patter of the auctioneer, but 'inexpressibly bored' by the lack of work or any alternative amusement. A number of hotels were out of bounds on the grounds that they sold spirits, which were apparently banned for the British Expeditionary Force. He met the village priest, who looked so much 'like the picture in the book that one felt one had met the identical man before'[6]. In contrast to the Russians, who used to stare at the unfamiliar sight of an Englishmen, the French 'rarely even look at you as you pass', and he said he only saw old men and women, apart from a few French officers. 'I did 2 operations this morning', he wrote, 'my first go with the knife. They have had a very busy time here after the Boche push but just now things are very slack and a good thing for us too after all as it will give our poor fellows a breather'[6]. It was at this point that he reminded Gertrude of the noise of the artillery at Lutsk (qv). He asked her to send him a stethoscope so that he could 'listen to some of the chest wounds'[6]. It is very surprising that he did not have one of his own with him, and the one she provided was later stolen.

Geoffrey must also have had some serious head injuries under his care for, in a letter of 16th May, he said that '...my cerebellar case is doing awfully well. The other man is bad and is developing a large cerebral hernia.... Both frontal lobes are badly pulped and I have felt all along that it will be rather miraculous if he recovers'[7]. His letter also included a request for some chocolates 'from Sissons in St Anne's Square'.

Clearly a number of letters are missing, for the next is dated 24th May, and he apologises for not having written for 2 days as there was nothing to say. There had been a severe gale, 'which had the advantage of keeping the Boche away'. He went for a long walk along the coast and back along the sands. There were only six patients in his beds, so his work was soon done. He mentioned a wounded soldier with gas gangrene on whom he had performed a delayed primary suture with success, after the usual initial excision treatment. This was the sixth good outcome among his cases of a similar nature. The technique of wide excision followed by delayed primary suture led to a much more rapid recovery than was usual with the standard routine, in which wounds infected with gas gangrene were left open and consequently took a long time to heal, and during this time muscle contractures always developed. Geoffrey enquired after Michael, whom he usually referred to by the Russian pet name, Misha, and continued: 'One goes to bed early. How we used to sit up in Russia.... I have read my paper that you sent me and it seems intolerably stupid. I shall have to rewrite it'[8]. One detects a yearning for Russia in these letters. It was an affection which never left him, an affection for the country he remembered from before the final revolutions, a world that even then, only a few months later, no longer existed. He was also missing the surgical activity and responsibility afforded him at Lutsk where he was in the midst of dramatic events. Events were not less dramatic in France, but he was not so directly involved in them.

During the next 2 days Geoffrey only admitted six patients, which gave him time for another walk to the village, where he had a glass of chocolate, and to the beach. He had played tennis at the weekend, but the balls would not bounce properly and he was hoping for some new ones. The state of the balls may have been an excuse for lack of practice, for he wrote candidly to Gertrude '...I am awful at tennis'[9], a contrast to his satisfaction with his game some years earlier. He even found time to read a novel or two in this relatively quiet period, so typical of military surgery in which slack times alternate with periods of frenzied activity.

Gertrude had now obtained a post with the Travelling Medical Boards for the examination of candidates for the Women's Army Auxiliary Corps (WAAC), the headquarters of which were in London. She therefore returned, for a week or so, to her former accommodation at 24 Gordon Street, Gordon Square, London, where she had lived 11 years before when working at the Royal Free Hospital Medical School. The work necessitated travelling to various cities, and she would frequently be kept busy and away from home for the whole day. Mabel Feury was now not only caring for Michael but for Gertude as well.

At the end of June, Geoffrey wrote to Trude that it was 'just a year ago today since I returned from Russia...and now before the year is up we have been separated again.... What a world it has been ever since we were married and how vain it will have been unless it ends with the surety that our children's happiness will be safe from a replica of these times'. As usual money worries beset him. 'I will send you £5 to carry on with later in the week if you are still stoney.... I have already given you all my allowance.... We are in the usual financial straits, nothing in hand, a lot owing, and a lot owed to us. We are jugginses I suppose to be so permanently like that but I spend a lot and you are always on the move and spending a lot although you earn a lot (no reproach implied)'[10].

Gertrude then decided to move from London, and stay with the Parsons in Hove while looking for suitable accommodation for herself, Mabel Feury (Pan) and Michael. She planned to travel from Sussex to her work in London by train although this meant getting up at 6 am. She quite soon succeeded in finding an apartment at 25 York Road, Hove, and told her mother that they had 'three rooms together on the ground floor, a nice sitting room and 2 bedrooms, one of which Miss F and baby will have which has a little private lavatory opening out of it, also a small conservatory where he [Michael] can lie in his pram with the door open on a wet day. It is all so much nicer than I thought we could get in apartments'[11]. There was an added advantage that the landlady was responsible for all cooking and catering tasks, which Trude was almost incapable of undertaking, and Pan was able to relieve her of any worries about her son. Gertrude wrote to her mother: 'I can hardly believe I did finally accomplish all there was to do. These days people refuse to move furniture and one's luggage must be under 100 lbs or cabs refuse to take you, and they won't take prams unless they are particularly amiable.... Some of Geoffrey's friends took our big trunks, files of medical journals, Russian trophies and household effects, dishes, saucepans etc. Another friend is keeping our big pram, and I sent all sorts of little odds and ends to Rochdale'[11]. On their arrival in Brighton she described queues to get ration books and the need to register with various shops.

The question had been raised, presumably by Trude or her mother, as to whether it would be better for Michael if he were to be sent to Canada and be cared for, with his sister, by their grandmother and the nursemaid. In reply Geoffrey wrote 'I had a long letter from your father yesterday, and although he sounds favourable to Michael going, it would be the greatest mistake in the world to let him go. Besides it is really dangerous and we do not know anyway whether we are going back or not, do we dear?'[12]. This is a very significant remark which shows that there had been discussions on the subject, and that Geoffrey had come to realise the restrictions that would be imposed on the development of his career if they did return to Canada. Those discussions may have taken place quite recently, for when Geoffrey joined the army he gave his place of domicile as Victoria BC and in Russia he had considered joining either the Royal Army Medical Corps (RAMC) or the Canadian Army Medical Corps.

Jeff was still under no pressure at work and found time for relaxation. In addition to reading Samuel Butler's *The way of all flesh* which had been published posthumously in 1903, he had begun 'to be resigned to being rather rotten at tennis and my hope now is to learn it well enough to be able to teach Monica and Michael to play better than their parents could'[12]. It was a great pity that he felt this need, for in the future he was to upset his children by his insistence that they should excel at games, in which none of them managed to perform to his satisfaction. The pressure that Jeff was to put on his own family is the more surprising since he had felt so strongly about the demands made on himself in his youth by his own father. So often does one generation reflect its predecessor. Sir Harry Platt once remarked how alike Geoffrey and his father were in temperament and behaviour[13].

A week later Geoffrey was worrying about the strain imposed on Gertrude by the Travelling Boards: 'I think it is very stupid of them to make you return to London between those Midland boards.... I can quite see that the Travelling Board business is too much of a good thing altogether.... I don't think you ought to do it any longer than you can help. I should suggest that you apply officially and formally for a job in the WAAC overseas contingent'[14]. Somewhat surprisingly, considering the Western Front was then only about 50 miles away from the hospital, in a letter dated 29th July 1918, Jeff remarked that he had just had a round of golf. The links at Wimereux were on the sand dunes beside the English Channel, and it was on this course that Alexander Fleming played when he was stationed, also during 1918, at a base laboratory in Boulogne, and where he invented a putting game which he played in the dark with candles inside the holes[15].

Jeff hoped to be able to get some leave after 7 months in France, with the prospect that he might be able to go home for Christmas, though he thought that in many ways a leave spent with Gertrude in France might be preferable. 'The south would be lovely, though it would be the wrong time of year'[16]. This astonishing statement presents an extraordinary contrast to the slaughter going on in the trenches and to his financial anxiety. Geoffrey repeatedly managed to produce ideas that would be to his own or both his and Gertrude's advantage, but which were divorced from reality. Nevertheless, he also anticipated that they would continue to be separated for some time hence[16].

On 1st August Jeff reported that Standing Orders prevented wives from residing within 40 miles of their husbands, unless working in a hospital. He thought that Gertrude might manage this if she joined the WAAC, but 'if you are in Paris or elsewhere I need not report your presence'. Geoffrey then consented to letting Michael be looked after by his uncle and aunt in Hove if they would have him. 'It is extraordinarily kind of them, I hope they won't get more than they bargain for'[17]. However, it seems most likely that Pan continued to look after Michael in York Road, with the knowledge that she could readily call on the Parsons if necessary.

On the clinical side, Jeff was very impressed with the antiseptic powers of Bismuth Iodoform Paraffin Paste (BIPP) which had been produced by the Newcastle surgeon, Rutherford Morrison, and he used this to sterilize those areas of wounds that he could not excise, preferring it to Flavine, though he commented that it was more expensive. He attended a meeting of the Base Medical Society at which he heard a paper on penetrating wounds of the knee and thought it somewhat tedious, despite reports of good results. One has to remember that there was virtually no clinical specialization in the army medical services, apart from ophthalmology and ear nose and throat surgery, and that Geoffrey had to treat whatever type of problem presented itself. He had operated on a boy with a lacerated superior longitudinal sinus due to a head injury. 'The haemorrhage at the operation was awful and almost uncontrollable. Still I think I should handle it better another time'[18].

Jeff knew that Gertrude really wished to return to Canada. She was always homesick to be back safely with her beloved mother in the beautiful environment of Victoria, which contrasted so sadly with the rain and grime of an English city, though she would clearly not object if Geoffrey decided to stay in Britain. The passing thought came to him that he might get an appointment on the junior surgical staff of McGill University, in Montreal, as that would be both in Canada and, at the same time, nearer to the Eastern United States and England. 'Still one cries for the moon. I have just about as much chance of getting the one as the other, but I can see your eyes flashing with pleasure at the thought and looking up the next boat for Canada!'[18]. In this letter he also mentioned the death following battle injuries, of Revere Osler. Harvey Cushing, the pioneer neurosurgeon, who was in France serving with the American forces, had operated on his friend Sir William Osler's son who had suffered abdominal, chest and thigh wounds, without being able to save him[19]. Jeff finally expressed his pleasure that Gertude had obtained an appointment as House Surgeon at Charing Cross Hospital and congratulated her on it[18].

It was the strain of the Board work that had prompted her to apply for a post at Charing Cross Hospital. She moved into the mess there on the 14th August 1918, leaving Michael in Hove under Pan and Mrs Parsons' care, but there is no record to say for whom she worked. She told her mother 'I have 2 wards full of soldiers and last week had three appendix cases to operate on and am very proud of this. Everyone is very nice to me, so I am as happy and comfortable as one can expect in these anxious times.... I hope to get to Brighton next weekend, it will be a fortnight since I saw Michael last'[20]. The appointment was only until 30th November; the reason for it being so short was that three of the junior staff at Charing Cross Hospital had left their appointments early, probably in order to join the forces. However, a note in the Charing Cross Medical Committee Minutes states that in future no honorarium would be awarded to the junior staff until they had completed their appointments.

Pan and the baby may have now been considering staying with the Parsons in Dyke Road, Hove, for Geoffrey wrote, 'I had a nice letter from Uncle Fred the other day saying how well he got on with Michael. He seems to be quite fond of him'[18]. But the situation was still under discussion, since just over 2 weeks later Jeff replied to Gertrude: 'If Aunt Ada and Uncle Fred really want the lad, they can have him'[21]; in the event this probably did not happen.

Meanwhile the lull in work experienced by Geoffrey earlier in the summer had passed and on 11th August he had no less than 28 operations to perform, in addition to his ward work, and he was very tired. On the following day he had important news to tell Gertrude. 'I had a long talk with the Colonel today. It is suggested by him that I should be made head [cranio-spinal] specialist (English) to the Base. Cushing is at present the spec. but apparently this might come off and I should do nothing else during pushes etc. It would be rather nice don't you think, but rather too good to be true as it would mean considerable kudos. I might be given some surgical chest beds as well. Rather hot stuff what. Don't breathe a word of it to anybody. You are the only person I have told and it is so nebulous & unlikely I am hardly justified in uttering it. Of course the Co. himself has no power to do it, but he may be able to persuade.... The very best of luck to you on commencing your Hosp. duties. I do so hope you will like it and be happy in the work. I am so sorry you didn't get down to see Misha'[22].

Geoffrey had become a strong advocate of specialization and the possibility of this opportunity to specialize, however uncertain, may have been brought about by his own persuasion, despite the remark that it was the Colonel's own idea. It shows that the aim of making neurosurgery his life's work was growing stronger all the time and that it was likely to influence his choice of appointments and opportunities in the future. Meanwhile head injuries were clearly now being channelled his way and, in consequence, his work load became increasingly heavier. 'We are horribly busy', he wrote on 30th August. 'Head work with our present tools — I haven't got my full Cushing outfit yet — is very tiring. All this boring with the hand trephine is tough manual labour. I am very pleased with local anaesthesia and have so far hardly used a general anaesthetic. I dope them well with hyoscine and morph[ine] first and they come in quite drunk. Morphia alone is no good. I did 6 or 7 today'[23]. It was the usual neurosurgical practice then to use local anaesthesia as much as possible, and this remained the policy until general anaesthesia became safe for long operations and could be given by remote control. Jeff had read about Cushing's techniques, but had not seen them or been able to discuss them with any member of his staff — a defect he was soon to put right. One cannot help remembering Geoffrey's lack of experience in cranial surgery and that he was entirely self-taught up to and beyond this point. Although it had been recommended that Jefferson should take over the care of head injuries, those in command knew little of the subject or of the skills that might be required. There was no designated British Neurosurgical Unit, though Percy Sargent and Gordon Holmes (both from the National Hospital for Nervous Diseases in Queen Square, London) were doing some specialist neurological work in France, particularly in the field of spinal injury. In this letter Geoffrey also told Gertrude that he had heard from Stephen Paget, who had been a surgeon on the staff of the Anglo-Russian Hospital but was not related to Lady Muriel, that 'his wife fell in love with you which is not surprising'[23].

The next letter was written in pencil on Army Form C 348. 'I have been so cross lately, I am rather ashamed of it, very snappy with everybody.... I have got two

Adrian huts going now full of heads (76 in the 2 huts) and about 25 more in the Casino, so I am pretty busy. I have very little cerebrum of my own left'[24]. In contrast, just 4 days later, he said: 'I have had little to do in the operating line though I have about 95 heads in still—a few lumbar punctures from time to time. I have to do a head tomorrow—decompression. Gordon Holmes was in today to see a cerebellar injury of mine. Its a great treat to watch him examining a case, he's most ingenious with his tests and a very nice and most enthusiastic man'[25]. It seems from a remark in this letter that Geoffrey was proposing to work up a paper on phantom limbs but, although he spent much time on it, it does not appear to have been published. He was also beginning to collect and preserve specimens of injured brains for later examination.

The 20th September found Geoffrey in bed with influenza, but it does not seem to have been very serious as he was only off work for 3 or 4 days. Nevertheless he felt 'groggy' for several more. He somehow persuaded the Colonel to stop any head cases being admitted to 14th General Hospital while he was off sick, and when he returned to duty he was given an assistant. It had been officially realised that Jeff had sometimes been over-stretched. While he was sick he managed to read a few novels, especially by Compton Mackenzie[26]. In the next letter Geoffrey advised Gertrude to go to see *Prince Igor*, the ballet derived from the opera, with choreography by Marius Petipa, which was on in London, as they had seen it together in Petrograd. He was delighted by reading Edward Marsh's memoir on Rupert Brooke. 'Its magnificent because he allows Rupert to talk such a lot of himself.' Finally he asked for some cigarettes to be sent out, 'I like 1) Notaras No 4 Virginian (Piccadilly rt. hand side somewhere near Albermarle Street). 2) Friebourg & Treyer or Evans & Evans or something, Haymarket 34, W. Straight cut Virginian. Tobacco is awfully difficult to get out here just now'[27]. His taste demanded the very best, war or no war.

Geoffrey had not expected to get home for several weeks, but had been overworked and the Colonel was sympathetic, so his leave may have been expedited. Back in England for a short spell, Gertrude and he discussed their future without coming to any firm conclusions. At all events Geoffrey wrote, on 14th October, that he was now back again at 14th General Hospital, having had 'such a happy time'. In characteristic form he 'only just caught the boat this morning by running'. Later that same day he had another talk with Gordon Holmes who was apparently impressed with his 'phantom limb stuff'[28].

After his return to France there were bombing raids over Wimereux, which were 'very trying' and had made the Casino 'hardly usable as a Hosp. now as every pane of glass has been broken by the blasted Boche and as we look out directly over the sea it is no longer weather-proof'[29]. His hopes for a designated Head Centre under his own care appeared to be reaching fulfilment. 'It seems very likely to come off, which would please me greatly if it were to be done on a big scale. I have no wish for any half measures.... The Colonel has been extremely nice about it, the difficulty is to get our Consulting Surgeon to do anything definite.... I have made a start by collecting my heads into one ward and today Maj. Gen. Sir Anthony Bowlby was taken round and it was described as the new head centre! I was so annoyed as I had no warning and no chance of putting my goods in the shop window.... My appointment as Surg. Specialist [general surgery] is through.... I went down to Harvard [The Harvard neurosurgical unit, which was the only one of its kind in France and treated head injuries from the American, British and other armies] yesterday and had a yarn with Cushing's first assistant [Gilbert Horrax], a very nice fellow. They are most friendly and will tell you anything you want to know about things. I attended one of their own little medical meetings which was interesting as one of them was just back from work in 2 or 3 British CCS's [Casualty Clearing Stations] and one liked to hear their views as outsiders'[29]. As it turned out, however, the end of the war was to come quicker than Geoffrey had expected and, as a result, his new Head Centre never materialized. Within a very few weeks there were to be hardly any surgical cases of any kind left in the hospital; instead it was full of medical patients, many of them suffering from complications of influenza.

Geoffrey had undoubtedly hoped to meet Harvey Cushing himself, when he visited the Harvard unit. Although a specialist surgeon, Cushing was Director of the American Base Hospital No 5 and later wrote its history anonymously. But on the very day that Geoffrey wrote to Gertrude about his visit, Cushing sent a letter to his own home as follows: 'Too poor on my pins to go to Vichy as planned. Marked increase of numbness and unsteadiness with a good deal of involvement of my hands.... Schwab [neurologist] shakes his head and talks about a multiple toxic neuritis with leucopenia'[30]. Cushing was in bed for 3 weeks, and he developed a deep vein thrombosis in one of his legs as a result. This explains why Geoffrey failed to see him on 17th October[30].

Even before the war ended, discussion of literary subjects had found its way back into the letters that passed between Geoffrey and his wife. In later life Trude's reading became more or less confined to professional work or religion, but at this time they were both reading general literature quite widely. We have seen that Jeff frequently gave her his own opinion on whatever novel or poetry he had recently come across and, presumably, her letters did the same, for it was a bond between them and a welcome relief from the many anxieties that beset them. On 20th October Jeff announced that he had purchased *The golden ass* of Apuleius, containing a number of tales written in the mid-second century AD*. He did not mention whether it was in Latin or a translation, for it is the earliest known Latin 'novel'. 'What a joy it will be to have our library again, and look over all our old treasures and add our new ones.... Who knows but that a few months may see the whole thing quite over.... Since I was back with you I have longed so much for our lovely Russian things, books and so forth. My heart goes out to the colour and sound and music of Russia. It was a wonderful experience and I am so glad that we shared it'[31]. Geoffrey was filled with a desire to write 'something beautiful and [I] am strangled by being perfectly inarticulate. I

*Apuleius.** He was a philospher of the time of Galen, active ca. 150 AD. His fame rests upon his *Metamorphoses* otherwise known as *The golden ass*. It consists of 11 books, elaborating upon a Greek tale. The narrator uses magic for amorous purposes, but it goes wrong and he is transformed into a donkey. From the fourth book onwards the adventures of the ass are described, except where they are interrupted by other tales. They are all told in the first person and eventually the story-teller, turned ass, is restored to human form by Isis. There is an autobiographical element to the work, for Apuleius himself was accused before the proconsul of having used magic to gain the love of his wife Pudentilla, a rich widow. He recorded his defence in his *Apologia*. (Boardman J, Griffin J, Murray O. *The Oxford history of the classical world*. Oxford, OUP 1986: 692–6.).

suppose with experience I could write good prose, in fact I know I could, but it is funny that anyone who <u>feels</u> the music of the <u>spoken</u> word of poetry as I do should be so incapable of writing it'[31]. It is surprising that Geoffrey appears not to have written any poems for Gertrude. We do not know of any, though it is possible that even if he had done so, she might not have preserved them for having been of too personal a nature.

At the end of October Geoffrey was again ill and in bed, this time with a cold, and his spirits were low; across the Channel Gertrude also had 'flu. Jeff's gloomy mood is clear from a letter: 'I am chronically and continually worried about my future — our future, and am rather depressed about it in a mild way. I do wish so much that you could get Monica, and yet suppose after all that we have to go to BC it seems such a waste of money and time. Of course I think it would do you a lot of good to have a month or two's complete rest.... I know you have lived on nervous energy now for over 2 yrs and don't want you to break down'[32]. He suggested that the matter be put on one side until they knew what chance there was of peace, and that she should plan to visit Canada as soon as the end of the war was established. The newspapers now carried news of the surrender of Austria, but Geoffrey still feared that they were over-optimistic.

Yet again, Jeff's extraordinary capacity for worrying about money, but at the same time spending it on simple luxuries, is revealed in his letter of 4th November. 'I have just got two absolutely splendid German shell cases of brass for our house ... you <u>will</u> like them though I had to pay quite a lot for them. I also wrote to Propert and got him to send me a catalogue of those Holbein prints that we thought so very beautiful.... I ought to enclose the promised cheque but so far my pass book has not materialised.... I suppose Austria is now absolutely out of it, so Germany cannot last long'[33]. Geoffrey had played hockey in the afternoon; 'Its the only game I have ever been <u>really</u> good at. Fancy, do you remember our football game at Lutsk! Great fun wasn't it when we played the Russian airmen'[33].

On Armistice Day, 11th November 1918, Geoffrey was buoyant and he wrote joyfully to Gertrude: 'Look we have come through. Well its true and the war is over, and all of us who are left alive ought to thank whatever Gods there be for their great mercy ... and that you and I, my dear, are amongst those who have survived.... There is a lot of cheering going on, mine sweepers were firing their guns in the Channel this morning, flags are flying everywhere, and they are shouting the Marseillaise in the Mess. All this in spite of its being a most cold dull and depressing day, raining steadily'[34]. Geoffrey wrote, interestingly, that the only medal ribbon he coveted was the Mons Star, 1914. Did he have some regrets that he did not join the RAMC until 1918? He continued: 'However, I think we have done our share. We have worked more or less unselfishly in the cause, suffered hardships and separation. Before long we shall be together again. One can't at all tell how soon it will be ... of course not a single man will be released until the peace terms are actually signed'[34], which had to be done by 26th November according to the armistice agreement. Then his financial worries crept back once more: 'I have at last got my pass-book and have less than I thought ... I shall only just have enough to pay expenses and may have to overdraw'[34]. This was written so soon after contemplating buying Holbein prints!

The Armistice celebrations in London were described by Gertrude in a letter to her mother, dated 'evening of 11th November 1918'. She mentioned the dense crowds of people in the street outside Charing Cross Hospital, excited men and girls shouting and singing, whistles and car horns blowing, many of the people drunk and a consequent stream of minor injuries pouring into the casualty department[35]. She also wrote to Geoffrey, who replied that there were celebrations in Boulogne, though he did not feel like going there to see them. Jeff was in fact involved in some horse-play whereby six members of the 14th General Hospital mess 'bagged an ambulance and went up with a kettledrum and some tin trumpets and so on to visit the neighbouring hospitals. We made a most appalling noise and I was quite hoarse yesterday as a result'[36]. Jeff emphasized again that he had no idea how long he would have to serve before demobilization, and hoped he would not be kept on the continent in the army of occupation. There were even doubts in his mind whether, in view of the extent of the revolution in Germany, there might be a situation in which there was nobody with whom to make peace. 'Its a pity Kaiser Bill didn't sit on his throne a few days longer, tho' the revolutionaries might have refused the terms. They might still, in which case there will be more war. I hardly think it is likely though'[36].

The great pandemic of influenza of 1918 had struck by now, and Geoffrey thought that, although the hospital would be full, there would soon be no surgical patients at all. He told Gertrude, who was about to end her appointment at Charing Cross Hospital and be reunited with Michael in Hove, that Sir RS 'the richest bachelor in England' was in the hospital and dying of 'flu. 'What a devil this flu has been. Great strong men are pretty fit one day and dead 48 hours later with very few physical signs'[37].

Geoffrey and a friend named Dale on 'looking out to sea saw 6 airships some sea-planes and a destroyer flotilla' from the cliffs where they were walking. So they 'hared down into Boulogne and saw the famous [HMS] *Broke* come in with the King and the two Princes Edward and Albert on deck. We went round and got a splendid view of them with Haig and Roger Keyes [Chiefs of the Army and Navy]. It was great fun, all the sirens in the harbour at full blast and crowds of people. The King and the whole party lunched at the Officer's Club quite publicly, no restrictions, anybody could go in just as in ordinary times. Rather nice wasn't it'[37]. Then, at the end of the letter, Jeff modified his usual request and asked for some pipe tobacco 'as its cheaper than cigarettes.... I'd like a few cigarettes soon though too if you have any money — but <u>cheap</u> ones'[37].

Geoffrey managed to get another brief spell of home leave and was able to spend Christmas with Gertrude after all, but he was back at Wimereux on 31st December, having left her that morning. 'It was so hard parting with you in that dimly lit noisy station.' They had again discussed their future and Geoffrey had told her finally that he wanted to settle in the Manchester area and that Canada was no longer a possibility. However, even this was not to be last word on the subject. He had heard that there was likely to be a vacancy on the staff of the hospital at Salford, and they must have talked about this. I appreciate your sacrifice about the M'ster decision so very much. It <u>is</u> hard for you my dear and I know it.... I shall write tomorrow to Garnett about Salford and see what he has to say. [Garnett Wright was a surgeon at Salford Royal Hospital, and a lecturer in operative surgery at the Manchester Medical School]. I feel I must now definitely declare myself for it and want it badly or I shall not get it'[38]. The possibility of sending Michael to join his sister in Victoria must have cropped up again, for

Geoffrey wondered what Mrs Flumerfelt thought about it, though he himself felt 'he really had better stay' in Britain[38].

The prospect of returning to England was now becoming imminent, and with it the absolute need to settle their plans for the future. Having given his address as Victoria, British Columbia, when he joined the army, the possibility arose of having to be demobilized in Canada, but it does not seem to have been seriously considered. When Geoffrey left Russia he was not only unwell, but had not got his ideas sufficiently clarified to reach any major decision. In any case he had said that he intended to join the Royal Army Medical Corps or the Canadian Medical Corps and would not have to reach a conclusion until the war was over. This moment had now arrived and he was about to return to Britain with very much clearer thoughts in his mind. He was hoping for a career in which neurosurgery would be his main concern, though he would inevitably have to practise general surgery as well, if only as a source of income. A return to Victoria would have made it almost impossible to achieve this, there being no medical school to provide research and teaching facilities, quite apart from the small size of the population in that distant Canadian town in the 1920s. Geoffrey felt, nevertheless, that if he stayed in Britain he would be unable to break into the London medical scene despite his high qualifications and influential friends, thoughts that were to return later in different circumstances. In Manchester and its neighbourhood, however, he was more at ease, was socially more comfortable, and a place on the staff of the Royal Infirmary, where there would also be a teaching commitment, seemed well within his reach. He needed a jumping-off point in the region, and Salford Royal Hospital would afford him that opportunity. Geoffrey was confident that he could obtain an appointment there, provided he overcame his earlier hesitation. The prospect of eventually going to Manchester was enough to satisfy his ambitions for the time being, and he would have more time to familiarise himself with neurosurgery, so that when he did apply to Manchester Royal Infirmary he could produce a strong case for the fulfilment of his dream of specialization in neurological surgery alone. Inevitably, it was to be several more years before this came about.

In the event Mrs Flumerfelt advised Gertrude to go to Canada with Michael, and Geoffrey expressed his approval, though he was not able to accompany them. In fact, they did not sail until April 1919. Meanwhile, arrangements had been made in France for Jeff's collection of brain injury specimens to be sent to the Royal College of Surgeons, where they would wait until he returned. He must have already negotiated with Professor Keith at the College to allow him to study them there.

Geoffrey had, by early January 1919, received a letter from Gertrude, passing on news of Monica from her mother. He wrote back: 'She must be perfectly lovely, I would love to see her but am happy for you to dear even if I can't. You really need her and she is becoming old enough to need to have the people she is going to live with around her, quite apart from the sentimental relationship'[39]. The present doctrines of child psychiatry had not then been formulated and Jeff's thoughts were quite spontaneous. In addition to the news, such as there was, he told her that his friend the Padre 'has just seen the Archbishop of Canterbury and is a little above himself in consequence!'[39].

On 25th January 1919, with tremendous enthusiasm, Geoffrey was able to write to Gertrude who was staying with the Parsons in Hove, that he would be coming home on Tuesday 28th, in only 3 days time. 'Isn't it splendid it will be lovely to see you. I'm so excited'[40]. However, although he was about to leave France he was not yet leaving the army, and the manner of his demobilization was still undetermined.

REFERENCES

GJ=Geoffrey Jefferson; GMJ=Gertrude Jefferson
1   Macpherson WG ed. *The medical history of the War.* Vol. 1. London: HM Stationery Office, 1921; **i**: 76–7.
2   GJ to GMJ. Letter 3rd May 1918.
3   GJ to GMJ. Letter 5th May 1918.
4   *Encyclopaedia Britannica.* 1962; **23**: 773.
5   GJ to GMJ. Letter 4th May 1918.
6   GJ to GMJ. Letter 6th May 1918.
7   GJ to GMJ. Letter 16th May 1918.
8   GJ to GMJ. Letter 24th May 1918.
9   GJ to GMJ. Letter 27th May 1918.
10   GJ to GMJ. Letter 30th June 1918.
11   GMJ to Mrs Flumerfelt. Quoted by Michael Jefferson, no date.
12   GJ to GMJ. Letter 8th July 1918.
13   Jefferson, M. Personal communication 26th March 1994.
14   GJ to GMJ. Letter 14th July 1918.
15   Maurois, A. *La vie de Sir Alexander Fleming.* Paris: Hachette, 1959: 98, 106.
16   GJ to GMJ. Letter 29th July 1918.
17   GJ to GMJ. Letter 1st August 1918.
18   GJ to GMJ. Letter 5th August 1918.
19   Fulton JF. *Harvey Cushing.* Oxford: Blackwell Scientific Publications, 1946: 424–5.
20   GMJ to Mrs Flumerfelt. Letter. 27th August 1918.
21   GJ to GMJ. Letter 21st August 1918.
22   GJ to GMJ. Letter 12th August 1918.
23   GJ to GMJ. Letter 30th August 1918.
24   GJ to GMJ. Letter 7th September 1918.
25   GJ to GMJ. Letter 11th September 1918.
26   GJ to GMJ. Letter 20th September 1918.
27   GJ to GMJ. Letter 22nd September 1918.
28   GJ to GMJ. Letter 14th October 1918.
29   GJ to GMJ. Letter 17th October 1918.
30   Fulton JF. *Harvey Cushing.* Oxford: Blackwell Scientific Publications, 1946: 435.
31   GJ to GMJ. Letter 20th October 1918.
32   GJ to GMJ. Letter 31st October 1918.
33   GJ to GMJ. Letter 4th November 1918.
34   GJ to GMJ. Letter 11th November 1918.
35   GMJ to Mrs Flumerfelt. Letter 11th November 1918, quoted by Michael Jefferson.
36   GJ to GMJ. Letter 13th November 1918.
37   GJ to GMJ. Letter 28th November 1918.
38   GJ to GMJ. Letter 31st December 1918.
39   GJ to GMJ. Letter 6th January 1919.
40   GJ to GMJ. Letter 25th January 1919.

---------------------------------- **Chapter 11** ----------------------------------

In Lancashire Again
1919–1922

When Geoffrey Jefferson returned from France at the end of January 1919, Gertrude and Michael were still living in the apartment in Hove. Just over 2 months later they sailed for Canada aboard the *Scandinavian*, reaching Halifax on 10th April and Victoria several days after that, an event noted in the local newspaper[1]. Geoffrey, however, remained in England and obtained lodgings as soon as possible, in London at 127 Queensgate, SW7, to be able to reach the Royal College of Surgeons easily. He wished to take up the offer by Sir Arthur Keith, made at the instigation of Professor Elliot Smith, for him to study the brain injury specimens which he had previously arranged to be sent there from France. He worked at the College until May, for only just over 3 months, during which time he produced the material for an extremely comprehensive paper on the physiology and pathology of gunshot wounds of the head[2]. He can have had time for little else other than work on this study and occasional visits to Hove. As has been mentioned, he was still on leave from the RAMC, for he had not yet been demobilized.

Early in that year Geoffrey at last succeeded in meeting Harvey Cushing, though he had long been, as he was proud to say, an avid reader of his papers. It was at a lecture at the College of Surgeons by Sir Arthur Keith on the subject of acromegaly. There are two letters from Cushing to Jefferson which pertain to the beginning of their acquaintance[3,4]. Geoffrey had written to ask him for copies of some of his papers. In reply Cushing said he remembered their meeting, but in response to the request for reprints, however, he wrote, 'I regret to say that such reprints as I still have are not particularly interesting ones for I have distributed the few papers of some possible scientific interest and have practically no copies remaining'[3]. He closed his letter by asking Geoffrey to let him have a copy of the paper on gunshot wounds of the head as soon as it was published. This was sent in due course, along with one other and, in acknowledging its receipt, Cushing remarked that Jeff had 'added greatly to the subject'[4]. 'A kindly bit of over-praise', was Jefferson's own comment many years later[5]. It is interesting, however, that by then Geoffrey had forgotten the subject of the remark, thinking that it had referred to acromegaly and the pituitary gland, whereas the reference was actually to the paper on gunshot wounds.

Geoffrey had attended a meeting of the British Medical Association early in April on the subject of surgical shock and had sat next to his old friend John Morley from Manchester but, generally speaking, he spent his days working at the Royal College of Surgeons in Lincoln's Inn Fields. On 5th April he met Harry Platt at the Imperial Institute, where they lunched together and then went on to watch the indoor tennis championships at Queen's Club. They were not impressed by the standard and came away before the close of play, but not without having spotted Hugh Walpole in the audience. That evening Jeff had a headache, one of several about this time, and a repetition of those he had suffered from during his time in practice in Canada. Then, a few days later, he took his notes on the brain trauma material to (Lord) Alfred Webb-Johnson. He explained in a letter to Gertrude, 'I'm trying to look at this head question from as logical an angle as possible and have laid down two dogmas to work from: 1) The importance of anatomical injury *per se*, because of the immense physiological importance of the functions which depend on the anat[omy]. 2) The paramount important of sepsis in raising the intracranial pressure. It seems to me that all injuries can be studied from these two view pts'[6].

Writing to Trude in Victoria later in the month of April, he began to address the letters to 835 Pemberton Road, rather than Ruhebühne, the change having presumably been demanded by the local post-office. There had been a gap of 3 weeks in the correspondence, occasioned by their inability to communicate while Gertrude was travelling, followed by a long letter covering a period of 4 days. He told her that he had asked for permission from the Medical Research Council to examine the detailed case histories of those patients whose brains he was studying, and that he had visited Gordon Holmes at 107 Harley Street more than once in order to show him what he was working on and to obtain encouragement. Jeff also revealed that he had written to (Sir) Charles Sherrington, who had been his father's friend, one of the most distinguished of British physiologists and by then the Waynflete Professor of Physiology at Oxford. Jeff wished to ask him about any possible correlations between his findings in the cerebral trauma cases and Sherrington's experimental work[7].

After much soul-searching Jeff finally decided to apply for the position on the Honorary consultant staff of the Salford Royal Hospital, with the possibility still at the back of his mind, of moving from there to the Manchester Royal Infirmary. Perhaps his thoughts may have reverted to a conversation some years previously in which he had remarked to one of his chiefs, Ralph Thompson, that Salford was no good for money, and he may then have remembered the reply, that 'personality could make a man anywhere'[8].

One of Jeff's problems was that he did not want to be appointed to Salford while still in the army, and then be sent to Canada to be demobilized since, as already mentioned, he had given his home address as Victoria, British Columbia, when he joined the RAMC. Another alternative was demobilization and deferred repatriation, which would open up a vista of 4 or 5 months separation, but would allow him to take the appointment at Salford if it was given to him. This was the option he finally chose, but when demobilization actually took place we do not know. As for repatriation, this had to wait for another 4 years. He had previously been wrongly informed that it was necessary to stay in the army until he was sent back to Canada.

Geoffrey expressed great sadness at the prospect of being apart from Gertrude for longer than they had expected, and also his anxiety to avoid any misunderstanding or misinterpretation of the choice that he clearly favoured. After all, he had written to her: 'I am not going to make up my mind on a course of final action until I am with you and we can decide together in Victoria'[9], a promise that was easier to write than to fulfil. Nevertheless, it was the first indication that he might join her out there sometime. The situation was that he would not commit himself to a life in Manchester for ever until he had experienced how he felt working there, and this was the 'final decision' that he said he would talk about, probably in Victoria. Gertrude, for her part, had both the children with her and still wanted him to join her there to discuss their future. A further encouragement to go out to Canada had been provided by her father in the form of a cheque which had, incidentally, eased Geoffrey's current financial situation. Not surprisingly, he had recently suffered more headaches and was very worried that his motives in applying for the Salford appointment would be misunderstood. 'I have been through torments trying to think out what will be best for all of us'[9]. Gertrude may not have given up all hope of Geoffrey returning to work in Victoria, and the tone of his letter suggests that he was still having to tread carefully.

Geoffrey went down to Hove at the beginning of May to spend a week with his aunt and uncle. He had been summoned to Salford for interview on 14th May or he would have stayed longer. He was both anxious and ambivalent (at least on paper) about the appointment. 'I am so afraid I am going to get the job, if they would only turn me down it would make things so much easier, and I would be able to come out soon. But I fear there is no chance of that and I shall have to work at Salford for some months waiting for a passage..., one must make up one's mind and follow the course of action decided upon'[10]. Although they had been talking together about not returning to Canada on a permanent basis, and even about the possibility of the appointment at Salford Royal Hospital, ever since they returned from Russia in 1917, the consequences for Trude of such an appointment, both emotional and professional, must have been obvious to both of them. It was $5\frac{1}{2}$ weeks since she had left for Canada, and by 8th May Jeff had still not heard from her[10].

To pass the time while he was staying in Sussex, Geoffrey went into Brighton with his aunt Ada and sat on the pier in the sunshine reading the *Morning Post*; he read various novels as well, on which he commented in some detail in his letters. However, he also said that he had looked through Harvey Cushing's *Tumours of the nervous system* 'which seems to me to be less good than I expected'. He told Gertrude that he was longing to hear what she would say about her reunion with Monica after 3 years of separation[10].

On 11th May a letter came from Gertrude but, of course, it did not contain any further comment on the matter of Salford or demobilization because of the postal delay. 'I'm terribly anxious to know all about Monica' Geoffrey wrote again, 'I hope she does not look too much like – whom I do not admire'[11]. It seems that Geoffrey did not have a recent photograph of Monica and he asked her to send him one. Michael's reaction on meeting his sister for the first time was to say 'Go away girlie from my mother', but this rather natural remark was not reported to Jeff in Gertrude's letter[12].

Writing before the interview for the job at Salford and still agonising about the decision to apply, Geoffrey said: 'Apart from [its] effect on prestige and being a useful bird in the hand to decoy something better elsewhere I shall not be at all sorry if I don't get it'[11]. These were probably not his true feelings, for he had previously determined to approach the committee with enthusiasm and had carefully weighed the pros and cons. The remarks were, however, symptomatic of his worry about the reaction of Gertrude and her family to the result of the interview, whether he was appointed or not. 'I am terribly anxious that your Father should realise that [if I am not given the job] I could have got it if I had wanted it, but as you know I have simply applied and refrained from working hard to get it, which would have made it almost certain. So Fate shall decide. Perhaps I was wrong to do this, and should boldly have said Yes or No to it, but the issues are so conflicting that it was very difficult to take such a course.... I am haunted by that knowledge, [of] what a supreme sacrifice it will mean to your people if we live in England'[11]. Nevertheless, he had made his mind up on that point very clearly when he was in France, and there is no reason to doubt that it was still his firm intention to practise in Britain. This prevarication was a symptom of the pressure being put upon him from Canada.

Following the interview on 14th May, Jeff was successful and he became an Honorary Assistant Surgeon to the Salford Royal Hospital. One only became a full Honorary Surgeon after a lapse of several years. 'My feelings about it were extraordinarily mixed but I'm coming round to it more now, particularly since I saw Dean* yesterday. He thinks he will be able to fix me up as a surg. path. worker at £250 which would be a god-send in these troublous times.... Altogether I've been in the lowest mental condition I've known for ages about everything. It has all seemed so hopeless. I don't see quite when I am going to get out to you'[13].

Then, somewhat astonishingly and contrary to all his previous plans, Geoffrey continued, in reply to a suggestion from Gertrude: 'I think you're right about Canada eventually, that we're going to settle there in the end. My chief mental worries were how on earth we were going to live for even a year here, but I feel a little better about that and think we shall undoubtedly win through and make a success of this'[13]. However, it cannot really have been his intention to return to Canada to settle in view of the decision so clearly expressed by him in the previous December[14], unless he thought vaguely of doing so in retirement.

Harry Platt had offered to share his own private consulting rooms at 26 St John Street, Manchester, with Geoffrey for a low rent (£30 per annum). It was essential to have somewhere of this nature in order to provide an income from a few private patients, since no money came from his hospital appointment, and so he placed an order for a small brass plate with his name on it to announce his presence there. Jeff had a heavy cold, which may have added to his recent depression. He had probably completed his work on the brain specimens before taking the short holiday in Hove, and he spent the last 2 weeks of May in Rochdale. Although he did not say it in so many words, he obviously found life much more congenial there than it had been when his father was alive to make demands on him. In the company of his brother and sisters he was happy. His mother was away when he arrived, but she soon returned together with two maids, there having been none for a year or two while the war lasted[13].

By now it was clear to Geoffrey that, after all, he would not be able to go out to Canada in the near future and that Gertrude and the children should return to England as soon as possible[15]. There were reports that Monica's health had given

*Dean. Henry Dean DM. FRCP. (1879–1961) was then Professor of Pathology at Manchester University. Later he became Professor of Pathology at Cambridge University, where he was also Master of Trinity Hall College and sometime Vice-Chancellor.

some cause for anxiety, and the question was raised as to whether she would be fit to undertake the journey from Victoria to England until it had improved, or even to tolerate the impure air of Manchester once she got there. Geoffrey continued to feel pretty miserable, for he was missing Gertrude very badly and needed to discuss his problems with her in conversation rather than by letter. In addition, he was again being troubled by further headaches. Only 3 days after obtaining the appointment as an Honorary Surgeon, Geoffrey mused, 'I don't know what has happened to me...I mean I had pretty clear ideas about what I wanted, all that I want just now somehow is quiet and rivers and trees. I don't feel as if I ever want to see any scientific stuff again.... Of course once I get a little bit interested again I shall feel less like a jellyfish with meningitis'[13]. It was very sad that, at the moment of his success in obtaining a consultant appointment, with the possibility of other work in a laboratory, and at the beginning of the surgical career that he had always aimed for, his pleasure was so completely marred by anxiety. Nearly all his troubles stemmed from the need to undo his earlier mistaken decision to work in Canada and the pattern of life that this had apparently established. However, in due course, Gertrude was to write to say that she had left all the decisions about their future to Jeff and that she had tried not to exert any influence.

Gertrude visited her sister in Seattle soon after arriving in Victoria and found Norma severely troubled by her marital problems. At Ruhebühne Monica was, not surprisingly, being 'rather difficile'. She had naturally become very attached to her nanny who had been chiefly responsible for her care. Now, at the age of nearly $4\frac{1}{2}$ years, this relationship was being severed. She can have had almost no memory of her mother, since she was only a year old when they parted. Although no arrangements had yet been made for Gertrude's return to England, Geoffrey wrote to ask that their instruments should be sent to him in Manchester, with as few other items of furniture etc. as possible, in order to save expense. He had begun to look for suitable consulting rooms of his own, while continuing to share 26 St John Street, Manchester, with Harry Platt. At last there was a plan of action which was being firmly followed.

The prospect of making a reasonable income still seemed a long way off. Geoffrey looked at his bank pass book and concluded: 'I can't have more than about £20 in the world, which is rather depressing', though it has to be added that he had not yet received his gratuity from the army. He decided, therefore, that somehow he had to find a paid job in addition to his hospital and private work. And, if they were soon going to be united again it was necessary to find a house. There was room at Rochdale for Gertrude and the children to be accommodated as a temporary measure, and Cecilia Jefferson had invited them, but that would be a last resort, for Gertrude and her mother-in-law could not have lived easily together.

Finding a house at an affordable price was a difficult task, owing to the number of men and women who were leaving the forces and who were also looking for somewhere to live. For the time being, Geoffrey had obtained accommodation for himself in a boarding house called Fernwood at 151, High Street, Chorlton-on-Medlock, Manchester, SE 'Not very nice but not too bad'. There were good practical reasons for choosing this neighbourhood. The area was rich in lodging houses that were convenient and socially acceptable, and which were occupied by many middle-class professional people as well as by students and actors and actresses. It was easy to reach the centre of the city from there and it was near the University and Oxford Road, which it joined. As yet the Salford Royal Hospital had given Jeff no out-patient clinic and no beds of his own, but he was more or less occupied by covering for other consultants who were away and for whom he did one or two operations. Some classes had also been started in order to prepare candidates for the FRCS examinations, and Geoffrey was made both secretary and organizer for these. The evenings were lonely for him unless they were relieved by the occasional invitation to dinner with the Garnett Wrights or other friends. To make matters worse, strikes in Canada were causing severe delays to the mail in both directions[16].

There were two unusual people among those sharing Geoffrey's lodgings, 'One a Russian called Na–, quite a nice and typical little Russkie business man. The other a weird cuss called No–, a YMCA worker, and electrical engineer, geologist and international socialist who calls himself a Bolshevik to frighten people. There was a terrific argument last night in the sitting room on socialism. No– was giving a disquisition on Karl Marx, really very interesting, but very intellectual and cold. It will smash when it comes into contact with Humanity. I've (I think) quite won No–'s heart and he has promised us security and protection in the event of a revolution! ...They are out entirely for material things and, as I told him, it can only become a world force when spiritual things are allied to it.... They are out to break up the capitalist system and establish communism in its place...but there is not enough preaching of unselfishness when once these things are got'[17].

Although no paper on phantom limbs appears in his bibliography, Jeff continued to work on the clinical material he had collected, and hoped to canvas Henry Head, Wilfred Trotter, Farquhar Buzzard and Percy Sargent for their opinions on his conclusions. 'I think I've got on to something rather good in the nerve bulbs, that is the escape of nerve fibres from the bulbs themselves and their spread into the fibrous tissue at the end of the stump'[18]. An important observation.

Geoffrey spent much time scouring the neighbourhood for a house, without any success, and he thought it might even be necessary for them to live in lodgings when Trude and the two children came back to England. 'There is still no sign of building wh. I can't understand'[19]. Houses were available for sale but none to be let, and purchase was out of the question. Things did not improve in the next 10 days and Jeff once more became very depressed for a while. 'I feel so miserable to think that you've been lonely and disappointed in me. Also so short of money, but I'm making nothing. I'm not even getting any assisting to do. So altogether its very worrying indeed and there's no house to be had anyhow'[19]. Jeff had not had a letter from Gertrude for several days, and none before that for 3 or 4 weeks; he was afraid that he had upset her by what he had written in his depressed state or by his appointment to Salford Royal Hospital. Indeed, in addition to his letter of 17th July, sent to Victoria, Geoffrey even posted a note addressed to her friend Beryl in Montreal with whom she would have stayed briefly before sailing to Liverpool, so convinced was he that she was already on her way home, though this was not in fact the case. And he excitedly gave Gertrude the news that he had admitted his first brain tumour and was about to operate, 'a left cerebellar as far as I can localise it'[19].

By July 1919 the Salford Royal Hospital had provided Jefferson with an out-patient clinic, which enabled him to begin to establish a relationship with the general practitioners in the neighbourhood, on whose goodwill he largely depended for private patients. He was also doing some coaching in anatomy on three days in the week, and his hospital beds had been increased to ten, plus any emergencies that he might admit on behalf of others. Two or three of the consultants had asked him to cover their duties while they were away on holiday, so that he was now quite fully occupied. There were very few consultant staff at the hospital at that time, in fact there were only four Honorary physicians and surgeons. These were George Langley (physician), James McAlpine (genito-urinary surgeon), Robert Ollerenshaw (orthopaedic surgeon), and Geoffrey himself (general surgeon). Anaesthetics were given by an Indian doctor named Ghosh. Robert Ollerenshaw, like Jeff, had a Canadian wife and they had two sons. With this in common it was natural that, over the years, these two families were to become friends.

Jeff commented in a letter of 25th July that he had listened to Harry Platt's excellent rendering of the Schumann Piano Concerto and that he was happy to hear that Gertrude had been playing the piano at Ruhebühne, though they would not be able to afford one themselves for a long time. He still hoped to see her soon but had no firm date for her return journey. Sadly, the patient with the cerebellar lesion had died only 3 hours after Geoffrey operated on her, which was 'disappointing in every conceivable way'[20].

Looking for a house continued to be a very unrewarding and depressing exercise. 'I spent Saturday evening "doing" Eccles again, Broughton Pk and Kessel but there is nothing to let. There was a most suitable house on the Eccles Old Rd but it was only for sale. I am quite sure that being in N. Manchester would be well worth while . . . at this end one is simply lost among the crowd . . . . The only way in which one can get a house is by knowing the people who are moving out . . . . I've made the best arrangement I can, and that is for you to send all our stuff to Stevenson's [Dr Scott Stevenson, MD], 36 Wellington Road, Eccles. He has a large clean dry empty stable where we could pile our stuff until a house falls vacant. People are offering £20 in the M'ster Guardian for information that will lead them to a house! I am sure we were wise in throwing in our lot with Salford. Applications for the FRCS class are coming in well. I'm making awfully little dear, and have practically nothing — a cable makes a big hole in my money. I never spend more than 1s 2d on lunch, coffee, a sandwich & a cake because I can't afford more.' Fortunately two of the Honorary staff at the hospital asked him to take care of their private patients while they were on holiday, 'otherwise the end of August would see me finally penniless. However, I am surprisingly confident about it all'[21]. Shortly after this Geoffrey was able to report that he had done a number of operations of a general nature at a private hospital or nursing home in Nell Lane; these included some limb re-amputations which provided him with more specimens of painful neuromata. Unfortunately, he had not been able to start any experimental pathology with Professor Dean as he had not yet received the necessary licence from the Home Office[22].

Apparently, Gertrude had written 'a long miserable letter' which showed some jealousy about Geoffrey's visits to his mother, brother and sisters in Rochdale, though these were very infrequent. One reason for her distress may have been that she did not get on well with her mother-in-law, probably through no fault of her own, and that she suspected that Mrs Cecilia Jefferson might try to undermine her son's affection for her. A factor in this discord had been the opposition by the Jefferson parents to Geoffrey's marriage to one whom they considered to be a relatively rich young heiress from abroad, who had enticed him away to go and live in Canada. It was compounded by the fact that his mother thought Geoffrey had also behaved irresponsibly by going to Russia, especially when his wife was pregnant though Geoffrey was probably unaware of her condition at the time. Jeff replied to Trude: 'I haven't been over to Rochdale for ages (5 or 6 wks) certainly not for a month, nor have I seen even Madge during that time, needless to say we haven't corresponded. All your fears are groundless'[23]. A further circumstance affecting her relationship with Jeff's mother was that, so it is said, Cecilia Jefferson regarded Jack as her favourite son, the one they could turn to for compassion or help, and that when Jack was doing his duty by serving in the RAMC, Geoffrey was still enjoying a supposedly affluent life abroad. It was apparently even argued that Jeff's absence had somehow been responsible for Jack having to leave the army and take over the practice. There was also a feeling that Jack had exceptional skills as a surgeon which had been thwarted by these circumstances. Of course there was some truth in all these arguments, though they were heavily biased and, if this story is true, these views were held by Cecilia Jefferson alone, Arthur having died, and certainly they were not held by Jack. Geoffrey reassured Gertrude further, saying 'I don't think there's the slightest need for you to fear that the Rochdalians will be a worry to us . . . . You have a quite just complaint — that I haven't written as often as I should, but when you think that the reason is because R'dle is replacing you in my affections its just too silly for words'. It had by now become apparent that Gertrude would not be returning to England before mid-September at the earliest[12,23].

Further efforts to find a house still being unsuccessful, Geoffrey decided to advertise and offered a £10 premium. He also resolved to book lodgings if nothing turned up by the 18th August. Despite Cecilia Jefferson's invitation for them to stay at 2 West Street, Rochdale, even lodgings were a more attractive alternative, though they did think that they might have to leave the children with their paternal grandmother for a time. Knowing his mother's attitude towards children, this would have been a last resort. To give an example of his problems, Jeff told Trude: 'I saw an awful [house] in Eccles that I found they wanted £60 a year for, the tenant to do it up and it lacked even gas fittings. We do want electric light if we can get it'[23]. It was not worth changing his own lodging before Gertrude arrived, but he had come to detest it for being 'such a beastly gossipy place'[23]. On the previous Saturday he had relaxed a bit and enjoyed an afternoon watching the cricket at Old Trafford, which must have reminded him of those carefree days in his youth when he was regularly able to applaud his favourite players[23].

After a full day seeing patients and operating, Geoffrey would walk from place to place looking at unsuitable houses, the only possible one having had holes in the floors from dry rot. Operations were coming Jeff's way with some regularity but he did not specify whether they were private or at the Salford Royal Hospital. Nevertheless, the increase in work indicated that he was beginning to be appreciated in the neighbourhood. The surgical instruments had arrived from Canada by 1st August, which must have been a relief to him for it saved him the embarrassment of having to borrow some in order to operate on his private patients. In response to further depressing letters from Gertrude, he was driven to remark, 'I must cable you, as I have made a guinea'[24].

Gertrude did eventually arrive back in England with Monica and Michael in the second half of September 1919. Geoffrey had arranged for them to spend the first night or two at the Queen's Hotel, Piccadilly, Manchester, near the former site of the Royal Infirmary. Michael remembers having breakfast in the dining room but, more bitterly, he recalls the tears he had shed when he discovered that he had left his much-loved teddy bear on board the ship at Liverpool[12].

Fortunately, Geoffrey had succeeded in renting a house called Holly Bank, in the Eccles Old Road, Pendleton, Manchester, before the return of his family. Whether or not this was the one he had seen and liked earlier, but which was then only for sale, we do not know. The cost of its rental was shared with someone named Miss A–, who lived in part of the first floor. She does not seem to have been a personal friend, and the arrangement was simply an *ad hoc* affair for the benefit of both parties[12]. Built at right angles to the Eccles road at a junction with a small side turning, it was a large house, memories of which were recalled by Michael who was still only a very small boy.

It had a large lawn surrounded by a high wall, mostly over 6 feet high, except for the frontage on the road where it was low, but with bushes that made the dining room rather dark. The playroom, was over the front door and near the bedroom which Michael shared with Monica, the two rooms opening from a corridor that ran the length of the house. At the end of this lay the abode of the mysterious Miss A–. There was a gas fire in the playroom in front of which was a loose floorboard. Through the gap between the boards he 'posted' any largesse that visitors gave him, such as pennies, threepenny bits, sixpences or the occasional half-crown. He even tried to persuade Monica to do the same. However, years later, his sister commented, 'well you would have lost it just the same if you'd put it in your money-box, because Geoffrey would come home from wherever he had been in a taxi and he often raided our money-boxes for his fare'. She added, more cryptically, that 'in those days no one ever knew where Geoffrey was', whether at Salford Royal, his consulting rooms, in the University (where he eventually had a small room of his own in the gallery of the anatomy museum after he was appointed a lecturer in Surgical Anatomy), out on a consultation, or operating in one of the three other hospitals to which he was later appointed.

Miss Mabel Feury (Pan) stepped in at once, as soon as the family arrived back from Canada, to take over the care of the children and, for at least part of the time that the family was at Holly Bank, Gertrude had the help of Lizzie Aldridge who had previously been her maid in London and Manchester. Pan would go forth from the house with Michael in a push-chair; Monica had to walk, which she thought very unfair. They would go up the hill to a pretty public park within which there was a building occupied by a small natural history museum containing stuffed birds, some butterflies and a variety of geological specimens. One show case stood out in Michael's memory since it was overlaid by a protective cover, which could be rolled back to reveal a number of stuffed snakes lying side by side in a kind of knot. On one occasion when Pan took off the cover he thought he saw one of them move. Since she had regaled him with stories of cobras in India, this became a source of real terror. Another recollection was of his third birthday party, which was held in the dining room at Holly Bank and at which, out of some embarrassment, he bit a semicircle from the edge of a glass of lemonade, fortunately without more serious consequences than a rather dramatic loss of blood[12].

The year 1919 saw the publication of a case report by Jefferson on myositis ossificans traumatica, which was one of the last of his papers on a general surgical topic[25]. It was a watershed in his medical writing, marking the change of his literary output from general to neurological surgery.

In the same volume of the *British Journal of Surgery* the results of his study of the brain specimens from France were published, under the title of *The physiological pathology of gunshot wounds of the head*[2]. In this paper he stressed the influence of sepsis on the outcome, and the importance of brain stem ischaemia as a result of anatomical injury and its consequent oedema, or of infection, or of both. Between July and October 1918, at the 14th General Hospital, Jeff had been responsible for 54 simple scalp wounds, 53 skull fractures with dural penetration, and 113 skull fractures with dural laceration. 'Only those with a pulse rate of less than 100 were admitted to Base Hospitals' and operations had to be 'all or nothing' with no place for useless half-measures. His results were good. Among his personal cases, 91 without dural penetration had no mortality. Of 79 with dural penetration the mortality was 29, or just over 37%. It has to be remembered there were no systemic drugs to use against infection. 'The result tallies very closely indeed with that obtained by Horrax in a neighbouring hospital', he wrote. Jefferson drew attention to the possibility of local brain damage in low velocity gunshot wounds that had not fractured the skull, but his most important conclusions related to ventricular injury with respect to cerebral hernia and brain fungus (cerebral herniation), and their effect on prognosis[2].

Jefferson realised that the bacteriology of those head wounds which proved fatal differed from that of the survivors, and that the most deadly aerobic organism responsible for this was *Streptococcus haemolyticus*. His concern was with the mode of spread of the infection within the brain and its route of entry into the cerebrospinal fluid pathways. 'He concluded that in the majority of cases of fatal brain sepsis a communication occurred between the ventricle and an area of encephalitis. These observations led him to investigate the anatomy and particularly the surface markings of the ventricular system.' As Schorstein pointed out[26], he had illustrated the paper with his own drawings. At that time no one possessed exact knowledge of the surface markings of the ventricles and, by means of this information, he had been able to foretell the future course of events more accurately than had previously been possible. His observation that ventricular infection was the chief cause of death from sepsis in gunshot wounds of the head was confirmed by experience in World War II[26]. Jeff was to write again on the same topic after World War II, when the paper incorporated his further experience, and was entitled *Head wounds and infection in two World Wars*. In it he reviewed his earlier cases and compared them with the more recent injuries that had been inflicted just over 20 years later[27].

Figure 14   *46 Birch Lane, Manchester.*

However, there was yet another and even more important publication by him in the same volume of the *British Journal of Surgery*. This concerned a review of fractures of the atlas vertebra, still often referred to as 'Jefferson's fracture', and a report on four of his own cases[28]. Jeff drew three conclusions: 1) that the resultant force of a blow on the head is horizontal and, in direct violence, causes separation of the lateral masses. The posterior arch of the atlas, being weaker than the rest, gives way most readily. 2) Extension of the neck crushes the posterior arch between the occiput and the neural arch of the axis. 3) The anterior arch of the atlas may be fractured by pressure from the odontoid of the axis when the head goes into extension[28]. Finally, there was yet one more publication that year. This was on gunshot wounds of the scalp with special reference to the neurological signs which they presented, and it appeared in the prestigious neurological journal *Brain*[29]. The amount of work involved in writing these three long neurosurgical papers was prodigious. However, although he had no private secretary his manuscripts were typed for him, saving him that necessity at least. No doubt this work helped to take his mind off the financial worries when there were not many patients to see and few of them private.

The family did not remain at Holly Bank for more than a few months, and in mid-September 1920 Geoffrey rented a furnished house, 46 Birch Lane, Longsight, Manchester. This was a distinctly smoky and not well-appointed locality in which to live, and the district later came to be officially known by the less tainted name of Rusholm, which had been the designation of the telephone exchange. Until then, to avoid the embarrassment of putting Longsight on their notepaper, the Jeffersons simply headed it 46 Birch Lane, Manchester S.E. Of course it had been financial constraint as well as lack of availability that had determined their choice of a new home. Birch Lane was not far from the centre of the city, but patients did not have to visit the house since they were seen either at one of the hospitals, in their own homes or in Geoffrey's consulting room.

Number 46 was semi-detached and slightly larger than its neighbour. It was about half way down the road and surrounded on either side and opposite by rows of smaller houses. On the heavy blackened stone pillars of the gate, there was inscribed in gold letters the never-used title of 'Sydenham Villas'. During the move Pan took the children for a fortnight to Marple, a village beyond Stockport and over the Cheshire border into Derbyshire, to stay on a working farm and have the benefit of some country air[12]. Lizzie Aldridge presumably helped Gertrude with all the household tasks that had to be done in the Jefferson's new home in Birch Lane.

In the March of 1920 Geoffrey had been appointed Consultant Surgeon to Grangethorpe Ministry of Pensions Hospital, where he had covered the duties of some of his colleagues from Salford Royal Hospital when they were on leave. There was an artificial limb fitting centre nearby that provided occasional patients suffering from painful neuromata and phantom limbs, thus helping to sustain his interest in these complications of amputation. At Grangethorpe he was in charge of head injuries and of those general surgical cases that were not of an orthopaedic nature. His success with the FRCS classes and his background as an anatomy demonstrator led to his first academic appointment after leaving the forces when, in the same year, he was made Lecturer in applied anatomy (neurological anatomy) at Manchester University. He also gave up the rooms he shared with Harry Platt and rented his own consulting room at 264 Oxford Road, Manchester, the road in which the Royal Infirmary is situated. The slow but steady growth of Jefferson's private practice produced a need for a motor car. In 1921 he became the possessor of a second hand Arrol-Johnston of 1913 or even older vintage, his choice again being restricted by affordability[12].

The Arrol-Johnston was a heavily built open machine with a maximum speed of 40 mph. The bonnet sloped down to the front of the car and between it and the windscreen was the radiator, which projected on either side. Its headlights were lit by acetylene gas, generated from carbide on which a supply of water dripped within a large container on the running board. However, the sidelights were lit by paraffin oil. Of course there was no self-starter and it had to be cranked by hand to bring it to life. The brakes worked on the rear wheels only. It was housed in a mews garage, for there was no garage attached to the Birch Lane house. Geoffrey continued to drive this remarkable vehicle until 1923, when he sold it and bought an Austin Twelve. According to legend, the Arrol-Johnston did not last long with its next purchaser. There was no petrol gauge, and to find out how much there was in the tank it was necessary to put in a dipstick. Instead of using this, the car's new owner was rash enough to peer into the tank with the aid of a lighted match. The consequences can only be imagined. It was the end of the car and very nearly that of the new owner[12].

Appointments to small outlying hospitals were common among the Honorary Consultants of large voluntary and, especially, teaching hospitals. This benefited the patients because they could be moved to a bed held by the consultant in the larger institution for any treatment for which the smaller hospital was ill-equipped or unable to supply. It also benefited the Honorary Physician or Surgeon, who of course received no salary from either source, by introducing him to the local practitioners. If the latter were impressed by his work in the voluntary hospitals, then they would send their private patients to him. One such small institution was the Eccles and Patricroft Hospital, to which Jefferson was appointed Honorary Consultant Surgeon in 1921. It was only a short distance south of Salford and so could easily be reached by car. In the following year, he also obtained a similar appointment at the new Knutsford War Memorial Hospital, which lay about 10 miles south west of Manchester, so that Jeff offered his services to a wide area covering the whole of the west side of the Manchester suburbs; but the city centre was his goal and the Manchester Royal Infirmary in particular. Some time in 1923 he additionally obtained a minor local appointment with the Ministry of Health.

During 1921 the Jeffersons, and Gertrude more especially, collected their correspondence with Sir William Osler and passed it on to Harvey Cushing, who was then writing his monumental and famous biography of the great physician. This was the beginning of a correspondence between Cushing and Jefferson that was to develop into a warm relationship. Cushing wrote that he was going to give the Cavendish Lecture on *Points of growth of the meningiomas* in June 1922, and that he would also be a Visiting Surgeon at St Bartholomew's Hospital; he hoped that they would be able to meet[30]. This they did, and it is likely that it was then that Jeff made some preliminary arrangements to visit the Peter Bent Brigham Hospital in Boston, though this journey did not actually take place until 1924. In 1922 a short paper by Jefferson, on bilateral rigidity in middle meningeal haemorrhage, appeared in the *British Medical Journal*[31].

In April 1922 the Manchester Surgical Society was founded, largely on the initiative of Arthur Burgess, who was its first president. The founder members included all the surgical honorary staffs of hospitals in Manchester and Salford, together with nine other 'hand-picked' members, one of whom was Jack Jefferson. At the opening meeting on 24th October 1922, Geoffrey Jefferson presented a paper on the gastric musculature, based on dissections he had carried out in Canada. He was to become the president of the Surgical Society for the 1938–39 session. In 1950 it became the Surgical Section of the Manchester Medical Society[32].

By September 1922 Jefferson could contain his ambition no longer and when a vacancy on the surgical staff of the Manchester Royal Infirmary was advertised he applied for the appointment. He presented himself as a surgeon with a particular interest in the nervous system, who was qualified to supply the expertise in this field that had been missing since Sir William Thorburn had retired from the hospital staff. In the manner of the day, the application took the form of a substantial printed booklet, beautifully set out in a blue cover. Geoffrey submitted his curriculum vitae and outlined his war service in Russia and France. He mentioned his research interests and teaching experience before submitting a list of ten neurological papers and 12 of a miscellaneous nature. His application concluded with testimonials from Sir Harold Stiles, Sir Arthur Keith, Sir William Thorburn, Sir Herbert Waterhouse, Mr Lawrence Pilkington, who was Chairman of the Salford Royal Hospital, and from the Professors Arthur Burgess, George Murray and John Stopford.

Needless to say they all had nothing but praise for Geoffrey's record and for his promise in the future. 'He is destined to take a high place in British Surgery', wrote Sir Arthur Keith, and Sir Herbert Waterhouse pointed out Geoffrey's suitability as a replacement for Sir William Thorburn, having 'devoted much attention to the Surgery of the Nervous System, in which branch he has already made for himself quite a reputation.... The Manchester Royal Infirmary...should welcome Mr. Jefferson as an Expert Surgical Neurologist'[33]. These persuasive remarks were, however, ineffective and Geoffrey failed to get the appointment. This must have been a bitter blow, especially in view of his strong desire to be on the staff of his own Teaching Hospital.

Life in Birch Lane went on as before. Gertrude gave birth at home to their second son, Antony Andrew on 13th June 1922. She employed a nurse who took up residence about a month in advance of the anticipated birth in case it should take place prematurely, as the other two had done. Miss Feury had already been sent off to a cottage in North Wales on a headland beyond Abersoch with Monica and Michael and, after about 6 weeks, they were joined there by Geoffrey and Gertrude and the new baby, who immediately became Pan's responsibility[12]. Their family was now complete.

The year 1922 had seen both the recent marriage of Jack Jefferson to Freda Stott, 'a thin witty elegant and ironic lady'[12], and Madge's qualification as a doctor, following which she joined the family practice. This brought about a considerable change in the situation at Number 2, West Street, Rochdale, and Cecilia Jefferson relinquished her command. She moved to a house called Greenbooth at Norden, a small village near Rochdale, and Madge went to live with her. From there Madge drove to her patients in a grey two-seater Morris Cowley, 'with a very reliable engine, designed by Hotchkiss you know'. She was extremely proud of this car[12].

Greenbooth was down a narrow cobbled road, a short distance along which there was a small disused cotton-mill. Beyond this the road curved so that the mill buildings were out of sight of the house, which lay about 200 yards further on. There was almost no traffic, for the road continued for only about another half a mile to peter out with just two or three cottages at its far end for company; then there was hilly woodland. Greenbooth was probably built about 1890, possibly for the owner of the mill. It was solidly constructed and well-appointed. In its grounds there was a tennis court, a little stream and, on the hillside, a small copse. Cecilia Jefferson lived there with her eldest daughter, two servants and a gardener until 1928, when Madge, now married to Jack Collins, took over the house. Cecilia then moved to a newly built and much smaller establishment at Bamford, outside Rochdale, her last home[12].

REFERENCES

GJ=Geoffrey Jefferson; GMJ=Gertrude Jefferson
1   *The Daily Colonist*. Victoria BC. 13th April 1919.
2   Jefferson G. The physiological pathology of gunshot wounds of the head. *Brit J Surg* 1919–1920; 7: 262–89.
3   Cushing H to GJ. Letter 9th August 1919.
4   Cushing H to GJ. Letter 26th December 1919.

5   Jefferson G. Harvey Cushing. *Manchester Medical Students' Gazette* 1943; **22**: 9–16.
6   GJ to GMJ. Letter 5th April 1919.
7   GJ to GMJ. Letter 29th April 1919.
8   GJ to GMJ. Letter 8th September 1912.
9   GJ to GMJ. Letters between 26th and 29th April 1919.
10 GJ to GMJ. Letter 8th May 1919.
11 GJ to GMJ. Letter 11th May 1919.
12 Jefferson, Michael. Personal communication.
13 GJ to GMJ. Letter 17th May 1919.
14 GJ to GMJ. Letter 31st December 1918.
15 GJ to GMJ. Letter 26th May 1919.
16 GJ to GMJ. Letters 2/3rd June and 1st July 1919.
17 GJ to GMJ. Letter 5th July 1919.
18 GJ to GMJ. Letter 7th July 1919.
19 GJ to GMJ. Letter 17th July 1919.
20 GJ to GMJ. Letter 25th July 1919.
21 GJ to GMJ. Letter 28th July 1919.
22 GJ to GMJ. Letter 1st August 1919.
23 GJ to GMJ. Letter 8th August 1919.
24 GJ to GMJ. Letter 19th August 1919.
25 Jefferson G. A case of myositits ossificans traumatica...the result of two separate traumata. *Br J Surg* 1919–1920; **7**: 135–7.
26 Schorstein J. War neurosurgery. *Manchester Medical Students' Gazette* 1946; **25**: 58–9.
27 Jefferson G. Head wounds and infection in two World Wars *Br J Surg* 1947; **War Surgery Supplement No 1**: 3–8.
28 Jefferson G. Fractures of the atlas vertebra; report of four cases and a review of those previously reported. *Br J Surg* 1919–1920; **7**: 409–22.
29 Jefferson G. Gunshot wounds of the scalp, with special reference to the neurological signs presented. *Brain* 1919; **42**: 93–112.
30 Cushing H to GJ. Letter 10th April 1922.
31 Jefferson G. Bilateral rigidity in middle meningeal haemorrhage. *BMJ* 1922; **2**: 683–5.
32 Platt H. The story of the Manchester Surgical Society. *Manchester Medical Gazette* 1971; **50**: 5–10, 19–24.
33 GJ. Application to the Manchester Royal Infirmary, 1922.

Chapter 12

Establishing a Neurosurgical Career
1923–1926

The foundations of Geoffrey Jefferson's career as a neurosurgeon were laid in the Salford Royal Hospital and, according to G F Rowbotham[1], it was here that Jeff began to study pituitary lesions in depth and to consider the treatment of intracranial aneurysms. In July 1923 he read the opening paper to the Section of Surgery at the Annual Meeting of the British Medical Association (BMA) in Portsmouth. It was entitled *Ventriculography as an aid in the localization of intracranial tumours*[2]. His early interest in radiology had encouraged him to adopt the technique of ventriculography that had been described by Walter Dandy a year or two earlier[3]. The paper given to the BMA dealt with the subject in very general terms, pointing out the enlargement of the ventricles associated with posterior fossa tumours, and the usefulness of the technique when tumours could not be localized clinically. However, Jeff very rightly emphasized its potential dangers and cautioned against what he called 'indiscriminate enthusiasm'. At the time when he gave the papers his personal experience was limited to only six cases.

In 1924 several important events took place. In the previous year Jefferson had applied for and been given a Hunterian Professorship by the Royal College of Surgeons, which he was now to take up. The title applies only to the delivery of a lecture, but the award has marked the beginning of many an important surgical career. Jeff's lecture, which was given in the February of 1924, was entitled *Remarks on fractures of the first cervical vertebra* and was based on the work he had published in 1919, though he now added an extensive review of the world literature and three more of his own cases. He was at pains to emphasize that, since the advent of radiology, the diagnosis of fractures of the atlas vertebra had become much easier, with the result that of 32 cases reported since 1900 only six had died, whereas previously it had been thought to be invariably fatal, for the reason that it was usually only identified at post-mortem. Also in this year Geoffrey was appointed Honorary Surgeon to the Manchester Royal Eye Hospital.

For some time Jefferson had been hoping to pay another visit to Canada and America, with the particular object of spending a few weeks in Boston with Harvey Cushing, and also taking the opportunity to visit other neurosurgical clinics in the United States. The fulfilment of these hopes now became a possibility. Gertrude's mother had undergone a 'routine operation' for the removal of stones from her gall-bladder and appeared to have made a satisfactory recovery. On 8th March 1924 she had been to the theatre with her husband and had looked and felt well. During the next 3 days, however, she had pain that was similar to the earlier gall-bladder symptoms, her condition deteriorated rapidly, and she died in the early hours of 12th March[4]. Gertrude was heart-broken; her intuition of her mother's death has already been mentioned. She became desperately anxious to see her father and sister. This was Geoffrey's opportunity to put his plan into action. He obtained leave from the hospitals and arranged for his duties to be covered. About 4 weeks after Mrs Flumerfelt's death, the house in Birch Lane was shut up and the Jeffersons, with all three children, set sail across the Atlantic. The family travelled by sea and the St. Lawrence river as far as Montreal, where they were met on the quayside by Mr Flumerfelt. Seeing him there alone would have brought home to Gertrude the full force of her loss; it must have been a very emotional return to her homeland.

Geoffrey set off for the United States almost immediately after arriving in Canada, on 27th April, leaving his family and Mr Flumerfelt to travel on to Victoria while he took the train to Boston, where he stayed at the Lenox Hotel. As before, it was Gertrude's father who largely bore the cost of the whole visit despite his now very difficult financial circumstances, but the help this time was also supplemented by a loan from someone named Arthur Furness in Montreal, who must have been better known to the Flumerfelts than to Jeff since there is a letter from him addressed to 'My dear Mr Jefferson'[5].

On the day following his arrival in Boston, Geoffrey wrote excitedly that 'I have just rung up the Brigham Hospital and find that Cushing is operating to-morrow morning at 10, so I am on the threshold of seeing what I have worked for for so very long. I shall probably be disappointed. I am glad to learn that he is operating at the Christian hour of 10 am'[6].

On the 29th April Geoffrey was at the hospital by 9.45 am and that day his letter included a number of percipient comments. It was his first real and prolonged exposure to Cushing's operating technique and his first opportunity of making the acquaintance of the famous neurosurgeon over a period of time. Jeff wrote later that until that visit he had 'taken only a correspondence course in Cushing'[7]. He told Gertrude: 'Well I've seen the great man do a laminectomy and tomorrow he is to do a pituitary so I am in luck.... He pottered about on odds and ends for a long time. He seems to be very indefinite and his staff never seem to know quite when he will do anything. My first impressions of him are good. He used no Spencer Wells [artery forceps] in his operation at all, placing one silver clip on the vessel and no more the whole time.... But one can see that his slowness and the great pains that he goes to to get good exposure and see where he is, must be a great help in difficult cases. He shelled out an extradural neurofibroma in the end ($2\frac{1}{4}$ hrs) very nicely indeed and sewed up the wound with innumerable tiers of interrupted black silk sutures'[8].

Following the operation Geoffrey attended an x-ray conference, where he was very impressed by the quality of the films from Dr Sosman's department, but less so by the discussion of them. He spent the afternoon on a ward round and some time in the Harvard medical library. Cushing appeared to be 'very nice and friendly, but I can see that his staff are rather uncertain of him and what my further opinion of his personality will be I cannot say'[8]. Sir D'Arcy Power, who was the senior surgeon at St Bartholomew's Hospital and also on the staff of the Victoria Children's Hospital in Chelsea where Geoffrey had worked, though not under him, was also visiting the Brigham Hospital at the same time. Jefferson noted with some surprise that such a well-known surgeon was referred to as "D'Arcy" 'and that Cushing calls his second assistant (Dott from Stiles' clinic in Edinburgh) by his Christian name'[8]. Coming from England, such familiarity seemed very unusual to

Jeff, for whom seniors would always have addressed their juniors by their surnames, and they in turn would never have used anything but 'Sir' in reply. In fact Sir D'Arcy Power is now chiefly remembered for having been 'the foremost historian of British surgery', though he also wrote on many other subjects[9].

That Harvey Cushing was an outstanding surgeon and the father of modern neurosurgery is unquestioned but, like a number of the surgical princes of that time, he had difficult relationships with many of his pupils and staff. His nickname of 'Pepper Pot' says much. In view of Geoffrey's remark, 'what my further opinion of his personality will be I cannot say'[8], it is appropriate to read now what he actually did come to feel about Cushing, after many meetings and after a long and warm correspondence over many years. Furthermore his final judgement was to be completely supported, though in less temperate phrases, by the account given later by Percival Bailey, who knew Cushing as well as anyone[10].

In 1953, 14 years after Cushing's death, Geoffrey wrote of him that he was 'charming, tiresome, petty, and admirable all by turns... the great qualities very heavily outweighed the others. Some folk thought him almost sadistic in the treatment of them, but such a statement would puzzle others who never saw a trace of it.... The fact, no doubt, was that Cushing was a difficult man in competition, and to those who failed to keep up with the pace or maintain the standard required in his clinic. Also he was apt to be querulous with any person who happened to hit on an idea independently and contemporaneously, for he was not as disinterested as Halsted* in priority.... Cushing pursued the scientific ideal with the utmost intensity and devotion. He sacrificed sometimes his friends to it. But of his honesty there is no doubt. He could be rough with his staff, he might nag interminably whilst operating, but he sent them away at the end of their training better men than they would otherwise have been; even if they had wounds to lick they were proud of the place where they had acquired them'[7].

Jefferson continued by describing how, away from the hospital, Cushing 'was a good talker, but a bad listener, except with those who knew what his interests were. Cushing would ruthlessly interrupt any talker, regardless of rank or importance, if he was not entertaining him. But often one could skim from one subject to another until suddenly his attention was arrested. He would then keep at it with remarkable tenacity. His outlook on life was definitely Puritan... yet he had a quick and deep sense of humour. Young and old of both sexes adored him; his quips, his deep voice, the queer flash of his tongue as he talked... the whole personality was stimulated to one end, the furtherance of his work and his ideals.... The only conclusion that one can reach after making the concessions that honesty compels is that a man may be as near great as mortals can, be incandescent in the scientific world, and yet have faults. Obviously it cannot be otherwise'[7]. This wonderful word picture of the man whose achievements Geoffrey admired above all others, is a good example of Jeff's ability to write clear, precise and vividly descriptive prose. His judgement of one who had become a close, but a departed friend by the time he wrote those remarks, was

---

*Halsted. William Stewart Halsted (1852–1922) was the famous surgeon at the Johns Hopkins Hospital in Baltimore under whom Cushing had trained. He was largely responsible for turning Cushing's steps towards neurosurgery and for the basis of his technique.

scrupulously fair, and it is quite certainly interesting that the last two sentences of the quotation could justifiably be applied to Jeff himself.

Jefferson's original plan was to spend a fortnight in Boston before going on to New York, but on 10th May he decided to remain there for an extra week and continue to learn as much as possible from Cushing and his team, besides paying visits to other Boston neurosurgeons. It is interesting that he witnessed several negative explorations, a reflection on the difficulties of diagnosis before the advent of contrast radiography and scanning, when the neurological history and examination was, in most cases, the only basis for the localization of tumours. One such negative exploration by Cushing was of a pituitary case and took place in the morning of 30th April. 'The pituitary operation was most beautifully done. I don't wonder that his mortality is so small. I'm learning a little all the time, and shall have gained a great deal in knowledge when I get back. It's a great experience. I am glad to be able to say honestly that it confirms me in the technical ways that I was following, and I am enriching my existing technique and not radically altering it—which is very nice. He aims at placing no haemostats [artery forceps] and no ligatures, totally avoiding crushed or devitalised tissues. Altogether most stimulating'[11]. After ward rounds in the afternoon Cushing drove D'Arcy Power and Geoffrey to the Harvard University campus in Cambridge, where they visited both the Widener* and the main libraries before going on to the beautiful suburb of Brookline and the Cushing home there.

In spite of Cushing's correspondence with both the Jeffersons over the matter of Osler's letters to them, and the letters to Gertrude in particular, he does not seem to have realised until that evening that Geoffrey's wife was Osler's 'Trotula', or else he had forgotten. 'It transpired at dinner that you were *Trotula* amidst great excitement. Cushing asked me to convey his gratitude to you for your very cheery account of Sir William. He says his letters (W.O's) were very few and he was most grateful for yours. He is publishing them. His book [*The life of Sir William Osler*] is finished and is about to go to the publishers. Power has been reading the MSS. We're getting on very well together .... I was sorry that you were not there to hear the excitement that prevailed when it became known that I was connected with Trotula—truly reflected glory. I can see that H.C. is not sure where this dark horse (GJ) stands. He'll find out before the week is out'[12].

On the following day Cushing arranged for Geoffrey to stay at the Harvard Club, for which he had to pay $3.50 per day, 'which is $1.00 more than I wanted ..., that only allows me 85c a day for food. I am being pretty frugal'[13]. He watched Sir D'Arcy Power operate and was not at all impressed. He also watched a negative cerebellar exploration by Gilbert Horrax, Cushing's first assistant for many years and on whom he leaned heavily. Another negative exploration was performed by Cushing on 2nd May. It is worth noting that Cushing very seldom carried out ventriculography which, being the invention of his former assistant and to some extent rival, Walter Dandy, made it suspect in his eyes. Jeff made the following sarcastic remark in a letter to Gertrude, which he was hardly in a position to produce in view of his own record of time-keeping: 'I saw a nice exploration for tumour that wasn't this morning. Cushing is pretty punctual, one hour later than

---

*Widener Library. The Harry Elkins Widener Memorial Library adjoins the large and impressive main library at Harvard. It is devoted to advanced studies and research.

he says he'll be. Operation at 11 actually began at 12.15'[13]. In the afternoon there was a clinico-pathological conference, carried out in the same manner that was to persist wherever such conferences were held for the next 30 years, and probably longer. Three cases were presented by the professor of pathology (Wolbach) and then discussed and diagnosed by the professor of medicine (Cabot) before the pathological findings were revealed. Geoffrey now felt that he was 'getting a good deal out of H.C..... With only one operation a day I should have got very little out of a brief stay. The whole subject is so large and presents so many points of interest and difficulty that one can only get things little by little. Also H.C. is a quiet and not very communicative fellow'[13].

On 3rd May Jefferson watched Elliott Carr Cutler do a valvulotomy on a dog's heart and then another negative cranial exploration by Cushing. Cutler who, according to Geoffrey had already successfully performed a mitral valvulotomy in a human by 1924, was Assistant Surgeon to Cushing in the latter's capacity as Professor in charge of the whole department of surgery at the Peter Bent Brigham Hospital. Cutler had been given cardiac surgery as his province. Eventually he succeeded his former chief as Professor, but not without some disharmony that led to Harvey Cushing and the Brain Tumour Registry* moving to Yale. 'Cutler had begun at once to rearrange the offices which he had inherited from Cushing and to alter the routine of the Operating Room .... Since Cutler knew Cushing's temperament, he acted in the belief that complete abrogation of Cushing's responsibilities was essential — not only in theory but in fact'[14]. In this Cutler was undoubtedly right, as has been confirmed by the experience of many whose retired seniors will not let go. During this visit to Boston, Jeff was impressed by the slow careful operating that he witnessed at the Brigham and the 'immense time' spent on haemostasis; also by the number of interns, for the proportion of 1 to 10 patients at the Peter Bent Brigham Hospital compared very favourably with that of 1 to 40 at the Salford Royal.

Geoffrey passed the next day with Horrax, watching perimetry carried out by Tracy Putnam (then a surgical assistant) and visiting the Boston Fine Arts Museum[15]. 'I am getting lonelier and lonelier as the days go by' he wrote to Gertrude. It seems that he was once more becoming depressed. 'I find I am really very ignorant about operations on the brain, but I am slowly absorbing it. H.C.....naturally feels that his views and his judgements, the results of such long experience, are final. For that reason I have to go rather slowly with him, as I don't want to show my ignorance or lack of experience. With some men it would not matter, but with him it would be unwise'[16]. On 6th May Geoffrey watched Cushing operate on an acoustic neuroma; he 'did it beautifully in 3½ hours. But it is terribly tiring standing on a stool for so long and craning over to look in'. To cheer himself up, in the evening he went alone to a cinema to see 'Douglas Fairbanks in "The thief of Baghdad" but there was standing room only at $1.00.

---

*Brain Tumour Registry. Beginning in 1905, Cushing requested all his brain tumour patients to write to him on the anniversary of their operations, in order to collect data concerning the end results of particular types of tumour. When he died in 1939 he was following nearly 1000 living patients who had had a brain tumour operated upon in his clinic. After the disagreement with Cutler, the records and pathological material of about 2000 cases were removed to Yale. Louise Eisenhardt, the neuropathologist who had once been Cushing's secretary, went with them. She later became the editor of the *Journal of Neurosurgery*.

Movies are more expensive here than with us, are fuller, are very hot, and (final insult and calamity) smoking is not allowed'[17]. At the end of such a day he was probably desperate for a cigarette.

It is remarkable, in view of all the discussion and correspondence over so many years on the subject of practising in Victoria, that he wrote on 8th May, 'I have not had any opportunity yet of talking to H.C. about neurosurgical prospects in Canada. From the propaganda point of view it would pay me better to stop off at Toronto and Montreal on the way back. I have not thought over the Canadian prospects very seriously. It is quite evident that they prefer to recruit from their own strength'[18]. This suggests that Geoffrey had promised Gertrude that he would make some enquiries while he was with Cushing. Obviously her overwhelming preference for living in Canada had been stimulated again by the loss of her mother and her consequent unhappiness. Perhaps Jeff's failure to obtain an appointment at the Manchester Royal Infirmary was making him consider all possibilities. He might well have been prepared to work in connection with McGill University or the University of Toronto if a likely opportunity had presented itself just at that time.

On 8th May Jeff had managed to get up at 7 am to go to the Lahey Clinic to see the surgeon for whom it was named 'do some thyroids at 8! I watched him till 2.30, and was pretty tired after six hours standing about. He's a good man, in a local sense, but a third rater on the international scale'[18]. Damned by faint praise; and Jeff was not yet attuned to the long neurosurgical operations lasting many hours, or as much as a day, that were to be commonplace in the 1930s, 40s and even later.

Harvey Cushing must have invited Geoffrey to attend a neurosurgical meeting that was being held locally, and it is surprising, in view of the fact that in only 2 years' time Jeff was to found the Society of British Neurological Surgeons, that he wrote 'I still feel that I don't want very greatly to go to it. I should like to some time, but in another 5 years or so would be keener on it as I am not likely to get very much out of listening to discussions'[19]. The likely interpretation of this is that he was fearful that, by entering a discussion, he might expose his own lack of experience. It was now that he decided to spend the extra week in Boston. The Cushings had invited him to tea at their home, and he was getting on well with Norman Dott, who was then an intern there. Geoffrey seems to have been prejudiced against the New York neurosurgeons whom he was due, reluctantly, to visit next, and he might have omitted to go altogether had he not previously been requested to do so by the editor of the *British Journal of Surgery*.

The extra week soon went by, watching operations, doing rounds and visiting libraries. 'I am moving on to New York tomorrow . . . . I am sorry to go, but I think I have got all the good out of this that I can get and it will be interesting to see something else for a change . . . . I gave Harvey a miss today as one can have too much of him. He is really a very trying fellow, and whilst everyone admires his ability he is anything but popular. He can be most charming, but is very changeable and moody, and it is pleasant to get away from him'[20]. A visit to the Massachusetts General Hospital brought Jeff's stay in Boston to a close.

In New York, Geoffrey found an affordable hotel on Broadway and wrote, on 18th May, that he had had 'a miserable day, nothing to do, walked along Fifth Avenue until I was tired, came back, and have just had dinner which cost me over $2, the first time I have approached that figure. I am hoping for a charity meal or two from Elsberg'[21], whom he was to see next day. Jeff even questioned whether he would have enough money for the railway ticket to Victoria. 'New York is a particularly beastly town.' However, during a long day spent with Elsberg, who had specific expertise in spinal surgery, not only was he treated very kindly by him, but Geoffrey had to admit that he had enjoyed himself. He continued to be very anxious about money. 'I cannot even buy a book to read or go to a theatre, which is damping my spirits. The fare to Victoria with an upper berth is $160, and as I have only $200 left the situation is grave. If you have nothing I wonder if Aggie* would be so good as to lend us some to be sent to Rochester.... It has been a wonderful experience for me and I am grateful to your father for having made it possible'[22,23].

Some money was telegraphed to Rochester. 'It is more than I shall actually need but I want to buy a few instruments while I can personally select them'[23]. He might have added that those specialized instruments would not have been available in England, where they would have had to be hand-made to order. The Mayo Clinic was in Rochester, Minnesota, and the chief attraction there was the possibility of seeing Alfred W Adson, to whom Jefferson had an introduction. He watched him operate and attended his ward rounds. He also had a chance of a word with William Mayo whose father had, by a strange coincidence, graduated from Owen's College in Manchester, and had founded the Mayo Clinic with his two sons, Charles and William. Jefferson also visited the Department of Medical Research and attended a neurological conference. In a letter to Gertrude he wrote that there were stories in the Clinic of trials of an antiserum cancer cure which, unfortunately, had less substance than another report he had heard of. The latter was a skin test for scarlet fever or scarlatina (the Dick test), though Jeff's message that 'within 12 months the scarlet fever scourge is prophesied to be finished' was over-optimistic[23].

From Rochester Geoffrey took the west-bound train to Canada, the *Mountaineer*, leaving at 11.40 am Sunday and arriving at Victoria at 3 pm the following Wednesday. He must have been delighted to be with Gertrude and the children once more. He probably spent another 3 weeks with them before returning home to England ahead of his wife and family for, on 25th June, he wrote to Gertrude in Victoria from the Canadian Pacific Railway en route to Montreal. 'It has been a lovely trip as far as weather goes. We are passing Lake Superior now and it looks lovely—what a magnificent country this is! Vancouver looked beautiful as we went out—the evening run up the Fraser River is quite beautiful, then the Rockies were magnificent again, fine and clear.... The place that impressed me most was Calgary, quite unrecognisably increased in size and solidity.... Winnipeg looked much the same, more rough-necks to the yard than any other of the larger towns or so it seemed to me'[24]. From Montreal he travelled on by sea to Liverpool.

Jefferson always took an opportunity to record his thoughts. Writing helped him to formulate them and his opinions, and the notes he made often became the basis of a future paper. It is therefore not surprising that he wrote an extensive record of his neurosurgical experiences in America, both at the time and in summary afterwards—probably on board ship on the way home.

---

*Aggie. Gertrude's close friend Agnes Renny, who had written her a kind and very sympathetic description of Mrs Flumerfelt's last illness.

Jefferson knew how important the visit to Harvey Cushing was going to be in the furtherance of his career and aspirations, and in order not to pass over or forget anything that he had learnt there, he made daily notes of all that he saw during his visit. This he now added to the longer *meditations*. The notes show how lacking in the knowledge of technique he was at the time, and also his lack of familiarity with neuropathology. This he had found disconcerting and depressing, as he had remarked in a letter to Gertrude early in May[16]. He had read all the papers and books on the subject that he could lay his hand on, but they could never substitute for observation and experience. It would be tedious to try to record these notes and not very profitable, for what impressed him then has now become the technique of neurosurgical operating which is almost universally adopted. So strong was Cushing's influence that, even today, the basic premises of his teaching are to be seen in nearly every neurosurgical unit, wherever it may be. Jeff drew pictures of Cushing's table and head rest, of some of the instruments he used and what he saw of the operations themselves. He made notes of the anaesthetic, the drapery, the assistants and, in fact, everything he wished to include in his own practice[11]. Interestingly, there are no notes at all about neurological examination and diagnosis and it may be assumed that Jeff's considerable knowledge of anatomy and neurophysiology had stood him in good stead in this field, for his expertise in it was never in question.

In addition, there is an unpublished *Notes on neurological surgery in the United States of America*[25], in which Jefferson was clearly exploring the possibility of attempting to make his career one of total specialization in neurosurgery. It is followed by a consideration of all the obstacles that would inevitably be put in his way. Written at the conclusion of this 1924 visit to the United States and Canada, it reads: 'There are now in that country some eight or ten men who devote themselves exclusively to the surgery of the nervous system, with a certain number of younger men in their services who will in the ordinary course of events subsequently plough the same furrow. It is interesting to see from the economic viewpoint that a sufficient subsistence can be derived to support a number of men in the sole practice of such a speciality.... There are few who have not felt at some period of their careers the special appeal which neurology makes upon us, the peculiar intellectual pleasure derived from the unravelling of neurological problems. But many who would have been willing and were even anxious to work in and to develop the surgical side of neurology have been discouraged by the ill success which has attended their efforts or by the gossip which they have listened to concerning the non-success of others.... It needs but a short acquaintance with this special branch of surgery for the observer to realise that a quite specialised and different technique is essential.... The technique which one witnesses in the various neuro-surgical clinics (to use the ugly phrase which has gained some popularity in the United States) is very similar in fundamentals... and is traceable to Halsted, though he does not appear to have been especially hopeful or even helpful in the development of this special work.... Halsted it was who proved by example and by experience (the word we are apt to use in place of "experiment" when speaking of human material) that it was not length of time that mattered during operations but what you did to your patient during that time. He demonstrated that one could operate if necessary for very long periods and have the patient in better condition and with a greater prospect of ultimate cure at the end of it than was the case in the hands of other surgeons who were apt to follow a rapid and rigid operative formula regardless of the special requirements of the individual case.... Difficulties of accurate diagnosis are often great. The actual approach to the lesion is often difficult and dangers often arise before a point in the operation has been reached where any positive curative measures have become possible. Finally the closure of the wound, in the skull no less than in wound closures elsewhere, is apt to be at least as difficult and as tedious, more so perhaps than the more spectacular steps which have preceded it'[25].

'We are left with the impression that the surgery of the nervous system has reached its present position in the United States because it has been on the whole rather more successful than similar efforts elsewhere. Greater facilities for animal experimentation...have played a great part in creating this success.... The limitation of such experiment is financial rather than legal. "Experiment" takes the place of "experience", in the meaning given to the words above'[25].

It is possible that Jefferson may have thought of trying to specialize at the Salford Royal Hospital, but circumstances were against him, and he knew that, even if it was allowed, it would never be successful at that time. In order to achieve his aim, it would be necessary to join the staff of the Manchester Royal Infirmary or to move elsewhere; to be part of a University Department of Surgery. This would be an unavoidable requirement if the essential support in terms of facilities, in the operating theatre, for neuroradiology, neuropathology services and research, was to be provided. There is no further mention in the letters of the possibility of neurosurgical practise in Canada, or that he spent time making enquiries in Toronto or Montreal on the way home.

Presumably Geoffrey's period of leave from the Salford Royal Hospital was limited and had determined that he must return home alone but, arriving before the family, and with some free days still in hand, it gave him the opportunity to assemble forces with which to remove the dust-sheets from 46 Birch Lane and have it ready to receive them when they arrived. 'I am sitting at the table at 46 writing this and waiting for Mother and Aunt Edie who are coming to prospect with a view to cleaning up for us. The house is very dusty but quite tidy. It will be a bit of a job getting it ready again. I doubt if they can really spring-clean it thoroughly as that would be too much. Of course with pictures down and dust-sheets over everything it looks a bit depressing. I've got the doors open to let a little air in but it's a horrible summer again — damp and cloudy and so lonely. It is miserable coming back by oneself.... I shall get the scullery done and so forth. I do wish we had a little money to do the range*. Next year we shall certainly have to paint the house outside. Everything does get so filthy in this place. However, perhaps before very long we shall be able to move into something better and a little further out'[26].

In fact, on his return to Manchester, Geoffrey stayed with Professor and Mrs Stopford initially and then, while still on leave, went to Rochdale where he found that Jack and his wife were on holiday in Switzerland. He dined with his sister Madge, who was looking after the practice at 2 West Street, and then visited his mother at Greenbooth. Jack and Freda returned very soon afterwards and the next

---

*Range. 'A fire-place having one or more ovens at the sides, and closed on the top with iron plates, having openings for carrying on several cooking operations at once'; first described thus in 1446. *Shorter Oxford English Dictionary*, 2nd ed, 1936.

day or two were spent between Rochdale and Greenbooth. A visit to Grangethorpe Hospital evoked the comment that 'It seems an awful drag starting again'.

His car was having a 'loose gudgeon pin in one of the piston shafts' repaired, but would be ready the next day, so making him more mobile. The good news was that 'there are two or three patients waiting for appointments, I am glad to say, and I hope before long my existence will be once more recognised'[26]. He still had his consulting room at 264 Oxford Road.

While Gertrude and the children were in Victoria the family had secured the services of a woman to act as a kind of governess with particular responsibility for Antony. She was known to the children as 'Miss B' and never achieved a place in their affections or the title of 'Nanny'. She was apparently English and, wanting to work her passage home, was glad to accompany Gertrude and the children on their return voyage; following which she disappeared from the scene[27].

The visit to Victoria had been both sad and painful for Gertrude, separated as she was for most of the time from Geoffrey, whose need to gain experience from the American neurosurgeons she may not fully have appreciated. The following letter from Jeff was probably addressed to her care of the shipping office in Liverpool, where Gertrude was due to arrive from Canada on the SS *Montroyal*; the envelope is missing and it is undated. 'This is just a line to welcome you home. I have got a temporary cook who is not bad, and Mother has lent us her maid whilst she is away (3 weeks)'[28]. The faithful Mabel Feury, Pan, had finally left the household for good when the Jeffersons went to Canada in April but a nursemaid for Antony, named Agnes Head, was found to replace her. Agnes came from Devon and her father was a Chief Petty-officer in the Royal Navy. Monica and Michael, being 7 and 5 years old, were both generally outside her care[27]. Jeff's letter continued: 'The house is habitable but not so far finished as I should have liked .... I went to the B.M.A. meeting on Friday and took part in the discussion on "Paraplegia" — I wasn't bad considering the small experience I have had of it or perhaps because I knew a little and was fairly lucid. I would not have gone if it hadn't been for the advertisement which one cannot afford to miss...'[28]. This second evidence of Jeff's hesitancy to attend a meeting and take part in a discussion is in striking contrast to his behaviour a very few years later, when his confidence had been restored. In fact the success he reported at this meeting may have helped in that direction. His letter continues, 'Sunday I went to Rochdale, the car behaving so badly that I daren't try to manoeuvre it into the garage so I left it in the garden all night. I went to the Northern to see Harvard and Yale v N. at tennis and then on to Old Trafford to see the test match'[28].

The Annual Meeting of the BMA at which Geoffrey spoke to the Section of Neurology and Psychological Medicine was held in Bradford and, as he mentioned to Gertrude, his motive for going was largely to let everyone know that he was back in circulation. In 1924 the commonest cause of compression paraplegia was tuberculous disease of the vertebrae (Pott's disease), and much of his paper was concerned with this. He discussed the appearances of the cerebrospinal fluid as an aid to the localization of spinal tumours and the value of the Queckenstedt test of compression of the jugular veins. Positive contrast radiography with Lipiodol (a proprietary solution of iodine in poppy seed oil) had already been introduced, but Jeff was cautious about its use. He 'endorsed Dr Feiling's remarks on the lamentable manner in which many cases of advancing spinal paralysis were allowed to progress to a hopeless condition'[29], but he did not mention the absolute urgency of relieving *acute* compression of the spinal cord, a necessity that may not have been generally recognised at that time[29].

When he returned to work at the Salford Royal Hospital that summer, Jeff operated on the arm of a patient to remove a blood clot from the brachial artery, becoming the first surgeon in the British Isles to achieve a successful embolectomy[30]. During this summer also, Harvey Cushing visited Oxford to see his biography of Osler through the press. Jeff did not meet him on this occasion but had previously asked him for his photograph. In October Cushing sent it and remarked in a covering letter that he had recommended one or two patients to Jeff and hoped that they had turned up[31]. He wrote again on 19th November asking if Geoffrey could recommend anywhere that his assistant Tracy Putnam might go for further training in general neurology and neuropsychiatry other than Queen Square—with an aside that he thought the consultants there might be 'so busy with outside work earning a living that they are not very much in evidence at the hospital'[32]. We do not have the reply, but one hopes that Jefferson refuted the insinuation. It does show, however, that Cushing appreciated Jeff's seniority despite his relatively recent exposure to specialized neurosurgery.

On her return to Manchester, Gertrude threw herself into medical activities with characteristic determination. Before they went to Canada she had been doing some part-time work with the Manchester Maternity and Child Welfare Services, and this she took up again. Then, for 2 or 3 years, she was also medical officer to Lewis's department store in the city. She was the kind of person who inspired confidences and on whose shoulder many were prepared to lean. Women, both medical and lay, came to her with their problems, recognising not only her sympathy and helpful advice but also her superior intelligence.

Thus the Jefferson family settled back into their life in Manchester and Salford and months passed with the rapidity engendered by a busy routine. The next event of importance was in April 1926 when Jeff made his mark at a meeting of the Société Internationale de Chirurgie, held in Rome, at which there was a discussion on the subject of partial seizures, then known as Jacksonian epilepsy. The term was first used by Charcot following the description of attacks of this type by Hughlings Jackson, and the eponym had become internationally recognised. Jeff pointed out that, although cortical scars were a common cause of fits of this nature, he had explored some patients most carefully without finding such evidence. In this he differed from Leriche, who asserted that there must always be a scar somewhere, but added that when one was present it had to be related to the precentral area of cortex. Jeff made the further point that epilepsy was relatively rare in civilian injuries when compared with war wounds, putting forward the concept that this was because the motor area was seldom involved in everyday mishaps. A case of Jacksonian epilepsy in civilian life was more likely to be due to a pathological lesion, vascular or neoplastic, than to trauma. Jefferson also remarked that he had 'discovered that Jacksonian seizures were, in their early stages, easily controlled by lumbar puncture and by bromide'[33], a telling comment on the therapy that was then current and available for the treatment of seizures. Of 60 cases of traumatic epilepsy in his own practice, 25 had been Jacksonian, and the more chronic ones had tended towards a natural cure.

His final remarks were slightly cynical: ' . . . those who believe most firmly in their particular method of treatment manage to convey to the patient a suggestion of cure which is very helpful'[33]. This was, of course, many years before cerebral corticography and stimulation at operation were employed for localization of the sources of fits, though Horsley had used electrical stimulation in animal experiments when working in his laboratory at the beginning of the 20th century.

With his increased confidence, and ever since his visit to Boston, there had been growing at the back of Jefferson's mind the possibility of forming a British society of neurosurgeons on the lines of the Harvey Cushing Club—the forerunner then of the Harvey Cushing Society (1931), now called the American Association of Neurological Surgeons (1967). He had written to Cushing to ask if they had a constitution and, on 21st October 1926, Cushing replied: 'I am interested to learn that you are *en train* to start a visiting group of British neurological surgeons. I doubt very much whether we have such a thing as a constitution but we may possibly have something of the sort. I would rather be inclined to say that our small American group constitutes a club rather than a society, and a club hardly needs a written constitution'[34]. He promised to ask Dr Francis Grant, the secretary of the Cushing Club, to write to Jeff further on the subject. This letter was addressed to 2 St John Street, Manchester, for it was here that Jefferson had now taken consulting rooms, having given up those at 264 Oxford Road. St John Street was where medical consulting rooms tended to be located in that city. It did not matter that the rooms were not near the Infirmary since Jeff had not yet obtained an appointment there, though his hopes of doing so had revived; it was the address that mattered now.

Events then began to move quite fast. The Board of the Manchester Royal Infirmary advertised for the appointment of an Honorary Neurological Surgeon. Jefferson applied and this time he was successful. He was only to be given four beds, and yet was responsible for an outpatient clinic. This time the application carried a list of appointments after Jefferson's name: he had become a full Honorary Surgeon at Salford Royal Hospital in 1925, was Lecturer in Applied Anatomy at Manchester University, Visiting Surgeon at Grangethorpe Hospital, Honorary Consulting Surgeon at the Eccles and Patricroft and at the Knutsford Cottage Hospitals, Surgeon to the Manchester Royal Eye Hospital, Late Hunterian Professor at the Royal College of Surgeons and Examiner in Surgery at Queen's University, Belfast. And he was now 40 years of age[35].

The application provides some interesting information, such as that Jeff had been teaching the applied anatomy of the central nervous system at the University and had recently begun to teach operative surgery as well. The latter academic commitment was shared with his friend John Morley. It also appears that Grangethorpe Hospital had provided him with opportunities to study post-traumatic epilepsy and that he was in charge of the patients with old gun-shot wounds of the head and spine who were admitted there. Naturally, in his application, he emphasised his experience of surgical neurology at the various stages of his career until this time, and his visits to Cushing and other surgeons in the United States and in Europe[35].

Jefferson's bibliography now included 16 neurological papers and the editorship of the section on neurological surgery in the *Medical Annual*. He also listed 13 papers on miscellaneous subjects. His referees were somewhat different from those of the previous application. First came Professor Sir Harold Stiles of Edinburgh, who emphasized the importance of Jeff's general surgical background and anatomical knowledge. Next was Sir Arthur Keith, who had accommodated him in his laboratory at the Royal College of Surgeons. Professor ED Telford of the Royal Infirmary gave a brief recommendation, followed by Dr FC Moore, the senior physician, who commented on Jeff's knowledge of neurology and his surgical skill. There was a testimonial from his old and much respected chief, Professor Elliot Smith, and a long and enthusiastic one from Professor JSB Stopford, the Professor of Anatomy and Dean of the Medical School. Geoffrey's credentials were irresistible and he was appointed Honorary Neurological Surgeon to the Manchester Royal Infirmary on 1st December 1926, thus achieving his first major goal[35]. He was presented to the Board of the Infirmary, who welcomed him to the hospital, at a formal committee meeting 7 weeks later.

On the very next day after Jefferson had achieved his ambition to join the staff of the Royal Infirmary, a meeting was held at the Athenaeum Club in Waterloo Place, London, to consider the formation of a Society of Neurological Surgeons. This was conjoined to a dinner hosted by Sir Charles Ballance. The foundation of the Society of British Neurological Surgeons (SBNS) was described by Jefferson himself, whose brain-child it was. 'Conversations had gone on before this between myself and Sir Charles, Mr (later Sir) Percy Sargent, Mr Wilfred Trotter, Mr Bathe Rawling and Mr Donald Armour, Mr James Learmonth and the young Mr Dott, all of whom favoured the formation of a neurological surgical group, something that would be as much a small scientific club as a formal Society. It had 14 members originally. I had had a considerable encouragement not only from Ballance but also from Harvey Cushing, who had inherited Osler's belief in the virtues of medical societies as centres for the exchange of knowledge and the encouragement of warm and friendly relations between members. There was then only one important specialist group in Britain—the Orthopaedic Association, founded by the enterprise of my friend Mr (later Sir) Harry Platt. The rules of that Association helped in the drawing up of our own but we laid more emphasis from the start than they did on foreign visits'[36]. Jefferson must have discussed the subject with his friend Harry Platt, who would have strongly supported him in his idea of forming a Society.

The note continues, quoting Jeff: 'The special meeting at the Athenaeum was attended by seventeen persons—the five of those already named and Sir David Ferrier, Sir Edward Sharpey-Schafer, Sir Grafton Elliot Smith, Sir Arthur Keith, Henry Souttar, Adams McConnell, James Learmouth, Blundell Bankart, LR Broster, Lancelot Bromley and Sir Charles's son, Dr AW Ballance. All these men except the last had some interest in Neuro-surgery though several eventually withdrew. Norman Dott was elected a Member of the Society which was then declared to have been founded. Sir Charles Ballance was elected President with myself as Secretary. Ballance was made Hon. President in 1927, a position he held until his death in 1936. Preparations had been made in advance for the first formal scientific session, which was held next day, 3rd December, 1926, at Queen Square'[36].

The importance of this event in the development of British neurosurgery cannot be overstated. The Society gradually assumed the rôle of unofficial governing body of neurological surgery in Britain, a rôle which is tacitly accepted today. It may be observed that the formation of the Society had preceded the development of complete specialization in the practices of its members, and it was very influential in obtaining recognition of the specialty in the United Kingdom. Further, there were no societies of a similar nature in Europe during the early years after its formation, so that the foreign meetings became a focus for neurosurgeons abroad until they themselves formed their own groups, and many became foreign members of the British Society. This fulfilled an aspiration of Jefferson's, that one of the two annual meetings should be held abroad at a foreign neurological or neurosurgical clinic. It may be said that Geoffrey was not only the source of inspiration for the formation of the Society and its ideals but, as Secretary and later as President, he continued to lead the Advisory Council in its decisions. He had given credence to the specialty in Europe and created a focal point for its future development on the eastern side of the Atlantic Ocean. For Jefferson himself, the exposure to demands of what was to be an increasingly wide-ranging organization, provided a useful preparation for the responsibilities that were to be put on his shoulders by the Ministry of Health during and after World War II.

It is fitting to continue this history of the foundation of the Society, by quoting a paragraph written in an edition of its Handbook some years ago (1984) by Joe Pennybacker, who was himself for many years its Secretary: 'From this account the reader may rightly infer that Jefferson was the prime mover, as he was to remain the presiding genius of the Society for many years during a long period as Honorary Secretary and as President for two terms. His keen intellect, sense of humour, and engaging personality combined in a superb surgeon the qualities which made him the perfect guardian of an infant Society. His immediate task was to arrange two meetings a year, as required by the Constitution, and it is a tribute to his interest and enthusiasm that with the exception of a Summer meeting in 1929, this commitment was fully honoured. Those who remember his utter disregard of time and punctuality may well wonder how this was ever achieved'[36].

Jefferson was almost as proud of his part in the foundation of the Society of British Neurological Surgeons as he was of his appointment to the Manchester Royal Infirmary, but in all this excitement there had been a background of tragedy at home. It was during the year 1926 that, owing to the development of a too friendly relationship between Jeff and a young woman, Gertrude had very seriously considered instituting divorce proceedings[27]. However, the bond between the Jeffersons was too strong and their respect for each other was too great for separation. The problem was settled between them and their previous warm affection for each other was restored. It is possible that from this time on Geoffrey was cast in Gertrude's esteem more in the rôle of hero rather than simply that of her beloved husband. She forgave him and it did not seem to alter the strength of her feelings for him, as far as those can tell who are best in a position to know. From now on nothing was too good for him, he was given priority in every detail of life in the home, and Gertrude made as sure as she could that she would never again experience the trauma she had been through. For Jeff, it was a salutary warning that caused him to count his blessings.

Other events took place in their normal course. On one occasion, Antony was taken to the seaside by Agnes Head where, at a single session on one day she/they made '80 puddings and 12 castles' in the sand. It seems that they joined Michael and Monica at Llangollen in mid-Wales; Lizzie, the maid, was there too but neither of the parents. Apart from the demands of work, Gertrude undoubtedly wanted to remain near Jeff[37]. So, if 1926 was Jefferson's wonderful year — he called it his *Annus Mirabilis* — it was not so for his wife, unless it be that the year ended happily after all.

REFERENCES

GJ=Geoffrey Jefferson; GMJ=Gertrude Jefferson
1   Visits to clinics. The neurosurgical clinic and neuropathological laboratories at the Royal Infirmary, Manchester. *Br J Surg* 1955–1956; **43**: 317–23.
2   Jefferson G. Ventriculography as an aid in the localization of tumours. *BMJ* 1923; **2**: 796–801.
3   Dandy W. Localization and elimination of cerebral tumors by ventriculography. *Surg Gynecol Obstet* 1920; **31**: 329–42.
4   Renny, Agnes to GMJ. Letter 13th March 1924.
5   Furness AW to GJ. Letter 8th May 1924.
6   GJ to GMJ. Letter 28th April 1924.
7   Jefferson G. Harvey Cushing. *Manchester University Medical Students' Gazette* 1943; **22**: 1–6.
8   GJ to GMJ. Letter 29th April 1924.
9   Charlton CAC. Sir d'Arcy Power: surgeon and historian. *J Med Biog* 1994; **2**: 137–45.
10 Bailey P. *Pepper pot.* In: Bucy PC, ed. *Neurosurgical giants: feet of clay and iron.* New York: Elsevier, 1985: 73–89.
11 GJ. MS Notes on his visit to the United States in 1924.
12 GJ to GMJ. Letter 30th April 1924
13 GJ to GMJ. Letters 1st and 3rd May 1924.
14 Fulton JF. *Harvey Cushing, a biography.* Oxford: Blackwell, 1946: 626.
15 GJ to GMJ. Letter 4th May 1924.
16 GJ to GMJ. Letter 5th May 1924.
17 GJ to GMJ. Letter 6th May 1924.
18 GJ to GMJ. Letter 8th May 1924.
19 GJ to GMJ. Letter 9th May 1924.
20 GJ to GMJ. Letter 16th May 1924.
21 GJ to GMJ. Letter 18th May 1924.
22 GJ to GMJ. Letter 19th May 1924.
23 GJ to GMJ. Letter 29th May 1924.
24 GJ to GMJ. Letter 25th June 1924.
25 GJ. MS. Notes on neurological surgery in the United States of America, 1924.
26 GJ to GMJ. Letter 7th July 1924.
27 Jefferson, Michael. Personal communication.
28 GJ to GMJ. Letter July 1924, undated.
29 Jefferson G. The diagnosis and treatment of compression paraplegia. *BMJ* 1925; **2**: 1156–7.
30 Jefferson G. Report on a successful case of embolectomy, with a review of the literature. *BMJ* 1925; **2**: 985–7.
31 Cushing H to GJ. Letter 23rd October 1924.
32 Cushing H to GJ. Letter 19th November 1924.
33 Jefferson G. *Discussion on Jacksonian Epilepsy.* 1927; Bruxelles: Imprimerie Médicale et Scientifique, 1927: 1–4.
34 Cushing, H to GJ. Letter 21st October 1926.
35 Jefferson G. Application of Geoffrey Jefferson...for the post of Honorary Neurological Surgeon to the Manchester Royal Infirmary, with a list of Contributions to Surgical Literature and Testimonials. 10th November 1926.
36 Pennybacker JB. Society of British Neurological Surgeons. *Notes on the History of the Society*, with quotation of GJ. Published privately, 1984: 39–44.
37 Head, Agnes to GMJ. Letter undated; also Jefferson, Monica to GMJ 6th August 1926; and GMJ to Antony Jefferson 9th August 1926.

The early neurosurgical years
1927–1930

In June 1927 Harvey Cushing had been invited to deliver the Macewen Memorial Lecture in Glasgow and to receive an Honorary LL.D from the university. He sailed to England on 4th June, with his daughter Betsey and his secretary Madeline Stanton. His Macewen Lecture was to be 'a landmark in the history of neurosurgery'[1]. Finishing touches were put to the address while Cushing was staying with the Oslers in Oxford, after speaking to the Medical Society of London on acromegaly. The Glasgow lecture was the 'first account of the use of electrosurgical methods in the removal of brain tumours', according to Fulton, who related that: 'he tried the electric loop for the first time on 1st October 1926 but did not have the technique really under control until January'. Describing Cushing's visit to England further, he added that: 'As relaxation from these formal responsibilities, there was a two-day visit to Manchester to see Mr and Mrs Geoffrey Jefferson and the John Rylands library*, and to attend a meeting of the Society of British Neurological Surgeons on 24–25 June'[1]. Cushing had suggested in a letter in May that they would stay at a hotel, but all three came to visit the Jeffersons at their home. Cushing wrote: 'I shall hope to have time to see the Rylands Library to meet Thos. Percival†, to play with Trotula and to do other things more historical than neurosurgical'[2]. This produced the following, very excusable, gaffe which Fulton recorded. 'Jefferson, who seldom nods, proceeded to look up Thomas Percival in the telephone book! H.C. much delighted, wrote to him from Oxford[3]; "Thomas Percival, he of the Code, I may have to leave undisturbed in his tomb. If you had asked Trotula about him, she would have told you who he was"[1].' The signatures of Harvey Cushing, Betsey Cushing and Madeline Stanton, written at the time of this visit, are in the Jefferson's Visitor's Book, on the cover of which is the title, 'The Open Door'; the Osler's homes both in Oxford and in Baltimore were known as 'The Open Arms'.

The meeting of the Society of British Neurological Surgeons in question was its second and it was, most deservedly and appropriately, held in Manchester at the

---

*John Rylands Library. In 1834 it was agreed to create an association of medical practitioners in the north of England and to provide a library and reading room. The Manchester Medical Society was founded in the following year. In 1872 the Society's library was accommodated in the library of the Medical School of Owen's College (later the Victoria University of Manchester). It is now the John Rylands University Library.

†Thomas Percival (1740–1804) was physician to the Manchester Infirmary from 1779 to 1780 and physician extraordinary from 1782 until his death. In 1781 he became one of the founders of the Manchester Literary and Philosophical Society, who own his portrait, and he held the presidency of this society for 33 years, having been joint president for 5 years before that. More than half the 24 original members were of the medical profession, but 50 years were to elapse before the purely medical society was founded in Manchester in 1835. He produced a code of ethics in 1792 to which Cushing refers[4]. There were several editions of this book, and it became the basis of the Code of Ethics of the American Medical Association before 1849, and was unaltered until 1957, hence Cushing's interest[5].

Royal Infirmary and at the Royal Hospital, Salford. Jefferson must have been highly delighted that Cushing was present. The subjects that were discussed then are still matters for debate, even 70 years on. The theme concerned vascular pathology. It has to be remembered that not only was this meeting taking place many years before cerebral angiography enabled vascular lesions to be demonstrated *in vivo*, but it was also only 5 years since the association between the signs and symptoms of subarachnoid haemorrhage and cerebral aneurysms had been demonstrated for the first time by (Sir) Charles Symonds, when working with Harvey Cushing, and almost at the same time by (Sir) James Collier in London[6]. At this SBNS meeting Jefferson showed two cases of carotid aneurysm and a cortical angioma. It was a subject which he was to make one of his own special interests, culminating in an important paper 10 years later[7] and other publications. Virtually the only surgical treatment then available consisted of ligation of the common or internal carotid artery, a procedure that carried its own considerable risks and could not guarantee even moderate success. It is hardly surprising, therefore, that many patients who had suffered a subarachnoid haemorrhage were not even referred by their physicians for a neurosurgical opinion. Sir Percy Sargent spoke on vascular abnormalities, the pathology of aneurysms was described by Dr Shaw Dunn and, perhaps surprisingly, their treatment was discussed by Wilfred Trotter who was better known for his work on peripheral rather than cerebral aneurysms. The meeting was a memorable event.

In the July of 1927 Harry Platt, Jefferson's long standing colleague, now an orthopaedic surgeon in Manchester, felt unwell one evening and did not want to eat. He spent a restless night, during which he had increasing abdominal pains and, eventually, he asked Jeff to come to see him. Jefferson diagnosed appendicitis and had his patient admitted to the High Elms Nursing Home in Victoria Park, Manchester; the most fashionable and best run establishment in the city, which he continued to use for his private patients until 1939. He then removed the appendix, assisted by another long standing surgical friend, John Morley. Legend has it that two minutes' silence was observed during Harry Platt's list at the Royal Infirmary that day, the operations there having been performed by the Resident Surgical Officer. Subsequently Harry Platt gave Jeff a fitted dressing case. In his letter of thanks Jeff wrote:

'My dear old chap,

I am of course delighted with your splendid presents, but above all by the charming letter which accompanied them. I appreciated it fully, the more so from the sentimentally aphasic fellow who sent it. We've run together side by side for 23 years now, and hope we shall be spared to double or treble it.

Yours affectionately,

Geoffrey Jefferson'[8].

While all this was happening, domestic events were naturally taking place at 46 Birch Lane. Children's parties were a rarity in the Jefferson household but Michael recalls one in 1922 or thereabouts, and another was held in the local church hall in 1927 when he was about 11 years old[9]. Monica, by now away at the Downs School in Seaford, Sussex, was receiving charming letters from her mother, one of which gave news of her pet mice and her dog Rollo, a Sealyham terrier[9].

Less happy were the letters that Gertrude received from her sister Norma in Seattle. She thanked Trude for Christmas presents and told how she had supplemented the family income by trying to sell books for a firm named Bookhouse, but was going to have to give that up. She probably had to purchase the stock herself, which she then sold, and she found the business of selling at the door very uncongenial. Although her husband, Herbert Ritchie, was the first violin in the Seattle Symphony Orchestra, the salary was small and there was no longer the steady support that they had assuredly received in the past from Norma's father. She described how she had to be out in 'all kinds of weather and the effort of trying to overcome people's rather natural antagonism before they know what a good thing I have to show them is rather too much'[11]. In fact she had intended to send nine of the books to the Jefferson children for Christmas, but had not been able to find 'the right sort of cardboard & then too the crowds in town were too much for my cold'[11]. Norma's marriage was in real difficulties and, now that their daughter Wanda had grown up, 'she and Herbert have as many differences of opinion as he and I have always had'[11]. Gillian Scaife's husband, Charlie, had turned up when he was acting in two plays in Seattle, but 'he didn't stay with us of course as we have so little furniture'[11]. Gillian Scaife and Charlie had been separated for some time, Norma and Herbert were about to become so and the Jeffersons themselves had very recently drawn back from the brink. Gertrude must have felt very upset by it all, particularly in view of her strong religious beliefs.

Gertrude's father had remarried late in 1926 and early in the next year Norma wrote of 'a constant dread of a meeting' and how she and her daughter were packing up the house in Seattle and putting it in order before selling it and moving to California[12]. Mr Flumerfelt wrote a birthday letter to Gertrude in April, in which he said that, although he was in his seventies, he felt well and was looking forward to pulling his business affairs together once more. However, his new wife, Lola, had caused him 'to have been for a long time trying to overcome bad feelings, occasioned by the gossip of some of our former friends.... Lola is peculiar, highly sensitive and perhaps a bit shy owing to the lack of early educational advantages'[13]. This remark left more to the imagination of his daughter than it actually explained, since she had never met Lola. It would have been inevitable for her to have compared her new step-mother with the beloved person to whom her father had once been married, and undoubtedly Norma did the same, for she had been extremely apprehensive of the possibility of their meeting[11]. Observations such as these can only have added to Gertrude's distress, and it is clear that neither she nor her sister were ever reconciled to their father's second wife. In this letter he also gave the impression, in a somewhat unromantic sentence, that Lola had saved his sanity and that this alone justified his remarriage, for '...I could not have preserved my health and mental powers had I been obliged to continue alone. Club or Hotel life would have killed me'. He recounted that 'My two objects in life are (1) To have her friendly with you and Norma and (2) to accomplish my life's ambition to clear up and pay my obligations.... I can however say quite freely I have never done anyone a wrong...and though many things have been done to me, I bear no ill will to any living person'[13].

At the end of August 1927, Harvey Cushing wrote to Jeff to thank him for an offer of the gift of the Nonsuch Press edition of William Harvey's *De motu cordis*, and promised that in return he would send Jefferson a full set of reprints of his 1926–28 publications. 'I am glad to know that you are getting off for a vacation and hope it will be a pleasant one, though you don't say where you are going'[14]—and neither do we have any record of where Jeff went. On 30th August, Cushing sent a hand-written letter to Jeff from Nyon-en-Suisse. He had gone there to stay at *Les Terrasses*, the villa of his friend Dr Arnold Klebs, 'since escaping from home after the Physiological Congress'[15]. Klebs was a bibliophile and historian, whose companionship and opinions were greatly valued by Cushing. The latter had enjoyed the Manchester meeting 'and what a splendid lot of cases you had to show!'[15]. Norman Dott had been with him in Boston for a month and 'I leaned heavily on him and let him do most of the work as I was busy with the Congress and trying to write a paper for Lund and another for Amsterdam. He's a fine lad...and from all points of view is a great credit to our neurosurgical field. I think Cairns will be another. All neurosurgeons should have—like you—wives that are superlatively acceptable to the guild and we shall have to look about for someone suitable for Norman Dott. Perhaps Trotula can help us'[15]. Although this is just an amusing aside, the manner in which this letter mentions the other two, younger, neurosurgeons who were together with Jefferson to pioneer the resurgence of British neurosurgery, emphasises once again how Jeff was so much more senior to them, both in fact and in Cushing's esteem. A further brief note from the Boston surgeon[16] thanked the SBNS for having elected him an Honorary Member or, to be more accurate, an Emeritus Member—an act by which they honoured themselves almost as much as the recipient. On this visit he had also been elected an Honorary Fellow of the Royal Society of Medicine and the Royal Academy of Medicine of Ireland, awarded an Hon. MChir of Trinity College, Dublin, and an LL.D from Edinburgh University (to balance the one from Glasgow no doubt!).

The Michaelmas meeting of the Society of British Neurological Surgeons that year was held at the London Hospital and University College Hospital Medical School. The responsibility for its organization fell on Jefferson's shoulders, but he now had the assistance of Miss Elizabeth Armistead, who became his devoted and very faithful secretary for the rest of his life. Hugh Cairns had been elected an *Associate* Member of the SBNS at the Manchester meeting and now read his first paper to the Society. His neurosurgical department at the London Hospital was the first specialized unit of its kind in Britain, though he had only a very small operating theatre and hardly any office accommodation. The 20 beds that he had been given were scattered in various parts of the hospital, and he had to take a share of the general surgery; 'but it was a beginning and, within the next ten years, he and the department were to establish an international reputation'[17].

In July 1928 the *British Journal of Surgery* had carried an article on the veins of the diploë, written by Jeff in conjunction with D Stewart[18]. This was mainly an anatomical paper, emphasising the variations in structure of the vertebrae, their radiological appearances, the alterations produced by tumours, especially meningiomas, and the rôle of the diploic veins in propagating infection.

Jefferson also took part in a discussion on spinal injuries at a meeting of the Section of Orthopaedics of the Royal Society of Medicine[19]. Once again, his detailed knowledge of anatomy was put to good use when considering the mechanism of various forms of spinal trauma. However, he left the consequent damage to the nervous system for other speakers to consider and mentioned treatment only very briefly, condemning early operation except in cases of cord compression, and favouring 'reduction rather than classical laminectomy'[19]. It is a comprehensive and very logical paper. Geoffrey also contributed a chapter on injuries and diseases of the spinal cord to *A textbook of surgical diagnosis*, edited by AJ Walton[20].

Despite Cairns' specialist neurosurgical unit at the London Hospital having been the first in the United Kingdom he, like Jefferson, had to continue to be a part-time general surgeon. Norman Dott, in Edinburgh, was the first in the British Isles to be allowed to specialize wholly in the discipline, though then without his own unit—a contrast to the situation Jeff had found in America several years earlier where dedicated departments were beginning to develop. Jefferson's beds at the Royal Infirmary had been increased from four to six, and he was soon to acquire two more, but this meagre number still severely restricted his activities, a state of affairs that was to continue for another 4 years.

Although not a founder of the SBNS, Dott had been elected a full member (unlike Cairns) at the first meeting of the Society. It was therefore to Edinburgh that they went for their fourth gathering, in the spring of 1928. Dott demonstrated an operation on an orbito-ethmoidal osteoma but, as he had not yet achieved a department of his own at the Edinburgh Royal Infirmary, the meeting was held at the Royal College of Surgeons of Edinburgh and at the University. Edwin Bramwell was one of the first to appreciate the association between internal carotid aneurysms and oculomotor palsy, a subject on which he spoke, and that great ophthalmologist, HM Traquair, read a paper on perimetry. According to Pennybacker, 'these early meetings in London, Manchester and Edinburgh, were evidence that these were centres of some enlightenment in which a new speciality might flourish. They did in fact prove to be the germinal centres from which most of the present generation of neurosurgeons sprang, either directly or indirectly'[17].

In August Cushing wrote a short hand-written letter to Jeff to thank him for the *De motu cordis*, which had now arrived. 'I shall treasure it, as I collect Harveiana'[14]. The 1928 Michaelmas meeting of the SBNS was again in London, but this time divided between Guy's Hopital, the National Hospital for Nervous Diseases in Queen Square, and Charing Cross Hospital.

As a footnote to the year 1928, it is of interest that Gertrude took the children to visit their grandmother at Greenbooth at least once during each of the school holidays. She was aware that she had never been accepted by her mother-in-law, who disliked her, and this was an endeavour to behave dutifully and as an act of placation. The only redeeming feature of these visits, as far as the children were concerned, was the 'super tea with marvellous cakes and fine thin sandwiches'[9]. Jeff came too when he was not too busy, so the visits probably took place on Sundays. During the summer, faithful Lizzie Aldridge came to visit the family in Manchester. Trude took them all down to Southport for the day. Lizzie had a sweet nature and continued to keep in touch with Gertrude, even during the poverty stricken years of her old age when her letters were very touching to read[9]. They were entering the period of the Great Depression, which lasted from 1929 to 1934 and affected the lives of most people, and not only in Britain.

In 1929 Geoffrey Jefferson moved his consulting rooms once more, this time from No 2 to No 10 St John Street. It was then also that Madge married Jack Collins. She left the partnership in her brother's practice and with her husband now took over Greenbooth, the house which she had shared with her mother. The month of May found Geoffrey and Gertrude in Switzerland, probably in order to attend a meeting the details of which are not available. However, they returned via Brussels and Bruges, where they climbed to the Belfry in the Grande Place and watched the carillon being played. The crossing from Ostend to Dover was rough. 'I was rather miserable towards the end & was finally sea-sick for a few minutes — Father managed to hold on', Gertrude wrote to her son Michael[21]. According to a letter written in the following year, Jeff and the family spent a holiday together at St Anne's-on-Sea, just a few miles south of Blackpool, where they had rented rooms that summer. It was probably only a short visit[22]. Whenever possible Jeff tried to share in the family holidays.

Hugh Cairns came to stay with the Jeffersons in July 1929. In his letter of thanks addressed, rather formally, to 'Mrs Jefferson' he wrote: 'so completely was I occupied in enjoying myself that I completely forgot to make a mental note about taking my umbrella — so when the time came to go away I left it behind!'[23]. His Medical Research Council Monograph (Special Report No. 125) entitled *A study of intracranial surgery* had been published recently. This was quite significant, for in it he had stated that it was up to the neurological surgeon to make his own diagnoses, independently of the neurologist; to this end an adequate knowledge of neurology on the part of the surgeon was assumed. 'It was this point, central to Cushing's approach and that of all modern neurosurgeons, which created difficulties between senior neurologists at the National Hospital Queen Square, and Cairns and Geoffrey Jefferson'[24]. This was a seed that was about to grow into a major problem in only a year's time.

Jeff had been unable to arrange a summer meeting for the SBNS, foreign meetings not having yet featured in the Society's calendar, and 'as there were so few neurosurgical "centres", our repertoire of places for conventional meetings was soon exhausted, and [so] in the autumn of 1929 we went to Sherrington's laboratory and the Radcliffe Infirmary in Oxford. Although the somewhat rarified neurophysiological atmosphere was unusual for practical surgeons, it was stimulating enough to make us repeat the experience eight years later in Adrian's laboratory in Cambridge'[17]. Jefferson had discussed the preparations for this meeting with Cairns who of course had, at that time, no official connection with Oxford, though he had been at Balliol as a Rhodes scholar and, certainly of equal importance, had married a daughter of the Master of that College.

As late as the beginning of October the programme for the meeting had not yet been settled. Cairns wrote to Jeff to suggest that Charles Sherrington should be asked to host the Oxford meeting by way, as an intermediary, of John Fulton*,

---

*Fulton, John F (1899–1960). American neurophysiologist in whose laboratory many of Cushing's trainees, including Cairns, spent some time. He had worked under Sherrington at Oxford, and became professor of physiology at Yale. Studies of the frontal cortex that he made and later discussed with Egas Moniz, led to the operations of prefrontal leucotomy. Finally he became Professor of history of medicine at Yale. He was known as a lover of mankind and books.

who was then working with Sherrington in the physiology laboratory. Fulton 'is a most likeable and approachable man...if you did this you would never regret it, because he has a library which would simply make your mouth water'[25]. The proposed topic was electrosurgery, the subject on which Cushing had given his Macewen Lecture. Cairns suggested that Dott should be asked to speak 'as he has been most recently out of Cushing's place'[25]. Jefferson must already have decided to ask Dott, for there is a letter from him to Jeff, crossing the one from Cairns, in which Dott said that he had brought back a very efficient diathermy machine from Boston, which he had 'left with Schall [the instrument makers] for some weeks for them to study and copy so far as they could.... I quite agree with you that this technical method is probably the most important contribution to surgery of recent years'[26]. Jefferson had also invited Dott to attend a committee meeting before the Scientific sessions began, to which the Scotsman commented, 'If there were anything likely to turn up at the Committee Meeting on which I could really be of service, of course I would make a point of getting down but if, as has happened, the Committee's chief function is to discuss the Dinner Menu, I am sure you would excuse me'[26]. These remarks obviously annoyed Jeff, and he wrote a record of his wrath in this comment at the end of the paragraph:- '(=oedema capitis. G.J.)'[26].

The occasion turned out to be very satisfactory. Cairns gave Jefferson his opinion: 'I agree with you that the Oxford meeting was a very great success. The one fly in the ointment from my point of view was that Trotter did not come along, though I must say that your contribution on Jacksonian Epilepsy was admirable. My feeling about the Club at present is that there are far too many people who do not take part in the discussions.... Of course, you may really think that all of us young things ought to sit tight and keep our mouths shut until we begin to get grey hairs, though I don't seriously believe that you do think this'[27]. Even though Cairns was but an associate member at this time, he did not hesitate to assert himself.

In his earlier letter of 8th October, Cairns had gone on to discuss the sterilization of electrodes and then turned to the subject of acoustic tumours. 'I am not surprised to hear of your fatality with an acoustic tumour.... I do know, however, that Harvey Cushing had a good many deaths on the table from acoustic tumours, from the same cause that you mention [possibly occlusion of the anterior inferior cerebellar artery]. When I was there he was very cautious indeed when he got up alongside the medulla and in most cases he only did a partial removal of tumour. Since then however he has become more radical, at least he says he has become more radical...I did not see him do one of these'[28].

Because Jefferson did not have suitable, boilable, electrodes for an operation he proposed to perform one weekend, Cairns offered to lend his own 'if you will promise to return them straight away'[28]. In fact, they were sent to Jeff but he did not need them after all: he returned them very promptly and they were acknowledged by Cairns just a week later in a letter in which he discussed the various merits of the Bovie, Wyeth and Schall diathermy machines. In the final paragraph of this letter Cairns commented on a remark in Jeff's note of thanks for the loan of the instruments: 'You sound rather down-hearted about only having 17 years to go. I dare say all the really keen workers have felt like that. I know Sherrington feels it acutely at the moment, not being in the least bit satisfied with what he has already done. You have got such a good record behind you that you could almost afford to retire on your laurels instead of worrying about the future'[29]. This shows that Jefferson had once again fallen into a period of depression which lasted for several weeks. In fact 17 years would suggest retirement at the age of 60, which was in no way a necessity for him. Perhaps his unhappiness was expressing itself here rather as slight enviousness that although Cairns and he were both on the springboard of neurosurgery in Britain together, Hugh Cairns was so much younger with, presumably, so many more productive years ahead of him. Neither could know what span was available to each. Jefferson even seems to have been hesitating to publish his comments on the subject of Jacksonian epilepsy for, a month later, Cairns wrote: 'I certainly think you should publish your remarks on Jacksonian epilepsy. They were absolutely first rate. I understand your feeling that you don't think anything of yours is good nowadays. It is, I suspect, the feeling that we all get about our work as we grow older, but it does not necessarily mean that the work is less good than the earlier work which was written with all the enthusiasm of youth at a time when writing was something of a novelty'[30].

Hugh Cairns was one of the two secretaries of the Section of Surgery of the BMA meeting due to be held in Winnipeg in August 1930, and he wrote to invite Jefferson to take part in a proposed discussion on spinal surgery, including trauma, and to ask who he might suggest should be invited to speak on the surgery of the sympathetic system. Leriche and Adson were already being considered[31]. In the event Jeff did not return to Canada for that meeting and we do not know who, if anyone, he may have proposed.

In the late winter of 1929 Jefferson suffered an acute mastoiditis, for which he was admitted to High Elms Nursing Home under his old school-friend Ashton Smalley who, with Frank Wrigley, operated upon it very successfully[9]. This illness proved debilitating, probably because Jeff had been working very hard and was not well when it came. As a result he and Gertrude took a month's holiday in Switzerland, at Interlaken, from where they went on to visit the Italian Lakes.

At the end of January 1930, Cairns sent Jefferson three books on peripheral nerves by Foerster, in order to help him prepare both a paper he was to read at the Royal Society of Medicine on injuries of the brachial plexus[32], and a chapter entitled The peripheral nerves for the Third Edition of Choyce's System of surgery, which was not published until 1932[33]. In the accompanying letter Cairns wrote: 'I don't envy you your job of writing the article but nevertheless I am very glad that you are doing it as I now will get much pleasure and profit from reading it'[34]. Some, possibly warm, discussion about the expansion of the number of beds under Jeff's care must have taken place at this time, although nothing materialized until 1932, for Cairns continued: 'I am delighted to hear about the prospect of the unit. That's the stuff to give them!'[34].

When the paper on injuries of the branchial plexus[32] saw the light of day, Jefferson confined his remarks to injuries of the roots and cords, and pointed out that the mechanism by which the damage took place was the same whether the trauma occurred during birth or later in life. He emphasised the variability of the tears that were found in the nervous tissue, and added comments about the sites of rupture and the importance of pain as a diagnostic indicator of plexus injury.

He quoted two of his own cases and pointed out how many lesions were not amenable to surgery, however much one wanted to help. 'I do not believe, in spite of the occasional good result that appears in the literature, that secondary suture of the branchial plexus is a possible operation, except on rare occasions.... I should like to lay it down for purposes of discussion that, whilst immediate primary suture may sometimes be feasible in those uncommon cases where two clean nerve ends are discoverable in an accessible position, secondary suture should never be undertaken. One should operate for plexus injury within a week or ten days or not at all'[32]. Jefferson was famous for his aphorisms.

Gertrude acquired mumps from Antony at the end of the February of 1930, but, although additionally suffering from a cold, she was well enough to go to St Anne's-on-Sea with Geoffrey, where they stayed in the same boarding-house that they had previously visited with the family. From there she wrote to Monica on 9th March: 'Dad and I are here for a short week-end as we were both feeling done up—Father with hard work and me after mumps and a cold. Everything in this house reminds us of our holiday together last year. Father and I have the same bedroom but Mrs– [illegible] has given us the upstairs sitting-room—(her room) which is even nicer than the one we had last time.... Last night we went to the pictures—very stupid—& this morning to church.... Last week we were quite gay as Mr. and Mrs. Platt took us to dine at the Midland on Tuesday & we went to a very good film afterwards—and then on Friday we took Dr & Mrs Langley to see Bernard Shaw's new play—The Apple Cart which was very amusing.... We have planted some seeds in small pots at home which we hope will come up in time to be transplanted to the allotment in April'[35]. This is the only mention in the letters of an allotment, an extra plot of land rented in order to grow vegetables, fruit or flowers for the house, and Gertrude hinted to Monica that they would need help in it during the holidays.

A little later, in March, Jeff was examining in Belfast, for he wrote to Gertrude from there. The crossing had been smooth but on arrival it was snowing. He had 'corrected about 20 papers before going to sleep. ... I came up to write after lunch but the room was so bitterly cold that I lay down and went to sleep and lost the chance'[36]. The letter ended with a protestation of his true and only love for her. He was then away in Bristol for Gertrude's birthday on 1st May, but wrote to wish her many happy returns. 'I really am very dependent on you, for your love and company and help and advice. I get very disappointed with myself at times, and I know you do with yourself, for you say so'[37]. These remarks are very revealing of the innermost thoughts of a man whose public stature was increasing all the time, and whose name was becoming familiar to anyone with neurological or neurosurgical interests. They were not insincere or due to false modesty, but were the result of true self-awareness; his personal ambition remained as strong as it had always been. In June he wrote again to Trude, this time during a visit to Seaford to see Monica and discuss her progress with the staff of the Downs School. 'I blew Monity up about not writing but she says she tried to often but couldn't get it done—so what can you say. Miss Cameron says they are all the same'[38]. Her school reports were not too encouraging either.

Jefferson must have had a post-operative fatality from hyperthermia at about this time, and have written to Harvey Cushing about it. A reply came from

Boston on 16th June that he could not possibly answer Jeff's question about how to avoid such a tragedy, and that diencephalo-hypophysial mechanisms would be the subject of his Lister Memorial Lecture which he was due to give at the Royal College of Surgeons later in the month. 'One has an occasional fatality from hyperthermia whether operating on fourth ventricle or third ventricle lesions and it is something you have to take chances on. I hope it may never happen to you again. And I do not see what else you could have done than the operation you carried out. I wish that I might find time to come up to Manchester, but I have made no definite plans as to what I shall do when I get this lecture off my chest'[39]. In fact he did not visit the Jeffersons on this occasion. However, they did have a guest who contributed a delightful limerick to their Visitor's Book, it having been related to him by the poet, Robert Bridges, who had written it at St Moritz in response to a remark that nobody could make a rhyme to St Moritz. It may not be among the Laureate's published works!

'There was an old Man of St. Moritz
Who said I don't care much for its —
When they said, For its what?
He replied, Its all rot.
Its only my rhyme to St. Moritz!'[40].

In formulating his ideas for the future Society of British Neurological Surgeons, Jefferson had always intended that one of the two annual meetings should be held abroad. Pennybacker later explained: 'and so in the summer of 1930 we made our way to Paris.... We were honouring two great Frenchmen, Clovis Vincent, neurologist turned surgeon; and Thiery de Martel, brilliant craftsman and designer of instruments; we were also paying homage to the Hôpital de la Pitié and the Salpêtrière, institutions with a famous neurological tradition'[17]. They also visited the Hôpital St Joseph. It was the first of many meetings on the continent of Europe. Trude probably accompanied Geoffrey on this visit, because no letters were written back to her from France that summer.

In August 1930 GF Rowbotham became Jefferson's registrar, known as his Chief Assistant. He was the first of the very few neurosurgeons who received their training entirely under Jeff's tutelage. He was with him in this capacity for the next 3 years and a firm friendship developed between master and pupil. During that time, with guidance from his chief, five papers appeared under Rowbotham's name and considerable responsibility was about to fall on his shoulders.

At the end of September Gertrude received a long letter from her father, in which he remarked that he was pleased to hear that she had been in Cornwall at the beginning of the month, when the family may have accompanied her. The letter also mentions that the Jeffersons had sold the lease of the house in Birch Lane although they did not actually move until the following year[9,41]. Concerning the Flumerfelt home in Victoria, her father wrote that it should have been converted into a girl's school, but the neighbours opposed the idea. 'There was so much trouble about it and the possibility of future litigation that we have dropped the idea'[41]. The same problems arose over a suggestion to turn it into a nursing home. It was too large for current needs, especially in the absence of servants, and the house was eventually pulled down. Norma had been visited in Los Angeles by her father, by which time she and her husband had finally agreed to separate. 'I am very very sorry for both', wrote Mr Flumerfelt, showing his understanding of the situation, and also regretting his inability to help Norma financially. 'It is too bad that my declining years should be shadowed by such a tragedy'[41]. He also remarked on his good health in this letter but, only a month later, he reported that he had some discomfort to his bowels. The results of x-rays suggested a need for exploration and he took himself to Montreal for a further opinion. The presence of 'a growth in the large bowel on my lower left side'[42], was confirmed, and operation was recommended without delay. He had some things to attend to in Victoria and was admitted to hospital in the following week. There were no more letters from him and, shortly afterwards, he died. He was a very brave, kind man, who achieved much and served his family and country well; we can believe that his misfortunes were solely the result of generosity and ill-advised investment. Sadly, however, the financial problems were not to end with his death.

Towards the end of 1930 a number of the younger neurologists at the National Hospital, Queen Square, 'felt that a new surgical appointment should be made before either of their surgeons, Sir Percy Sargent CMG, DSO and Donald Armour, retired or died. They had both been appointed in the first decade of the century to support Victor Horsley. Cairns, Dott and Jefferson were canvassed. The post was advertised and all three applied'[24]. Dott was disqualified for having an Edinburgh Fellowship and not that of the English College. In the beginning of the new year there was the usual ritual of calling on the senior members of the consultant staff and 'the election was the talk of Harley Street'[24]. Cairns and Jefferson both made known their conviction that it was important that a neurosurgeon should be appointed who would be 'making his own diagnosis, determining the management, and operating with extreme care and gentleness'[24]. This was at variance with the 'principles established at Queen Square, by which the physicians made the diagnosis and decided the management; if that involved an operation, this was carried out by a general surgeon with an interest in neurosurgery'[24]. The Board of Governors refused to accept the recommendation of the Medical Committee and, at first, no appointment was made. The divisions were such that Armour had voted for Cairns and Sargent had threatened to resign if Cairns was appointed![24]. The time was not yet ripe for reform. Julian Taylor, a general surgeon at University College Hospital with a very considerable interest in neurosurgery, was eventually given the appointment.

From the financial point of view, Jefferson regarded the period leading up to and a little beyond 1930 as the most difficult there had been for him. Some years later, during World War II, he had time on his hands when waiting for a flight to America. As he was wont, he put his thoughts on paper: 'We had some tough years from 1919 on for 10 years and more and Trude was a brick, a marvel, a wonder through all those years. She worked and helped and earned money that kept us just about afloat. If she'd been a different sort of woman we might have sunk. I shall never forget the relief when I got £500 a yr. from the pension that Harry Platt got for me. It was nearly all we had for years'[43]. Life was not easy for a conscientious surgeon who was dependent on private patients for his income, yet wanted to give his time to his hospital work and to writing and research.

Added to which the Salford area was 'the most unlucrative in the country I should say'[43]. However, all three children received their education, during these lean years and beyond, at expensive boarding schools; in the case of the boys, at the Dragon School in Oxford, Rugby School and Oxford University. Jeff wanted to give them something of which he may have felt the lack himself. Though this was a severe financial strain, its very possibility does not suggest penury.

REFERENCES

GJ=Geoffrey Jefferson; GMJ=Gertrude Jefferson
1 Fulton JF. *Harvey Cushing, a biography.* Oxford: Blackwell, 1946: 549.
2 Cushing H to GJ. Letter 15th June 1927.
3 Cushing H to GJ. Letter 17th June 1927.
4 Percival T. *A scheme of professional conduct relative to hospitals and other medical charities.* 1792.
5 Brockbank EM. *Sketches of the lives and work of the Honorary medical staff of the Manchester Infirmary, 1752–1804.* Manchester: Manchester University Press, 1904.
6 Symonds CP, Cushing H. Contributions to the clinical study of intracranial aneurysms. *Guy's Hospital Reports* 1923; **73**: 139–63, also in Symonds CP. *Studies in neurology.* Oxford: Oxford University Press, 1970: 8–9, 27–47.
7 Jefferson G. On saccular aneurysms of the internal carotid artery in the cavernous sinus. *Br J Surg* 1938; **26**: 267–302.
8 GJ to Platt, Harry. Letter 23rd November 1927 (In the Jefferson Memorial Library).
9 Jefferson, Michael. Personal communication.
10 GJ to Monica Jefferson. Letter 11th May 1927.
11 Ritchie, Norma to GMJ. Letter 30th December 1926.
12 Ritchie, Norma to GMJ. Letter 17th January 1927.
13 Flumerfelt AC to GMJ. Letter 26th April 1927.
14 Cushing H to GJ. Letter 27th August 1927.
15 Cushing H to GJ. Letter 30th August 1927.
16 Cushing H to GJ. Letter 29th September 1927.
17 Pennybacker JB. *Handbook of the Society of British Neurological Surgeons.* Published Privately. 1984, 40–41.
18 Jefferson G, Stewart D. On the veins of the diploë. *Br J Surg* 1928; **16**: 70–88.
19 Jefferson G. Discussion on spinal injuries. *Proc Roy Soc Med* 1928; **21**: 21–44.
20 Jefferson G. Injuries and diseases of the spinal cord In: AJ Walton, ed. *A textbook of surgical diagnosis.* Vol. 1. London: Edward Arnold, 1928; **1**: 435–52.
21 GMJ to Jefferson, Michael. Letter 7th June 1929.
22 GMJ to Jefferson, Monica. Letter 9th March 1930.
23 Cairns H to GMJ. Letter 28th July 1929.
24 Fraenkl GJ. *Hugh Cairns.* Oxford: Oxford University Press, 1991: 67, 74.
25 Cairns H to GJ. Letter. 8th October 1929.
26 Dott N to GJ. Letter 9th October 1929.
27 Cairns H to GJ. Letter 30th November 1929.
28 Cairns H to GJ, Letter 8th October 1929.
29 Cairns H to GJ. Letter 15th October 1929
30 Cairns H to GJ. Letter 4th December 1929.
31 Cairns H to GJ. Letters 16th and 19th October 1929.
32 Jefferson G. Injuries to the brachial plexus. *Proc Roy Soc Med* 1929–1930; **23**: 1282–5.
33 Jefferson G. The peripheral nerves. In: Choyce CC, ed. *Choyce's system of surgery.* London: Cassell, 1932; **3**: 271–331.
34 Cairns H to GJ. Letter 31st January 1930.
35 GMJ to Jefferson, Monica. Letter 9th March 1930.
36 GJ to GMJ. Letter 19th March 1930.
37 GJ to GMJ. Letter 30th April 1930.

38   GJ to GMJ. Letter 10th June 1930.
39   Cushing H to GJ. Letter 16th June 1930.
40   Campion GG MS in Jefferson visitor's book. 26th November 1930.
41   Flumerfelt AC to GMJ. Letter 19th September 1930.
42   Flumerfelt AC to GMJ. Letter 25th October 1930.
43   GJ. MS *Notes* December 1942.

Chapter 14

A time of consolidation
1931–1935

Life in the Jefferson household in Birch Lane now had a settled routine. Breakfast was never served until after 9 am; during it Geoffrey would read the *Manchester Guardian* and exchange with Gertrude the various letters that had arrived with the morning post. The only occasions when breakfast was at 8 am were when Jeff was due to lecture at the University. Then there was near panic to see that he was not delayed, and he was dispatched for this event which, unlike most others, was not subject to his own very personal conception of time[1].

Jefferson did not return home from the hospital or elsewhere until about 8 pm, when he would have dinner. The exact time of arrival was quite unpredictable, and his food often had to be kept warm after the rest of the family had eaten, for the meal was officially at 7.30 pm. If there was time, he would then sleep in his chair until the 9 o'clock news on the radio, for the news became almost the one fixed point in his schedule, particularly during World War II. After the news he went to his desk to write letters or notes, which were typed up the following day by Miss Armistead. He had a phenomenal memory for the details of his case histories and wrote operation notes and letters about his patients at home without the aid of clinical notes. He once tried a dictaphone—the old wax cylinder variety—but did not like it and soon reverted to manuscript. The letters and notes that he wrote out for typing were always on yellow paper. This was a useful habit, copied from Harvey Cushing, which distinguished the contributions from the 'chief' from all other records, since nobody else was allowed to use that colour.

At 10.30 pm Jeff had tea, which he would allow to get cold before he drank it. On one afternoon occasion in America he asked for a second cup, but the pot had not been renewed and the tea was tepid when it was handed to him. He commented on this, whereupon he was told that since he always let it grow cold it really did not matter. Jeff replied 'Yes, but I like to let it grow cold myself'[2]. After this late cup of tea he would usually work on papers or speeches, or whatever was in hand until 1 or 2 am, during which time he smoked, as he always did when not with patients. He sometimes invited his first assistant to come along in the evening to discuss a paper or some clinical matter, and would talk long past midnight without considering the effect on that individual's family, or the need for rest before another heavy day's work. He just did not notice such things. Nor had he any concern for domestic issues or responsibilities within the home. This meant that the hours he spent there were available for work, writing letters or reading, for he gave very little time to the family. With Gertrude, when they created a free hour or two together, they devoured a lot of non-medical books which were discussed between them, and sometimes one or other would read a whole book aloud for their mutual enjoyment.

Entertainment at the Jefferson's house was generous though not frequent, for both Jeff and Gertrude were too busy to spare evenings unnecessarily and the days were completely filled. However, neurosurgical colleagues were always made welcome if they were visiting the neighbourhood. Gertrude did not always remember when she had invited a guest, who might turn up to her complete surprise. The burden of catering and looking after the needs of the family fell almost entirely on the domestic staff. Jefferson never drank whisky or gin, and wine was only served on special occasions; though there might be a glass of beer or cider at lunch on Sunday, and a single glass of sherry if there was a visitor. But such wine as there was was of the best, delivered by a Bristol firm whose traveller called once a year and persuaded Jeff to buy two or three cases of claret or burgundy and some good white wine. As for Trude, half a glass of sherry or a single glass of wine would have been enough for her. It was tea that Jeff really liked to drink, some kind of Indian variety and nothing fancy. It was a taste developed in the hospitals in which he spent his life, and he particularly enjoyed it after a long and tiring operation when chatting to the ward sister or his assistants; and, of course, there were always those regular evening cups[1].

The Jeffersons managed a short break away from work in the spring of 1931. Monica wrote to her mother from Seaford: 'I am so very sorry to hear that poor darling Dad is so tired, and I am very pleased to think he is going to the Lake District for a rest at Easter time'[3].

By the beginning of that year the Estate of Alfred Flumerfelt was being wound up, with the worrying discovery that his assets barely covered the amounts that were owed. A succession of letters came to Gertrude from The Royal Trust Company in Victoria, which was a firm of Executors and Trustees. The first of these, dated 26th February 1931, gave news of Ruhebühne, in Pemberton Road, Victoria, where she had been married and which had always been associated with recollections of her mother and her youth. The solicitor's letter said: 'We canvassed the situation regarding its possibilities very thoroughly and came to the conclusion that nothing could be done with it, and we have arranged to have it torn down and are to receive $200 for the salvage'[4]. Although the house was less than 40 years old, and would have cost $30–40,000 to build anew at 1931 prices, it was now virtually worthless. Gertrude must have been devastated by these further blows, which produced the final crumbling of the sources of her memories of childhood and youth. A few friends remained, such as Aggie Renny and, of course, her sister Norma, now alone with her daughter and impoverished. Victoria was no longer the paradise it had once been.

From Canada Mr Davis, the solicitor and friend of the family, continued to write. He told Gertrude that her father's will 'left everything he had to Mrs Flumerfelt [Lola], but it appears extremely doubtful as to whether she will ever receive any benefit from the estate'[4]. He was very sympathetic about Mr Flumerfelt's difficulties, adding that he believed that his mistakes were only those of ill-judgement. 'He was one of those very brilliant men who are impatient of detail and who are consequently led by others into taking steps that would not have been taken if the detail of the particular transactions had been more carefully considered'[5]. As much as 8 years later, with characteristic rectitude and consideration, Gertrude was to send the solicitor a cheque for $500, which she could ill afford, in payment of a long-standing account owed by her father to his doctor. Yet, even by then, the affairs of the estate had still not been finally settled[6].

Meanwhile, Jefferson had finished the preparation of his article on the peripheral nerves for the third edition of *Choyce's system of surgery*[7], and he had sent the manuscript to Cairns to read before giving it to the publisher. Cairns replied: 'I have read the greater part of your article and think it is first rate. Articles and books on peripheral nerves are usually rather monotonous & much of a pattern, but this is a strikingly individual and valuable essay. Please be an angel and ask for 2 page-proofs and send the extra one to me, as I don't want to have to buy a new Choyce if I can avoid it'[8]. There then followed three pages of suggestions and comments, mostly concerning the sympathetic nervous system, and finally he wrote: 'The only really important thing that occurred to me in the article on peripheral nerves was that I could find nothing about slowly produced tension as a factor interfering with conduction of nerves eg. 6th nerve palsy, ocular palsies with advancing exophthalmos, delayed ulnar palsies from chronic stretching at the elbow after old fractures (I have also seen that lesion from a non traumatic arthritis of the elbow)'[8]. This was valuable help and criticism from Cairns, and illustrates how meticulous he was about the content and style of any paper, whether his or by a colleague.

A very important friendship had developed between Jefferson and Cairns, who were now working closely together for the SBNS and were to be jointly responsible for the establishment and control of British neurosurgical services during World War II. Cairns thought he had a slight influence with the Rockefeller Foundation at that time, for they had given him a Travelling Fellowship to go to the United States, and he wrote to them on Jefferson's behalf to see if some funds could be attracted to Manchester in order to develop a specialist neurosurgical centre there. 'I'm jolly glad we had that talk but sorry that we couldn't finish it', Cairns wrote to Jeff, 'I have written to Gregg'[*8]. That particular effort was unsuccessful, but Cairns' support in other directions was to be of inestimable benefit later on. Probably having copied Cushing, who often commented on some current case or problem in the course of correspondence on another subject, both Jefferson and Cairns did the same. There is a postcript to the above letter, which begins: 'That man with the glioma that I did on Thursday had a complete paralysis of Lt arm and leg after the operation. The leg is now moving well . . .'. He continued, 'The *Geheimrat*[†] went off yesterday highly pleased, I think, with his visit to this country. He believes that the future of neurosurgery lies in this country because clinical neurology is so good here'[8]. In March 1931, in addition to his appointment at the London Hospital, Cairns joined the staff of the Maida Vale Hospital for the Treatment of Epilepsy, Paralysis and Diseases of the

---

*Gregg. Dr Alan Gregg, an officer of the Rockefeller Foundation, whose interest in neurology and psychiatry led to the establishment of the Montreal Neurological Institute and of Cairns' own department at the London Hospital, and to many other munificent acts. (GJ Fraenkl. *Cairns*. Oxford: Oxford University Press, 1991: 61).

†Geheimrat. Literally, a privy councillor. In this context it probably refers to Harvey Cushing, although no visit to England at this date is mentioned in Fulton's biography, and he had been ill in the early part of the year. The term is also used as a title in Germany, but there is no biographical record of a German visitor to either Jefferson or Cairns in May 1931.

Nervous System, which was then independent of the National Hospital, Queen Square.

In response to one from Jefferson, a letter from Cushing arrived in June, just a year after his last. 'What fun it would be if you could come over here for a spell. It would be a great stimulus to me.... I hear glowing accounts of your work from various sources from time to time and rejoice to know that you and Dott and Cairns are making such headway. But I am not sure that any form of surgery ought to be "subsidized" for this rather suggests that it cannot stand on its own feet. And after all, it is nothing more than a special field of surgery which must continue to grow out of general surgery if it is to have any real excuse for existence.... I shall look forward to seeing your Savill Oration with interest'[9]. Cushing then told Jeff that he was preparing his book on the meningiomas[10]. He went on to say that Horrax was doing all the trigeminal operations on his unit, for which a complete section by the temporal route was performed, with apparently little or no trouble from corneal anaesthesia. He was magnanimous enough to show interest, at the same time, in Dandy's posterior fossa approach to the trigeminal roots and wrote that he had suggested a comparative trial of the two methods, but this had not been approved by Dandy. He ended by commenting on the disappearance of tuberculomas from his New England practice, though there was still a good deal of bovine tuberculosis about, and how he had hoped to have the opportunity to remove a tuberculoma from the posterior fossa using diathermy—or electrosurgery as he called it.

In the June or July of 1931 the Jeffersons' move to a new house finally took place. It was to No 33 Belfield Road, Didsbury, Manchester, in a more attractive part of the city than Rusholm, and much further from the centre in a southerly direction. It was the district, though not the house, in which the Jeffersons were to spend the rest of their days. Belfield Road had trees at intervals along its sides and was at that time 'unadopted', which meant that the road was still gravelled. The Jefferson home was a detached brick house with three floors and a basement. There were neighbours on all sides—Monica was sure that the curtains on the other side of the road twitched every time she came and went[1]! There was a small garden in front and one behind in which there was just enough room for restricted games such as deck quoits and 'Kum Bak', in which a tennis ball suspended on elastic between two poles was hit with a racquet, ostensibly for stroke practice though the action and reaction did not much resemble that of a ball on a tennis court. The soil was too poor for there to be any serious attempt at horticulture, though there were borders in which a few plants grew, nasturtiums in front of the house and lupins, delphiniums and sweet-peas behind. The garden was inhabited by Monica's three tortoises, who rejoiced (if that is the right expression for a tortoise) in the delightful names of Amos, B-mos, and C-mos[1].

The entrance to the house was at the side and led into a passage from off which the sitting and dining rooms opened. At the back, separated by the staircase from the reception rooms, were the scullery, kitchen and, most important of all, Jeff's book-lined study. This seemed to be almost completely filled by his desk, which was one of two that he had had sent back from Canada in 1919; the other was at St John Street in his private consulting room. On the staircase were signed photographs of various neurosurgical friends, such as Dott, Cairns, Olivecrona and Lindau; Cushing's portrait was exalted to a place in the study. The family bedrooms were on the first floor, above which were those for the cook and the maid. There was also a 'playroom', allocated to the younger members of the family for their amusements. The basement was entered from the kitchen and contained the coal store, larder and the necessaries for washing clothes etc.

Although the next summer gathering of the SBNS was being organized by Jefferson, the local arrangements were made by his friend Adams McConnell in Dublin, where the meeting took place at the Richmond Hospital and in Trinity College, the university founded in 1591. Jeff always had a soft spot for Dublin, with its memories of his days at the Rotunda in the company of Harry Platt, and he was looking forward to the event. He also found time to publish a paper, in collaboration with Raymond Whitehead, on a rare tumour in the petrous bone. This was a single case report, but one of particular note occupying no less than 47 pages, for nothing exactly similar to this tumour had been recorded previously. The lesion was a papilliferous cystoma, associated with a hypernephroma and a cystic pancreas[11].

In August 1931 a notable event took place when the first International Neurological Congress was held in the Swiss Capital of Bern. It was of neurosurgical significance since it was the first public occasion on which the physicians, who had been impressed by the knowledge and achievements of the Cushing group, had recognised the possibility that some surgeons might even aspire to the status of *neurologist*. Among the 700 delegates were such luminaries as Harvey Cushing, Otfrid Foerster, Ivan Pavlov, Charles Sherrington and Howard Welch. Geoffrey Jefferson was there, of course, and so were Norman Dott and Hugh Cairns, among no less than 25 of Cushing's trainees. At a dinner given for them by the "Chief", 'Cushing reminded them that they should be proud to be accepted as neurologists, but they should not get too far away from general surgery, for their roots were in that fertile soil'[12]. That advice is as relevant today as it ever was though, no doubt, Cushing would by now also have had something to say about placing too great a reliance on technical rather than clinical methods of diagnosis.

Jeff wrote a long letter to Gertrude from Bern, describing his train journey. At the neurological meeting, 'I met dozens of people and its been so much worth while coming—I had lunch in the Casino Restaurant out on the terrace with Olivecrona and Cairns, more meetings all the afternoon till just on 6.0 with a nice speech by Nonne to round off the day's work. Then to tea with Sachs [Ernest Sachs, from St. Louis] and Hirsch of Vienna at the crack hotel, the Bellevue, and met Cushing who was delightful'[13]. He went shopping and then to dinner as the guest of Arnold Klebs. Over coffee Jeff, CP Symonds and Cairns 'discussed the symptomatology of head injuries for ages instead of going to the official reception'. The subject may well have been brought up by Jefferson, since he was due to speak on it at the Royal Society of Medicine and had to prepare a paper[14]. They walked back to their hotel together and 'met Dott and had tea with him at 11.45 pm'[13]. It must have been well past midnight before Jeff began his letter to Gertrude. He reminded her of the time when they had visited Switzerland during his convalescence after the mastoid operation less than a year ago, and how much they had enjoyed the country and their holiday together. He briefly mentioned a dinner with Cushing and concluded with a list of names of the various people he wished to remember[13]. This was a useful social *aide-memoire* which he often employed.

Shortly afterwards, and breaking new ground not for the first time, Jefferson reported in the *Lancet* the first case of glosso-pharyngeal neuralgia operated upon in Britain. He had divided the nerve in the neck in October 1929 at Salford, with complete relief of pain until a recurrence took place in 1931. The root was then divided in the posterior fossa at a second operation, but the success or failure of the procedure could not be assessed since the patient unfortunately died of pneumonia on the fourth day[15]. Another product of Jeff's evening and nightly writing was a paper on trigeminal neuralgia, to be read at the annual meeting of the British Medical Association that was due to be held in Eastbourne. It was soon published[16] and Cairns wrote enthusiastically: 'I have just read your paper on Trigeminal Neuralgia and felt I must write to congratulate you on doing so very well something that has been attempted many times before. It is an elegant article and I envy you the wisdom which makes it possible for you to write like that. This is the sort of paper that will advance British Neurosurgery and make people like Harvey Cushing admire British Medicine more than ever'[17].

Hugh Cairns was elected a full member of the Society of British Neurological Surgeons at their Michaelmas meeting, held at the Medical Society of London's house in Chandos Street and at the London Hospital. Throughout 1931 there had been a correspondence between Jefferson and Dott, who was trying to create a specialized neurosurgical unit at the Edinburgh Royal Infirmary. Dott wrote: 'I may have to compromise. The staff at the Royal are rather pressing me to start work there. I have held out long enough to be able to secure fairly good conditions but to hold out longer might be misunderstood. What I hope to be able to do ultimately is, that having secured a hold on the Royal here, I can get a more ideal clinic going in the next few years and then quietly and unobtrusively transfer all the work there!'[18]. This quotation from Dott's biography is followed by the comment that, although the department was finally created in 1939, the new unit was not opened until 1960, a war and more having intervened. On 3rd November, Dott wrote again to tell Jeff that he had obtained good operating facilities and everything that 'a man can reasonably desire in that direction'. He had also written earlier to tell Geoffrey that he was engaged to be married, so Cushing had worried unnecessarily, and this had happened without the aid of Trotula[18]!

The Savill Prize with its Oration, which Cushing, in his letter of the previous June, had mentioned that he was looking forward to reading, was one of the first of many similar honours that Jefferson was to receive in the years to come. He wrote and spoke well, what he had to say was always worth listening to and worth reading carefully when published. He delivered a lecture in his own particularly attractive and inimitable style, which differed little from his ordinary conversation. The Oration, in memory of a neurologist at the West End Hospital for Nervous Diseases, was given on 27th January 1932 at the Royal Society of Medicine, with Sir Charles Ballance in the Chair, but it does not appear subsequently to have been published. It was entitled *The hypophyseal tumours and the tuberal syndrome*.

Early in 1932, Cairns and Jefferson were hoping to arrange a joint visit to Edinburgh to see Dott operate. They were both going to a meeting in Leeds where Cairns was talking on the pituitary gland as a preliminary run for a paper to the Hexagon Club* which he was due to give on 8th April, and he invited Jeff to meet him there: 'Do come to the lecture before dinner if you can and have a go at me in the discussion'[19].

Geoffrey had arranged another continental visit by the SBNS, this time to Amsterdam at the Wilhelminagasthuis, thereby providing an opportunity for the Dutch to give papers and meet their colleagues. The Michaelmas meeting was held in London at St Bartholomew's Hospital.

In September, Cushing wrote to say that he was sorry not to have seen Jeff when he had been briefly in England in order to visit Sir Charles Sherrington; this was on his way back from attending an International Physiological Congress in Rome. Jefferson must have expressed some anxiety about his personal prospects, for the letter reads: 'You need have no misgivings about your own future, for your name is far better known on the Continent than you have any idea about. Indeed I had a long visit from Martel in Paris who told me things about your work that would make your ears burn. That it has all been hard sledding getting established and that it must seem to go very slowly I can well understand. Indeed, I can understand it better than you perhaps appreciate, for all of you have now reached a position and are doing more and better work than I was doing after twenty years at this job in which we are engaged'[20].

However, a reward was to come, for the facilities provided for Jefferson at the Manchester Royal Infirmary were about to be increased. They were still far from all that was necessary to constitute a specialized Neurosurgical Unit, but it was progress. He now shared a female ward with Harry Platt, in which 24 beds were equally divided between neurosurgery and orthopaedics, plus three side-rooms for very sick patients of both disciplines. The male ward was divided into 24 orthopaedic beds and 12 for neurosurgery, plus four side-rooms. They shared their own operating theatre, in which Jefferson was provided with sessions on Tuesday, Thursday, Friday afternoon and Saturday, Platt having Monday and Friday mornings. The chance for these two to work together cemented their friendship still further. Radiology was provided by Dr EW Twining†, of whom Jeff was also very fond. He once told Cushing when referring to x-rays, 'I have a man here whom I call "super"'[21,22], and later he wrote of him in terms of considerable endearment.

An idea of the amount of operating that Jefferson was doing at this time can be obtained from a list of his tumour cases between the years 1928 and 1932. He would have done virtually all the operations himself. He comments: 'This does not represent the whole material which might have fallen into the statistical

---

*Hexagon Club. Hugh Cairns was a founder member of this exclusive club of only six members. They dined together every 3 months and listened to a paper by one of the group, who were undoubtedly free with their criticism and opinions. Cairns was the only surgical member, all the others being medical neurologists, Russell Brain, Denny Brown, George Riddoch, Charles Symonds, and Macdonald Critchley (Critchley M. *The citadel of the senses*. New York: Raven Press, 1985: 109–20).

†Twining. Edward W Twining (1887–1939) may be regarded as the pioneer of British neuroradiology. As a student he suffered an injury from an infected needle which handicapped him throughout his life, and from the complications of which he eventually died. He was invited by Barclay (qv) to a specially created post at the Manchester Royal Infirmary. He was very inventive and wrote on many aspects of radiology in addition to his important work on the nervous system. He is commemorated by medals in the Royal College of Radiologists and the Society of Neuroradiologists.

survey because, owing to the exigencies of beddage, a number of lesions have been studied outside my own department and never admitted into it'[23].
The list is as follows:

Meningiomas	26
Acoustic neuromas	23
Pituitary tumours	48
Gliomas	116 (Hemisphere, 86 Cerebellar, 30)
Secondary carcinomas	8
Blood vessel tumours	9
Tuberculomas	13
Syphilomas	8
Pseudo tumours	19 (Serous meningitis)
Unverified tumours	66

Unfortunately the manuscript page stops abruptly just as Jeff was about to comment on the unverified cases. Omitting these from the list, and assuming that the rest had craniotomies, the total is 270 over the 5-year period. These were only the tumour cases, and there were undoubtedly also a large number of head injuries, and other patients with abscesses or spinal problems, together with an unknown number of general surgical cases who would have been under Jefferson's care.

Jefferson had his work spread between the two main hospitals, in Manchester and in Salford, the latter having remained his chief commitment until now, but there were also private patients to be operated upon at High Elms, consultations to be done in the smaller hospitals and Grangethorpe, and his private practice was steadily growing. This very strenuous life was beginning to take its toll by undermining his health.

In April 1933 Jeff was struck with a serious illness, repetitions of which would occur on several future occasions. Severe abdominal pain led to a diagnosis of peritonitis and he was admitted to the High Elms nursing home as an emergency. An exploratory laparotomy was carried out by his senior colleague at the Salford Royal Hospital, Garnett Wright, who found Jeff to be suffering from diverticulitis which might lead to peritonitis. He made a good recovery from the operation, which seemed to set him back rather less than the mastoidectomy had done[1]. On hearing of this illness, Hugh Cairns wrote to invite him to spend his convalescence at South Stoke, his newly acquired country home near Arundel in Sussex, an invitation which was willingly accepted. On 30th April, Cairns wrote: 'We are delighted that you will go to South Stoke next Sunday. All will be in readiness for you there and I feel sure that it will do you good. South Stoke is a village on the Arun about 2½ miles north of Arundel.... The village consists of a farm, some cottages, a church and our house which is the Old Rectory. We have only had it for 4 months and it is very wild and dishevelled outside & rather bare within, but it is tolerably comfortable.... PS. There are very few books at South Stoke as yet. HC'[24]. Geoffrey and Gertrude spent 2 weeks there and will have had no difficulty in supplying their own reading matter.

Recognition of the existence of neurosurgery as a specialty by the neurologists at the International Congress in Bern, may have been the trigger which brought about the appointment of Geoffrey Jefferson to the Honorary staff of the National

Hospital for Nervous Diseases, Queen Square, London, in May 1933. It is now designated the National Hospital for Neurology and Neurosurgery, but usually referred to still as 'Queen Square'. There were many letters of congratulation on obtaining such a prestigious post. Hugh Cairns was also appointed at the same time but, according to Sir Charles Symonds, he only operated there on one occasion[25]. This was a very strenuous commitment to add to Jeff's busy Manchester practice, even though he attended Queen Square just for one day every fortnight. Normally, he went up to London in the late afternoon of the previous day, often staying the night at the Langham Hotel, Langham Place, and not far from the Royal Society of Medicine. Sometimes the pressure of work in Manchester would not allow this and he would go by train, taking the midnight sleeper and having breakfast at the Euston Hotel before going to Queen Square for a heavy day's operating, teaching and seeing cases in the wards. More often than not he would return to Manchester the same day, travelling again by sleeper, which arrived at 4.30 am next morning. Passengers were allowed to remain on board until 7.00 am, when his son Michael would pick him up if he was at home[1].

For WR Henderson and others at Queen Square, Jefferson's fortnightly visits 'soon became important events. The atmosphere was a happy one, and they were looked forward to by his colleagues and the resident staff . . . . The question "When is Jeff coming?" was often asked. Why? Not only was everyone very pleased to see him but, more important, we expected a novel approach to the patients which his colleagues had referred to him. He did not disappoint us, and we liked his pithy comments. These visits were too short for the demands on his time, but their importance lay not in the number of patients treated — for they would still have been treated — but in his influence, both personal and academic. What his own clinic may have lost through his absence was more than compensated [for] by what the other gained, and the benefit he derived from new associations. He liked discussions with the neurologists, and when he disappeared — as often happened — he was usually found in the laboratories in the basement discussing and learning something of pathology from Dr Greenfield, and the clinical applications of neurophysiology with Dr Carmichael'[26].

After a year or two suggestions were made, unofficially, that Jeff should consider having a full position on the medical staff of the National Hospital, as opposed to the fortnightly visits that he was making. This would mean moving to London, and the possibility of such a change was to stay with him, with force and much soul-searching, until the advent of World War II.

Jeff wrote two review articles during the year 1933. The first was on spinal injuries[27]; the second was based on a paper he gave at the Annual Meeting of the BMA in Dublin, the subject of which was the treatment of acute head injuries[28]. In addition to these, from 1927 to 1946 he produced a review chapter on the *Surgery of the nervous system* for the *Medical Annual*, which was published every year by John Wright of Bristol. Each article, usually covering several different topics, was a summary in the form of an essay drawing attention to the most important recently published papers and to aspects of surgery of general interest. It demanded an extensive review of the international literature.

In October an important event took place when GF Rowbotham, who was already working closely with Jefferson, was appointed to the more prestigious post of Assistant Surgical Officer in the Neurosurgical Department of the

Manchester Royal Infirmary, a post which he held until July 1938. As has been mentioned, he was the first person who might be regarded as having been entirely trained by Jeff, and he had become a strong and reliable anchor man and deputy. They worked well together and were good friends. Rowbotham had been a house surgeon at the Salford Royal Hospital in 1925 and first assistant in the Neurosurgical Department at the Royal Infirmary since August 1930. He was therefore extremely familiar with Jefferson's methods and practice and, during Jeff's illnesses and when he was away at meetings or on holiday, the running of the neurosurgical department had been entirely in his hands, including all the operative work. He later became a consultant neurosurgeon in Newcastle and is particularly remembered for his work on head injuries[29]. A year or two later Jeff wrote to Professor Brouwer of Amsterdam: 'My first assistant [the title he perferred to use] gets two weeks holiday commencing the middle of next week and I have suggested to him that he spends it in Amsterdam seeing the surgical work of Oljenik. I have already spoken to Nick [Oljenik] about him, but I want him to see the whole Clinic at work and will be grateful if you will take him under your wing and let him see your own work too'[30]. In those days a holiday was seen as an opportunity to extend neurosurgical experience. 1933 was also important for being the year in which Harvey Cushing, having retired, moved from the Peter Bent Brigham Hospital in Boston to Yale University.

Also in 1933, anxiety arose within the family with the discovery that Gertrude was suffering from a carcinoma, which was then treated with radium. She was naturally nervous about this, and arranged a 24 hour exeat for Michael from Rugby School. On this occasion Gertrude wanted sympathetic company, and she found it with her elder son. They drove together in her fabric-covered Austin Seven to a hotel in Oxford and, in the evening, went to a performance of *Hamlet* at the New Theatre. The radium treatment was entirely successful[1].

During the Michaelmas term Gertrude took Michael out for a picnic. On returning to the hotel Trude discovered that she had lost a diamond brooch during the afternoon; almost miraculously, she found it on going back to their picnic spot on the following day. She wrote of this to Antony and, in the same letter remarked that they had a new cook and that Bridget liked her, 'which is a good thing'. This is quite significant because keeping servants was a constant difficulty in the Jefferson household at this time, but it is unlikely that this cook stayed much longer than the rest[31].

A letter which Gertrude wrote to Michael in March 1934 gives a vignette of some aspects of life at 33 Belfield Road shortly after the move from Rusholm. 'Monica went off to skating with Mrs Ferguson in the morning & to the Goodfellow's dance in the evening. There was a Bridge Evening at the Kingsway Hotel in aid of the Babies' Hospital..., it was not as bad as I thought.... Dad had to go into Cheshire to see a case so the maids had a quiet evening after their hard work.... Today Dad is playing golf with Dr Elias.... I think you will find the hall, bathroom and kitchen greatly improved. I wish we could have the dining-room done too as the paper is very dirty.... I read in the paper that they put...[the play, *Clive of India*] on in Berlin & there was rioting round the theatre as a protest against Elizabeth Bergner & her Jewish origin—Too absurd isn't it!'[32].

A diary kept by Antony during the summer holiday of 1934 reveals a delightful picture of the Jefferson family entertaining itself and then going on holiday to Germany. It is clear that Jeff joined in whenever he could manage it. There were visits to the cinema and a memorable one to what could now be called an amusement park, at the Belle Vue Zoological Gardens in Manchester, where there was target shooting (creditable results by Antony and his father), a ghost train, and miniature Brooklands car racing in which Jeff's foot slipped from where 'the pedal that you press down to make the car go was' so that Antony, then aged 12, 'won easily' — perhaps a kindly parental mistake. The highlight was a portrayal of the Siege of Delhi, in front of a huge panorama and accompanied by fireworks[33].

On 16th August the Jefferson parents and all three children set off by car for Germany. Jeff being in control, it is not too surprising that they arrived late for the ship from Harwich to Antwerp, so that the car had to travel on deck instead of in the hold. They then journeyed via Cologne and Heidelberg to the Titisee in the Black Forest, where they spent a few idyllic days bathing and catching butterflies. Munich came next and on to Garmisch Partenkirchen, from where a visit was organized to the Passion play at Oberammergau — they arrived late for the opening scenes. The weather was kind and the holiday was most enjoyable[33].

Harvey Cushing wrote to Jefferson from Yale in September 1934, mostly on the subject of pituitary basophilism, a syndrome first described by Cushing himself and associated with basophil adenomata. 'I don't think we have gone far enough with this syndrome to make 100% diagnoses until we have more cases verified at autopsy. When we have enough of them I think it will be quite possible to distinguish them clinically from the occasional cases of adrenal cortex tumors that may closely simulate them'[34]. Jefferson had apparently told Cushing that Dr S–, his pathologist, 'had found at least a dozen basophil adenomata in cases which have shown no signs of basophilism'[34]. Cushing wrote that he was very much disturbed by this and asked for sample slides to be sent to him. He reported further on the subject of tumour pathology: 'My collection is just being set up down here [at Yale] to serve as a tumor registry'[34]. That the possibility of a move to London must have been very much on Jefferson's mind at this time is shown here, for Cushing ended his letter as follows: 'Do let me know something of your own plans, whether you are moving to Queens [sic] Square or staying in Manchester. I hope you won't try to shuttle between two places or you will be worn to a frazzle. It's hard enough doing proper neurosurgery and getting something out of it from one focus of activity. I hope you are flourishing. My best to your wife and much power to your elbow. Always yours, H.C.'[34].

After the summer meeting of the SBNS, which was held in Edinburgh and Aberdeen, and after the Jefferson family had spent their holiday in Germany, the second gathering of the Society that year was held in Manchester at the Royal Infirmary; it marked the beginning of Jefferson's first Presidency of the Society, which lasted from 1934 until 1936. He had been its secretary since 1926, but his influence over the Society's affairs did not lessen in his new rôle. The Manchester venue entailed much extra work for him, for not only was his department the greatest single contributor of papers, but each one was very carefully rehearsed and vetted by him before it was presented by any member of staff.

Following up his earlier report on the general surgical subject of embolectomy in 1925[35], Jeff produced another article on that topic in the same journal in 1934[36], which excited some correspondence. A chapter in *Carson's Modern operative surgery*, on the surgery of the sympathetic nervous system, was also contributed by him in that same year[37].

However, the stress of his journeys to London and the desire to specialize in neurosurgery to the exclusion of all else, led Jefferson, in February 1935, to write to the Chairman of Salford Royal Hospital to offer his resignation from his appointment as Honorary (General) Surgeon, 'for I am no longer able to devote sufficient time to the work'. He hoped, however, that he might 'continue in the Neuro-Surgical work of the hospital'[38].

Not long after this the Rockefeller Foundation, who had awarded a large building grant to the National Hospital which would include neurosurgical facilities, extended their deadline from 1935 to 1937. This gave him more time to think about his future, whether it was to be in Manchester or London.

A profound disagreement arose in the following month between Jefferson and a histologist in the Department of Anatomy of Manchester University. It appears that there were differences of view on matters of neurohistology, and that the histologist felt she could not continue to report on Jeff's material any longer. However, he pleaded with her, 'I shall very greatly need your help in giving that paper to the Pathological Society, because you have all of my most important material in store, so please do not leave me completely in the air'[39]. Although it is not clear what paper he was referring to, this was a very real crisis, for without his pathological and anatomical material Geoffrey could not produce most of his original work. A paper by the histologist in question on the relationship between oligodendrocytes and astrocytes had been refused publication, and this may have been the source of contention. Jefferson wrote further, in answer to a letter from her: 'I am very sorry the paper was not accepted, for it was an interesting idea. However I realise fully now that work together would have been impossible as you so deeply resent any criticism, and without the give and take of ideas constructive scientific work cannot be done. At the same time I want you to know how much I appreciate the help you have given me in the past.... It is a thousand pities that it should all be to no end. About my material. I shall have to arrange for the removal of the wet specimens.... Some specimens exist now, I think, only in blocks. Will you be good enough to set these on one side as I gather you do not wish to part with any slides. I cannot over-emphasise the importance to me of my material, and if you have any duplicate slides I should most greatly like to have them. The whole thing is part of my life work and I cannot replace much that you have'[40]. The seriousness of the situation has not been exaggerated.

In the spring of 1935, Jefferson had received a letter from Dr CH Frazier of Philadelphia, well-known for his operation for trigeminal neuralgia, concerning the possibility of an American contingent attending the forthcoming meeting of the SBNS in Stockholm. He replied: 'What we would like ourselves is that your members should address ours and bring over short papers, or long ones for that matter. I can see a difficulty in this, of course, and that is, whatever people have that they have really worked up they will be letting off at the Congress [the International Congress of Neurology], but some people have probably got another barrel to fire still, and they might let us have that'[41]. In fact, a special combined meeting with the American Neuro-Surgical and Harvey Cushing Societies took place instead, on 3rd August 1935 at Queen Square, and included papers by Horrax, Penfield, Putnam, Adson, Mackenzie, Coleman, Peet and Fulton — a real feast.

The summer SBNS meeting of 1935 had been held in June, in Stockholm at the Serafimer Lasarettet, before which Jeff had visited Copenhagen. Gertrude did not accompany him, and he had travelled by air, which was a new experience. He wrote to her from Denmark: 'The plane was a marvel. We were taken down to Croydon in a 'bus and after a short wait embarked. It was a four engined monoplane, 20 seater, about 14 people in it. The body is so strong that it gives you a great feeling of security and there was no particular sensation going up, down or along the flat. You can see a lot of geography, and we should have seen more if it had been a better day but it was raining when we left, the clouds very low as it turned out. We flew above them all the way, the first hop to Amsterdam at 4000, the rest at 8000. It all seems very simple and very easy and I should not hesitate a moment about going again. You'd love it in one of these big machines, you might just as well be on the ground'[42]. He also wrote from Stockholm about the meeting, which he found very tiring but successful, and he gave her his impressions of Herbert Olivecrona[43], which he would elaborate in more detail to Cushing in due course.

Jefferson, in his fairly regular communications with Cushing, reported his latest news in a letter on 17th May 1935, and continued with a further note on his personal situation with regard to Queen Square. 'My twenty-four beds have kept me pretty fully occupied, and every other week I put in a day in London. You wonder why? Actually I am only marking time to see what I should do. They have now the chance of making the most marvellous neurological centre anywhere in Europe and I rather think it will come true. If so I don't know that I can afford to be out of it as it will be that first and the rest nowhere. I expect you know that they have got $300,000 for building [from the Rockefeller Foundation], and what is more important, the same amount for endowment of research workers. I don't think buildings matter much, what matters enormously is funds within one's gift for promising fellows. That is the thing which I covet most. Some folk seem to manage to drive along content with their personal production, but I like a lot of people round me. I enjoy my visits to the National as there are plenty of brains there, and almost magical opportunities when they all get to pulling in the same direction. I like rubbing my wits against the best brains I can find. One of the most salutary states, I feel sure, is the one when you feel that you are no good compared with one or other else. Were you immune from that? Maybe the feeling doesn't last long but some permanent advantage probably comes out of the stimulus .... Your years, now that you are out of the immediate turmoil, will be largely spent in being sought out by scientific gunmen demonstrating that here you were at fault, that that needs modification. But I can't think that you will mind that much. Your achievement as a whole has been so tremendous that you can afford to throw bits away here and there'[44].

Cushing replied at length. 'Your promised contribution to the Jackson Centenary has not yet reached me, but John [Fulton] meanwhile brought over the copy that you sent to him and I have read it with delight, not only for its information but for the vivid way in which it is presented. If Hughlings Jackson had written as well as you do, more people would have read him and understood him while reading .... By this time you will be about on the way to Stockholm to sit at the feet of Olivecrona and abundantly partake of hors-d'oeuvre and schnapps. They are a great race, the Swedes, and have perfected themselves in gastronomy no less than in other directions[45].'

He then referred back to his letter of 12th September 1934 on the subject of basophil adenomata and the assertion by Dr S– that he had found a significant number of examples in patients in whom there were no signs of pituitary basophilism. The requested slides had not been forthcoming, and Cushing wrote that this he 'rather judged would be the case after I had read his article. It rather sounded as though he was out to prove that there was nothing much in the basophilism idea, and perhaps he is correct. It takes a long time to get a syndrome properly evaluated and established, and the more brickbats and fewer bouquets are handed to it at the outset, the better it will be for me as they tend to show up the weak points of my thesis. I now have about twenty additional verified examples and shall some day hope to get round to making a modest review of the subject and at the same time try and answer some of the questions that have been thrown at me, not all of them as yet easily answered. I ventilated myself mildly on the subject before the H.C. Society group, someone of whom I hope and believe will ere long venture in surgically upon a case and suck out the small adenoma which is usually visible on the upper surface of the pars anterior. So far, the only real therapeutic support has come from the cases that have been successfully treated by radiation. To be sure these are not histologically verified, but they nevertheless hint that irradiation of the pituitary body rather than of adrenals or thymus can abolish the symptoms'[45]. The condition is now referred to as Cushing's syndrome and, as he predicted, these tumours can be removed surgically, with dramatic results.

After the Stockholm meeting, Jefferson wrote again to Cushing and told him all about it, including a description of Olivecrona's operating technique. 'You do write lovely letters, a supreme gift.... All this highly mechanised surgery seems to me to lack style in its best sense. By that I mean lacks the perfection of artistry that makes the greatest performers in work or sport. At cricket and golf—and maybe at baseball—there are fellows who get first class results by methods not so elegant as some others. Elegance is the word. I have very little doubt that Olivecrona is as good, or better, than most of us but if you use these pronouncedly mechanical instruments it spoils somehow the stylistic effect. That's equally true of Martel. I must add that Olivecrona has struck an extraordinarily happy mean and once the dura is open he is a different man, most painstaking and exact. Altogether we felt a little crestfallen to see how well he did his work in such a short time'[46]. Jefferson concluded by asking for two portrait photographs of Cushing, one for Manchester and one for Queen Square.

A reply came from Yale in September. 'Your delightful letter of July 15th mailed on September 6th has just reached me like a belated Christmas present. It is none the worse for wear and highly acceptable.... There is a young lad named Willie Henderson at the National Hospital who tells me that the only great day for him is when you turn up to operate'[47]. Henderson was shortly to produce a brilliant survey of Cushing's pituitary cases, to work for some time with Jeff and eventually become a consultant in Leeds. He was president of the SBNS from 1956 to 1958.

Meanwhile plans were afoot to build a new operating theatre at Queen Square and Cairns, who had an operating table that they were interested in, wrote to suggest that Geoffrey Jefferson and Julian Taylor should meet him at the London Hospital to discuss its design. He concluded by asking Jeff to see a patient with an infection, about whom he was very worried[48]. Jefferson must have operated on a pineal tumour early in July, a very difficult task in those days. He was watched by Almeida Lima from Lisbon, who had worked with Hugh Cairns. Cairns wrote to Jeff: 'Lima tells me you had a great day yesterday with your pineal tumour and I hope today was just as good. Lima was most enthusiastic about it and said you did a beautiful job'[49]. The Anglo-American meeting at Queen Square that August was very satisfactory, as Cairns agreed: 'I am glad to have an excuse for writing to tell you that I thought your speech the other night was a masterpiece. The dinner was a howling success in every way and so indeed was the meeting'. More remarks followed, about the construction of the new operating theatre[50].

The Jeffersons took the chance once again to have a short holiday after the American visitors had left, and joined their friend John Morley and his family for a boating vacation on the Norfolk Broads. The Broads life did not entirely suit Jeff, for he wrote to Rowbotham, who was holding the fort for him in Manchester: 'The weather here is marvellous. I got myself badly burned playing golf yesterday.... We are shortly going out in a motor launch from Potter Heigham.... I had a golf lesson yesterday and felt like a candidate for the first MB. Apparently I'm all wrong about this game, and have been instructed to study certain movements which are physiologically impossible but, it would appear, essential for the performance of a stroke. So I have not played today'[51]. And in another letter: 'I was disturbed to find how horribly out of condition I was, but can now stand up better to this sort of Olympic Games life. I've done little else. We had a long day's sailing yesterday and then only 2 sets of tennis. I go to bed every night with a severe arthritis in the Rt shoulder joint! I have rewritten part of the optic foramen paper[52] but have got stuck again, momentarily'[53]. The rest of both letters concerned patients and arrangements to be made for his return to work. At the beginning of September Jeff spoke at the British Association meeting and took part in a discussion on the pituitary gland before attending the Michaelmas meeting of the SBNS, which was again hosted by Cairns at the London Hospital.

In the November of 1935 Jefferson had some correspondence with GL Girdlestone, the Nuffield Professor of Orthopaedics at Oxford, who had written a paper on femoral artery embolism. Jeff wrote to him concerning the possibility that the clot might shift: 'If you will look at that paper that I gave at Bournemouth[36] you will find that I have forecasted exactly that happening.... I believe that this shift can occur spontaneously into a less important vessel and is the explanation of sudden recovery of patients without intervention.... I have not so far had a case of my own in which this very thing has happened during palpation and manipulation of an artery...and I need hardly say that I am very pleased it is you who have had the first definite success'. Jeff goes on to advocate operating under local anaesthesia in such cases, since it was 'the patient's sudden recognition of a return to normal put you wise as to what had happened'[54]. In a further letter, he wrote 'It is the hammering of the blood column behind the clot that had a good deal to do with the shifting.... I feel that one ought to control the main artery to the limb before trying to push the clot into a subsidiary vessel, because you might dislodge it from the profunda bifurcation and have it stick at the popliteal.... A finger on the superficial femoral...might be just as good as dissecting it up and putting a temporary controlling band on it.... In old people with brittle arteries it would be just as well to try with digital control first'[55].

This correspondence exemplifies Jefferson's continuing interest in the wider field of general surgery at that time. It also demonstrates the need he had always had to communicate with others in order to share his problems and burnish his thoughts. In the early days Gertrude had acted as the foil, particularly in the field of literature and music, and he still always insisted on absolute silence during dinner if the Promenade Concerts were being broadcast on the radio. By this time, however, his focus had become almost entirely neurosurgical and she was no longer able to stimulate him in the same way. Instead, Harvey Cushing, EW Twining and Hugh Cairns had come to fill the rôle, and Harry Botterell was soon to join these favoured few.

Jefferson had written a letter to Cairns to congratulate him about something, the details of which are unfortunately missing. It drew the following reply: 'Thank you for that perfectly charming letter. No one but you could write a letter quite like that. When the rest of us have all forgotten our Medicine we will still remember you as a personality who bit deep in ways that were not ordinary'[56]. The next paragraph has the first mention in the extant Jefferson correspondence of a neurosurgical unit for Cairns at Oxford, and that might have been the subject of Jeff's letter. 'I have been itching to talk to you about Oxford ever since the night of that dinner at New College. You can imagine what a strain it has been to me not to talk. However, things should be settled before long and whatever happens your letter has given me and will continue to give me great pleasure. I can't say any more now because I haven't let myself think about practical eventualities very much, ever since the incredible good fortune of having the scheme accepted came to pass'[56].

During this busy year Geoffrey also wrote papers on the treatment of head injuries in general practice[57], on Jacksonian Epilepsy[58], on Hughlings Jackson[59] and, on intracranial tumours in the *Medical Annual*[60].

REFERENCES

GJ=Geoffrey Jefferson; GMJ=Gertrude Jefferson
1   Jefferson, Michael. Personal communication.
2   Bridges, Elizabeth to White JC. Letter 14th March 1961.
3   Jefferson, Monica to GMJ. Letter 8th March 1931.
4   Royal Trust Co to GMJ. Letter 26th February 1931.
5   Royal Trust Co to GMJ. Letter 27th February 1931.
6   Royal Trust Co to GMJ. Letter 10th February 1939.
7   Jefferson G. *The peripheral nerves* In: Choyce CC, ed. *Choyce's System of surgery*. 3rd edn. London: Cassell, 1935; **3**: 270–300.
8   Cairns, H to GJ. Letter 3rd May 1931.
9   Cushing H to GJ. Letter 25th June 1931.
10 Cushing H, Eisenhardt L. *The meningiomas*. Springfield Ill: Chas C Thomas, 1938.

11   Jefferson G, Whitehead R. Papilliferous cystoma of the petrous bone associated with hypernephroma and cystic pancreas. *Br J Surg* 1931; **19**: 15–62.

12   Fraenkel GJ. *Hugh Cairns.* Oxford: Oxford University Press, 1991: 78.

13   GJ to GMJ. Letter. 31st August 1931.

14   Jefferson G. The diagnosis and treatment of head injuries. *Proc Roy Soc Med* 1931/1932; **25**: 742–51.

15   Jefferson G. Glossopharyngeal neuralgia. *Lancet* 1931; **2**: 397–9.

16   Jefferson G. Observations on trigeminal neuralgia. *BMJ* 1931; **2**: 879–83.

17   Cairns, H to GJ. Letter. 14th November 1931.

18   Rush C, Shaw JF. *With sharp compassion — Norman Dott.* Aberdeen: Aberdeen University Press, 1990: 156, 246.

19   Cairns, H to GJ. Letter 14th February 1932.

20   Cushing H to GJ. Letter 26th September 1932.

21   GJ to Cushing H. Letter 15th July 1935.

22   Guthkelch, Norman. Personal communication.

23   GJ. MS Notes.

24   Cairns, H to GJ. Letter 30th April 1933.

25   Symonds CP. *Tria Juncta in Uno. The Cairns Memorial Lecture 1970.* SBNS. Published privately.

26   Henderson WR. Professor Jefferson at Queen Square. *Manchester University Medical Students' Gazette* 1946; **25**: 56–7.

27   Jefferson G. The treatment of spinal injuries. *The Practitioner* 1933; **130**: 332–47.

28   Jefferson G. The treatment of acute head injuries. *BMJ* 1933; **2**: 807–12.

29   Rowbotham GF. *Application for the Appointment as Assistant Surgical Officer in the Neurosurgical Department of the Manchester Royal Infirmary.* 1933.

30   GJ to Brouwer B. Letter 1933 undated.

31   GMJ to Jefferson, Antony. Letter 10th December 1933.

32   GMJ to Jefferson, Michael. Letter 11th March 1934.

33   Jefferson, Antony. *Diary* 1934.

34   Cushing H to GJ. Letter 12th September 1934.

35   Jefferson G. Report of a successful case of embolectomy, with a review of the literature. *BMJ* 1925; **2**: 985–7.

36   Jefferson G. Arterial embolectomy. *BMJ* 1934; **2**: 1090–4.

37   Jefferson G. The surgery of the sympathetic nervous system. In: Grey-Turner G, ed. *Modern operative surgery.* 2nd edn. London: Cassell 1934: 533–70.

38   GJ to Frankenburg S. Letter 11th February 1935.

39   GJ to ERAC. Letter 22nd March 1935.

40   GJ to ERAC. Letter 25th March 1935.

41   GJ to Frazier CH. Letter 15th May 1935.

42   GJ to GMJ. Letter 4th June 1935.

43   GJ to GMJ. Letter 7th June 1935.

44   GJ to Cushing H. Letter 17th May 1935.

45   Cushing H to GJ. Letter 30th May 1935.

46   GJ to Cushing H. Letter 15th July 1935.

47   Cushing H to GJ. Letter 17th September 1935.

48   Cairns H to GJ. Letter 19th June 1935.

49   Cairns H to GJ. Letter 12th July 1935.

50   Cairns H to GJ. Letter 7th August 1935.

51   GJ to Rowbotham GF. Letter 1935 undated.

52   Jefferson G. The value of radiology in neuro-surgery; radiography of the optic canals. *Proc Roy Soc Med* 1936; **29**: 1169–72.

53   GJ to Rowbotham GF. Letter 27th August 1935.

54   GJ to Girdlestone GL. Letter 11th November 1935.

55   GJ to Girdlestone GL. Letter 20th November 1935.

56   Cairns H to GJ. Letter 16th November 1935.

57   Symonds CP, Jefferson G. The treatment of head injuries in general practice. *BMJ* 1935; **2**: 677–80.

58   Jefferson G. Jacksonian epilepsy; a background and a postcript. *Postgrad Med J* 1935; **2**: 150–62.
59   Jefferson G. John Hughlings Jackson. *Manchester University Medical Students' Gazette* 1935; **14**: 185–9.
60   Jefferson G. The surgery of the nervous system; intracranial tumours. In *Medical Annual*, Bristol: John Wright, 1935.

Chapter 15

Achievement
1936–1938

The 1936 summer meeting of the SBNS was in Dublin, once again at the Richmond Hospital; it was the only one held that year. In the spring Jefferson had spoken to the Section of Radiology of the Royal Society of Medicine on the value of radiology in neurosurgery, with particular reference to the techniques of obtaining satisfactory views of the optic canals[1]. He had been making a study of their anatomy as a support to his major paper on compression of the chiasma, optic nerves and optic tracts by intracranial aneurysms, which was to be published in *Brain* in 1937[2]. That changes in the optic foramina and canals could be shown radiographically, was a new and extremely important factor in the diagnosis of lesions in that area, but their accurate demonstration was well beyond the technical capacity of most x-ray departments at that time. Jefferson spoke again to the Section of Orthopaedics of the BMA at their annual meeting in Oxford, this time on the subject of injuries to the spinal cord. He described 75 personal cases and paid appropriate tribute to the researches of Sir Charles Sherrington[3]. Jeff also read a paper to the Hull Medical Society on 27th March.

In the second half of August 1936 the Jefferson family had a holiday in Austria. It was to be the last time that they all went on vacation together. They travelled by car and were met in Vienna by Jeff's aunt Ada (Parsons) from Hove.

At the end of October 1936 Gertrude paid a brief visit to London, probably to attend lectures by Professor Mapother at the Institute of Psychiatry, then housed within the Maudsley Hospital, in south London. She had realised that many of the problems that she had to deal with at the Welfare Centres where she worked required a knowledge of this subject. The determination which had manifested itself throughout her life again became evident and, now in her mid-50s, she had decided to qualify as a psychiatrist. Her absence from home produced a letter from Jeff. He had enjoyed a concert on the previous Saturday evening which he had attended with Jack Small, later to be a neurosurgeon in Birmingham. 'I never heard better playing', he wrote[4], and he passed on an invitation from a mutual friend for Trude to be taken to an opera on the following Wednesday, after dinner at the Langham Hotel. Sunday had been employed visiting a patient in Derby, taking Rowbotham with him. This was a sign of the growth of his private practice, for he continued: 'Finances are a bit relieved by yesterday and other things coming along, too, I think'[4]. It was not often that Jeff was so buoyant on that subject.

Towards the fulfilment of her new direction in medicine, Gertrude took Part 1 of the examination for the Conjoint Board Diploma in Psychological Medicine (DPM) at the beginning of December 1936. Antony wrote from Rugby School, 'I expect you are dreading your exam, next Friday isn't it?'[5]. Following the written part, Jeff commented to her: 'I was so glad to hear that all went well, or at least that there had been nothing unexpected in the paper. I told you you would know

Figure 15   *Gertrude Jefferson, in 1936 or 1937.*

as much as the examiners. Good luck my dear, in the viva. It ought to be all right. We shall be thinking of you on Tuesday afternoon'[6]. Gertrude must have been staying in Hove with the Parsons and travelling up to London daily by train for he sent his love to Aunt Ada. She passed the examination and completed Part 2 in the following year. Eventually a letter from the Examining Board told her that she would receive her diploma on 27th January 1938[7].

Jeff's review of neurosurgery for the 1936 edition of the *Medical Annual*[8] covered the treatment of cerebral abscesses, facial paralysis, intracranial tumours and the surgery of spinal lesions. He wrote to Cushing in November in support of WR Henderson, who had worked with him and was about to go to Boston: 'I feel I must write to tell you what a grand fellow I think Willie Henderson is. You will not need this news from me. Latterly he has become more and more impressive and he was becoming indispensable at Queen Square. What I like is the impression he has been making on the physicians, who receive them [the surgical residents] ordinarily about as easily as a piece of cold sealing wax.... To talk of something else. All the more thoughtful folk in this country, as well as the others, have been profoundly moved by Nuffield's gift to Oxford. It is not merely the generosity of it but the imagination. Quite a few people have good ideas but they rarely have any money (is the ratio inverse?, not always of course). Money plus imagination, generosity for an ideal of this kind, has not blossomed on the same tree in this country, though in your own it is a commoner affair. Although there is nothing official I gather that Hugh [Cairns] is going there. He will have all my good wishes for he has the right ideas, the right ideals, to help make this something quite different from anything that has existed here before. I think he will succeed in doing it'[9].

Cushing replied: 'I am glad that you feel as you do about Willie Henderson. He is stirring us up here about these old pituitary adenomas, the end results of the early operations even of the transphenoidal group being far better than I would have believed. A succession of these patients have been coming in every day to have their fields taken and to be checked up, and I think he ought to make quite an important communication about them, more important in a way that Hugh's paper which merely dealt with the general group that he saw in his year'[10]. The letter continued with comments about the proposed unit at Oxford and the lack of further Rockefeller support for Donal Sheehan's anatomical work[11]. Henderson's 'important communication' was published in the British Journal of Surgery two years later[12].

The SBNS, unusually, had a meeting in January 1937 to make up for the lack of a Michaelmas meeting in the previous year. It was held at the London Hospital and at the Royal College of Surgeons in Lincoln's Inn Fields. It was presided over by Jefferson of course, who gave one of his most impressive and important addresses, on the subject of the tentorial pressure cone. It was to be built up into a major article published in 1938[13]. The paper brings together a large number of earlier reports dealing with separate aspects of the phenomenon in addition to his own observations and experience. He emphasised the dangers of lumbar puncture when coning was present, the unreliability of papilloedema as the sole criterion of raised intracranial pressure and the need to follow ventriculography by immediate operation. His efforts to draw attention to the condition and its dangers were to lead to the saving of countless lives. He concluded: '...the shadings, the variabilities and the nuances of the clinical picture which can be induced by pressure of the uncus on the crus cerebri can be better evaluated if the observer is alive to the possibility of this complicating factor. He will know that not all fixed and anisocoric pupils indicate a tectal or pineal tumour; he will look with a more understanding eye on diencephalic signs, and he will seek by operation to undo, as best he can, the mischief that the cone produces'[13].

The possibility of a move to London, and an appointment which would give a much greater commitment to Queen Square, had reached the point of a letter and a memorandum written in January 1937 by Jefferson to Gordon Holmes, the senior neurologist there, whom he had first met in France 20 years earlier. Gordon Holmes replied: 'You may be interested to have my own "reflections" on them [Jeff's observations].... Of course the first thing that strikes me is the wonderful facilities you have at present, or will soon have, in Manchester and how noble it is of you to think of throwing them over in order to have "an opportunity of making a bigger contribution to neurosurgery" in London, I really admire you for it. It was I who first suggested inviting you to come to Queen Square and like everyone else on the Staff I would be glad & proud to have you as a more intimate colleague ... '[14].

Holmes then took up several specific points that Jefferson had raised in his letter: 'I feel it would be undesirable to have a Professor of Neurosurgery only; it would help the tail to wag the dog. My own feeling is that the title should be reserved for "whole time men". If not why should not Wilson, Walshe, myself enjoy the honour — if you think it is one. I have worked and taught at the Hospital for 35 years — for the first 9 of which I was a whole time man'. Holmes emphasised that he believed that the surgeons should have the right to admit to their own beds those 'patients referred to you, but I feel very strongly that it would be a tragedy for the Hospital and do it a lot of harm if every tumour, or suspected tumour were sent at once to the Surgical Wards.... After all only a proportion of suspected tumours turn out to be so & it should be the job of the trained physician who is familiar with all neurology to decide.... We don't want other experiments e.g. Penfield's duplicated here'[14]. Holmes was referring to the dominance of neurosurgery in the Montreal Neurological Institute, where a neurologist played little or no part in the diagnosis of patients referred for neurosurgery. Although agreeing with a need for follow-up facilities, he thought that 'an ordinary O.P. [outpatient appointment] for any case thought to be possibly surgical inadvisable'[14]. The question of the cost of surgical assistance and the need for extra nursing accommodation was also a serious matter, despite the very generous grant from the Rockefeller Foundation of £60,000, and especially in view of the hospital being £40,000 in debt, plus a deficit of £7000 in the previous year; figures which would hardly be an embarrassment now, but were significant enough then. Furthermore, the physicians would not countenance any reduction of their own staff in order to provide for the surgeons. The letter ends by saying that there was plenty of time for discussion. 'I see no probability of the surgical wards being opened for 2 years or so .... Excuse a long scribble, but its Sunday evening'[14]. This letter tells one much about the protectionist attitude of the physicians at Queen Square at that time, and their desire to maintain clinical control over most, if not all of the patients if possible. There was to be no doubt about who was the 'dog' and who was the 'tail' in Holmes' letter, and Jefferson could not accept that definition of the likely situation. It is also conceivable that, although the physicians received no remuneration for their services at the National Hospital at that time, the loss of most 'surgical' patients would reflect on their private practices before very long. To them this was critical for, despite the apparent affluence of some consultants, their real assets were often very different. Their expenses were considerable; even if they did occasionally include a Rolls Royce car and chauffeur, there were the more essential secretary and consulting rooms with a 'good' address to be provided, together with a life-style consistent with the popular idea of a 'Harley Street Consultant'. Soon, of course, this situation was to change with the advent of the Emergency Medical Service during World War II and the later arrival of the National Health Service, when consultants were to be remunerated for their hospital work.

Cairns' move to Oxford from the London Hospital was now assured, though it did not take place until April 1938. However, this meant that the neurosurgical field in the capital would be left more widely open, since those left practising the specialty were also general surgeons, with but an 'interest' in the subject. Jefferson must have felt that he might now be able to achieve that which he had always perceived as the pinnacle of medical practice — to work in London and be entirely dedicated to neurosurgery. He had yet to realise that to work in the capital was not an essential requirement for perfection. For several years there had been the prospect of moving to London, and Jefferson obviously wanted to clarify the situation. It would seem that he wanted a personal chair in neurosurgery on a par with the arrangements proposed for Oxford, but he had suddenly received negative messages from the very man who had initiated his part-time appointment to the National Hospital. He was still ambitious, both for his specialty and for himself, and he could be excused for feeling downhearted and discouraged that the person he had gone to for advice on several occasions should show such prejudice.

Gordon Holmes wrote again just 3 days later, in response to Jeff's acknowledgement of the above letter[14]: 'I am very surprised to see from your letter that you regarded some of my remarks in my letter of Sunday evening as bitter or unfair.... My aim was to write to you a very friendly letter merely emphasising my own point of view, and pointing out some of the difficulties that the scheme presented by you may involve'[15]. Apart from the matter of professorial status, Jefferson had also suggested that Harvey Jackson, who was already an Assistant Surgeon at Queen Square and had a considerable degree of autonomy, should be the Assistant Surgeon to Julian Taylor and himself. Holmes opposed this idea with the thought that Jackson was worthy of a higher status and assumed this to be the main point of contention. In fact it is much more likely that the reservations Jeff had expressed really concerned future relationship between the physicians and surgeons at the National Hospital.

While these letters were flying back and forth, Gertrude had been in London to meet Aunt Ada and Monica, to go to the theatre (*Two bouquets*) and to visit friends. She wrote to Geoffrey. 'We had such a very nice time but it was spoilt by your not being able to share it — I hope you got home safely & that all is going well. Monica didn't get back until about 1.15 am & I was beginning to feel very fidgety — especially as I didn't really close my eyes on account of having to let her in. N– took her to a private dance club & she forgot the time & so was late. She was so nice about it when she came in that one couldn't really be cross.' Gertrude too had been invited out to dine: 'I had a very successful evening with F.H. She gave me a very delicious dinner & I met her husband whom I liked. They have a very roomy flat not far from Bryanston Square, but even that size of flat would be too cramped for us'[16]. She was looking at the practical and domestic possibilities of a move to London. This was an aspect of the projected departure from Manchester which Jefferson had hardly considered, the effect on her own commitments not having been acknowledged either.

Meanwhile, JG Greenfield, the famous neuropathologist at the National Hospital, made a proposal to Jeff that they should write a book together on the surgery of the central nervous system. He wrote, on 14th February 1937: 'I had an interview with Mr Tindall of Baillière Tindall & Cox on Friday & suggested to him that you and I should write the book.... We must have a talk about it & see how much can be done soon. I don't feel that there will be any difficulty about explaining things to Taylor. What about Cairns? He & Symonds have been writing up cerebral tumours for Rolleston's Encyclopaedia—a waste of energy compared with a book on Cerebral & Spinal Surgery. Anyway he won't have time for anything at the moment. I should like you to dine with me before the meeting on Thursday evening, so that we can discuss it'[17]. There are some very brief notes about the proposition, in Jefferson's handwriting and possibly made during the dinner, but the book was never written.

At the end of April 1937 Geoffrey and Gertrude travelled to the United States; they crossed the Atlantic in the RMS *Queen Mary* and arrived in New York on 3rd May. While Jeff was in Philadelphia and St Louis, visiting clinics on the east coast and seeing Cushing at New Haven before going to Canada, Gertrude was to fly to see her sister Norma in the State of Washington. The local newspaper, *Seattle Star*, recorded her visit, and announced her intention of staying with the Ritchies until the end of the month, when she would fly to New York to meet Jeff and sail for home on 5th June[18]. Most of Jefferson's visit to America was recorded by him in diary form, with many comments about what he saw, where he went, and whom he met.

The diary begins with a summary of his impressions of the meeting of the Cushing Society at Temple University Medical School in Philadelphia. This university, though only founded in 1888, was then almost as large as the much older (1740) University of Pennsylvania in the same city. Jeff was impressed by the youth of the participants at the meeting. 'Clearly the young men of today are getting along very fast, but its much easier—they step on to the lift in this skyscraper of scientific knowledge much nearer the top than we did.... The chief impression that I gain from the talk at this Meeting is the mechanistic view of neurology rather than the more neural side of matters. There was no neurological paper except one on chiasmal injury. I told Tubby [Francis] Grant that the impression that I gained was that the head contained meninges, blood vessels, and cerebro-spinal fluid, and that there was scarcely a mention of that queer pulpy mixture of gray and white matter that fills the interstices between these other structures.... At the moment I can't help being shocked by the absence of neurology or any discussion of neural mechanisms in the assessment and treatment of head injuries. The only 3 papers of great interest . . . were 1. Fulton's on V.M.C. [vasomotor] centres, in or near the motor cortex. 2. Van Wagenen's on diabetes insipidus. 3. Freeman and Watt's on lobotomy'[19]. The last of these, with its apparently dramatic results, was seen at that time as heralding the solution to many psychiatric problems. However, instead it was to launch the catastrophic, and largely uncontrolled, spate of prefrontal leucotomy (lobotomy) and other similar operations which not only brought the field of psychosurgery into being but also brought it into disrepute, despite the undoubted benefit it conferred in many cases.

In St Louis, Jefferson watched several operations performed by Ernest Sachs and enjoyed his company. 'This evening we discussed a book on errors (I should think he makes less than most people). My objections were 1. One's errors are always more interesting to oneself than anyone else. 2. No two people make just the same mistakes, they partly arise from intellectual content and temperament and each of us makes different mistakes in different directions though there must be a field of common error. 3. They need very brilliant, journalistic writing to make the cases live again.... Ernest has an innate courtesy which is most impressive to me.' John Fulton 'was very amusing at Fay's cocktail party—talking French in a Louis Seize manner to Mme Rossier.' On 11th May Jeff gave a lecture after watching Sachs operate, but its subject is not mentioned. He then flew to Chicago with a 10 minute 'convenience' stop at Pittsburgh, such were the problems of commercial flying in 1937. While he was in Chicago he watched operations and attended clinical rounds as usual, but also found time to visit the Art Museum and the Field Museum of Natural History. He dined with Percival Bailey but 'was too tired to be intelligent'. Next, he flew on to Baltimore. 'I am a bit short of money', he wrote on the plane. 'I have 24 dollars, the best part of a fiver and I ought to be able to have a night in Philadelphia and buy my return ticket with that amount.... It's pitch dark and we have passed over two sizeable towns. In case we fall and crash in landing I had better send my love to T [Trude].... Night at Philadelphia. Felt awful on Sunday—too much cream I verily believe'[19]. On 19th May, Madeline Stanton, Cushing's secretary, forwarded two cheques she was holding for him which were gladly received[20].

While he was in Baltimore he spent time with Walter Dandy and a number of other luminaries, including Max Broedel, the famous medical artist. At the Johns Hopkins Hospital he saw Dandy remove an acoustic neuroma–'total extirpation through a unilateral incision, avertin and ether blown with an atomiser bulb, air over ether in a large bottle. Nurse anaesthetising sitting under the table.... I told Dandy that I would be feeling like Hell after a case like the one he had just done. He said that is how he felt'[19]. There can be few more exhausting occasions in surgery than a long neurosurgical operation, and Dandy was a more rapid surgeon than Cushing. There was much shop talk over dinner at the University Club that evening. Jeff watched some more operations on the following day. 'Dandy evidently has little interest in the more cultured side of surgery. It is queer that he should have accomplished so much. Next he did an 8th nerve section, this took him about 40–45 minutes. Rarely using clips—relies on diathermy. After that he did a right temporal lobectomy..., did it very well'[19]. It is probably significant that Dandy rarely used Cushing's blood vessel clips and, in the same way, Cushing rarely used Dandy's air studies, for there was a scarcely veiled antagonism between them. The idea of outlining the ventricles of the brain with air had been suggested by his observation of the appearance of air under the diaphragm in a case of perforated intestine. 'Dandy told me...that's how he came to think of air and used it'[19]. This refutes the idea that it was suggested by a 'spontaneous ventriculogram' in a patient with a fracture of the skull involving an air sinus.

Jefferson's next stop was at New Haven, Connecticut, a visit to which he had been looking forward greatly. He had travelled by train, 'nine hours...in a smoker, fumes so dense everybody's pipes went out and we finished in a quite salubrious atmosphere'[19]. On arrival he stayed with the Cushings at their home at 691 Whitney Avenue. While in New Haven he took the opportunity to spend some time with Louise Eisenhardt, the neuropathologist, and going over the basophil adenoma cases in the Tumor Registry. Cushing showed Jeff round two of the Residential Colleges at Yale and 'spoke longingly of his youth, the smell of the ground, the lighted windows round the courts, silhouettes of the trees and a piano, or music floating from a room.... He spoke of the old days, how simple life was, a total then of 300 [undergraduates].... H.C. can skim from one subject to another fast enough but he will suddenly seize on to something that interests him and sticks fast and shows great tenacity in going deep into it'[19]. It is interesting that this trick of behaviour was a particularly noticeable trait adopted, along with a number of other characteristics, by his pupil Hugh Cairns. John Fulton, in his biography of Cushing, referred to Jeff's visit to Yale on this occasion and remarked: 'Cushing enjoyed nothing more than showing guests about the University, and in this instance the pleasure was enhanced by the stimulating exchange of ideas since H.C. looked upon Jefferson as having one of the most searching and original minds in British medicine'[21].

While in New Haven, Jefferson wrote a paper on removal of the right or left frontal lobes in man[22]. This was referred to by Cushing in a later letter which begins: 'Dear Geo. F.: To think the admirable paper in the July issue of the B.M.J. should have been written by you in one morning on the back porch, screened against interruption by flies or homos, at 691, Whitney Avenue, New Haven! I shall put up a tablet to that effect. Much power to your elbow and love to you both. Always aff^y. H.C. #John says you were two hours late at the lab^y in consequence'[23]. The full witticism at the beginning of the letter, which appears elsewhere, was 'Geo. F. Frey'. On that visit, Cushing presented Geoffrey Jefferson with his own fountain pen, commenting that he had already sucked all the ideas out of it.

Three days later Jefferson heard Fulton give a paper to the Beaumont Society (of medical history) on Sir Kenelm Digby, the 17th century sailor-diplomat-philosopher, and he viewed Fulton's library. 'Marvellous show of books by John—including some copies of [William] Harvey. Digby fond of H., used... [Harvey's works] in his own book on Body and Soul'[19]. After visiting Westport for the day, Jeff went with Cushing to watch a baseball game. 'H.C.s interest in the ball game was keen—most rigid attention to it, but he played three years in the teams and understands all the moves of it. Said he supposed they knew more about it now, but they used to play a few professional teams in the old days and beat them, but the professionals certainly are better now than then'[19]. Commenting further on the ball game in a letter to Antony he said: 'H.C. sat there like a school boy recording all the plays in pencil on the score card, a thing that requires more knowledge than I had'[24].

While staying with Cushing, Jefferson also wrote to Rowbotham: 'I have often thought of you of course and wondered how the patients were progressing.... I have been so busy that I have had very little time to write to anyone.... H.C. is in marvellous form, going about as if there was nothing whatever the matter with him* and as full of fun as ever.... On Wednesday I go to Boston to stay with Gil

*Cushing's health. In November 1935 Cushing had been hospitalized with symptoms of a gastric ulcer. At the same time he had suffered severe pains in the left foot, which were of vascular origin. He eventually developed a gangrenous middle toe, which had to be amputated under local anaesthesia, and he did not leave hospital until the 6th February 1936. His foot continued to be very painful, and he referred to it in a letter to President Roosevelt's secretary, Miss LeHand, in December 1936. In April 1937 he went to New York and Washington. 'All this I accomplished without assistance other than for a porter and a wheel chair at both ends of the line. What's more, wearing my own boots. So you see I am very much on the mend.' (Harvey Cushing to Arnold Klebs, letter of 29th April 1937. Fulton J. *Harvey Cushing*. Oxford: Blackwell, 1946: 681–2 *et supra*).

Horrax—then up to Montreal, he is going to drive me there by car which will be nice'[25]. That letter was written on the 22nd May 1937. The visit to Canada was in order to see Wilder Penfield and the new Montreal Neurological Institute, after which Jeff returned to New York and a meeting at Atlantic City, before rejoining Gertrude and sailing home to England.

Two weeks after returning home, Jefferson attended a meeting in London and spent the night at the English Speaking Union's club house in Mayfair. Characteristic of his sense of humour, and in view of his location, he chose to write this letter to Gertrude in German. It was not altogether successful, for he began by failing to make 'My dear' feminine. It amused him that he had gone to London by train and, being unable to find a first class seat, had shared a compartment with only one other person in the third class[25].

In less than another fortnight, Geoffrey was writing to Gertrude from a hotel in The Hague, on his way home from the 1937 summer meeting of the SBNS in Berlin. His description of the Berlin meeting held portents for the future that were largely unrecognised. There were about 500 participants, and present at the dinner were the German 'heads of the Army, Navy, Air Force and Army Neurological Services all in full dress uniform and their satellites in the same.... I had to make a speech of course, in which I referred to our gratitude to the Govt. for having sent its special envoys. A thoroughly Nazi affair and quite out of keeping with the intentions of our small (but very important) Soc...'[26]. On the previous day he had 'sat next to Frau Sp–... she was young, fair, plump, niceish looking—but DULL.' At dinner the next evening, 'terribly expensive', he sat between Foerster* and Olivecrona and opposite Sauerbruch. 'The latter is a queer fellow, impulsive, proud, humorous all by turns. Immediately we sat down to dinner he "*Prosit*"-ed me, but my glass had not yet been filled. So he reached over and poured some of his wine into my glass, slopping it all over the table cloth without the least concern. From then on he toasted all through dinner and caused a consumption of wine equal to 18 Marks a head—an incredible quantity, of which I had very little.... After that we went and drank beer in the Heidelberger till 1.30 am. Next morning, ops by Sauerbruch at ˙9.0—a transthoracic oesophageo-gastric anastomosis and a thyroid'[26].

At the same meeting, but on another occasion, Jeff wrote: 'I made a speech— adequate. We made... [Foerster] an Emeritus member of our Soc.—the idea came to me as I was dressing for dinner—the effect electric. Foerster was so moved by it that he walked about, everybody standing round the candle-lit tables, in dead silence like a man walking in a trance—emotional sleep walking.

---

*Foerster. Professor Otfrid Foerster (1873–1941). A brilliant neurologist and neurosurgeon, who practised in Breslau, then in Germany but now called Wroclaw, in Poland. He remained an Emeritus member of the SBNS even during World War II, despite his German nationality and, in August 1937, he may well have realised that Britain and Germany were soon to be in conflict with one another. His wife, who died just two days after husband, was Jewish, and they both assisted Jewish refugees to come to England before war broke out. He was held in the greatest respect by those who knew him, including Cushing, who said: 'Apart from the fact that his presence in the clinic was a constant stimulus to every member of the staff, I do not believe that any visitor has ever endeared himself more to our hospital family, nor have we been obliged to make our farewells to anyone with more profound regrets than to him.' (Fulton J. *Harvey Cushing*. Oxford: Blackwell, 1946: 599.). This respect for Foerster seems to have extended even to Nazi officialdom, despite his precarious position with regard to his marriage. (Bucy P, ed. *Neurosurgical giants*. New York: Elsevier, 1985: 128–37).

I never saw anything like it, nor had anyone else. He kept two or three of us here till 2.40 am. afterwards to continue drinking. No one the least "lit up" though. He has a patent method of dealcoholing champagne by putting peaches into it . . . '[26]. It is to be observed that there was no question of Jeff consulting the SBNS Council before creating an Emeritus member. It was enough that he had decreed that it should happen. During the meeting he invited Foerster's sister to stay with them in Manchester, an invitation that was to have a sequel. It seems that Foerster collapsed sometime during the Berlin meeting, following which, Jefferson told Cushing, ' . . . at the close of the first morning, he took me off to his favourite café to try to revive himself with a cup of coffee. He put his hand on my knee and with the greatest impressiveness said: "My dear Jefferson, you have no idea how ill I am". He speaks as if he does not expect to live more than a few months, but frankly, I could not be sure whether he really was mortally sick or just greatly overwrought — "Troubled by fast-coming fancies that will not let him rest"'. Changing the subject, Jefferson continued: 'The new Queen Square looks more than good. Its going to be the best thing in Neurology yet, and give neurosurgery a chance to pay some worthy tribute to its begetters'[27]. Foerster lived for exactly 4 more years, when he and his wife both died from pulmonary tuberculosis. After the meeting Jeff returned from Holland by train and ship, and immediately went to Queen Square to see patients with Symonds and Walshe before going home to Manchester.

Another very important paper, on compression of the chiasma, optic nerves, and optic tracts by intracranial aneurysms, was given in brief by Jefferson to the Section of Neurology of the Royal Society of Medicine, and published in full in *Brain* later in the year[28]. He also spoke to that Section on colloid cysts of the third ventricle and on frontal lobectomy[29]. In the paper on compression of the chiasm etc. by aneurysms, he analysed 66 recorded cases and added 12 of his own. His conclusion, that 'there is only one useful treatment for these cases, and that is carotid ligature'[28], is not acceptable today, but it was a fair judgement in the context of the surgical techniques available when it was written. However, his clinical description of the visual field defects produced by these lesions, and their manner of development, still remains one of the clearest expositions of the subject[28].

Jefferson also addressed the Osler Society in Oxford, ostensibly on the effects of removal of the right or left frontal lobe, for it was he who had shown that there was little or no neurological or intellectual deficit following the removal of either, provided the speech areas were preserved but, archly, he used this theme to speak on the future development of medicine and surgery. He made the talk into an article for the *Manchester Medical Student's Gazette*; it was entitled *Thoughts on Medical Schools*. 'Surgery is too easy' he wrote, 'Medicine, though I may seem a renegade to say it, is the subject which will more permanently satisfy those with the best brains'[30]. Although he pointed out that the two disciplines should not be totally separated from each other, in 1937 it was necessary to encourage students to become physicians, for the surgical field seemed to him to be reaching saturation. However, Jeff did not mention the contrast there was at that time between the sometimes dramatic results of surgery and the limited resources that were then available in medicine. This made surgery seem more attractive to those who desired, like Geoffrey himself, not only to diagnose but to be able to cure illnesses.

'The great need of the present is the physiological laboratory in the hospital, the research institute if you prefer that title, to make studies under properly rigid conditions of those diseases which need unravelling.... So much of what one knows has all the imprecision, the blurred outline, the vagueness, of a thalamic impression'[30]. Jeff made a plea for the integration of universities and medical schools, for collaborative research between the academic, scientific and clinical departments, and for better evaluation of the results of treatment. The new Nuffield units and medical school at Oxford had provided an opportunity which, he considered, ought to be followed elsewhere. His contributions to the *Medical Annual* in 1937 were on various aspects of the surgery of the nervous system, spine and spinal cord[31].

Jefferson and Cushing exchanged several letters that autumn. In one of them, Jeff described his recent visit to Penfield: 'Wilder was in good form, but thought everything was very bad all the time, as intelligent people will of their own work. I like him but I couldn't write a thumb-nail sketch of him to save my life, probably because he takes more knowing than most people'[27]. Jeff also sent copies of various photographs that he had taken during his time in the United States, and asked Cushing, once more, to sign two desk portraits, one to keep at home and the other to hang in the Royal Infirmary[32]. Cushing replied: 'Thanks for the enlargements of the kodaks. I regard the entirely bald one with Trotula at the fountain as the pleasanter of the two, which is altogether natural. The other, ruefully regarding a sheet of what may be one of your own works, is less pleasant in its expression, which is also as it should be'[33].

The 1937 Michaelmas meeting of the SBNS was held in Cambridge at the Department of Physiology and at the Strangeways Institute. Finally, as the year closed, Jefferson made a detailed assessment and balance sheet of the arguments for and against a move to London and Queen Square[34]. What he really needed was a permanent salary in order to be, at least partly, independent of private practice, and there had been a suggestion that the Rockefeller Foundation might be persuaded to support him with a personal grant until he became established[35].

The analysis covers four foolscap pages; it is not clear if it was intended for Jefferson's own private reference or, possibly, to be addressed to Alan Gregg of the Rockefeller Foundation. The practical pros and cons appear to come down quite strongly in favour of Manchester, though the prestige and research facilities of Queen Square could not be discounted. For instance, he had 24 beds in Manchester and was offered only 14 in London. There were unlimited private beds in Manchester with a new private block about to be opened, whereas he would only have 6 in London. He had a house surgeon and first assistant in Manchester, but Queen Square had not yet decided the matter and pleaded poverty. A private secretary was provided by the hospital in Manchester but would have to be a personal arrangement in London. The cost of living was much greater in London, whereas rents were relatively cheap further north. In London Jeff feared that he would be 'pulled away from the hospital' in order to make sufficient income from private work to cover his expenses. He concluded that the research facilities available in London were, in fact, the only clear advantage. 'From a business man's viewpoint, it would look an unwise move to transplant myself.... The difficulty is that I am going to be forced to make as much money as I can, and the more I succeed the less shall I be able to do the very thing for which I want to move.... Unless I can immediately get a sufficiently well paid and promising first assistant, I am going to start with conditions worse than I leave here.... Let us suppose that I should pay these assistants and all others that I need out of my own pocket. I have the example of Cairns there to guide me, for he had to carry in the end such a burden that he had less and less time to put into his hospital work'[34]. This, of course, referred to the time when Cairns was at the London Hospital, before he relinquished that position and became the Nuffield Professor of Surgery at Oxford in 1938. 'One last point, St. Thomas's Hospital has asked me if I would go there.... It would be either Guy's or there I suppose, but I should feel myself in honour bound to give all my real service to the National Hospital. What would cause me to accept the move to London without hesitation would be two thousand pounds a year for the rest of my working life and five hundred pounds a year for assistance...subject to review, say, every three years'[34]. The question of a move still remained undecided.

In one of his letters to Antony, in November 1937, Jeff was able to report that 'The new private block at the MRI was opened by Lord Dawson on Monday and John Morley made a better speech than his, I understand. I shall be sending my patients there instead of High Elms'[36]. The year had been one of achievement and this was appropriately, but rather surprisingly, marked by an honorary membership given to Jeff by the Estonian Neurological Society in December.

In January 1938 Gertrude completed the examinations for her diploma in psychological medicine and was appointed to the staff of the Manchester Royal Infirmary as an Assistant Psychiatrist in the small department run by Dr Howard Kitching. He had an outpatient clinic there, but no beds. With this appointment Geoffrey and Gertrude had, in a sense, eventually achieved their earlier plan of working together, for they were now at least in the same institution and, with the development of psychosurgery, there was even some overlap of their disciplines. Not only was there this possibility but they also 'worked as a team in making a comprehensive appraisal of a wide range of behavioural and cognitive functions, especially in patients whose tumours were to be radically removed'[37]. This research showed that it was possible for more extensive excisions of brain tumours to be undertaken than had previously been considered safe, without causing serious psychological deficits[37]. Gertrude, in addition of course, continued her work with the Manchester Maternity and Child Welfare Centres and as an adviser to her friends, a rôle that she undertook throughout her life.

Jefferson wrote to Cushing in that same month in order to tell him that nothing had yet been decided about a move to Queen Square, and to comment on some photographs[38]. He sent a longer letter in the same direction in April in which he said, amongst other things, that he and Gertrude had been 'to the Lake District for Easter and spent a good deal of the time breathing on our fingers to thaw them out'[39]. He often told Cushing about the papers he had in hand or projects that were in his mind, and he mentioned that he had started a study of the intracranial extensions of pituitary adenomas[39]. This work did not reach maturity for nearly 2 years, when it became Jefferson's presidential address to the Section of Neurology of the Royal Society of Medicine[40]. He continued: 'We had an important meeting at Queen Square two weeks ago, at which the Physicians (I must out of respect give them a capital P) most graciously and good-humouredly removed the Ban on Surgery, and ceded independence to the surgeons (small s,

Figure 16   *Gertrude Jefferson and Harvey Cushing in 1938.*

but in future allowed a Capital) both as regards beds and out-patients. There should be a gentle rustling of wings in Heaven. I suppose this means that I shall be going, if only, and it is a big if, they can afford me. What a nuisance this financial business always is'[39]. In humorous vein, however, Jeff remarked: 'I met Thomas Percival the other day outside the Rylands Library. He sent you his cordial, most esteemed greetings. He said he never heard of meningiomas. Poor fellow'[39]. Geoffrey was thinking of the joke against himself and his failure to recognise Percival's identity in 1927, a slip which may still have rankled slightly. Cushing replied a week or so later, and remarked on some references to extrasellar extensions of pituitary adenomas in his own writings. 'The news about the change of mind at Queen Square interests me greatly, and it is too bad that they could not have made this concession to the Surgeons (with a capital S) long ago. It is a triumph for you, and I hope things will so pan out that you can see your way clear to take on the job, for there is much missionary work to be done and you could swing it better than anyone else I know'[41]. However, these persuasions were to be in vain.

The centenary meeting of the Swiss Surgical Society (Schweizerische Gesellschaft für Chirugie) was held in Bern in the May of 1938, and there Jefferson gave a further paper on resection of one of the frontal lobes, together with reports on 13 personal cases[42]. He recommended block resection of the affected frontal lobe for patients with non-enucleable frontal lobe tumours, having found that it gave the best chance of long survival for these patients. In his experience, no important mental, moral or other disability had followed as a result of this treatment.

After the Swiss meeting, Jefferson wrote a brief report of it to Cushing, and added the following remarks: 'Our visit (Trotula went too) coincided with all the tension over Czecho-Slovakia, and it was interesting to talk with the continental folk about things in general. They were scared stiff in Basel, as they feel sure the Germans will come through Switzerland. On the other hand I had some grand talks with the Germans, who say they will not come through anywhere and have no intention of attacking anyone. Which is as it may be, but reassuring none the less. On the whole I believe them. It upsets one's work too much to think of anything else'[43]. The desire to believe that which is most wished for is very strong, and Jeff succumbed to that desire then, as he had in connection with the advent of Lenin in 1917, and would do again in the future. The meeting in Bern was on 20th May 1938 and it had been on 11th of March, only 2 months previously, that Germany had annexed Austria. The Munich agreement between Hitler, Daladier and Chamberlain was entered into on 30th September 1938, and Czechoslovakia invaded approximately 6 months after that. The tide of war was advancing, and it was clear that Hitler's word meant nothing. On the way back from Switzerland Geoffrey and Gertrude visited Clovis Vincent in Paris, where the summer SBNS meeting was taking place. To Cushing, Jeff delivered his verdict on Clovis Vincent: 'He's a queer chap, working in conditions that seem bad to me, for he has too many beds, too many patients, too much operating'[43].

Harvey Cushing was to come to England for the last time that July, in order to receive an Honorary Doctorate of Laws at Oxford. Jeff had hoped that his friend might be persuaded to be present on another auspicious occasion, due to take place at the National Hospital. 'I am wondering whether you would come to the opening of the New Wing at Queen Square on the 19th. Queen Mary is going to officiate and I think you above all people should be present'[43]. The visit of Cushing to Oxford in July 1938 has been long remembered in the annals of neurosurgery. He was in very good form and the degree ceremony went off well. On his return to New Haven, he wrote to Jefferson: 'It was marvellous to have seen you and Trotula in Oxford, and I appreciate hugely your coming on for the ceremony. I was sorry to have failed you at Queen Square, for had I realized that I would be invited to inspect the buildings with Queen Mary I would have gone more suitably attired or at least have covered my informal garments with my newly acquired Oxford gown. But to perlustrate with the Queen was not what took me there. I merely went accompanied by Klebs and Pat as a tribute to the newly appointed surgeon who is going to make things hum when he takes over the job that has so long awaited him'[44].

The long drawn out and even unsettling problem of making a decision about moving to London had been slightly modified by a letter that Jefferson had received from Dr Grainger Stewart in June. It was in this letter that he had been told about the acceptance by the staff of Queen Square of the right of surgeons to have their own beds and outpatients. But there was no answer to the financial aspect of his appointment and, as yet, no official approach had been made to the Rockefeller Foundation, although the hospital Board of Management appeared to be depending on their aid[45].

Gertrude took the opportunity of a journey to London to study the housing market. Both she and Geoffrey had visited Antony at Rugby School in the middle of June, and in her letter to him on the following weekend she reported that 'I saw a number of houses in London but of course it was only a preliminary survey. I hear that a nice house in Manchester <u>may</u> be falling vacant soon and if this happens it may affect our decision'[46]. This was a rather startling remark, almost a *non sequitur*, in the light of Jeff's continuing considerations. Writing again on 3rd July she remarked that: 'Father had a letter during the week which referred to the question of London. Nothing definite came out of it but there was some comfort to know that things are moving'[47].

Although the Jeffersons took a short holiday in Scotland in August, visiting Gleneagles and fishing at Strathpeffer, there was no time for relaxation on their return, for the Michaelmas meeting of the SBNS was to be held in Manchester and Jeff had also been elected president of the Manchester Surgical Society, an honour which demanded that an address should be given. He was meticulous about attending meetings of the SBNS and, even after he had ceased to be its president, he could be relied on to be there, and was usually asked to make some comments. In July, Joe Schorstein had replaced GF Rowbotham as first assistant, and Richard Johnson was appointed second assistant surgeon. Jefferson wrote a most appreciative letter to Rowbotham. 'You have assisted in the formative years of Neuro-surgery in this town and, as I think therefore in England. In the years yet to come you will probably look back on it all with amused tolerance for our ignorance and clumsy gropings towards the light.... This is not a letter of farewell, for you were appointed to a Research Fellowship on Wednesday.... I want you to know how much I appreciate the toiling that you have done at my side, and now after the sowing I shall look forward to the scientific harvest'[48].

Meanwhile Gertrude was, as ever, administering aid to all-comers, and now Fräulein Foerster was among those who sought sympathy at Belfield Road. Beginning on the 27th September, she stayed for 8 days at the Jefferson's house. It was during this visit that Chamberlain returned from Munich with his message of 'Peace in our time'; war with Germany had been delayed but it had also become inevitable, and the persecution of any Jews that remained in Germany or the countries that had been overrun was certain. It transpired that the main purpose of Fräulein Foerster's visit was to ask that the Jeffersons might give accommodation and help to some Jewish refugees. This they agreed to do.

The presidential address to the Manchester Surgical Society was delivered by Jefferson on 18th October and was entitled *The special field of neurosurgery*[49]. Much of the lecture was devoted to the relationship between medicine and surgery, for neurosurgery bestrides the two major disciplines. These days, it may seem strange or even superfluous to explain such a matter. However, even as late as in the 1950s, ignorance of what neurosurgery was about was widespread. Wildly exaggerated and uniformed opinions about the nature of the cases that were operated upon and the results of operation, were held both among the laity and in the profession. Generally speaking, very few head injuries were seen by a neurosurgeon at this time, and it was assumed that little could be offered in the way of effective treatment for tumours or other similar conditions. Jefferson gave a brief analysis of 1000 of his own intracranial cases, among which were 110 meningiomas, 117 pituitary adenomas and 70 acoustic neuromas. Spinal and traumatic cases were not included in this survey[49].

Jefferson's address to the SBNS was probably on the subject of the saccular aneurysms of the cavernous sinus when, as host, he gave the first paper of their November meeting at the Manchester Royal Infirmary[50]. It was a masterly analysis of the various ways in which these lesions may present, and the means of their diagnosis and identification that were then available. If he had known of the advances which have taken place since this important paper was written, he would have taken much pleasure in amending it and expressing his views on new techniques. All the presentations at the meeting were by Mancunians, with the exception of one by de Vet from Holland, and all would have been criticised and rehearsed in front of Jefferson beforehand, as was his custom. He had remarked in a letter to Antony: 'I am going to have rather a bad time this next three weeks preparing for a meeting that we are going to have here. A lot of papers have to be written and listened to by me before it'[51].

The possibility of war was still too dreadful for Geoffrey to contemplate, as it was for most of those who remembered the carnage of World War I. In the same letter to Antony at the beginning of November 1938, with reference to the recent crisis, he wrote: 'It is interesting to hear how disturbed everybody is at what happened and the need for greater efforts still in arming. However—its all too difficult. I doubt if there'll be any fighting really. I think things are going to settle down'[51].

In mid-November, Cairns asked Jefferson if he would like to have 'a really good neuro-histologist, who was a Jewish refugee from Austria'[52]; an offer which was readily accepted. The doctor in question was Eugen Pollak, who was to become an invaluable asset to the neurosurgical team.

Called back by the school which he had not loved and for which he still had no particular affection, on 15th December 1938 Jefferson gave a speech at the Old Mancunian's dinner; this was not the one quoted earlier (Chapter 3), which he did not deliver until 1949. Jefferson and Cushing exchanged Christmas letters, Jeff being especially appreciative of the gift of a copy of the book on meningiomas by Cushing and Eisenhardt. In his letter, as usual, he also described the papers that he was preparing, of which there were no less than five at that time[53,54]. In addition to Jeff's extensive output of lectures and other writing throughout the year, the Medical Annual carried his regular review of neurosurgical progress. But an important contribution written in collaboration with his ear, nose and throat colleague, AA Smalley, must not be overlooked. It was Smalley, who had operated upon Jeff's mastoid in 1929. The subject was progressive facial palsy, in this case in connection with intratemporal epidermoids[55]. Six cases were reported, in each of which the diagnosis of 'an obscure neuritic process' had first been made. They gave a clear description for the first time of every aspect of the condition as it presented in this way—a key paper. Another collaborative article on a similar subject also appeared that year. James Hardman had worked with Jefferson on a Medical Research Council Fellowship, and their joint paper was entitled *Cerebellopontine angle signs produced by ependymomata*[56]. Only two cases were described. Hardman became a consultant neurosurgeon in Sheffield.

And all the while, Jefferson was making his fortnightly journeys from Manchester to London and back in fulfilment of his surgical responsibilities at Queen Square. Thus was completed the last full year of peace before World War II.

REFERENCES

GJ=Geoffrey Jefferson; GMJ=Gertrude Jefferson
1   Jefferson G. The value of radiology in neuro-surgery; the radiology of the optic canals. *Proc Roy Soc Med* 1936; **29**: 47–50.
2   Jefferson G. Compression of the chiasma, optic nerves and optic tracts by intracranial aneurysms. *Brain* 1937; **60**: 444–97.
3   Jefferson G. Concerning injuries of the spinal cord. *BMJ* 1936; **2**: 1125–30.
4   GJ to GMJ. Letter 2nd November 1936.
5   Jefferson A to GMJ. Letter 29th November 1936.
6   GJ to GMJ. Letter December 1936, undated.
7   Examining Board to GMJ. Letter 15th December 1937.
8   Jefferson G. *Medical Annual*. Bristol: Wright, 1936.
9   GJ to Cushing H. Letter 10th November 1936.
10   Cairns H. Late results in the operative treatment of intracranial tumours. *Lancet* 1936; **1**: 1223–8.
11   Cushing H to GJ. Letter 21st November 1936.
12   Henderson WR. The pituitary adenomata. A follow-up study of the surgical results in 338 cases (Dr Harvey Cushing's series). *Br J Surg* 1938/1939; **26**: 811–921.
13   Jefferson G. The tentorial pressure cone. *Arch Neurol Psychiat (Chicago)* 1938; **40**: 857–876 and in *Selected papers*. London: Pitman Medical, 1960: 251–68.
14   Holmes G to GJ. Letter 31st January 1937.
15   Holmes G to GJ. Letter 3rd February 1937.
16   GMJ to GJ. Letter 12th February 1937.
17   Greenfield GJ to GJ. Letter 14th February 1937.
18   *The Seattle Star*—Personals 22nd May 1937.
19   GJ. MS Notes on his visit to the United States, 1937.
20   Stanton, Madeline to GJ. Letter 19th May 1937.
21   Fulton J. *Harvey Cushing, a biography*. Oxford: Blackwell, 1946: 681.
22   Jefferson G. Removal of right or left frontal lobes in man. *BMJ* 1937; **2**: 199–206.
23   Cushing H to GJ. Letter 19th August 1937.
24   GJ to Jefferson A. Letter 22nd May 1937.
25   GJ to GMJ. Letter 27th June 1937.
26   GJ to GMJ. Letter 6th July 1937.
27   GJ to Cushing H. Letter 9th August 1937.
28   Jefferson G. Compression of the chiasma, optic nerves and optic tracts by intracranial aneurysms. *Brain* 1937; **60**: 444–97.
29   Jefferson G. Colloid cyst of the third ventricle. *Proc Roy Soc Med* 1937; **30**: 850–1 and Two cases of left frontal lobectomy. *Proc Roy Soc Med* 1937; **30**: 851–3.
30   Jefferson G. Thoughts on Medical Schools. *Manchester University Medical Students' Gazette* 1937; **16**: 131–7.
31   Jefferson G. *Medical Annual*. Bristol: Wright, 1937.
32   GJ to Cushing H. Letter 26th October 1937.
33   Cushing H to GJ. Letter 1st November 1937.
34   GJ. MS undated notes on a possible move to Queen Square.

35   Jefferson M. Personal communication.
36   GJ to Jefferson A. Letter 18th November 1937.
37   Sweet WH. Personal communication.
38   GJ to Cushing H. Letter 26th January 1938.
39   GJ to Cushing H. Letter 26th April 1938.
40   Jefferson G. Extrasellar extensions of pituitary adenomas. *Proc Roy Soc Med* 1940; **33**: 433–58.
41   Cushing H to GJ. Letter 4th May 1938.
42   Jefferson G. Frontalappenresektion. *Helvetica Medica Acta* 1938; **5**: 777–82.
43   GJ to Cushing H. Letter 30th June 1938.
44   Cushing H to GJ. Letter 5th August 1938.
45   Stewart TG to GJ. Letter 1st June 1938.
46   GMJ to Jefferson A. Letter 26th June 1938.
47   GMJ to Jefferson A. Letter 3rd July 1938.
48   GJ to Rowbotham GF. Letter 30th July 1938.
49   Jefferson G. The special field of neurosurgery. *BMJ* 1939; **1**: 147–50.
50   Jefferson G. On saccular aneurysms of the internal carotid artery in the cavernous sinus. *Br J Surg* 1938; **26**: 267–302.
51   GJ to Jefferson A. Letter 7th November 1938.
52   Cairns H to GJ. Letter 15th November 1938.
53   GJ to Cushing H. Letter 7th December 1938.
54   Cushing H to GJ. Letter 22nd December 1938.
55   Jefferson G, Smalley AA. Progressive facial palsy produced by intratemporal epidermoids. *J Laryngol Otol* 1938; **53**: 417–43.
56   Hardman J, Jefferson G. Cerebellopontine angle signs produced by ependymomata. *Zentralblatt für Neurochirurgie* 1938; **3**: 137–45.

Chapter 16

World War II
1939–1941

It is astonishing to find that, as early as January 1924, a committee had been set up to report on the precautions that should be taken in the event of air raids. As situations changed, so other committees followed and, in March 1935, a White Paper on Defence included recommendations for the care of civilian casualties sustained in attacks from the air. This resulted in the setting up of an Air Raid Precautions Department, responsible for training and the provision of shelters etc. Its brief was to have a complete civil defence system in place by 1939. Following those actions were the Air Raid Precautions Act of 1937 and a survey of hospital facilities throughout the UK, which had been completed by the beginning of 1938. Special arrangements were made for the London area, which was divided into sectors based on the teaching hospitals. Other committees, such as the Central Medical Emergency Committee of 1937, had their specific responsibilities. The emergency services were expanded and, during the last months of 1938 and in 1939, arrangements were made for the evacuation of hospitals in vulnerable areas, while mental hospitals were warned of the need to surrender their beds. By June 1938 all these efforts were being co-ordinated under the Emergency Medical Service (EMS), with responsibility to the Ministry of Health. The EMS was to be in control of all civilian medical and ancillary facilities. The actual evacuation of London hospitals and others which were considered to be endangered, took place on the declaration of war in September 1939[1].

The early months of 1939 were to pass in an uneasy state of peace, and during this time preparations for conflict were only too apparent. Jefferson and Cairns, as Consultant Advisers to the Ministries of Health and Pensions, were jointly made responsible for the organization of neurosurgery throughout the country, but the exact date of their appointment is not clear. However, though there was a demarcation between them of two areas of responsibility, their ideas were completely co-ordinated. The Voluntary and Local Authority Hospitals had been brought under State control in the Emergency Medical Service, and it was through this agency that Jefferson and Cairns put their plans into action, not only to provide for normal and continuing peace-time neurosurgical requirements, but also to cope with the anticipated flood of civilian and service casualties from air raids. An increase in military activity and movements produced its toll of extra cases as well. In June 1940, however, Hugh Cairns was to join the Royal Army Medical Corps, and from then on the entire responsibility for the organization of civilian neurosurgery throughout the UK fell on Geoffrey Jefferson's shoulders.

Cairns had already been the prime mover in setting up the Military Hospital for Head Injuries at St Hugh's College, Oxford, which opened in February 1940, and at first he worked there as a civilian. Having been civilian consultant to the

Queen Alexandra Military Hospital, Millbank, London, from the early 1930s[2], he knew those whose influence was necessary to co-ordinate the treatment of head injuries, from all three services if possible, though the Royal Navy in fact looked after those of its own. Nevertheless, this required delicate and far-reaching negotiations throughout 1939, which culminated in the opening of the specialized hospital in Oxford. He also organized the neurosurgical services within the army, so that the transition of his civilian responsibilities to Jefferson had virtually taken place by the time Cairns gave up his position with the Ministry of Health. But this anticipates events and, in many respects, life for Jeff was temporarily to go on much as it had previously done.

Early in the January of 1939 Jefferson wrote to Rowbotham, soon to be a consultant neurosurgeon in Newcastle, to congratulate him on two papers that were to appear in the next issue of the *British Journal of Surgery*, both of which had been written from, and were based on work in, Jeff's department. The first was on epidermoids arising in the diploë of the bones of the skull[3], and the second on hyperostoses in relation with [*sic*] the meningiomas. Jeff wrote: 'Two in one number would be good enough, but the thing that counts is their quality. I am very pleased indeed with the look of them. It was worth while agonizing over the meningiomas and turning them this side up, now that, because I think it will be the standard work for 25 years or more. It will do us all credit, you most of all'[5]. In the final paragraph of the meningioma paper Rowbotham acknowledged his indebtedness to Jefferson for his criticism of the scientific studies, and for his guidance. We may be sure that this contribution to the work was very significant, without detracting in any way from the praise justly given by Jeff to the author. It is noteworthy that Jefferson's name does not appear as a contributor, for he wished the credit to go entirely to his protégé.

A letter to Cushing, written on 28th January 1939, confirmed that Jeff had been unwell and in bed with a respiratory infection. He had taken the opportunity to read 'quite a lot of medical history'[6]. Included in this study had been the memoirs of Sir James Paget. 'I found something that amused me. Do you remember that delightful Professor of Greek or Latin that we dropped in on rather informally (by peering through his window) one night at Yale? The one, I mean, who had that graduated set of chairs according to the time that he wished to snooze. I find that Palmerston, like him, had to write standing up, because, he told Paget, "if he fell down that woke him". What a conservative statement!' The letter continued on the subject of a biography of Halsted. 'I have lent my copy to someone and can't remember to whom. What used you to do with the young men around you, how did you get books and reprints back? . . . The keener they are the more acquisitive and the more easily do they persuade themselves that the late owner no longer needs them as much as they.' There then followed a very significant remark with reference to the projected move to London. 'I am held up in any ideas of changing my pitch by the international situation. It is either going to settle in the next few weeks or months or blow up all together. Possibly things are not so black as they seem. Hitler may enlighten us on Monday as to his fate as well as ours'[7].

Cushing replied on 10th February. He recalled their meeting with the Emeritus Professor of Latin, GL Hendrickson, and remarked on the difficulty Jeff would have in obtaining another copy of Halsted's papers, or, indeed, even of his biography. On the loss of books he said: 'I quite agree with what you say about the disappearance of books. Mine have ways of walking out of the room, or at least changing their places on the shelves just when I am most anxious to put my hands on them. It is a good rule never to lend books or umbrellas, for one never remembers who has them and it's safe to say they will never be returned'. Then, finally, he commented, 'I had supposed of course that you would ere this have definitely set up your staff in Queen Square, but I judge from what you say in your last paragraph that you apprehend that Hitler may be more likely to bomb the place than your present quarters in Manchester. There is evidently only one thing that Hitler at all respects and that is a man with an umbrella, so most Englishmen can feel themselves reasonably safe anywhere'. This somewhat flippant remark suggests that Cushing had little idea of the feelings of most people in Britain, and their increasing anxiety during the months leading up to the declaration of war. It is true, on the other hand, that up to the very last moment, there were still many even in Europe, who continued to hope that the worst might not happen[8].

In the same week Geoffrey had addressed the Leeds University Medical Society on the *Contributions of surgery to neurophysiology*[9]. This was a subject that was close to his heart, for he regarded all expressions of pathology in the nervous system as a means of illustrating the function of whatever part might have been affected, and failure to observe or make use of these messages was negligent. His approach to a clinical problem was through neuro-anatomy and neurophysiology, in both of which he was a master. Having first located and described the abnormalities in each field, he then considered what might have caused them. Finally, he produced his diagnosis and recommendation for treatment. This shows how Jeff, a master clinician, had just those qualities that were required by one of the founders of his specialty in Britain.

Part of a communication, written by Dott to Jefferson at this time in connection with the possible form of a European Society of Neurosurgeons, may be quoted as an example of the way in which Dott, at least, still held hopes that the future might be peaceful. 'I am not sure but what a European Society of Neurological Surgeons is more urgently desirable now than in more normal times', he wrote. 'I suppose the only thing likely to avert the catastrophe of war, in the long run, is a degree of mutual respect and trust between the peoples of different nations and I should suppose that science generally and medicine in particular constitutes one of the best international bridging systems. Possibly we should not lose the opportunity to do what we can in that direction.... I should incline to do our bit by showing rather exceptional friendship in medical matters to those whose national policies we find so disagreeable at present'[10]. Clearly, he was referring to Nazi Germany, and equally clearly, again like many others, he did not appreciate the impossibility of exerting any influence whatsoever over Hitler. Unfortunately we do not have Jefferson's reply. In April 1939 Britain introduced general conscription.

An interesting recollection by Michael Jefferson provides an insight into Jeff's practice at this time. Michael was living at home, while he was a clinical student, and had been asked to act as chauffeur to drive his father to see a patient at the Lancaster Royal Infirmary. She complained of back pain and was feverish. After a brief examination, and without the benefits of special x-rays, Jefferson diagnosed a spinal abscess and said that he must operate urgently. The operating theatre did not have diathermy to coagulate bleeding vessels but there could be no delay.

Jefferson asked Michael to assist him with the operation and carried out a mid-thoracic laminectomy, the level of which was based entirely on the clinical evidence. When the dura mater around the spinal cord was exposed there was no sign of any pus, a point which Michael remarked upon. His father looked up at him and said 'Ah, well, Mike, just wait and we'll see'. After a little further exploration pus welled up from the vertebral body in front of the spinal cord. Jefferson's clinical acumen, his knowledge of neuro-anatomy and his surgical skill, had been enough for an accurate diagnosis and treatment in the absence of any of the usual diagnostic aids that are now routine, and without some of the equipment which is now taken for granted. It was four o'clock in the morning when they returned to Manchester[11].

In the United States, special celebrations for their patron's 70th birthday were now being arranged by the Harvey Cushing Society, to take place at New Haven, Connecticut, on 8th April 1939. He had been given a *Festschrift* on his 60th birthday. There was to be a dinner, accompanied by the presentation of a complete bibliography of his writings. Jefferson had hoped to be able to attend 'but the Dictators have dictated otherwise', he wrote to Cushing in reply to the invitation. 'I feel that the extreme uncertainty of the European situation makes a visit unwise, although I am heartbroken not to be there.... I feel that I, as the senior neuro-surgeon in this Country, and by reason of my feelings towards you, ought to have been present. You know well what those feelings are, a mixture of admiration for the man who has made the greatest surgical achievement of his time and the warmest imaginable personal devotion. I cannot say more. Others who for geographical reasons can attend more easily will be able to pay you just homage, and I can imagine what joy it will be for you to have all your children around you. Please think also of one who will be attending as a disembodied spirit, I mean of course, Your devoted...'[12]. With this he enclosed 50 reprints of Henderson's monograph on Cushing's pituitary operations.

This letter and the safe arrival of the reprints, sent via the liner RMS *Queen Mary*, were acknowledged. In his reply, Cushing said he had 'interceded with the Post Master General to hurry the packages off from the boat without the delay of sending them through the Customs Office.... It was nice of you to have written this personal note, and I like to think that some at least of the pleasant things you have said may be partly true'[13]. It was to be Cushing's last letter to Jefferson, apart from an acknowledgement of a cable, for he died 6 months later, on 4th October 1939.

Possibly prompted by the overtures that had been made by the National Hospital, Queen Square, Manchester University now offered Geoffrey a personal professorial chair in a neurosurgical department at the Manchester Royal Infirmary, with research facilities, suitable staff and freedom to continue private practice. Funding for it had been negotiated with the Nuffield Foundation, apparently with backing from Cairns. It was to be the first neurosurgical chair in England, since Cairns was head of the Nuffield Department of Surgery at Oxford and hence was a professor of surgery in general. A similar chair, in orthopaedics, was also to be provided at Manchester University for Geoffrey's friend Harry Platt, with whom he shared the wards and an operating theatre. This situation, coupled with the prospect of attacks on the capital if there should be a war, left no more room for doubt in Jeff's mind as to the wisdom of staying in Manchester, and his flirtation with the idea of working in London was finally over. Together

Figure 17   *The Manchester Royal Infirmary (Courtesy of British Journal of Surgery Society Ltd). Drawing by Albany Wiseman.*

with Gertrude, Geoffrey's thoughts now turned to finding a more agreeable place in which to live that would be in keeping with his future status as a professor and with his, now considerable, reputation at home and abroad. Furthermore, the lease on the house in Belfield Road was nearing its end[11].

A very suitable property came on the market in Didsbury, due south of the city but still within the suburbs of Manchester. It was in Stenner Lane and known as 'High Bank'; a big house, standing in its own grounds, with a large garden that sloped downwards towards the river Mersey. It was a substantial rectangular building with deep eaves, two main floors and an imposing appearance of solidity and importance. The purchase price was only £2500, but this was more than Jeff could then afford. In a revealing, but undated, fragment of a letter to the owner of the property, he wrote: 'If only taxation had not been so crippling during the relatively few years that a specialist can make any money in, the problem would not have been so difficult to solve. However the point is not whether one might have afforded "if only" (for that is the economic dilemma of everybody's life) but whether one actually can'[14]. So, as with the other houses in which he had lived, Jeff negotiated a lease which was signed on 9th May 1939, and agreed to rent the property for the next 10 years.

Figure 18   *High Bank, Didsbury, Manchester.*

The laurel-lined drive up to the house was rather gloomy, being separated from a public park by a high wall. The broad front of the building had a glass-embellished front door. An inner door opened into the hall, which included a splendid flight of wide stairs with shallow risers, black metal banisters and a polished wooden rail. The tiled floor of the hall was partly covered by a deep red carpet, which was continuous with similar carpeting on the stairs and first floor landing. There was a passage leading to Jeff's non-medical library and informal sitting room—previously a billiard room. The door at the foot of the staircase opened into his study which was dominated by his desk and papers and books spread around. Built-in bookshelves and glass-fronted bookcases, together with various chairs completed the chief furniture of the room. The hall also gave access to the sitting room and dining room. The sitting room was spacious, with big easy-chairs and a large sofa, as well as a tall-boy and other pieces of furniture, including a radiogram. The huge windows, extending from floor to ceiling, looked on to the garden, and there was a rather austere marble and steel fireplace. An assorted collection of oil paintings relieved the white-painted walls. There were no less than three doors from the dining room, and it was here that Jeff chose to hang his collection of etchings and engravings. A large silk shade covered the lights which hung over the polished table. There was another entrance to the house, leading to the kitchen and back staircase; this door would later achieve particular significance[15].

The garden was Gertrude's delight, and was managed with the aid of Sims, their elderly gardener. It faced south and was, of necessity, terraced where it fell away steeply beyond some flower beds and a narrow strip of grass next to the back of the house. The large vegetable garden was surrounded by brick walls on the east side of the property; they also enclosed a delapidated greenhouse, the sole remaining function of which was to provide warmth and shelter for Sims while he ate his lunch. Beyond some railings at the bottom of the garden there lay a meadow, which was frequently flooded by the river during the winter[15].

The day that the lease was signed, Gertrude wrote enthusiastically to Antony, telling him of her plans for redecoration. 'The hall is to be a sort of creamy brown, as light as possible, but the paint in the hall and dining room will be left brown'[16]. However, a month later she had to report: 'We are now racking our brains as to what can be cut out. I cancelled our new bedroom furniture this morning. I would rather have nice decorations and carpets.... The garden is full of lovely flowers and <u>birds</u> which ought to be fun'[17]. She loved the garden from the start, and took a great interest in it.

After staying with the Jeffersons later in the year, Hugh Cairns was to write to thank Gertrude saying: 'My visit to Lancashire was a bright spot in a dismal and harassed month. I loved your new house and its warmth and kindness were like the last'[18].

Early in May, the dignity of Professor was conferred on Geoffrey Jefferson by the University of Manchester, and with it came the full-time services of a Lecturer and a Research Assistant. He gave up his visits to London and the National Hospital and, having already severed his ties with the Salford Royal Hospital, he was thus able to concentrate his activities between the Manchester Royal Infirmary and his new consulting rooms. These were at No 3 Lorne Street, an unpretentious road adjacent to the Infirmary but near the recently built Private Wing, in which he could now care for and operate upon his private patients and be within the curtilage of the voluntary hospital, where he still devoted the greater part of his attention and skill though, of course, he received no payment for the latter services. The professorial chair carried a stipend which relieved him, to some extent, of total dependence upon his private practice. Jeff sublet a room of the house in Lorne Street to a thoracic surgeon, a colleague at the Infirmary, and Gertrude had a consulting room upstairs. In this she saw some of her private patients, while others visited her in the library at High Bank.

Congratulations on the professorship poured in from Jeff's many friends, and from the family. He wrote to Antony on 21st May, 'I can't get used to being a Professor, but as time passes of course it will no longer sound so novel...it is a nice thing to have happened. I must admit pleasure at my elevation to the Academic Peerage. But I don't see that it will make any fundamental difference to my duties, which remain those of being as good a doctor as I can. So here's good luck to me'[19]. He had been busy during that week putting together and revising a paper by his radiological colleague and friend, EW Twining (see footnote Chap. 14), who had recently died after an illness of only a few days. The manuscript was not yet ready for publication, although the subject had been that of a Hunterian Lecture given by Twining at the Royal College of Surgeons in 1936. The second part of the paper, which was in two sections and entitled *The radiology of the third and fourth ventricles*, was only in draft form and required much attention from Jefferson; when it was published it was to be of landmark importance in its time[20]. The loss of his friend had been deeply felt by Jeff, who told Antony, 'I have been so upset at the loss of Gobbo, I loved that man, he was a lovely person, so intelligent and such a completely nice individual at the same time. People who are both those things are rare'[19]. Gertrude observed that his death had clouded their pleasure regarding the professorship and the move to High Bank[21].

That June Jeff wrote a brief birthday greeting to Antony: 'I hadn't realised it was tomorrow until Mums pushed the pencil into my hand.... Isn't she a marvel—here everything is, paper, stamped envelope, blotter, pencil (to be blotted).... Affectionately, Father. Signed, sealed, and blotted'[22].

An example of the work that Jefferson was carrying out at that time on behalf of the Ministry of Health, can be gleaned from his unpublished and incomplete manuscript, *Summary of the neurosurgical facilities in Britain in June 1939*. '...Whereas the few original centres arose through the special endeavour of local pioneer spirits, backed by their colleagues, others came into being in recognition of local needs and a surgeon was imported or subsidised. Even as late as 1938 there were only seven surgical beds in the National Hospital, Queen Square, the acknowledged original home of neurosurgery. With these few beds a large number of cases were actually handled, because the patients were passed rapidly through the surgical beds and back into the medical wards from which they had come. However, in the new Rockefeller part of the building opened in the summer of 1938, there were two separate floors for surgery alone. Owing to the difficult finances of the hospital only one of these was ever handed over to surgery fully. The shadow of the war had a paralysing effect on development.... In addition to the National Hospital, good surgical work was also carried out at the Maida Vale Hospital for Nervous Diseases, and at the West End Hospital...'[23]. Apart from documenting the unfulfilled intentions of the London County Council to bring their patients with nervous ailments together into one centre, the manuscript unfortunately ends without completing the survey of facilities in the rest of the country. However, he was to write later, consequent upon the expectation of war, by the middle of 1939 'a number of Neurosurgical Centres had arisen based on the University Medical Schools. Most of these were recent or new creations'[24]. Arrangements were made for several new civilian centres to be set up by makeshift conversions in mental hospitals and similar institutions throughout Britain. For example, the neurosurgical department of the National Hospital for Nervous Diseases was to be evacuated to Hurstwood Park Hospital, Haywards Heath, Sussex, and all the other London teaching hospitals had similar arrangements prepared for their dispersal. In Scotland, Norman Dott was to work at Bangour Hospital west of Edinburgh, and in Hertfordshire, Wylie McKissock set up a new unit at Leavesden Mental Hospital near Watford; other moves were designed to take place elsewhere in the country. Most hospitals outside the major cities were enlarged by the construction of hutted wards connected by open corridors, and similar accommodation was provided for the ancillary departments.

Jefferson's appreciation of the situation was that: 'This war would be a new sort of war, worse than any before because something was going to happen that all Peace Conventions have prohibited—the killing and injuring not only of men of the fighting services, not only of the non-combatant male civilian population, but of women and children. Nor would hospitals and their staffs be in any way immune from disaster.... Work could not be carried out in the Hospitals in the great cities, certainly not in London.... Innovations were therefore planned at Cabinet direction by a new division of the Ministry of Health — the Emergency Medical Service.... Two neurosurgical centres were first established north and south of London and one in the North-west'[24].

As if to prepare the medical profession for war, in the spring and summer of 1939, Jefferson wrote two papers. The first, on the *Special field of neurosurgery*[25], was based on his Presidential Address to the Manchester Medical Society; it was followed by a two part article on *War wounds of the head*[26]. In July he spoke at the Royal Society of Medicine on tumours of the lateral and third ventricles[27]. He also wrote on tumours of the frontal lobes for the *Postgraduate Medical Journal*[28] and produced his usual contribution for the *Medical Annual*.

And then the inevitable happened; Britain, once again, was at war. Austria had been the first state to fall victim to German expansionist policy, on 11th March 1938. Almost exactly a year later, on 14th March 1939, Czechoslovakia had also been engulfed. Italy and Germany formed the Axis pact in May 1939, and in August a totally spurious treaty of non-aggression for 10 years was signed between Moscow and Berlin; this was to be broken when Russia was invaded by Germany only 2 years later. On 1st September 1939 Hitler invaded Poland, with the direct result that, after 2 days, Great Britain and France declared war on Germany and Italy. The 3rd September was a Sunday, and Geoffrey Jefferson, Gertrude and the family were in church at the time of the announcement by the Prime Minister. Everyone's worst fears having been realised, the Jeffersons went to the home of Dr Benton, an anaesthetist, where the implications of the fact that the nation was at war were discussed over a glass of sherry. There is no way of knowing what was said, but the family was at least spared some anxiety by the knowledge that Jeff was 53 years old and would not be conscripted and that the two sons were, for the time being, in the reserved occupation of medical training.

On 17th September Russia attacked Poland's eastern frontier, and that of Finland on 30th November. It had been anticipated that, on the declaration of war by the Allies, there would be an immediate onslaught by Germany against France and the Low Countries, accompanied by severe bombing of Britain. This did not happen. A period of relative inactivity ensued while the German forces regrouped. Plans for attack were made on both sides, but they were either rejected or postponed for differing reasons. This so-called 'Phoney War' was to last until 10th May 1940, when the 'Blitzkrieg' air raids on London began. However, it provided valuable time during which the Emergency Medical Services were put on a war footing and those plans that had been in the making since the time of the Munich crisis came into action. The whole of British medicine was affected.

From America, Madeline Stanton sent Jefferson a cable to tell him of Cushing's death on 4th October 1939 from a coronary thrombosis. This was associated with generalized arterial disease which may have dated from as far back as 1918; he even had occlusion of both femoral arteries. Jefferson, who had not been asked to write an obituary for any of the weekly medical journals, responded by sending letters to the *Lancet*, entitled *Harvey Cushing, A surgeon's appreciation*[29] and to the

British Medical Journal[30]. John Fulton wrote to Jeff to say how he found that Jeff's note in the *Lancet* had surpassed all the others. ' . . . your superb letter seems to me to show deeper insight, feeling and real understanding of his personality and contribution than anyone else's. . . . Mrs Cushing has given me a heavy responsibility in asking me to undertake a life of the Chief and I am counting on you and others for help'[31]. When the book was eventually published in 1946[32], Fulton's biography of Cushing was to win him a Pulitzer prize, as indeed Cushing's *Life of Osler* had done for its author in 1926.

The year 1940 began quietly enough but brought increasing work for Jefferson. He became a member of the Brain Injuries Committee, which had been set up by the Medical Research Council, and met in London for the first time on 7th March. Professor ED Adrian (later Lord Adrian of Cambridge) was the chairman; among the members, in addition to Geoffrey Jefferson, were Hugh Cairns, Norman Dott, George Riddoch and Charles Symonds, J Godwin Greenfield, EA Carmichael and Aubrey Lewis. It is strange, though significant, that there were only three neurosurgeons in the group, the other members represented different aspects of neurology and psychiatry. However, Jefferson and Cairns were among the very few neurosurgeons in Britain who were still available and who had any previous war experience; Jefferson alone of them had been a surgeon with responsibility for wartime head injuries. The committee later published a glossary of terms to be used for recording head injuries, giving definitions of stupor, traumatic delirium and so forth. This essential step was taken, with considerable foresight, in order to be able in the future to study, assess and compare the case histories of those who were unfortunate enough to sustain head injuries. The committee also advised on grants in aid of work on new developments in the neurosciences[24].

The Section of Neurology of the Royal Society of Medicine is a meeting ground for all the neurosciences and, as its current Section President, Jefferson gave his address on 18th January 1940 on the subject of extrasellar extensions of pituitary adenomas. It was another study of lesions in an area which was of particular interest to him. Many years later, his Sherrington Lecture was to be a further development of this theme[33,34]. In his presidential address Jeff was at pains to point out that Cushing and others had been most interested in those pituitary tumours which were mainly confined to the sella and which, in consequence, gave the best results when they were operated upon. He emphasised that unless 'extensions of the pituitary adenomas beyond their average confines were included in any survey the history would be but half told'[34]. It was in this paper that he first discussed the malignant adenomas, later to be a controversial subject, but here he made his first attempt to 'designate malignancy with more precision' than earlier authors had done, and to distinguish between mere size, malignancy and invasiveness[34]. As president of the Section Jeff would have attended its monthly meetings, again in London, with the necessity for a choice between an overnight stay or a sleeper on the train back to Manchester. It was during his term of office that the bombing of London began, when air-raids took place almost every night.

Meanwhile the war was not going well for the Allies, and on 25th June 1940 Germany signed an armistice with France, the evacuation of troops from Dunkirk had taken place, and the siege of Britain followed. The whole country became vulnerable to attack, and, as Jeff was to write later, 'this possibility was soon turned into fact.... Stage by stage ten Special Head Centres were set up in England and two in Scotland.... Most of them were originally replacements of the peace-time centres, moved to safer places, some were new. These 12 centres did not all come into being at once..., the latest were added only in the summer of 1944 for the Invasion of Europe'[24]. Not only did these units care for cranial and spinal wounds in the sectors of which the Teaching Hospitals formed the nuclei, but they also provided for the neurosurgical needs of the civilian population. The staff of each unit consisted of a neurosurgeon and his chief assistant, two house surgeons, an anaesthetist, a pathologist, an electro-encephalographer and two secretaries. Radiology was supplied by the hospital to which it was attached. There were usually some rehabilitation beds, with their special staff, within the same or an affiliated hospital. A problem existed in finding enough civilians with the necessary expertise to staff these units, a difficulty made worse by the fact that there had been no regular peacetime neurosurgeons in the forces and the services were now calling on as many as they could get. In the event, Jefferson's neurosurgical centres were to play a major rôle in dealing with service casualties as well as those of civilians, and by the middle of 1943, a year before the invasion of Europe, the total admissions to just six of them had reached 5638, of which 46.8% were service personnel[24]. It is not surprising that the SBNS held only one meeting in 1940. Oxford, where so much training and care of head wounds was going on, was the natural choice of venue. Jeff took part in a discussion on gunshot wounds[35].

The compulsory notification of all head injuries that were admitted to EMS hospitals was Jefferson's next move. As he put it, '...notification was imposed not without some expostulation by the general surgeons'[24]. In this way the neurosurgical centres could keep track on head injuries that were in general hospitals and accept their transfer where necessary. It also led to the discovery that industrial head injuries were not very common, that most head trauma was the result of traffic accidents, and it made available precise details of the number of cases that were due to enemy action. Jeff emphasised the important part played by rehabilitation in reducing the period of sickness and the incidence of post-traumatic disability after head injury[24].

Jefferson was also responsible for a study that was undertaken in order to find out what effect on the condition of these patients, if any, could be attributed to the transportation of head injuries to special centres; for this was a point of objection put forward by those who wished their care to remain in general surgical hands. After the end of hostilities, he was to write: 'It has been one of the outstanding lessons learned in this war that head injuries can be moved without any decline in condition. On behalf of the Medical Research Council I undertook to find out about the pulse rate, blood pressure and temperature before and after a journey of 3 hours or so by road.... This removed the greatest bar to transfer and segregation'[24]. It also justified Jefferson's demand that civilians with head injuries should be transferred to specialist centres. A similar policy had been adopted by the army on a basis of their findings that a higher incidence of complications occurred, and there was a need for a longer period of recovery, when military patients with head injuries had been treated by general surgeons. 'When the battles began in Europe we were able to apply these lessons, and many hundred head wounds were flown home for their definitive treatment in conditions much better than the battle-field provides[24].'

At the Jefferson home at High Bank, in Didsbury, the remarkable and near-indispensible Bridget Hennessy had now arrived; she was Irish and was to be their cook for the next two decades. In fact, responsibility for most of the details of household management fell upon her shoulders, not only the cooking, but also the shopping, cleaning and almost any other requirement. There was some additional domestic help in the house from a 'daily'. Guests remembered her with affection and concern and enquired after her in their letters. She was to remain with the family until she had a stroke almost 20 years later, when the whole mechanism of the ménage fell to pieces as will be seen.

Geoffrey Jefferson had adopted a routine in which he had breakfast brought up to the bedroom in the morning, while he and Gertrude read the newspaper and each looked at their individual mail. This was a habit that he had copied from Sir Charles Sherrington, whom he used to visit at the Nursing Home in Eastbourne where the great physiologist ended his days. Jeff used to sit up in bed like Winston Churchill and appeared to be quite oblivious of the need to get up, sometimes staring for ages at the ceiling while he pondered over a problem. Suddenly, however, he would jump out of bed, be dressed in about 20 minutes and on his way to one of the hospitals—woe be to anyone who kept him waiting[11]. He would probably not return until dinner time, which was still nominally at 7.30 pm, but he was habitually late. Antony was now reading medicine at Oriel College, Oxford; while Michael, having graduated from the same university, was doing the clinical work for his final medical degree at the Manchester Royal Infirmary and was still a part of the family then living at home. Ultimately both Jefferson's sons were to follow their father and make their own marks in the field of neurology, Michael as a neurologist and Antony as a neurosurgeon.

In the summer of 1940 Monica was married. Geoffrey had suffered a flare-up of his diverticulitis just before the wedding and was in bed with a fever at the time. He could not attend the ceremony and had to arrange for his daughter to be given away by her great-uncle, Sir John James. Her husband held a managerial position in the steel industry and had a very successful career, but the marriage later floundered.

Then the arrival of four Jewish refugees provided a not entirely unexpected, but considerable, addition to the Jefferson household. They were a husband and his wife in their mid-40s, and a young boy and girl of about 16, who were unrelated. It had been arranged that the older couple would give some help with cooking and in the house, but they came from a professional background and were unhappy with the situation. After 2 or 3 months something more suitable was found for them[11]. Both the younger refugees remained at High Bank and, with Gertrude's help, quickly learnt to speak English. The boy found work in a hotel but, though this did not prove to be very congenial, he stuck to it and returned to Germany in 1945. The girl became very fluent in the language and obtained work as a secretary; eventually she married a lawyer and settled in Britain[11].

Among the many Jewish medical refugees in the United Kingdom, two were to work closely with Jefferson. One of them, Eugen Pollak, the distinguished neuropathologist who had been recommended by Cairns, had been interned in the Isle of Man as an alien on the outbreak of war. He had now been released and was able to work in the pathology department of the university, but was apparently not allowed access to the Royal Infirmary. He had trained and lived in Vienna when it was the centre of European culture, alive with fresh thought in many fields; he was a scholarly and cultivated man. However he led a lonely life in Manchester, his wife having died and his married daughter, who had also escaped from Germany, was living elsewhere. His arrival filled a gap and provided the essential expertise in neuropathology on which every neurosurgeon depends. He died shortly after the end of the war. Later, a neurosurgeon named FK Kessel came to Manchester and became an important member of the neurosurgical department[11].

In 1940, towards the end of April, No 1 (Canadian) Neurological Hospital arrived in Britain. Jefferson, with the Minister of Health, and in the midst of the confusion after Dunkirk, helped to locate the unit on the estate of Lord Camrose at Hackwood Park, Basingstoke. Hackwood became the central neurological, neurosurgical and psychiatric hospital for the Canadian army. Jefferson then arranged for its use also in the British EMS system as a head and spine centre. This meant that for the next 5 years Jefferson became a regular visitor to the hospital, where he often spent the weekend. According to report, his arrival was always invigorating and stimulating and as welcome as a fresh breeze to a becalmed sailor. On the staff of the hospital was Major Harry Botterell, a neurosurgeon from Toronto whom Jefferson had met and corresponded with before the war. He was to become one of Jeff's most intimate friends, one might even say a temporary member of his family which was, after all, half Canadian. Botterell provided exactly the independent confidant that Jefferson needed, having lost both Cushing and Twining, though their relationship did not develop fully until a year later. However, a letter written after the war shows a considerable exchange of ideas at an early stage in their relationship; in it Botterell remarked that, even in 1940, they had discussed plans for the creation of a Neurological Institute in Manchester, inspired perhaps by the Montreal Neurological Institute[36].

About this time, in the middle of 1940, Geoffrey Jefferson developed an interest in the problem of concussion — a difficult subject about the nature of which there were, and still are, several theories; a sure sign of uncertainty and lack of proof. In his diary he had written contemporaneously and without revision the comment, quoted in a letter to Botterell, that his ideas on concussion had little to do with treatment. '...I should do better were I more empiric. The need to have a wide and deep understanding employs my thoughts and I have always assumed that treatment springs from it necessarily. But in that I think I have erred by not thinking out deeply enough what treatment is possible. I could, and do, claim that the more important things are the fundamentals of causation, of nature, of progress, of valuable result and that, given that, others can think up treatment. None the less I detect a disinclination to be very exact about treatment in my writings. I must remedy that in future'[37]. He commented in the same letter to Harry Botterell when the war was over: 'I don't know that I ever profited much by that homily to myself. Understanding things was my province — the borderlands of neuro-surgery, neurology and neurophysiology'[37]. This extract tells much about Jefferson's self-analysis and his way of thinking, even if the self-criticism is not entirely justified. It also shows how close to his younger Canadian friend he became.

Botterell was 35 years old when he came over to Britain in 1940, Jefferson was 54 at that time, and we are lucky to have Jeff's thoughts about him, quoted from the diary that he was keeping at the time. '[H.B. is] a real worker when there is work to do, level headed and intelligent with a buoyant good humour.... It has been a great joy to have him around. He does me good'[37].

From August 1940 to May 1941 Norman Guthkelch was house surgeon to Jefferson and has described what it was like to work for him at the Manchester Royal Infirmary during that period. There were then about 25 resident doctors at the hospital, but the neurosurgical team was always on call for its own emergency admissions and the house surgeon had also to take his turn in the Accident and Emergency (Casualty) department and in giving anaesthetics. The result of this was that he frequently had to ask colleagues to cover for him when any of his various duties coincided. In that case, the favour had to be returned, so that his tenuous allowance of off-duty time almost vanished. As there was no Intensive Care Unit at the Infirmary in those days, post-operative patients returned directly from the operating theatre to the wards, where it often happened that they could not be left for more than a few minutes. The house surgeon had also to prepare patients for operation, attend to laboratory investigations and carry out minor procedures such as lumbar puncture. This last could be very demanding, since the practice then was for most post-operative patients to have lumbar punctures on a daily basis, sometimes even twice daily, until there was no longer any sign of raised intracranial pressure[38].

At the same time, and in the Cushing tradition, Jefferson expected a high standard of history-taking and examination. The notes were another of the house surgeon's responsibilities, and visual field examinations had always to be done personally by him too, afterwards to be very critically examined by Jeff whose discussion of every aspect of his cases was penetrating. Jefferson was not interested in classifications of disease and never mentioned such a thing as a syndrome; each case had to be viewed and dealt with on its own merits. The comments that he made on his own observations, which were typed in red on blue paper, were always fascinating to read and often showed brilliant insight. Incidentally, his Chief Assistant's notes were on pink paper and the house surgeon's on white[39]. Nevertheless there was a certain lack of organization in the department and no regular follow-up system had yet been established during Guthkelch's time. Jefferson had little conception of setting up a clinical trial or of the use of statistical methods[38], but that may have been attributable to his seniority, for such things were barely thought of in the pre-war era. It was an unwritten law that the pathological examination, whether of tissues or at a post-mortem, was of supreme importance, and the utmost trouble was taken to obtain specimens. Failure to examine a brain, even if the diagnosis seemed certain, was seen as a missed opportunity to learn something, for examination often revealed unsuspected and completely new information.

As a teacher, Jefferson 'was indeed a fine lecturer with a very adequate (though not overwhelming) presence, an unhurried delivery, and often a delightful turn of phrase. Another quality...was his concern that what he said should be understandable by the less bright members of his audience. This showed itself rather touchingly in the one regular annual lecture course which he gave, which was to fifth year medical students'[38]. Jefferson had asked a question of a member of his audience who was considered to be somewhat of a dullard, and he had gently guided him towards the correct answer; he ended by praising him. Thereafter, Jeff made a point of asking the same person a question almost every week. The result was that the student's confidence and determination to learn rose with each session. By the end of the course the other students had come to regard their colleague with a new respect and, in turn, he became devoted to the professor, who had a 'capacity to suffer fools gladly so long as they were respectful fools'. But he had no time 'for people whom he perceived as thinking that they knew it all'[38]. The advertised topic of the course was Applied Anatomy, but Jeff's method was to select neurosurgical subjects which interested him and to discuss their anatomical implications. He made no attempt to be systematic and moved from one subject to another quite freely. Indeed, he professed an abhorrence of systematic lectures[38].

Norman Guthkelch did not speak for himself alone, when he said that 'GJ's unpunctuality and habit of disappearing back to his consulting rooms or to a meeting, or wherever, without warning and, worse, without giving any indication when he would return, was difficult to tolerate.... GJ's disregard of the comfort of his juniors could be very frustrating, and I often felt that he treated his team pretty much as his personal property'[38]. However, it has to be said that this was the way things were before World War II, and even in the years immediately following it. Such behaviour by their seniors, and burdens of this sort that were imposed on young doctors, were accepted by them in exchange for the privilege of being taught by those who undoubtedly commanded enormous, sincerely held, and usually well deserved respect. Geoffrey Jefferson was revered by those who worked for him, and the words 'Master' and 'Genius' were used by them with genuine feeling and no cynicism. This enabled his staff to forgive the shortcomings which could be so irritating; his unpredictability, his sarcasm, his lack of sensitivity for the feelings of others, or his sharp chastisement of transgressors. These faults were amply compensated for by his generosity and understanding on other occasions and by his charisma. As Sir Harold Himsworth wrote in an article in the *Dictionary of national biography*: 'The basis of Jefferson's unique authority was the mind behind the wit.... His perspicacity became legendary in his lifetime and his salty aphorisms were treasured with delight by his contemporaries'[40].

In 1941, 'A typical operating day would start at 7.30 with the HS [house surgeon] making burr-holes under local anaesthesia ready for ventriculography. By about 8.15 (if all went well, which it didn't always) the air would have been injected, the patient returned to bed in the sitting position and the bed, mounted on a trolley, wheeled by the HS to the X-Ray Department.... By this time the Chief Assistant had usually arrived, and as soon as he and the radiologist had agreed that the filling of the ventricles was adequate, GJ would be contacted by phone.... He would come down to the X-Ray Department, review the films and tell us what operation he proposed.... GJ would typically tell his Chief Assistant to turn down the bone flap...and he would disappear again'[38]. Before an operation it was the job of the HS to cut down on a vein for an infusion; which was sometimes a further source of delay, so that the craniotomy seldom started before 10 am[38].

Jefferson was very particular about having the patient, and especially the head, in the correct position on the operating table; a most important consideration which could affect the whole procedure and one which was very difficult to correct once the drapes were in place. It 'became something of a matter of honour for the Chief Assistant to get as much done as soon as possible,...' in the hope that he would be given permission at least to start to take out the tumour. 'However GJ did not often delegate authority in this, or indeed in any other sphere'[38].

Those who were scrubbed up for an operation wore long rubber aprons beneath their gowns, which, in Jeff's case, made his rather protuberant abdomen even more conspicuous. He disliked tight-fitting surgical masks and always wore a length of sterile surgical gauze attached to a sort of metal spectacle-frame instead of the usual, much lighter, protection. 'Having put on gown and gloves, GJ would stroll almost casually to the head of the table, possibly ask a few questions and check the position of the patient, [but] he would not talk much until the tumour was out.... He was slow by any standard, but he was also gentle and always careful to be certain of exactly where he was before proceeding'[38]. His complete understanding of the anatomy left this in no doubt. Nevertheless, Guthkelch felt that, despite Jeff's care and slowness, he spent insufficient time controlling bleeding vessels and sometimes seemed to lack a strategy[38].

This criticism brings to mind the very different operating conditions that existed before controlled respiration, controlled blood pressure, bipolar coagulation and osmotherapy had been introduced. These later techniques reduced the amount of haemorrhage and slackened the turgidity of the brain considerably, thereby improving visibility and producing less need for firm retraction; the operating microscope, lasers and the ultrasonic knife were to be further aids. It seemed like the dawn of a new era of brain surgery when these things arrived on the scene many years later, as indeed it was, and the time needed for any procedure became considerably shortened. The advent of micro-surgery was a milestone that would have fascinated Jefferson, but it is doubtful if he would have adopted it himself had he then been alive and operating. He belonged to a different age and even described himself as a Victorian.

'Once the tumour was out and the haemorrhage arrested, GJ would relax. It was his practise to close the dura himself in most instances, and during this time he would often talk about neurosurgery and neurosurgeons in general, though sometimes he would conduct a somewhat unnerving inquisition into the progress of patients on the ward. Despite the ease and enjoyment with which he seemed able to produce somewhat barbed witticisms about people and institutions, he had a sense of loyalty to his colleagues...', and after these conversations no hard feelings were ever left behind[38].

At the end of the August of 1940 Jefferson snatched a brief holiday in Scotland, as one can gather from a letter he wrote to Rowbotham concerning the consultant post which his former Chief Assistant was eventually to obtain in Newcastle. After describing what he had been doing, he continued: 'I have been busily engaged writing the story of concussion, the thing that I had in mind to appear eventually as a book. I shall content myself with trying to place it as a long paper. Its an immense length already and its not finished yet. At the present moment I feel rather satisfied, but I've no doubt it really needs rewriting. I can never tell until I see it in type and nothing has yet survived the "ordeal by typing"; I don't anticipate this will be an exception. How one does run to those weakening conjunctions, ands, buts, nows etc. The blue pencil needs freely using. I expect some of those conjunctions are prepositions?'[41]. The paper eventually appeared in 1944 in a much abbreviated form under the title of *The nature of concussion*[42]. Such were Jefferson's second thoughts about it, not only after typing but after publication, that he did not consider it worthy of inclusion in his *Selected papers*[43].

His work for the Ministry of Health and the EMS demanded many journeys away from Manchester, mostly by train and, in addition, Jefferson had his normal duties as Professor of Neurosurgery to perform and a huge work-load in the neurosurgical unit to sustain. Nevertheless he published no less than six papers in 1940. They included his presidential address to the Section of Neurology of the Royal Society of Medicine on extrasellar extensions of pituitary adenomas[34] and an obituary for Harvey Cushing in the *British Journal of Surgery*[44]. Other papers were on tumours of the optic nerve[45], cervical spine dislocations[46], and his participation in a discussion of a similar subject[47].

In November 1940, since there was little activity in the Canadian Hospital at that time, Harry Botterell arranged for leave in order to work with Jefferson in Manchester for a month or two. His visit proved stimulating and useful, since he saw patients for Jefferson when asked and took a part in teaching the junior staff, in addition to accompanying Jeff in whatever he was doing. Manchester was bombed on several occasions while he was there; the infirmary was hit and there were casualties among the staff. Jeff referred to this in a letter to Botterell later in the war: 'It is just two years ago since those horrid nights of noise, dirt, and emotional disturbance that you, personally, helped us so manfully to survive and to overcome. The peace of yesterday and of to-night call up feelings of deep thankfulness that the horror has not been repeated .... We are grateful to you all for having come to our aid at such sacrifice when we needed help so badly, and with such invigorating effect on all of us'[48].

Harry Botterell was with the Jeffersons for Christmas, when the house was quite full and Gertrude feared that the beds might be 'rather queer'. Coventry too had sustained severe bombardment at the end of November and, after visiting there, Geoffrey had gone on to Warwick, to which city the casualties had been evacuated, in order to see the situation regarding head injuries for himself. It was a time when one never knew when a raid would take place or what might be the target, and this was especially unnerving in large towns and railway centres. His anxious wife wrote: 'He is away again at the moment. In London today — at St Albans yesterday, and is due home at lunch time. I shall be very pleased to see him safely home'[49]. Jeff had paid a visit to Liverpool following the severe raids on that city, and his impressions were vivid. 'I shall never forget that weekend. What a dreadful time it was'[50]. He travelled a great deal during the war years in his capacity, in fact if not in name, as the chief civilian neurosurgeon, calling on the various neurosurgical centres that he had established throughout the country. 'These it was his delight to goad, inspire, and enliven by a series of pastoral visits', even when there had been no enemy activity[40].

Despite the precarious situation in which Britain found herself at the beginning of 1941, there were those who, even then, were looking towards the aftermath of the upheaval. Jefferson had received a letter from the Principal of Glasgow University in which he suggested that there might be a danger 'that there would arise a number of rather petty neurological units in Glasgow, and that this should be guarded against'[51]. Jefferson was asked to consider the matter and possibly use his influence eventually to create 'one substantial neurological unit'[51]. The result was a memorandum from Jeff in which he gave his whole-hearted support to the idea. Further letters at the end of January and in March confirmed the progress of the scheme, which was passed on to the Vice-Chancellor. The ultimate result was the creation, after the war was over, of the Institute of Neurological Sciences at the Southern General Hospital in Glasgow.

Hugh Cairns wrote an interesting letter to Jeff in February 1941: 'The Army are going ahead with the equipment of two more mobile neurosurgical units. I suppose it will take several months.... They knew about *your mobile units* [author's italics] and asked me if there was any likelihood that you might not need them after all. I said that I felt sure from our talk that you did not think there was any chance of a transfer at present; but that if the summer went by without your finding use for them I thought that you might be glad to have them transferred to another theatre of war where they might be more useful — but this, I said, was only supposition on my part. On this basis they decided to go ahead and build two more at once, since it takes about six months. Do you think this is all right?'[52]. The importance of this letter is that these civilian units, if they existed, must have done so in secret or still have been under construction, for there is no record of them in the official history of the EMS, and no personal memory of them has so far been traced. Cairns was responsible for the creation of Mobile Neurosurgical Units in the army, the first of which was donated by Lord Nuffield. That Unit was unfortunately captured after the fall of France, together with its staff, among whom was Willie Henderson; but it was soon replaced and seven more were commissioned during the war.

Richard Johnson, who had been a junior assistant to Jefferson, had left the Manchester Royal Infirmary at the end of 1940, though he was to return after the war was over. He sent Jeff some forceps from Thackray, the instrument maker, as 'a small and I fear much belated memento of my extremely profitable and happy year on the neurosurgical unit'[53]. After a spell at Hill End, in the St Bartholomew's EMS sector hospital near St Albans, where there was a 'constant dribble of air raid casualties'[53], he was posted to the Military Hospital for Head Injuries in Oxford, and then commanded one of the Mobile Neurosurgical Units (No 3) in India and Burma.

Jefferson had reported to the Brain Injuries Committee on the civilian head injuries that had so far been sustained as a result of air raids. Following this, in March 1941, EA Carmichael, a senior neurologist at Queen Square, wrote: 'I am sure that you will feel happy at the appreciation by the Services of your Report.... Whittingham writes in high praise of the report, and states that he would like to supply a copy to each of the R.A.F. Hospitals — 24 in all — for circulation to the medical staffs'[54].

In May, Jefferson visited Cambridge to give a lecture. Afterwards, the vote of thanks was proposed by Sir Charles Sherrington and seconded by ED Adrian; to have such eminent speakers to acknowledge his address was indeed a compliment in itself. On his way to Cambridge by train Jeff had travelled as far as Peterborough with Gertrude, and she met him there again on his return. Immediately after they got back to Manchester he drove directly on to Sheffield to see more head injuries. Gertrude, who had continued to accompany him, described contrasts of the kind that became so familiar during the war years. 'It was a lovely drive back over the Snake [Pass]—the cloud effects were wonderful, but it was very late for our dinner & we had just finished it when an alert went at 10.30...we slept in the cellar'[55]. Once again, only one meeting of the SBNS was held during the year and, as in 1940, the Radcliffe Infirmary, in Oxford, acted as host.

In the midst of a life of concentrated clinical and administrative work, Jeff yet found a place for his other interests. In a delightful letter to wish Antony good luck for his examinations, he asked various questions for his own information, such as 'what Reil's dates were and when he named the insula', and concerning Vieussens. He then delivered *obiter dicta* on the 'good' and 'bad' in music and poetry; remarks which he cannot have thought through very completely: 'I envy you your ecstatic listening of Bach. I love him because he is so simple. But some of his things seem dull to me. I suppose at bottom the difference between the good and bad [musicians] is that the good rise to great heights a few times, more rarely lots of times, but some of their work is dull. Its the same in writing, in poetry, the very best wrote some poor stuff, but their best is untouchable in quality. A time will come no doubt when instead of the Complete Poems of so and so, we have thin books called the "Good Poems of ——". At present we have "Selected Poems" but they always include rubbish. I believe that those little slips like you have of Eliot, Auden etc. are about as big as most greater poets could fill. Perhaps the greatest would be twice as thick. This must be true of music. I do hope you find the papers not the hardest for ten years'[56].

An article on scalp wounds had been written by Jefferson and even submitted to the editor of the *British Medical Journal*, who said he would accept it, but Jeff was worried that it was not up to standard. So in May he wrote to Harry Botterell at Basingstoke for his opinion: 'Do you think it is any good or not? Is the stuff on mechanism and types too juvenile, and if not do you think it is right?.... The voice of mediocrity is very loud'[57]. In reply, Botterell had recommended revision but Geoffrey had difficulty in finding the time to do this and excused himself. He wrote 'I have lost interest in the Scalp Wound affair'[58] and 'Geo. Riddoch and I are too fully occupied with "Rehabilitation" to allow time to think of anything else'[59]. However, in September 1941, he decided that he must get the paper out 'before blitzing starts seriously'[60]. Botterell agreed with this, and went so far as to suggest that Pennybacker, Northfield, McKissock and Rowbotham should be sent round the country to talk on the subject, so important did it seem to him[61]. The paper was eventually published in a shortened version in *The Practitioner*[62], but later expanded significantly for the *British Medical Journal*, with Botterell as joint author[63]. This gesture by Jeff of co-authorship, indicates that Botterell had made a considerable contribution to the work, for Jefferson had few collaborators. It was at the same time, an accolade for the Canadian.

Jefferson, through the Brain Injuries Committee, hoped furthermore to arrange for Botterell to analyse the cerebrospinal fluid (CSF) findings from head injuries in his Canadian Hospital and at the Military Hospital for Head Injuries in St Hugh's College, Oxford. John O'Connell, who was the senior neurosurgeon at Hill End, had been given the task of analysing the EMS cases 'and the idea is that you should work together and present a joint report to the MRC [Medical Research Council]'[58]. Jeff also suggested to Botterell that he should write a 'History of the Cerebellum . . . . I should have liked to hear that you were hard at it, for it would be a fascinating subject properly presented'[58]. Two months later he wrote to ask for news of the CSF report and to say that he had 'spent 3 days in London with Penfield [from Montreal] and Jim White [from Boston] last week and we had a grand time musketeering around. Now I have to go to London to-morrow, back again on the midnight train, two days here and off to Bristol on Friday'[60]. It may come as a surprise that, in spite of war conditions and the hazard of U-boat attacks on trans-Atlantic liners, the close relationship between British and north American neurosurgeons managed to continue. Jeff also paid a pastoral visit to Wales at the end of October[64].

In July 1939 an American neurosurgeon named William H Sweet had begun a planned research year at the National Hospital, Queen Square. When war was declared he generously felt that there must be a way in which he could lend a hand in the struggle against Nazi Germany, and hoped that he might be able to join one of the army's mobile neurosurgical units that had been organised by Cairns, who was now a Brigadier. However, 'the vagaries of war precluded that course of action'[65] for him and it was not until the early autumn of 1941 that the need for a neurosurgeon in Birmingham provided a suitable opening, and Jefferson arranged for Sweet to join the staff of the Queen Elizabeth Hospital in charge of the neurosurgical department there. He was one of a number of American doctors who gave their services to Britain during those crisis years, long before the United States entered the war, and who are owed a debt of gratitude. Established in Birmingham, Sweet felt the need for someone to whom he could go for clinical advice when it was needed, for he had not then had any previous experience as the head of a department. Jeff not only acted in the capacity of a freely available consultant to him but, to some extent, also filled a paternal rôle as Sweet's adviser in personal and professional matters, for the young American's father, who was also a surgeon, had died when his son was in his final year as a medical student. Bill Sweet very greatly appreciated Jeff's kindness and wisdom, and his ability to appraise events dispassionately and comprehensively, always in his characteristic and unhurried manner. Jefferson became, in Sweet's own words, 'the man whose example I have most sought to follow'[65]. In later years, as the head of the Neurosurgical Service at the Massachusetts General Hospital in Boston, he was to pass on some of this example to others.

Sweet was interested in trying to improve the reliability of Sjöqvist's operation for the relief of facial pain by cutting the pain tracts in the bulbar region of the brain stem. Jefferson saw the possibilities in a modification suggested by Sweet and not only encouraged him but supervised the new operation when he successfully performed it for the first time. Careful examination, on which Jefferson always insisted, of the sensory loss thereby produced, led to further discoveries concerning the pain pathways in the neighbourhood of the lower end of the fourth ventricle and their local distribution. When this work was published Jeff generously did not allow his name to be associated with it, giving all the credit to the author[65,66].

In November Botterell became Chief of Neurosurgery at the Canadian Neurological Hospital at Hackwood Park, with the rank of Lieutenant Colonel. Jefferson, who never allowed an opportunity to escape, was not slow to react to this news. It would be 'a chance to canalize your abounding energies.... Lets have a clinical meeting and everybody read a paper on something'. Botterell agreed[67].

It was in the December of that year, 1941, that FK Kessel came to work for Jefferson. He was about 40 years old, and a fully trained neurosurgeon. As such he was able to provide much needed help with some of the operating, especially during the many days when Jeff was away from Manchester. In addition, Kessel saw some of the private patients when requested. He remained in Manchester until about 1948, when he went to live and work in Switzerland.

Gertrude Jefferson was Chairman of the Manchester Branch of the Medical Women's Federation at about this time. Numbers of workers, especially women, had been sent to factories all over the country to take the place of the male employees and to fill the jobs created by the need for armaments and all the other essential requirements of a country at war. Manchester, being an industrial centre, had received large numbers of these women, who were billeted in houses in and around the city. Gertrude wrote, in an undated report on behalf of the Federation, that: 'It would seem that a considerable amount of disease is being brought into this district by transferred industrial workers'[68]. She gave several examples and concluded her report by advocating that pressure should be brought about 'to enforce legislation for a full compulsory medical examination of industrial workers at their place of origin. This would have the advantage of ensuring treatment for those who need it and would avoid the unnecessary spreading of disease in other towns'[68]. Unfortunately this suggestion was not adopted, and the problem remained. Her work in the Maternity and Child Welfare Clinics, among her private patients and outpatients at the Royal Infirmary, and among those who simply lent on her for support and advice, was now augmented by more general responsibilities which filled her time to such an extent that whenever she was at home she was always kept busy writing letters or seeing people who visited her at High Bank. This was made possible by Bridget and the help of her secretary, Elizabeth Bridge.

As an interesting aside, Antony Jefferson had written to his mother from Oxford in the summer of 1941: 'I had dinner with the Medical Society lecturer, a Russian called Chain, the other evening...Florey and some other guys have got hold of some red-hot stuff...the publication is not yet out. They've got some stuff they call Penicillin which they've isolated pretty pure...extracted from a mould called penicillium notatum. It has the same range as M&B and the other sulphonamide drugs, with the advantage that its terrifically more potent as a bactericide, is non-toxic, the patients feel better not worse after injection and it...can be used in suppurating wounds etc. where the sulphonamides are destroyed'[69]. He did not mention how extremely painful the early three or four hourly intramuscular injections of the, relatively impure, substance were. Only very small amounts were then available and, in 1941, they were reserved for service personnel only. Hugh Cairns, Ian Fraser and Howard Florey were shortly to take it to the armies in North Africa and Italy, where its value was shown to exceed even their high expectations. This discovery was a pivotal point in the future of medicine, and may have had some influence on the outcome of the war.

REFERENCES

GJ=Geoffrey Jefferson; GMJ=Gertrude Jefferson; EHB=Harry Botterell
1   Dunn CL. The emergency medical services. In: MacNalty A, ed. *The medical history of the second World War*. London: HM Stationery Office, 1952.
2   Fraenkel CJ. *Hugh Cairns*. Oxford: Oxford University Press, 1991: 136.
3   Rowbotham GF. Epidermoids arising in the diploë of the bones of the skull. *Br J Surg* 1939; **26**: 506–14.
4   Rowbotham GF. Hyperostosis in relation with the meningiomas. *Br J Surg* 1939; **26**: 593–623.
5   GJ to Rowbotham GF. Letter 15th January 1939.
6   GJ to Jefferson, Antony. Letters 19th and 27th January 1939.
7   GJ to Cushing H. Letter 28th January 1939.
8   Cushing H to GJ. Letter 10th February 1939.
9   GJ MS Address on *Contributions of neurosurgery to neuro-physiology*. 7th February 1939.
10 Dott N to GJ. Letter quoted by Rush C, Shaw GF. In: *With sharp compassion — Norman Dott*. Aberdeen: Aberdeen University Press, 1990: 165.
11 Jefferson, Michael. Personal communication.
12 GJ to Cushing H. Letter 30th March 1939.
13 Cushing H to GJ, Letter 7th April 1939.
14 GJ to the owner of High Bank. Letter undated fragment.
15 Jefferson, Antony. Personal communication.
16 GMJ to Jefferson, Antony. Letter 9th May 1939.
17 GMJ to Jefferson, Antony. Letter 12th June 1939.
18 Cairns H to GMJ. Letter 20th September 1939.
19 GJ to Jefferson, Antony. Letter 21st May 1939.
20 Twining EW. Radiology of the third and fourth ventricles. *Br J Surg* 1939; **12**: 385–416, 569–600.
21 GMJ to Jefferson, Antony. Letter 9th May 1939.
22 GJ to Jefferson, Antony. Letter 12th June 1939.
23 GJ. MS *Summary of the neurosurgical facilities in Britain in June 1939*.
24 GJ. MS *Large scale planning for head injuries*. Undated.
25 Jefferson G. The special field of neurosurgery. *BMJ* 1030; **1**: 147–50.
26 Jefferson G. War wounds of the head. *BMJ* 1939; **2**: 347–9, 407–10.
27 Jefferson G, Jackson H. Tumours of the lateral and third ventricles. *Proc Roy Soc Med* 1939; **32**: 1105–37.
28 Jefferson G. Tumours of the frontal lobe. *Postgrad Med J* 1939; **1**: 170–8.
29 Jefferson G. Letter *Lancet* 1939; **2**: 856–7.
30 Jefferson G. Letter *BMJ* 1939; **2**: 832.
31 Fulton J to GJ. Letter 3rd November 1939.
32 Fulton J. *Harvey Cushing — a biography*. Oxford: Blackwell, 1946.
33 Jefferson G. *The invasive adenomas of the anterior pituitary*. Liverpool: Liverpool University Press, 1955.
34 Jefferson G. Extrasellar extensions of the pituitary adenomas. *Proc Roy Soc Med* 1940; **33**: 433–58.
35 Jefferson G. Discussion on recent experiences with gunshot wounds of the head. *J Neurol Neurosurg Psychiat* 1940; **3**: 343–6.
36 EHB to GJ. Letter 19th March 1947.
37 GJ to EHB. Letter 11th August 1955.
38 Guthkelch N. Personal communication.
39 Hardman J. Professor Jefferson as a teacher. *Manchester Medical Students' Gazette* 1946; **25**: 52–5.
40 Himsworth H. *Sir Geoffrey Jefferson*. In: *The dictionary of national biography 1961–1970*. Oxford: Oxford University Press.
41 GJ to Rowbotham GF. Letter 28th August 1940.
42 Jefferson G. The nature of concussion. *BMJ* 1944; **1**: 1–5.
43 Jefferson G. *Selected papers*. London: Pitman Medical, 1959.

44 Jefferson G. In memoriam Harvey Cushing. *Br J Surg* 1940; **27**: 442–6.
45 Jefferson G. Tumours of the optic nerve. *Proc Roy Soc Med* 1940; **33**: 688–90.
46 Jefferson G. Cervical spine dislocations. *Proc Roy Soc Med* 1940; **33**: 657.
47 Jefferson G. Discussion on fractures and dislocations of the cervical vertebrae. *Proc Roy Soc Med* 1940; **33**: 651–60.
48 GJ to EHB. Letter 22nd December 1942.
49 GMJ to Jefferson, Antony. Letter 1st December 1940.
50 GJ to EHB. Letter 18th May 1941.
51 Russell J to GJ. Letter 7th January 1941.
52 Cairns H to GJ. Letter 20th February 1941.
53 Johnson RT to GJ. Letter 28th January 1941.
54 Carmichael EA to GJ. Letter 13th March 1941.
55 GMJ to Jefferson, Antony. Letter 2nd May 1941.
56 GJ to Jefferson, Antony. Letter 30th June 1941.
57 GJ to EHB. Letter 12th May 1941.
58 GJ to EHB. Letter 9th July 1941.
59 GJ to EHB. Letter 15th July 1941.
60 GJ to EHB. Letter 9th September 1941.
61 EHB to GJ. Letter 29th November 1941.
62 Jefferson G. The treatment of scalp wounds. *The Practitioner* 1941; **12**: 164–5.
63 Botterell EH, Jefferson G. Treatment of scalp wounds in air-raid and other casualties. *BMJ* 1942; **1**: 781–3.
64 GMJ to Jefferson, Antony. Letter 4th October 1941.
65 Sweet WH. Personal communication.
66 Sweet WH. Medullary tractotomy of descending cephalic pain pathways. In: White JC, Sweet WH. *Pain and the neurosurgeon.* Springfield Ill: Charles C Thomas, 1969: 627–32.
67 GJ to EHB. Letters 24th November 1941 and reply of 29th November 1941.
68 GMJ. MS Undated report on behalf of the Medical Women's Federation.
69 Jefferson, Antony to GMJ. Letter 8th June 1941.

Chapter 17

World War II
1942–1943

The German invasion of Russia took place in June 1941 and by December its armies had reached the suburbs of Moscow. The beginning of 1942 saw Hitler's forces concentrated in Russia, while he assumed that Britain was in a sufficiently precarious military position for her surrender to be inevitable, and there was therefore a pause in the threat of offensive activity against the United Kingdom, apart from the continued bombing of her cities. At the same time, the Battle of Britain was being fought and won in the air and the Battle of the Atlantic continued at sea. Actual invasion of the British mainland was not seriously considered by the Germans until it became apparent that the expected surrender was not going to take place. The failure to invade allowed the Royal Air Force to build up its resources until it had sufficient strength to attack Germany in return. This prompted Hitler to order the ill-planned operation code-named *Sealion*, for which barges were assembled in the French channel ports preparatory to a proposed invasion across the English Channel in October. However, the barges were destroyed and the threat of invasion came to nothing.

In Africa the tide of battle had gone back and forth along the northern coast. June 1942 found the British forces driven back to within the borders of Egypt. But, like other tides, it turned once more, and this time decisively. The counter-offensive of the battle of Alamein began on 23rd October. From then on, although there were set-backs, the balance began to go in favour of the allied armies and against the Axis forces of Germany and Italy. The year 1942 was to see a turning point against Germany, on the Russian front as well.

At home, Geoffrey Jefferson continued to look after the neurosurgical services in Manchester, and in the country as a whole. Anxiety at the prospect of invasion with only the almost token preparations to counter it, gradually became replaced by a new pride in what was slowly being achieved and the realisation, leading to conviction, that victory could eventually be won.

During January 1942, Jefferson's correspondence included a letter from Cairns thanking him for reprints of Jeff's papers, and congratulating him on his achievements. 'You have managed to get your spirit and personality into every page, and that is still the most important thing in life, even though it cannot be weighed and measured.... When doctors can write as you do, they should do it every day. Perhaps when the boys are qualified you will be able to profess without having to do outside practice, and with the University paying you a good salary and allowing practice in the MRI'[1].

Considering the desperate war situation, it is interesting that Jeff also received a letter from Henry Schuman, a dealer in rare books in New York, in response to a request for a copy of the special catalogue of Cushing's works that had been issued to mark his 70th birthday. Mr Schuman wrote: 'I don't mean to play hard to get, but actually there is but a solitary copy remaining, not including our file copy. I am glad to send it, and shall feel that it could not have been relinquished into more suitable hands than those of a distinguished colleague and co-worker of Dr Cushing'[2].

In the last week of February, Jefferson gave the Dr John Burns lecture to the Faculty of Physicians and Surgeons of Glasgow. He spoke on the acute head injury as a neurological problem[3]. The subject gave him the opportunity to expound his approach to clinical problems in terms of the disturbances of neurophysiology that they caused. This sound basis for diagnosis carried the greatest security against error that could be achieved before the advent of brain scanning, and it still remains as necessary a method as it was then.

Antony Jefferson had applied for one of the dozen or so Rockefeller scholarships that had been offered in order to enable a few medical students to complete their training in the United States or Canada. His father and mother passed on the wise advice that he should bear in mind that 'should you feel that after the war you wanted to live in Canada or USA you would not get much chance in the way of plums in research or better jobs except in the University where you had been as a student'[4]. Clearly they pointed the way quite strongly towards McGill University in Montreal where, incidentally, Wilder Penfield was to be found, but they actually suggested putting Harvard forward as his first choice[4]. At the end of May Gertrude was able to send loving and enthusiastic congratulations to Antony on obtaining one of the scholarships. 'We are all united in our pleasure and excitement over the news.... It is lovely to think that you will get, even indirectly, in touch with the places and people who were part of the old days'[5]. She gave him the news that Jeff was studying the works of Marshall Hall, Bridget had a cold and various guests had been coming and going at High Bank[5]. Jeff sent him a telegram, that was followed by a letter in which he also mentioned how busy he was, not only with the Ministry of Health but also preparing lectures and articles, 'a total of 6 on the stocks, all to be out this year, bless me. I suppose if I do get them out I can order myself a neon halo. I should be entitled to it'[6]. Antony was soon to be accepted by McGill University.

Not every action that Jefferson took, as part of his organisation of neurosurgery in the EMS, was universally appreciated. There could be no better example, however, of real appreciation than a letter from Wylie McKissock, who was in charge of a temporary neurosurgical unit attached to Leavesden Emergency Hospital (University College Hospital) near Watford, Hertfordshire. 'Any success we have been able to achieve here in Leavesden has become possible only by reason of your unfailing help and encouragement and every member of my team is deeply sensible of this'[7]. The idea of a unit in which all the patients were together, in wards that were close to a specialised operating theatre and x-ray department, was new to most surgeons in Britain at this time. McKissock continued... 'I have realised how great an advantage it is to have every patient continuously under my control; you may be sure that, when the war is over, I shall be one of the first to co-operate in the development of neurological surgery along improved lines'[7]. The lines to which he referred were those long envisaged and frequently advocated by Jefferson, and they finally became the foundation upon which post-war neurosurgery developed in Britain.

A protégé, Martin Nichols, wrote to Geoffrey from a prisoner of war camp in Germany on 31st March 1942, asking for neurosurgical news and worrying about his future. In the event he became a consultant to a new unit in Aberdeen after the war was over. However, he was able to give no information concerning the welfare of Willie Henderson, who had been taken prisoner with him and the rest of the personnel of No. 1 Mobile Neurosurgical Unit[8].

Acceptance of the scalp wound paper by the *British Medical Journal*[9] enabled Jeff to pass on the news of its future publication to Harry Botterell, together with a copy of a book by Damon Runyon. Their friendship was expanding beyond the confines of neurosurgery, and perhaps Jeff sought to establish something of the literary give and take that there used to be in the letters he had exchanged with Gertrude in his youth. When the proofs of the scalp wound paper came through, he sent them to Botterell to scrutinise[10]. Among Jefferson's publications in 1942, there was one which defined his views on the future of specialisation. 'Every specialty looks mighty queer to the other fellow.... One of the chief bars to progress is the conviction of the general physician or surgeon of his superiority which is, in the end...derived from the historical beginnings of medicine.... I shall be content if I can wring from him an admission that in a properly balanced hospital scheme less space must be allotted to him in the future'[11]. Jefferson's foresight was to be realised in due course.

In July 1942, Jeff was planning the programme for a meeting of the SBNS at Queen Square due to be held in the autumn, and he wrote to Harry Botterell about it. There was to be a discussion on the treatment of prolapsed intervertebral discs, with Botterell proposing surgical treatment and Harvey Jackson opposing it, followed by John O'Connell, who had operated on 30 or 40 cases, and then Joe Pennybacker 'to close the discussion with his hundred cases.... I think it is a good plan to get some of the "antis" in before the "pros"'[12]. Mixter and Barr had elucidated the pathology of disc prolapse more than 6 years earlier but, in 1942, there was fairly widespread scepticism about the wisdom of operating for it, particularly among British neurologists. Referring to another occasion, the letter continued: 'In the afternoon of August 1st I shall want you to do the subdural haematomas. I am looking forward to it'[12]. Invitations from Jefferson of this sort were virtual commands.

The Medical Research Council's subcommittee on Brain Injuries was due to hold a meeting on 28th of August, and Jefferson was arranging for Botterell to present his report on the cerebrospinal fluid findings in head injury cases to the members though, as it happened, he was unable to do so in person. Writing to Botterell earlier in the month, Jeff suggested that the report should be studied by four neurosurgeons plus Paterson Ross (a general surgeon who had collaborated with Botterell in producing it). 'I think', Jefferson wrote, confident that the remark would go no further, that 'if we get rid of the physicians we should get something done'[13].

Alarming news was then received by the Jeffersons, that Antony's ship had been torpedoed on its way to the United States. He had been rescued from a raft by a destroyer which had been accompanying the convoy, after sliding down a rope over the ship's side and burning his fingers in the process. The result of this was that he lost all his baggage and landed in Nova Scotia instead of New York, with no documents and no luggage. He travelled to Montreal, where the

Penfields could not have been kinder. They reclothed him, and Wilder Penfield became his guide and adviser during his medical course at McGill. Penfield's colleague, William Cone, and his wife were also very good to him. Jeff almost at once received a sympathetic letter from Hugh Cairns: 'Antony seems blessed with a happy mixture of energy and tranquillity and [will] be none the worse for it. But that doesn't make it much easier for the parents'[14]. He also gave Geoffrey Jefferson a warning that Joe Schorstein, who had been working in Manchester, would soon be called up to join the RAMC. When that happened, Schorstein was replaced by a Canadian, RA Bailey, as Chief Assistant.

In a letter to Antony, his father wrote: 'We were of course deeply interested in all that you had to tell us.... I am sorry you got torpedoed, you were just unlucky. I expect you regret your beautiful clarinet above all else.... It will be a long time before we see you again, confound it, but its just as bad for so many thousands of folk whose sons and husbands have gone overseas. Nor will they all come back, poor things. However that won't do, no depression allowed'[15]. It was a delightful letter, full of questions about life in Canada. 'I suppose you went up by train, and haven't their engines lovely whistles. I feel quite homesick for that smell and the sound of an engine whistle in the distance, which spells America to me'[15]. There was also plenty of news of Jeff's doings at home, including the award of an Honorary FRFPS from the Faculty of Physicians and Surgeons of Glasgow. Unfortunately, Jefferson was taken ill on the day he was to receive the diploma, and it was given *in absentia*!

Jeff had escaped to Temple Sowerby, in Cumberland, for a brief holiday early in September 1942, and he wrote from there to Botterell asking for a description of his neurosurgical experiences consequent upon the recent and tragic raid on Dieppe that had taken place on 19th August, in which Canadian troops had suffered severely. He explained, using Osler's nickname for Gertrude and thereby revealing how close their friendship had become: 'Trotula and I are up here with the Morley's fishing—well you know what I mean—its raining like mad, the rivers are in flood and thick with mud, tree trunks and so on—perfectly hopeless. Its always wrong for fishing—too little or too much, too soon or too late, too fine or too wet.... I've been reading a biography of Sir Wm Macewen and am confirmed in my belief that a history of neurology must be painfully written bit by bit, as the author overpraises him neurosurgically through ignorance of the background against which he must be seen. I rely on you for the history of the cerebellum. Its a cultural exercise that will determine your future for you, don't be put off by its difficulty and make a small start this winter if nothing special has happened. I think, though, that something special will happen—its anybody's guess'[16]. The proposed history of the cerebellum was never written[17].

There was an ominous remark in a letter, dated 23rd September 1942, written to Antony who had by now enrolled as medical student at McGill University, Montreal. 'I've had another abdominal pain episode for twenty four hours but am all right again. I spent it reading Thomas Browne's* letters. I cannot do better

---

*Sir Thomas Browne (1605–1682) Physician of Norwich, who had studied medicine at Oxford, Montpellier, Padua and Leyden. Author of *Religio Medici*, the most famous of several well-known works by him. His *Christian Morals* was published posthumously in 1756, when it was edited by Samuel Johnson.

than conclude with a copy of a letter from Lady Browne to their son Tom. Spelling was her weakness. "Dear Tom, I am glad to hear that you will judge prudently of things and if you do not find them according to expectation com home to us a gaine. If you want more monyes then you thinke fit to take of my cosen...but be suer to spend as lettle as you can." '[18]. Advice which was apt in the circumstances, if not entirely practical.

Jefferson had put forward plans for a Neurological Institute in Manchester in a letter to Sir John Stopford, the Vice-Chancellor of the University, who replied hopefully at the beginning of October: '[The Neurological Institute] is very near to my heart and therefore I welcome the proposal that it should be put forward for prior consideration by the Nuffield Trust'[19]. This was very welcome encouragement for Jeff, who was still unwell. The abdominal pains had persisted and it was clear that another attack of peritonitis had developed as a result of the chronic diverticulitis from which he continued to suffer. 'I am laid up again', he wrote to Antony at the end of the month, 'I have had the usual disgusting Autumn cold and cough, one of my biennial lay-ups.... Well right on top of that I've had a recurrence of my diverticulitis which got so bad yesterday that I could scarcely walk about. I came to bed and shall be fit to operate tomorrow. I am only doing so because I must (see a doctor) and shall return to bed. I think I shall go to Ruthin [the hospital at Ruthin Castle, Clwyd, North Wales] for a couple of weeks' treatment because I've had this blight for about 2 mos. now in attacks. What happens is that I get a mild pelvic peritonitis that quickly subsides, but it's tender and painful on movement, rapidly subsiding with rest'[20]. There was also news that Michael, who had now graduated in medicine with degrees from Oxford University, would soon be called up for service in the RAMC. Jeff reported that he had acquired four volumes of John Hunter's complete works (1835 edition). Several dealers in old medical books kept him informed when something turned up that might interest him. However, the demands of work and the incapacity resulting from his illness had interfered with his routine, and he was despondent. 'I have not progressed one millimetre in my own writings in two months, a bad, black record'[20].

In reply to a letter from Jeff, Harry Botterell had said, 'I think we are all becoming "Parlour Socialists" regarding medicine'[21]. To this Jefferson responded from his bed at Ruthin Castle: 'I do not mind you being a socialist at all because I know that you are the same sort as me, varying from extreme right to extreme left all in the course of 24 hours. The only doctrine I will not swallow is communism. I shall never accept the notion that all men are born equal in a biological sense.... I am laid up more or less by my blasted diverticulitis. I have had an awful time this last month with one indisposition after another, and I am beginning to feel both depressed and angry'[22]. Gertrude was anxious too and was trying to arrange to visit Ruthin for a few days, though her Manchester commitments made it difficult for her to do so[23]. Jefferson's progress was slow, and a month later he was still in hospital. But he wrote to Botterell on 27th November: 'I am recovered, having all sorts of humiliating treatment and tomorrow the further indignity of a squirt of Barium. I'm going home Sat. to do a couple of operations, going to London for Thursday's meeting at [the] Ministry and then back here for another week'[24]. The demands that Jeff was putting on himself were determined by his own conscientiousness, but may also have had something to do with his knowledge of the sacrifices being made by those in uniform.

Cairns wrote to Jefferson from Oxford, giving his views on the future deployment of various neurosurgeons when the war ended. 'I have been thinking lately about post-war arrangements for head injuries, and I would like to have a talk with you about it all soon. I was sorry to learn that you had gone to Ruthin Castle, but relieved to know from your letter that it was in the nature of a rest, for purposes of contemplation. You ought to have more of such periods, because it seems to me that something good always comes out of your periods of communion with yourself'[25]. Cairns does not seem to have appreciated that 'rest' in Jeff's terminology meant the medical alternative to surgery, neither did he realise just how ill his friend had been. Incidentally, Cairns was also asserting his intention to have more than a little say in 'post-war arrangements'.

Back at Ruthin Castle at the beginning of December, Jefferson wrote a note for his diary: 'I came here because ever since the Monday in Sept. when at Temple Sowerby, that day I had to go to Glasgow and didn't go to get my Honorary FRFPS, I've had 3 fairly bad attacks of pain in the lower abdomen with pelvic peritonitis in the 1st and 3rd. So John Morley got me in here with Sir Edmund Spriggs and Dr. Paterson'[26]. Fortunately, there was a library in the hospital of which Jeff made good use. He was upset because Antony had read an article by an American criticising the English for not getting rid 'of their stupid castles...and so on', and he was angry with the Canadians for deploring his son's English accent. This produced a minor outburst in reply: 'I was pleased to be reminded that it was Englishmen who brought about and carried through the War of Independence and wrote the Declaration of Independence' he expostulated[27]. Jeff was writing to Antony from his bed. The letter continued: 'Well, the Beveridge Report [proposing a National Health Service and Social Security] is out and is the absolute apotheosis of boredom, though hailed by all as a great work. I daresay it is but its interest is mainly for actuaries. There's no poetry in this report, and, by golly, very little imagination. I see my profession (and yours to be) turn into a State Service. Very well, I don't mind, I quite welcome it. I know very well that a Jefferson ends up at the top whatever the rules of the game are. Whilst I am comforted to see that £20 will be paid for my burial expenses. So look out for the new aristocracy, the undertakers, my lad, that's who..., they will turn into "Morticians". I wonder whether you had better take a Morticians course, at £20 a wallop; counting the number of folk who die every day, it should be the best "profession" in England.... I'm here another week for more humiliating treatment but x-rays a week ago show my colon looking less second-hand'[27]. He did, however, add a postscript which was more generous to the Report, in which he said: 'I feel that this is a somewhat irresponsible comment on Beveridge, fundamentally its sound and will be accepted, the people will demand it. I wish that other countries would do the same—we're such pioneers, the States have nothing nearly so democratic as our pensions for the common man even now. They'll be way behind now'[27].

With time temporarily on his hands Jefferson, as usual, wrote notes describing and recording his random thoughts. He had been very pleased with his address on the acute head injury as a neurological problem[3], which he had given in

Glasgow. 'But I don't suppose anyone will write to me about it. Reminds me of
what Lewis Weed said to me in Gordon Holmes drawing room at 9 Wimpole St
over tea, the pleasant front room with his small Rembrandt etching in it, — a
summer day early in August 1938 I think — Weed said folk always clamoured for
reprints of his less important stuff and left him with wads of reprints on his
hands of the really (in his view) important stuff'[26].

Allowing his thoughts further freedom, Jeff set down more ideas. 'I told Rock
Carling something of my views on conversation, started by FR Lindsay's
question: "Is there anything worth discussing?" The decay of religious beliefs
and the rise of science had left nothing but facts to talk of and they were dull, you
could only make statements which, as Dr Johnson said of questioning, is not a
form of conversation suitable for gentlemen! But I don't think Lindsay's right, we
talk for preference very little about what we know for certain (i.e. scientific
measurement, knowledge) I never do. It does not seem to be suitable for
conversation. I conclude that we talk to extract, not impart, information — to hear
what others have to say or to find out what we think ourselves by "behaving" in
a conventional way (Lloyd Morgan's *Meaning of behaving*). Otherwise as Lindsay
says there is nothing to talk about but other people's lives, which he decides is
not a fit subject — but God bless us all this is probably the No 1 subject among the
$\frac{1}{2}$ or un-educated population of the world and represents 95% of what passes for
talk between friends. I was always impressed by the avoidance by Harvey
Cushing of talk about contemporary personalities, he rarely spoke of them
though he spoke often enough of the heroes of his youth and so on. I'm writing
this with Cushing's fountain pen that he gave me at New Haven in 1937'[26]. He
had spent 2 hours in the library that day, and notes on ten or more books
followed these comments. He probably returned home for Christmas.

However, at the beginning of February 1943 Jefferson was once more back in
hospital at Ruthin Castle, writing again to Antony: 'I went in last time feeling bad
(mainly tired) and came out better. This time I went in fine and came out
lousy...but I've recovered'[28]. Despite his recent illness, he planned to visit
Canada and the United States in May for a lecture tour sponsored by the British
government, and he hoped that he and Antony would be able to meet again then.
For some unknown reason, though possibly because the arrangements were
awaiting finalisation, this letter was not posted but was enclosed with another,
written a little over a month later. In this Jeff complained that his clinical work
load was keeping him from writing papers. 'I get no time to go over material and
work it up. I ought to stop operating — the trouble is that I do it so much better
than anybody else. This is not complete vanity, a bit perhaps'[29]. It is, however, the
reason often given by those who have some difficulty in delegating
responsibility.

About the 18th April Geoffrey went to London with Gertrude and stayed at the
Paddington Hotel to await news of the departure of his plane for the United
States. At the hotel he passed the time once more, by writing musingly,
introspectively and perhaps a little apprehensively: 'I've had an interesting life, I
wouldn't like to live it over again, I might do worse. There's been a lot of fun and
there's still a lot to come, but I certainly am beginning to feel older. I think I
operate better than ever, with more judgement.... I can now, I think, do pretty
well what I want technically, succeed in doing nothing wrong.... But there's still

a lot to do. I wish I hadn't to spend so much time planning things — not only the EMS, and the Neurol. Inst. but the shape of neurosurgery after the war. I quite like planning except that one has to keep at it so long and it uses up energy.... I want to write more scientific things and some philosophical ones too — the soul for instance — that is pretty well roughed out, and a life of Cushing* that would be a synoptic history of neurosurgery.... I've got over any wish to be in London now. That's a very recent thing and I don't know its reason, for the number of folk with real leisure in M/C [Manchester] is very few.... How I miss Twining, we just vitalised one another somehow, stimulated one another, made one another think better. He was a lovely man.... Yes, I have enjoyed life. Such suffering as I've had, and this had [sic] been a good deal — tho' whether more than other folks I wouldn't know — probably not than many with the instability that a curious and experimental mind always must have. [That] I have had enough ballast not to do anything hopelessly foolish, though fairly bad maybe, has been due to my temperament and is or was my own fault. Trude has been a great help, so intelligent and she's provided a lot of antibodies that I needed. God help and bless her, the love'[30].

These notes were intended to be the beginning of a diary of his journey, and Jefferson mulled over his forthcoming tour and various possible projects. In his writing there is more than a hint of anxiety, as well as a suggestion that he was putting down certain notes for the benefit of posterity, should he fail to survive. 'If I get bumped off I will be an angry ghost haunting around. So much still to do. I need a good ten years of it yet.... There's the follow up on the last War cases, which is a very rough diamond in need of the polishers art'[30]. He must have been considering undertaking a long-term follow-up of his 1914–18 head injuries; he never managed to do this, though the wording implies that a start had been made. Further, he had read an article on Descartes, which stimulated him to consider that philosopher's 'notion that true ideas were always clear and distinct... [this must be] one of the greatest fallacies of all time, as its author unwittingly proved.... I wish I knew where to publish my Pineal article on Descartes — I wish I'd written it, if it comes to that. I really must get on and finish the history of concussion. I could do it in a three mos. period I think. But I shall have to make some money to pay my collosal income tax. What a slogging labour it will be'[30]. In this extract one has a glimpse of the sequence of ideas recorded by Jeff just as they came to his mind, and with the thinnest of threads connecting them. There followed a list of five papers that he proposed to write, all of which were eventually published.

After almost a week of waiting he finally left for America, starting the journey on a special train to Bristol. He flew from there in a 'land plane... after an oral and written examination by the Passport, Customs and Censorship Authorities' to Limerick, in the Irish republic, where there was another delay. Next evening they flew in a flying boat from Foynes, opposite Shannon airport, to Lisbon where they arrived in the early hours of 27th April. He spent the day in Estoril with Egas

---

*Cushing. Though by no means a 'synoptic history of neurosurgery', Jefferson did publish an excellent article on Cushing in a biographical series in the *Manchester Medical Students' Gazette* in 1943. Two years later, this was followed by one on Cushing's books in a different journal. He never wrote a history of neurosurgery. (Harvey Cushing. *Manchester Medical Student's Gazette* 1943; **22**: 7–46 and Harvey Cushing and his books. *J Hist Med Allied Sci* 1945; **1**: 246–53).

Moniz and Almeida Lima. At about 7 pm he rejoined the plane which flew over Casablanca and Dakar to Bolam in what was then Portuguese Guinea, now Guinea Bissau. After passing a further 24 hours on the ground, the plane flew on to Liberia, where it landed on 'Fisherman's Lake'. He now joined a Boeing flying boat of Pan American Airways, which may possibly have been the same one in which he had left from Ireland, and flew during the night to Port Natal in Brazil, north of Recife from where, after a short stop for refuelling, they went on to Bolem further up the coast. One of the four engines needed repair, so they spent the day there. Tantalisingly, the manuscript ends at this point and we do not have a record of the number of stops there were from here to his destination in Montreal. His absence from England on his own, having so recently been ill, was clearly a source of much worry for Gertrude, quite apart from the anxiety induced by air travel itself in 1943. Jefferson's proposed itinerary in Canada and America was extremely demanding, for the plan was to visit Montreal, Toronto, Ottawa, New York, Detroit, St Louis, Boston, 'and I bet Ann Arbor, Chicago and the Mayo Clinic come in too'; so wrote Geoffrey in his notes[30].

A number of letters associated with this undertaking have survived. They included invitations to visit various clinics, or comments on visits that Jefferson had already made. Typical is one from Ann Arbor, Michigan, in which Max Peet says: 'I am so sorry you could not stay longer with us. There were so many things I wanted to discuss with you and never had a chance. Could you possibly come back after visiting Toronto? .... You did not look around your room carefully before leaving. Mrs Peet found the two enclosed [dollar] bills on the table behind the door. You may need them before you get back home'[31]. In other letters he was asked to give a talk in Montreal at McGill University, to visit Kenneth McKenzie's 'Cabin' and see if Antony could join them for the weekend, to take part in a meeting of the American Psychiatric Association and the International League against Epilepsy, and also to attend a meeting of the Neurological Subcommittee of the National Research Council in San Francisco. All this in addition to an already overcrowded schedule.

Having apparently received a letter from Geoffrey that was written in a somewhat apprehensive vein while he was waiting to depart, Gertrude wrote in reply as soon as she heard that he had arrived safely: 'Your letter meant a great deal to me, more than I can say — but did add temporarily to my nervousness by its suggestion of a permanent farewell .... By Easter Monday evening my ability to have faith was re-established & by the time the cable came I already felt sure you had arrived safely. Thanks be to God'[32].

The tour went ahead as planned, and Jefferson wrote an excited letter to Antony from New Haven on 17th May, telling him 'I had dinner with the Whiteheads* last night, and they've asked me to go in and talk to them another night.... I was thrilled by the couple'[33]. He had previously written in his diary: 'Whenever I feel cocky I ought to read Whitehead (I've just been reading some *Adventures of ideas*) — the limitless range of things to be known is gratifying.

---

*Whitehead, Alfred N. (1861–1947), British-American mathematician and philosopher who collaborated with Bertrand Russell in writing his *Principia mathematica*. Among Whitehead's many works are those in which he formulated a tentative philosophy, aimed at unifying all the complex components of the world, in order to provide an effective guide for living. His *Adventures of ideas* was published in 1933.

There's no doubt that when one is absorbed in a scientific problem one is in need of a corrective'[30].

The second visit to the Whiteheads having taken place, Geoffrey described the event to Gertrude: 'On Thursday night I went to see the Whiteheads by myself and was there from 9.0–1.0 am. He doesn't go to bed till 2.0 because he doesn't sleep v. well. I had a delightful evening, they are a charming pair.... The following are jottings made between 1 and 2 am. when I got back'.

'**A.N.W.** "The Brain is a storehouse of the body's experience" — I think he's right in a big sense that one can't properly think of the nervous system existing apart from the body. He's very keen on feeling, of the feeling of all of oneself, "body image" though he doesn't know the term. He knows no neurology.'

'**Mrs W.** on Bertrand Russell — "Bertie is clever, oh intensely clever, but he's not wise, oh no! He is one of those folk who can express everything in words and thinks that there is no more to say. He has never had any difficulty in expression but he's missed a lot."'

'**A.N.W.** — feels that thoughts are so difficult to express, that there is so much pre-supposition in sentences and that deep thought carries these pre-suppositions that may not be shared by other people. He holds quite different views from Russell in this important way. He got nearest to what he wants to say in *Adventures of Ideas* after trying to do it for years.' On the difficulty of turning sense into words which were in fact unnecessary: 'That was a view that "Bertie" could never have understood. "He was always so sure".'

'**A.N.W.** on Julian Huxley — a lovely phrase — "He's encased in his own certainty". He disapproves deeply of JH's finality of belief chopping the world off now and not admitting how much there is to know. "He's so afraid of nonsense"! As if this was a crime! Adventure was the great thing, one must adventure in ideas, "Every single fact or law that I was taught in mathematical physics between 1880–1885 has been altered." But few good beliefs need total alteration. So amazed by "dogmatism of scientists, as bad as ever the theologians were. If they would only admit the tentativeness of what they do and of the rules and laws they make".'

'**A.N.W's** views on God given in the last chapter of *Advent. of Ideas*. He said he had not dared to use the name God — I forget what he does call him or it. Told him what Prof. Robinson said to me of the difficulty of knowing what W. means by God. He said with a laugh that he didn't know himself.'

'**Mrs W.** — on people that you like and get on with — "resonance is so important in pleasant association." I like that—that congenial folk resonate with you. Also that others make you feel self-conscious and that ruins everything.'

'**A.N.W.** loves Plato because he discourses, a great discusser and talker. How they started discussions with the students when they first came to Harvard — 30–60 at a time Sat. nights, gave them chocolate to drink and cakes. He loves Hume because he wrote so beautifully that it was possible to see exactly where he went wrong.... He is quite sure that the universe has a plan and equally sure it is proper to ask Why? As well as How? Thinks the antiteleologists are stupid.... I've left no room for anything else. A.N.W's a little cherub-like man with a slow very precise donnish way of talking but he's a pet. She is as good as I said, she smokes like a chimney at 80!'[34].

Jefferson wanted to convey the pleasure of the evening to Gertrude, and did so in these recollections of his conversation with the famous philosopher and his wife.

A comment made by Sir Francis Walshe, in a letter to Jefferson some 12 years later, brings Bertrand Russell and AN Whitehead together once more: 'It is interesting to find that in Bertrand Russell's *History of Western Philosophy* there is not a word about Whitehead's philosophy, while Aquinas is written off as no more than a stooge of the Church. Whatever he might think of Aquinas, he could not honestly have omitted all mention of Whitehead from a work bearing the title he gave his book. In other words, Russell's intellectual integrity is imperfect—to put it mildly. Perhaps the truth is that Russell is a symbolic logician and not a philosopher at all. This is how the Thomist experts regarded him'[35]. Walshe himself was probably very familiar with the teachings of St Thomas Aquinas.

Brown University in Providence, Rhode Island, wanted to award Jefferson an Honorary Degree, but his itinerary prevented him from attending the ceremony and so he had to forgo the distinction. Correspondence had to be fitted in, and Jeff wrote to Adams McConnell in Dublin: 'I have got so sick of everybody sending their love to you by me that I think I had better get rid of it before it breaks my back .... I have had a most entertaining trip, and am leaving now to go up to Toronto and then on to the Mayo Clinic [to give the Mayo Foundation Lecture]. At either of these places I may, if conditions are unnaturally favourable, catch a fish'[36].

Jeff's stay in the United States had been extended in order that he could travel to the Pacific Coast to speak at the University of California and to the Los Angeles Neurological Society[37]. Alan Gregg, of the Rockefeller Foundation, wrote to confirm Jeff's return to the UK on the 17th June, but he was anxious about the strenuousness of the visit and concluded: 'I can only hope that you are not allowing your friends to exhaust you with acts of friendship, hospitality, etc. There are more agreeable deaths than being killed by kindness, glad as I am that so many people feel that way about your visit'[38]. Jeff himself told Antony: 'The kindest thing they could do would be to show me to a room with books and papers and leave me alone for a couple of days'[39].

Jefferson had not known before he left for the United States that he had been recommended for the honour of Commander of the Order of the British Empire (CBE), as the letter arrived too late for him to receive it. Of course, the proposal had to be kept secret until it was officially announced. On 2nd June however, following the publication of the Birthday Honours list, Gertrude was able to break the news to Geoffrey: 'This has been a great day, the first time—(but not the last I imagine) in which your name appears in the birthday honours list .... I have been wishing so much I could tell you'[40].

Antony did manage to meet his father, in Montreal on 5th May, and they both stayed with the Penfields, but examinations got in the way of them seeing much of each other. Later, however, Antony was able to travel to New York with Jeff[41]; this was after Jefferson had visited Rochester and St Louis, and before he returned to Montreal for 2 days in order to speak to the Montreal Neurological Society on the subject of Marshall Hall, the neurologist who, in the mid-nineteenth century, described spinal shock and the grasp reflex[42].

How Jefferson came home to England is not clear, but it has been said that he flew home in a Liberator transport aircraft of the American Air Force, which would seem likely, especially since Lord Beaverbrook and the United States Ambassador Averil Harriman were among his travelling companions. 'It was an exciting time with exciting prospects fulfilled', he was to write almost a year later[41]. He arrived back in London by train, where, to his great surprise, Gertrude met him on the platform. She gave him the news that Michael had been married, and that Geoffrey was to go to Buckingham Palace on 8th July to receive his decoration. In due course, in a letter to Antony, he wrote: 'I appeared at Buckingham Palace (do the bright young things still call it Buck House?) and had the most impressive ribbon and decoration hung round my neck by H.M. [King George VI]. Which was very kind of him and very graciously done. Mother and Hy. Botterell used my 2 complementary tickets and saw me "done". There was a crowd of us including the marvellous R N captain who attacked cruisers with destroyers off Norway last winter. He very deservedly got the V.C.'[43]. Jeff had greatly enjoyed the short time that he and Antony had been able to spend together and added: 'I don't know whether I have made it sufficiently clear how much I liked being with you in those various places. We had a grand time I thought everywhere. You're a good companion and no mistake'[43].

As Jefferson said on his return to Manchester, 'Things go on here much as when I left them'[43]. Dr Kessel and the rest of the staff had managed very well, probably greatly aided by Jeff's invaluable secretary, Elizabeth Armistead, to whom Harry Botterell wrote: 'I was lost in admiration at your skill in taking histories, doing visual fields and being generally indispensible'[44]. In war-time the distinction as to who did what was often defined by necessity rather than qualification.

In September 1943 Geoffrey took a week's holiday near Kelso, in Scotland, and Miss Armistead wrote urgently to Botterell: 'Please return the plan of the river — I don't know what river. He is going away on Monday and thinks he may get some fishing'[45]. History does not record how he faired on that occasion; perhaps the weather and the water were satisfactory for once. His next letter to his Canadian friend was to ask for Botterell's views on which hospitals in the mid-south area of England should be retained for neurosurgical purposes after the war, since a meeting was being arranged with the various Consultant Advisers to the Ministry of Health, who were 'beginning to look ahead (possibly far ahead) to demobilisation and the return of EMS centres to their peace-time ownership'[46]. Discussion of the matter was to take place after the SBNS meeting, which was due to be held at the end of that month at Chase Farm Hospital, Enfield, Middlesex. During that week, Jeff received an Honorary MSc from Manchester University and addressed the Northern Section of the British Medical Students Association.

Jefferson's interest in books surfaced once more in another letter to Antony: 'Your book purchases interested me. I have 3 or 4 Charcot's, and that's not all of them. Your purchase of the Brown-Séquard at 25c. was a masterpiece — I have one. I saw one listed in a catalogue a while ago, they were asking £7 or 8 for it'. Jeff then took obvious pleasure in describing various patients on whom he had recently operated. 'I haven't written a line of my multitudinous papers in 2 wks or more. I'm too tired, too many letters to write in the evgs. I finish at 1.0 am. I always think there will be an end to it but there never is'[47]. He was shortly to attend an important meeting of the Medical Research Council in London on peripheral nerve injuries, and to hear Cairns' Presidential address to the Section of Neurology of the Royal Society of Medicine on the subject of Penicillin, whose efficacy in preventing and treating wound infection Cairns had assessed with Ian Frazer and Howard Florey in North Africa and Italy. 'Its good but not the final word that we all wistfully thought it would be'[48], commented Jeff.

Manchester University now proposed that Jefferson's appointment should become that of a full time professor in charge of the neurological laboratories, including responsibility for teaching and research, but still with permission for a restricted amount of private practice and duties as an honorary consultant to the Infirmary. The new arrangement would involve less in the way of clinical commitment and, hopefully, allow more time for his writing, research and his administrative duties with the Ministry. He wrote to Harry Botterell: 'What sort of salary would you want to come here after the War with a view to taking over this place eventually?'[49]. Needless to say, Botterell did not feel prepared to settle away from Canada.

Antony had now obtained his MD from McGill University and was about to take up an internship in Durham, North Carolina, at the hospital associated with Duke University. Strangely enough, his father seems to have assumed that, because a cable had not arrived to tell him the result of the examination, Antony must have failed it! He wrote accordingly and then continued: 'Did I tell you that I'd got the Morgagni *Seats and Causes of Disease* and a lovely *Works of Francis Bacon* 3 vols 18th cent. calf?'[50]. He asked Antony to look out for Reil's physiological essays, Descartes' letters and a report on Phineas Gage, the American lumberjack who had sustained a brain injury from an iron bar driven through the frontal region of his skull. Jeff had not been well and had spent 2 days at home but 'I shall, I fear, have to admit that I'm better again tomorrow and go back to work — a great nuisance. I could have done with a week at home to get some writing done — Kessel's laid up with appendicitis so its a bit tough. I've no one to fall back on with a sounding "plop"! So I've got to work'[50].

He continued busily to plan and was now looking towards the end of hostilities. The expression 'for the duration' (of the war) was on everyone's lips. It neatly conveyed the sense of an end at some unknown time.

REFERENCES

GJ=Geoffrey Jefferson; GMJ=Gertrude Jefferson; AJ=Antony Jefferson
1   Cairns H to GJ. Letter 25th January 1942.
2   Schuman H to GJ. Letter 3rd January 1942.
3   Jefferson G. The acute head injury as a medical problem. *Glasgow Med J* 1942; **11**: 77–94.
4   GMJ to AJ. Letters 5th and 8th March 1942.
5   GMJ to AJ. Letter 31st May 1942.
6   GJ to AJ. Letter 1st June 1942.
7   McKissock W to GJ. Letter 30th March 1942.
8   Nichols M to GJ. Letter 31st March 1942.
9   Botterell EH, Jefferson G. The treatment of scalp wounds in air-raid and other casualties. *BMJ* 1942; **1** 781–3.
10   GJ to Botterell EH. Letters 23rd May and 8th June 1942.

11   Jefferson G. The future of the specialties. *Br J Radiol* 1942; **15**: 283–5.
12   GJ to Botterell EH. Letter 9th July 1942.
13   GJ to Botterell EH. Letter 5th August 1942.
14   Cairns H to GJ. Letter 13th August 1942.
15   GJ to AJ. Letter 14th September 1942.
16   GJ to Botterell EH. Letter 6th September 1942.
17   Botterell EH. Personal communication.
18   GJ to AJ. Letter 23rd September 1942.
19   Stopford JSB to GJ. Letter 2nd October 1942.
20   GJ to AJ. Letter 30th October 1942.
21   Botterell EH to GJ. Letter 16th September 1942.
22   GJ to Botterell EH. Letter 31st October 1942.
23   GMJ to GJ. Letter 10th November 1942.
24   GJ to Botterell EH. Letter 27th November 1942.
25   Cairns H to GJ. Letter 4th December 1942.
26   GJ. MS. Undated, December 1942.
27   GJ to AJ. Letter 2nd December 1942.
28   GJ to AJ. Letter 10th February 1942.
29   GJ to AJ. Letter 18th March 1942.
30   GJ. MS. Notes. April 1943.
31   Peet M to GJ. Letter 15th May 1943.
32   GMJ to GJ. Letter 5th May 1943.
33   GJ to AJ. Letter 17th May 1943.
34   GJ to GMJ. Letter 22nd May 1943.
35   Walshe FMR to GJ. Letter 16th December 1955.
36   GJ to McConnell A. Letter 23rd May 1943.
37   GJ to Fraser R at Ministry of Health. Letter 22nd May 1943.
38   Gregg A to GJ. Letter 24th May 1943.
39   GJ to AJ. Letter 29th May 1943.
40   GMJ to GJ. Letter 2nd June 1943.
41   GJ to AJ. Letter 5th May 1944.
42   Jefferson G. *Selected papers.* London: Pitman Medical, 1960: 73–93.
43   GJ to AJ. Letter 12th July 1943.
44   Botterell EH to Armistead E. Letter 11th August 1943.
45   Armistead E to Botterell EH. Letter 7th September 1943.
46   GJ to Botterell EH. Letter 27th September 1943.
47   GJ to AJ. Letter 17th October 1943.
48   GJ to AJ. Letter 23rd October 1943.
49   GJ to Botterell EH. Letter 22nd November 1943.
50   GJ to AJ. Letter 7th December 1943.

Chapter 18

World War II
1944–1945

For many months the Russians, in a manner reminiscent of World War I, had been asking the Allies to open a second front in Europe in order to relieve some of the pressure that the Germans were exerting on them. The commitments of the forces in Africa and Italy had so far prevented this from being an option, but now that America had entered the war and the invasion of Italy had been well established, it became first a possibility and then a necessity. Operation Overlord was agreed at the Cairo conference in November 1943. This was to be the invasion of northern France, which eventually began on 6th June 1944.

As early in the year as the beginning of February, Jefferson wrote to Antony in Canada: 'I'm up to the neck in preparations for the last (we hope) stages of the War. Winston was a bit cross the other day with the insane optimism of folk who thought the war would soon be over. He <u>may</u> be right, but its certain that we've got to act and plan as if he was. The only sensible way'[1]. The invasion of Europe from England meant that casualties, and head injuries in particular, would be sent straight from the fighting zones to EMS hospitals in the UK, often, owing to the speed of their evacuation, without any preliminary intervention beyond first aid. Facilities for the reception and treatment of the wounded had to be created, beds had to be set aside and the distribution of casualties so organised that no single hospital or neurosurgical centre was overloaded. This explains why Jefferson was involved in the planning. He wrote again from Manchester, on 5th May: 'The Boche have not been up here, there was a daylight alert for 10 mins today, probably a Reconnaissance plane stooging and snooping for information useful to them in getting themselves knocked out in the Second Front. At close quarters here we take this so-called "Second" Front pretty seriously. Its going to be anything but a push over and we are soberly and quietly awaiting its start, not over tense, just waiting quietly. Nobody knows when it will come—nobody I mean except the Tops, and I would rather not know because it would be a secret that would worry me, lest I accidentally divulge it'[2].

Gertrude sometimes accompanied her husband on his visits to London. 'Mum and I were in London last Sat. as I expect she has told you', he wrote to Antony: 'A fine shoot went on while we sat holding hands in a cinema seeing *Carnet de Bal* and not knowing a better nearby 'ole to go to'[1]. Intermittent bombing of London and elsewhere continued, but in June the German attack was enhanced by the use of a jet-powered Flying Bomb, which came to be known as the V1 or Buzz Bomb, most of which were directed at London. Their potential was reduced by attacks by the allies on the launching sites, and more than half of the approximately 8000 that were sent were destroyed in the air. Nevertheless they added to Jeff's problems during his frequent visits to London, and these were made worse in September when the V2 rockets were used. These were 46 feet long and carried a ton of explosive at about 3000 miles per hour, so that there was neither warning nor any possibility of protection from them. Although the V1 and V2 missiles between them killed almost 9000 people and injured 23,500, they did not have the effect, expected by the Germans, of paralysing the capital and halting the war. They did, however, add considerably to Gertrude's anxiety on behalf of her husband when he was away from home.

Jeff still managed to find time for some non-clinical writing, perhaps even as a contrast to his other obligations. 'I've rehashed the *Soul*—gave it to the Lit and Phil [Manchester Literary and Philosophical Society] here the other day and got a short leader in the M/C Guardian on it (say I, vainly)'[1]. This paper was not published until 1949, when it had been the basis of the John Mallett Purser lecture, given in Dublin[3,4]. It later formed part of a longer article on René Descartes[5]. The much larger work that Jeff had planned, on the 'localization' of the soul, was never completed.

Then, one day, following a visit to Rowbotham in Newcastle, Jefferson became aware that his heart was not behaving quite as it should. He wrote to Antony: 'I've had a burst of extrasystoles but don't pay any attention to that, for no expert takes them very seriously. I feel fine.... Are the smells nice in the woods around you? Its the smells that most recall Canada to me'[6]. Though he may have been right about the insignificance of these symptoms, Jeff was a heavy smoker of cigarettes; he was to suffer much more serious heart trouble several years later.

The pressure of work continued: 'Too many sick people and too much 2nd Front', Jefferson wrote to his friend Harry Botterell[7].

In May, he produced a short paper on the management of head wounds in battle casualties. It was a general directive to all the EMS hospitals in preparation for their reception of wounded from the impending fighting on the continent of Europe. It began: 'It will be understood that all head wounds must be sent for their primary surgical treatment into a Special Centre (see D.G.L.343)'[8], thus confirming the policy that he had already instituted. It is a comprehensive document in which Jeff uses the first person singular and signs it, Geoffrey Jefferson. Characteristically, it contains Jeffersonian aphorisms, such as: 'I know of nothing more likely to do harm to the many than the decision to call a surgeon away from his work to see a desperate and probably hopeless case'[8]. He re-iterated and emphasised the arguments in favour of transferring casualties with head wounds to a Special Head Centre, and concluded: 'Although early operation gives the best results it is evident that delay is in the main fully justified if the time is spent in getting the patient to the right place'[8].

The article which Jefferson had published on the life of Harvey Cushing[9], in a relatively obscure student's journal, received warm approval from John Fulton who thought 'it was better in its beginning than Macaulay!'[10]. He relayed Fulton's comment to Antony, adding: 'But I have not got M's encyclopaedic knowledge of the arts and humanities and quite lack his terrific storehouse therefore, from which he draws apt illustration of a point or parallels. He really had a terrific mind even if he was a Whig—"I perceive, Sir", said Dr Johnson, "that you are a vile Whig!". I'm a Whig, I feel sure, though I'm capable of being something different at different hours of the day!'[10].

In the long letter of 12th April, in which Jeff replied to Fulton, he remarked: 'I am an immense admirer of Macaulay who had one of the most tremendous minds that this country has produced . . . . I began reading him at the height of the Blitz with some prejudice against him. It soon evaporated'[11]. The paper by Jefferson which so impressed Fulton begins as follows: 'The praise of famous men must always reveal something of the convictions, and incidentally reveal no few of the prejudices of the writer. The last two decades have seen the brilliant accomplishment of a form of biography, interesting and amusing, which focussed attention on those blemishes of character from which no man is wholly free. Doctors and their achievements are no more exempt from the possibility of ironical or belittling analysis than their brothers in other fields of work. An age that became shy of confessing beliefs, discredited causation, doubted the value of purpose and denied all influences but those of environment, found in such essays support for a negative attitude towards existence, for what H.A.L. Fisher aptly called "*Lues* intellectualis*". Yet it is hard to believe that in this period of progression backwards there was any true declination in that kindly feeling in young and old towards their fellow-creatures, which has evolved in society . . . '[9]. Fulton himself was a prolific writer in many rôles — as physiologist, medical historian, correspondent and diarist. Jeff's association with him, and with Cushing, may well have increased his own literary aspirations.

Ruminating further on the subject of biography, in the same letter to Fulton, Jefferson mentioned his thoughts about writing a book on Cushing which was to be 'an outline of neurosurgical progress during HC's life'[11]. The letter continued: 'I dare say I ought to push on with it and get it out. But I wonder if I really could in view of the terrible amount of work that I have just now with all these Second Front preparations and then there will be the actual care of . . . [the wounded]. It is a biggish job having the whole of the Country under one's wing for head wounds — some wing! . . . My wandering thoughts betray how much I'd like to do and how little I think I can effect. I haven't finished the story of reflex action. I have finished the "Localization of the Soul" but only the Descartes period . . . . I have got a paper brewing on Wilfred Trotter comparing him with the fascinating Joseph Glanville 300 years before.† Add five papers on neurosurgery unfinished and you see my unresolved complexes in their full beauty'[11]. In the end the paper on Trotter joined those that were never written.

Still writing to Fulton with the pen that had belonged to Cushing and which had acquired something of the nature of a talisman for him, Jeff pondered what its previous owner would have undertaken next, after he had managed to finish his work on Vesalius. 'I was always sorry that he'd never written anything much on Halsted; he was the one to have done it even if it was only a long short paper.

---

*Lues. The meaning is that of a plague or pestilence. Its use as a synonym for syphilis arose as a contraction of *Lues venerea* or *syphilitica*.

However, in a corrigendum added in typescript to his own copy of the above paper, Jefferson wrote: 'Fisher's label "Lues intellectualis" . . . should have been "Tabes intellectualis". It was Macaulay who used the other word (a pestilence rather than a wasting), calling the over-praise of briefed biographers the "Lues Boswelliana", a more unkind appelation so far as Boswell was concerned though it was not quite justified in the much less important instances that Macaulay had in mind. That great artist was very partial to a scholarly joke with a sting in the tail' (GJ MS addendum to his *Harvey Cushing* paper, ref. 9).

†Joseph Glanville or Glanvill. (1636–1680). English philosopher who believed that whereas there are isolated facts, they are not connected by causes so that no one gives rise to another. He was superstitious and wrote in defence of witchcraft, but also in defence of the Royal Society.

Not that Macallum's Life isn't good, but its too polite. We must both beware of what Macaulay calls "Lues Boswelliana", too much adulation, though it is unfair to set out to debunk.... The art lies in getting the dosage of good and of imperfect right'[11]. Fulton at that time was writing his own biography of Harvey Cushing.

Jefferson had now been made an honorary member of the American Neurological Association, and a member of the Advisory Board of the *Journal of Neurosurgery*. He had also been asked to join the editorial board of the newly renamed *Journal of Neurology Neurosurgery and Psychiatry*. Although these appointments were a recognition of his ability and seniority, their 'reward' became that of yet more demanding paper work.

As D-Day and the Second Front approached, Jefferson, who had only recently celebrated his 58th birthday but was surely over-working, confessed to Antony: 'I feel just a tired old man, isn't it utterly disgusting to have to work so hard. In the morning I shall probably feel a lively youngster again.... I wonder how many years' war there is going to be, it will be about six I guess and would be seven or eight taking everything in. I do want to live for as many years as possible in an unblacked out High Bank'[12]. In the event he did not have to wait very long before D-Day, which marked the beginning of the closing stages of the war in Europe and arrived on 6th June 1944; with it the long expected casualties began to return to England from the landing zones in Normandy. Five days after the initial assault Jefferson, who had been visiting various hospitals around London and the south of England, wrote to Gertrude: 'My chief concern [about visiting Southampton] is the probability of having to make exasperatingly slow journeys because of heavy traffic on the road. It has all been very interesting, the wounded are cheerful and in very good shape—the mortality remarkably low—less than one per cent in those that I've seen, some of them are bad but not many. I spoke to one or two German prisoners, one of them said that when they saw our invasion fleet at dawn they said "This is the end of the war—its unbelievable!" I suppose they had expected a handful of landing craft and ships. They are operating on about 25 per cent of the cases at the Transit stage and evacuating the rest, so the next thing is to go up to the Midlands to see how they are getting on.... My plan now is, as I said, come home Wed.—do the exams. Thurs. Fri.— go to Winwick [North of Warrington, in Cheshire] Sat, have Sun. at home and come back here.... I think that if I spend that week on it [war casualties], everything should be tied up and I can take a more normal round of duties again'[13]. Jeff's figures, of course, referred to those with head injuries who had survived the first few hours after wounding, and did not include the immediate battlefield mortality.

The Athenaeum Club provided Geoffrey Jefferson with a convenient London base and, just over a week later, he wrote to Gertrude from there: 'I've just been to the Ministry to report progress. Fortunately I was able to say that everything was going well and that I had at present no further demands to make.... I must confess I don't like these robots [V1 Flying Bombs]...I read the German account this morning with some amusement—they said that you could not see London or most of the S. of England because of the smoke of devastation. This is a thumping lie.... The only upsetting thing is the uncertainty of it'[14]. He wrote to ask Botterell for information about the Canadian head injuries from France that they had received at Hackwood Park[15]. Ten days later came the reply that 185 had been admitted to the hospital, most of which were British[16].

Experience of penicillin was still limited, and Botterell had asked Jefferson how to combat pyocyaneus infection in the wounds of patients on penicillin injections. Jeff's astonishing reply was that 2.2% Glycol 'cures it', but that this remedy had not yet been tried 'on brains or in CSF'[17]. On 24th July he wrote to Botterell regarding the transfer of casualties from France: 'I do not know how much will still come by sea, maybe quite a bit. But it is evident that if AVAC [evacuation by air] were to expand it should be done by increasing the landing fields by using those further north so as not to put too great a strain on one area'[18].

By the end of September, Miss Armistead was so worried about Jefferson's health that she wrote to Harry Botterell to ask him to use his influence to reduce Jeff's burden of work. 'I wondered if you would let me know confidentially what you think of Mr Jefferson. I feel very worried about him and do wish he could have more rest. I was horrified when he wrote to me while I was away, saying they had cancelled their holiday at Penrith and were going to London. I do wish you could persuade him to go somewhere for a real rest . . . someone will have to take him in hand'[19]. During that month Jefferson had been taken ill with another attack of diverticulitis while in London, for his friend John Morley wrote: 'I am disturbed to hear of your plight, but glad that you seem to be weathering the storm. I suppose the good old tablets have been invoked?'[20].

The SBNS was due to meet on 4th November 1944 and Jefferson was making plans to invite several American surgeons to attend. They accepted, but Jeff had

Figure 19   *Geoffrey Jefferson, Winchell Craig, Glen Spurling and Hugh Cairns. (ca. 1944).*

to explain that he 'could not throw the Meeting quite wide open to the world because of the feeding'[21]. He also found an opportunity to indulge himself during a visit to London, by spending some time in HK Lewis's bookshop. Afterwards he wrote to Botterell that 'Miss Murrells [of HK Lewis] told me that you did not take any of these books because you had not got any money, which seems to me to be a very inadequate reason for not buying them straight off.... It was extremely kind of you to come down to Brighton to see me. I am perfectly well again. I only wish I could go on playing truant for another six months'[22]. Botterell had obviously hurried over to Sussex to see his friend in response to Elizabeth Armistead's appeal.

A few days later, Miss Armistead was able to report to Harry Botterell that, after all, 'Mr Jefferson decided to go away for a few days, so he and Monica went last Thursday to Windermere.... I had a letter from him this morning and he says he feels perfectly all right and doesn't know what he has gone away for'[23].

Preparations continued for the SBNS meeting, which was to be held at the Canadian Neurological Hospital, near Basingstoke. Jefferson was planning to spend the preceding night in London with Gordon Holmes, which shows that their former disagreements over the details of the proposed Queen Square appointment had been set aside. He had invited Major General Monro, the head of the Army Medical Services, to the meeting and told Botterell: 'you had better get the red carpet out for he has accepted. I have asked Holmes, Riddoch, Walshe and a lot of other luminaries of lower seniority but high intelligence'[24]. The meeting took place on 4th November as arranged and, in the manner of all SBNS meetings, was proclaimed to have been the best ever!

Although it was by no means a perfect time of year for such a visit, after that meeting Jefferson managed to take a short holiday in the Trossachs, hill country in Perthshire, Scotland. He found time for some reading and, in pencil on the fly-leaf of a book by Sir Clifford Allbutt entitled *Science and medieval thought*, he wrote the following comments: 'It is just possible that a reader beginning this book at, say, p.73, might find it tolerable. Taken as a whole it is just one long muddle. Although one recognises that it has a theme it remains submerged beneath every bit of junk that the author had collected in 30 yrs.... Compare this book with the work of a real master — e.g. Coulton's *Studies of medieval thought* and Willey's books and one sees clearly how addled Allbutt was. C.A's pursuit of knowledge was extremely laudable in a Leeds' man. Perhaps they took warning for they certainly have pursued hard cash rather than learning ever since — and that with great devotion'[25]. This is a good example of Jeff's cynicism, which could be very sharp at times.

The Editor of the *British Journal of Surgery* proposed to publish an article on the Canadian Neurological Hospital in the series on visits to war clinics and he left it to Jeff, who had probably suggested the idea in the first place, to provide an author. Naturally he chose Harry Botterell. As he said: 'You'll hate it but you'll have to do it'[26]. The article appeared in the next volume of the journal[27].

It should be noticed in passing, that Geoffrey Jefferson's standing in Manchester society was certainly not confined to his professional work. He was a much respected citizen, and as such had been appointed a Trustee of St Nicholas Church, Burnage, an adjacent parish to Didsbury. This had been the church that the Jeffersons attended when they lived in Belfield Road. Jeff himself was not regularly in the congregation, since he usually visited his hospital patients on Sunday morning. It was Gertrude, of course, who was the most devotional of the family. The Bishop of Manchester wrote a letter in October 1944 concerning the choice of a new incumbent and asked if Jeff would like to see the candidate who was favoured by the other Trustees, since he had been unable to attend the meeting[28]. Much later, in 1958, another rector of that parish wrote to say that he had been appointed to a church in Lewes, Sussex, and to thank the Jeffersons for their help during his time at Burnage[29].

As the approach of the end of hostilities in Europe was perceived, the siting of new post-war neurosurgical centres, and the fate of those that had been set up during the years of the emergency, had to be decided. The manner in which Cairns and Jefferson worked together, and subsequently presented ideas to a Planning Committee, can be judged from a letter from Cairns in the January of 1945. He wrote to Jeff after visiting the Haywards Heath unit, which had been derived from Queen Square. He had watched Harvey Jackson operate and had talked with Brodie Hughes. 'They have about 70 patients there—mostly tumour material. There is very little head injury work, though while I was there they were waiting for some patients from a bomb explosion in Kent.... Obviously the sooner the tumour work can be kept at Queen Square instead of being moved down to Haywards Heath the better. When that is done there will be little work for Haywards Heath.... Why not, therefore, try to develop something to take its place?'[30]. He suggested training a local surgeon in the care of head injuries, or running it as a subsidiary head centre with a surgeon from Queen Square 'on call from London for the more difficult cases'[30]. Neither of these ideas would have had much appeal for those working in the centre and would not have attracted a surgeon of quality to the unit. However, Cairns continued: 'Some transition of this sort to post-war medical services would seem to be required for all these centres which have proved so useful in war time. You have doubtless been thinking of this'[30]. Inevitably, with the coming of peace and a realignment of responsibilities, Jefferson was soon no longer to have the 'whole of the Country under one's wing for head wounds'[11]. As it turned out, he did not easily relinquish his position, and in fact this was not expected of him. He still had influence through the Ministry of Health, whose adviser in neurosurgery he remained, and through the Council of the SBNS. However, Cairns was a much younger man, Cushing-trained and very ambitious, and in the next few years his standing was steadily to grow, along with that of the SBNS itself. This relative change of status between Cairns and Jefferson did inevitably lead to some degree of competition between these two remarkable men. In such circumstances, 'if ever rumour hinted at discord or rivalry it would be silenced with such a disarming declaration as, "You know the reason X. and I have never for a moment been jealous of each other is because each one of us has secretly believed himself to be the better of the two"'[31].

Eventually Germany capitulated, at midnight on 8th May 1945, but it was many months, even years, before normality was restored in Britain; rationing continued, there were shortages of fuel and, above all, the war in the Far East had yet to be won. The Voluntary Hospitals gradually resumed their previous status, but were soon to become part of the National Health Service, as would almost all general practices. Medicine would change beyond belief when compared with the pre-war situation, and many of the administrative changes met with initial resistance. Those who had served in the forces were slowly demobilised, hospital posts were created for specialist training, and young doctors returning from the forces became available for the new civilian appointments, which of course included some at the Manchester Neurosurgical Centre.

On the 5th July Jefferson delivered the Doyne Lecture at the Ophthalmological Congress in Oxford, entitled *On compression and invasion of the optic nerves and chiasma by neighbouring gliomas*[32]. This was an extremely comprehensive and well illustrated survey of the subject and Jeff, referring to himself, hoped 'that some of what he has to say may be new to a few, and that what is old will not be, at the worst, inaccurate'[32]. It is a lecture that should be read by all aspiring neurosurgeons. It contains yet another of those aphorisms so typical of Jefferson, and so well worth remembering: 'Dorsal compression of the chiasma is likely to induce early macular defects'[32]. One hopes that examination of the visual fields, and the exercise of clinical deduction from them, will not be entirely displaced by imaging techniques or handed over to other specialists, although this is already starting to happen.

The years immediately following World War II were a time of beginnings, not least in the field of neurosurgery. The SBNS, as the representative body of the specialty, took centre stage and set up a Planning Committee to consider the neurosurgical needs of the population, the staff which a Neurosurgical Centre required, the qualifications and training of that staff, and the relation of neurosurgery to those branches of medicine to which it is most closely allied. The chairman of this planning committee was Hugh Cairns, and Geoffrey Jefferson was its secretary. The other members were Norman Dott, Paterson Ross, FAR Stammers, Willie Henderson now safely home again, Harvey Jackson, Wylie McKissock, Douglas Northfield, John O'Connell, GF Rowbotham and Julian Taylor, who, when taken prisoner by the Japanese when Singapore fell, had been held in the notorious Changi camp. With such an important and all-embracing brief it is not surprising that it included several of the leaders of the next generation of surgeons. It took 2 years for them to report but, when they did, their deliberations had a profound effect on the future of British neurosurgery[33].

Life at High Bank in the summer of 1945 was at times quite hectic, as can be gathered from one of Gertrude's letters. 'Monday night 3 young American Army doctors—Wednesday Mater [Mrs Arthur Jefferson] arrived...in the evening Mrs Bailey & Capt. Peterson from McGill.... On Tuesday Mrs Green arrived from Ireland on her way home and spent the night at High Bank—On Thursday Dr Sweet came from Birmingham & will stay until to-morrow'[34]. This was followed by a christening and a dinner party. Poor Bridget!

For two reasons, Jeff was again thinking hard about additional help in the Neurosurgical Unit and a possible successor for himself in Manchester. In the first place, he wished to reduce his clinical commitment in order to have more time for writing and research, and he may have had some intimation that this would become possible later in that year. Secondly, his retirement was due to take place in 1951, in only 6 years' time. He asked John O'Connell, who had been running the St. Bartholomew's Hospital neurosurgical unit in their sector at Hill End, St Albans, if he would be prepared to come to Manchester. Once again Jefferson received a negative reply: 'I have given a great deal of thought to the problem of whether I should go to Manchester or stay here. In the end I have decided that I ought to stay.... It seems that it would be wrong to leave Bart's just when there is a possibility of getting a good neurosurgical service working there. One thing I feel quite certain about and that is that I shall always be sad to have missed the opportunity of working with you'[35].

The war in the Far East finally came to its end with the capitulation of Japan on 2nd September 1945. Whatever the present sentiments may be about the use of the atom bomb, the feelings at the time were almost solely of immense relief that, after 5 years of world-wide slaughter, the war had been brought to an end.

Somewhat surprisingly, during this summer, Jefferson gave at least two broadcasts to China on the BBC World Service and the subjects may seem rather strange. The first, given in August 1945, was on the *Management of closed head injuries and fractures of the skull*; the second was on *Brain surgery*. The purpose was to bring the latest information about British surgical methods to the Chinese, who had been isolated from Western developments by their war against the Japanese and then by World War II. One gathers from correspondence that Jeff was not so much at home with the impersonal microphone as he always was in front of an audience[36].

An important and rather remarkable skirmish in the fields of neurology and neurosurgery broke out at this time. The *British Medical Journal* carried a report on the deliberations of the Neurological Committee of the Royal College of Physicians in an editorial in its 1st September 1945 issue[37]. Two weeks later a very significant letter from two of the consultant neurologists at Queen Square, FMR Walshe and CP Symonds, appeared in the same publication. They picked up the point, mentioned in the editorial, that the relationship between neurology and neurosurgery had still not been determined. The letter amounted to a provocative statement of the dominance of neurology. 'The neurologist... has diagnostically to handle neurology and whatever his colleagues may believe to be neurological, whether in fact it is so or not.... To exclude from his purview all clinical neurological material which investigation may ultimately show to call for surgical intervention is arbitrarily to mutilate his proper field of experience... and have unfavourable consequences for those who seek his advice as patients... [Neurosurgery] is predominantly a therapeutic specialty... The dominance of therapeutic thinking is also reflected in the routine to which these cases are commonly subjected once they enter the neurosurgical clinic.... The neurologist faced by a new case instinctively asks himself, "What is the matter with this patient?".... Whereas the neurosurgeon instinctively asks "Has the patient a space-occupying lesion, and where is it?".... It leads also, no less inevitably to undue use of... [ventriculography and encephalography] and when these fail to yield relevant information, too often a negative diagnosis, and to the ultimate handing over of the patient to the neurologist, to whom in such cases — if we are to be perfectly frank — it would have been better to refer in the first instance'[38]. They went on to say that even if neurosurgeons were to have a formal neurological training (as was mentioned in the Report[33]), their experience and judgement would be inadequate. 'It would be as unreasonable for the physician to claim to be able to employ surgical techniques without due training and practice as for the surgeon to ask to be accepted as completely equipped to meet the wider range of diagnostic requirements it is the physician's prime duty to acquire'[38].

This letter stung Jefferson to the quick, and revived the controversy that had surfaced and annoyed him before the war, during his correspondence with Gordon Holmes concerning the clinical responsibilities of neurosurgeons at Queen Square. The International Neurological Congress might have accepted some neurosurgeons as *bona fide* neurologists, but Queen Square still did not. Jefferson replied in a published letter at the beginning of October. He mentioned that a scheme for the training of neurosurgeons was under consideration by the Planning Committee of the SBNS and, referring to the Walshe/Symonds letter, wrote: 'They regret that the medical neurologist has lost too much valuable clinical material to the... [surgeons] and believe that this stunts the growth of the physician. It is a fact that the neurological physician no longer sees every case of suspected brain tumour before it goes to the surgeon, as was the custom in former days. It needs little imagination to comprehend that this is disappointing to the physician, but it has happened in many branches of medicine and is a sign of (at least) commencing maturity.... The state of affairs... has occurred as a natural process which needs new adjustment—that of partnership. I am well aware that the emancipation which the neurosurgeon now enjoys carries with it heavy responsibilities. He is called upon to make the greatest contribution that he can to our knowledge of the nervous system (for which he has exceptional opportunities) and, more important from the humanitarian point of view, to avoid the infliction of unnecessary trauma.... Neither medical neurologist nor neurosurgeon is impeccable, and it would be a fatal error to try to build the future on any other understanding.... What deeply concerns us all is so to educate ourselves and our successors that mistakes shall be minimized. This will be done by the freest possible interchange of opinion between the physician and surgeon.... The loadstone that draws the surgeon into neurosurgery is not surgical technique but neurology.... A happy relationship, mutually educative, to say nothing of friendship between the medical and surgical subdivisions of neurology is possible.... No good will come of repressive action in which one branch seeks to dominate the other'[39].

This was the voice of reason replying to a prejudice that was not without arrogance, and the justice of Jefferson's judgement can now be measured. Over the last 50 years, the fruitful collaboration and mutual respect asked for by Jefferson has not been completely achieved, but it does exist in most centres. That such a relationship can take place, in which there is a free interchange of opinion, friendly collaboration, mutual education and reciprocal respect for each other and for the two disciplines, has been amply demonstrated.

As soon as the Walshe/Symonds letter appeared, Cairns wrote to Jeff that he had decided not to reply; but he also reported that 'Queen Square has decided to revert to the old practice of admitting all cases under the physicians'[40]. The surgical patients were even cared for by neurological house physicians. This confirmed Jefferson's fears and showed his wisdom in countering a clear move to establish an acceptance of neurological dominance over surgery elsewhere. Privately, he must also have been relieved that he had not uprooted himself from Manchester a few years earlier and transferred to Queen Square. Cairns, who had just become the new president of the SBNS, had the temerity to ask Jeff to withdraw his reply, having presumably been sent a draft copy for his perusal and comment. He seems to have been afraid of difficulties arising from the fact that the surgeons at Queen Square had already accepted the new ruling, and he believed that the SBNS should express its view as a body. This might have been interpreted as capitulation to the neurologists, but he was anxious not to restrict the freedom of individuals by laying down rules. The SBNS Planning Committee was due to advise the Ministry of Health about the needs and locations of future neurosurgical centres, and Cairns continued: 'We must see to it that the neurologists don't try and cramp our freedom there—not likely I suppose after the excellent work of your centres'[40].

We have reason to be grateful that Jefferson did not heed Cairns' request. His reply had not only stated the neurosurgical position quite clearly but also gave a logical and friendly answer to the authors of the letter, of whom Walshe was undoubtedly the motivator. Cairns even suggested that Symonds, with whom he had collaborated at the Military Hospital for Head Injuries throughout the war was, according to him, 'already showing signs of not being sure that he has done the right thing'[40]. Within a very few years, Symonds was collaborating with certain neurosurgeons in just the friendly and mutually beneficial way that Jefferson had suggested. It would probably have amused Jeff that when he died, his own obituary in the Biographical Memoirs of Fellows of the Royal Society was to be written by Sir Francis Walshe[41]. In due course the separate autonomy of medical and surgical neurology at Queen Square was eventually established, and the title of the hospital even changed to *The National Hospital for Neurology and Neurosurgery.*

Jefferson, in his capacity as secretary of the SBNS Planning Committee, sent a draft memorandum to the chairman, Hugh Cairns, concerning proposed recommendations for neurosurgical training and for future centres. This shows the extent to which Jeff was responsible for moulding the final report, and he later admitted that it was largely his own work[42]. Cairns commented: 'I am alarmed at the tendency to lay down a long apprenticeship. If we make it harder to attain specialist rank and pay in neurosurgery than in general surgery, we won't get any recruits'[43] and he suggested they should also consider the size and staffing requirements of proposed centres. Rather surprisingly, Cairns even suggested that possession of the Diploma of Fellowship of one of the Royal Colleges of Surgeons was not necessarily essential[43], and he failed to foresee the diminishing rôle of general surgery consequent on the increase in subspecialties. In these matters Jefferson was clearly the more farsighted.

The Committee's recommendation, when it came in 1947, was: 1) That higher qualifications would be obtained in 'less than four years after graduation—the first year in Junior Resident appointments in medicine or surgery, the second in whole time studies in the basic sciences, the third as Senior House Surgeon, and that six months of these years should be spent as a House Officer in medical or surgical neurology. In addition, 'The surgical neurologist will be a better recruit if he has done another year in general surgery after obtaining his F.R.C.S. diploma.' 2) 'A minimum further period of four and a half years is required before an apprentice can be considered as competent to stand on his own feet'[33]. There were many more recommendations, such as that 6 months should be spent in medical neurology and that one year out of the four of the apprenticeship should be spent in one of the related disciplines, such as neurophysiology or neuropathology. Thus the Committee suggested a minimum of 8 to 9 years of training following qualification[33]. This was before the introduction of the pre-registration year after obtaining the first diplomas or degrees. Since the report was made, the whole structure of specialist training has changed, but it is of historical interest to read of the first attempt to lay down an approved course, and it was Geoffrey Jefferson who was mainly responsible for drafting these requirements. First and foremost he was seeking as high a standard of expertise as possible, with plenty of emphasis on the adjacent disciplines.

Antony had by now returned from America, had completed his Oxford degrees and was about to enter the Royal Navy for his National Service. He went with his parents on a few day's holiday in Bamburgh, Northumberland. 'Father admitted he was broken-hearted, I don't think I have ever heard him say so much before', Gertrude afterwards wrote to him. 'He does enjoy your companionship so much & this holiday has been one of the happiest ever'[44].

Just before the publication of the Report of the Goodenough Committee on Medical Education[45] of which Jefferson was not a member, the Senate of Manchester University had been discussing a proposed Chair of Medicine, and had recommended that it should be a whole-time appointment without the right to private practice. Jefferson proposed an amendment by which the words 'with restricted private practice' would replace the embargo. He spoke at length in the Senate and first put the arguments in favour of the proposal of total restriction, four closely reasoned points against his own amendment. He then argued for the amendment as follows: 'By far the most usual custom throughout the world is for the University paid professors to do limited practice'[46], and a rigid whole-time framework would effectively reduce the quality of the applicants for the post and the prestige of the position. Travel was an absolute necessity for a Professor of Clinical Medicine and the funds would not be available without these private resources. Finally, to be whole-time without private practice would reduce the Professor 'to artisan level and indeed unless the holder of the Chair becomes known to doctors through contacts or private approach and so to the Community, the Professor will be held in less esteem than his colleagues who are free to do what they will.... Whether he does research depends on the man we choose not on his opportunities to add to his income...[and] if his reputation is such that some people at least wish to consult him privately I feel that they and he should have that right'[46].

It was important to establish the principle of limited private practice from Jeff's own point of view also for, on 29th September 1945, he was given a new contract with the University and was appointed 'Professor of Neurological Surgery (Part-time) and Director of the Neurological Laboratories'. It was stipulated that he should 'be required to devote two-thirds of his time to the duties of the post'[47]. He now had a mandate to spend more time on academic activities and his writing.

The Brain Injuries Committee of the Medical Research Council no longer had a rôle and its work, and that of its subcommittees, was summarised by Jefferson[48] as part of the winding up process. Initially the committee had been concerned with basic factors in head injury such as brain damage and the nature of concussion. This had resulted in the demonstration that it was sudden acceleration and deceleration of the head, and associated shearing strains, rather than deformation of the skull or brain which caused the mischief. It had been shown that dehydration had no place in the treatment of head injury, except in exceptional circumstances. They had produced the Glossary of Terms, which brought about uniformity in the records of brain injured patients. Mandatory notification of head injuries, especially those due to enemy action and motor-cycle injuries, had been introduced. Helmets for motor cyclists had been made compulsory in the army, which led to a decrease in the number and severity of their head injuries. Improved treatment of dural tears, of brain abscesses and methods of repairing skull defects had been brought about. Research on the use of the sulpha drugs and penicillin was financed, and the long term mental incapacity of those who had suffered head injuries had been investigated. Mental incapacity was found to be rare, although manual skills were frequently lost[48]. It was a significant record of achievement.

But Jeff had been feeling gloomy. Michael was serving in the RAMC in India, Antony was on his way to Australia, and 'our food has been worse than ever, but is picking up again slightly and will soon be at its old high of mediocrity'[49]. He cheered up a bit and wrote a long letter to Harry Botterell, who was now back in Canada at the Toronto General Hospital: 'I wrote you a black-edged sort of letter I fear, but I feel better about things'[49]. He related that he had received John O'Connell's rejection of the offer of an appointment in Manchester, but thought it likely that Richard Johnson would be appointed as his first assistant. He had begun working under his new contract, 'I started my job on part time and I have succeeded fairly well in beating off patients. Its a funny business deliberately wrecking a consulting practice but I almost enjoy it, for I'm too tired to enjoy seeing them. Also we have one sanguinary committee after another, plan, plan, plan. We're busy planning neurosurgery for the country and writing (in fact I've written most of it already myself) a fine manifesto on the Training of the Neuro-surgeon[33]. I've just been up to London to answer questions at the Ministry about the hospital arrangements, staffing in particular — I passed, I think. This Gov't of ours [Labour under Clement Attlee] is planning our heads off, they are wizards at stopping everything but, come to think of it, that's the only easy thing a Gov't can do. I fancy we shall be mighty sick of them in 3 or 4 years time, at the moment it doesn't seem to matter...'. Jeff told Botterell about the various papers he was writing and the moves of some of those neurosurgeons that his friend would have known. 'Q.S. [Queen Square] have re-imposed the rule that all cases must be admitted under a physician. Walshe and Charlie S. [Symonds] wrote a stupid letter to the BMJ.... I've got a lot to do and not very much time. Its hard to believe and as for really recognising it, its impossible, for I feel the same as ever I did. They say Wilfred Trotter looked round the room at the Athenaeum one day and said, "All these Johnnies think they're immortal. But of course they do! I know I'm not but I feel as if I were" '[49].

And Gertrude Jefferson was working hard too, in her clinics at the Infirmary, at her Welfare Clinics and at home. She had her own secretary and had adopted a somewhat similar practice to Geoffrey, of writing in the evenings, though not to such a late hour. She had a consulting room in the same house as Jeff in Lorne Street, next to the Royal Infirmary, where she also spent time writing and seeing patients. In connection with her work at the hospital Jefferson wrote: 'She has to do everything and is doing it very well too I'm proud to say, not showing the strain too much. But she'll be glad to have less to do, though she'd hate to have nothing to do. I should like to have nothing to do. Well I suppose one only has to wait long enough'[49]. The thought of the approach of his sixtieth birthday in a few months' time was probably adding to his low spirits.

REFERENCES

GJ=Geoffrey Jefferson; GMJ=Gertrude Jefferson; AJ=Antony Jefferson; EHB=Harry Botterell

1   GJ to AJ. Letter 3rd February 1944.
2   GJ to AJ. Letter 5th May 1944.
3   Jefferson G. René Descartes on the localization of the soul. In: *Selected Papers*. London: Pitman Medical, 1960; 45–69.
4   Jefferson G. René Descartes on the localization of the soul. *Irish J Med Sci* 1949; **285**: 691–706.
5   Jefferson G. René Descartes (1596–1650), philosopher, mathematician, physiologist. *London Hospital Gazette* 1950; **53**: 69–78.
6   GJ to AJ. Letter 7th March 1944.
7   GJ to EHB. Letter 10th April 1944.
8   GJ. MS *Management of battle casualties — head wounds*. Instructions, signed but undated.
9   Jefferson G. Harvey Cushing. *Manchester Medical Students' Gazette* 1943; **22**: 1–16.
10   GJ to AJ. Letter 10th April 1944.
11   GJ to Fulton J. Letter 12th April 1944.
12   GJ to AJ. Letter 5th May 1944.
13   GJ to GMJ. Letter 11th June 1944.
14   GJ to GMJ. Letter 19th June 1944.
15   GJ to EHB. Letter 19th June 1944.
16   EHB to GJ. Letter 30th June 1944.
17   GJ to EHB. Letter 10th July 1944.
18   GJ to EHB. Letter 24th July 1944.
19   Armistead E to EHB. Letter 30th September 1944.
20   Morley J to GJ. Letter 27th September 1944.
21   GJ to EHB. Letter 9th October 1944.
22   GJ to EHB. Letter 7th October 1944.
23   Armistead E to EHB. Letter 16th October 1944.
24   GJ to EHB. Letters 25th and 27th October 1944.
25   GJ MS on the fly-leaf of Allbutt TC. *Science and medieval thought*. London: C J Clay, 1901. In the possession of Dr Denis Leigh.
26   GJ to EHB. Letter 7th November 1944.
27   *Visits to clinics — The Canadian Neurological Centre at Hackwood Park, Basingstoke*. Unsigned article. *Br J Surg* 1944/1945; **32**: 525–30.
28   Bishop of Manchester to GJ. Letter 18th October 1944.
29   Williams Rev J to GJ. Letter 14th January 1945.
30   Cairns H to GJ. Letter 14th January 1945.
31   Morley TP. Obituary. Sir Geoffrey Jefferson. *Acta Neurochir* 1961; **9**: 718–20.
32   Jefferson G. On compression and invasion of the optic nerves and chiasma by neighbouring gliomas. *Trans Ophthalmol Soc UK* 1945; **65**: 262–303.
33   SBNS Planning Committee *Notes on the neurosurgical needs of the population and the training of neurosurgeons*. 1945–1947. Published privately.
34   GMJ to AJ. Letter 8th June 1945.
35   O'Connell J to GJ. Letter 31st July 1945.
36   GJ. MSS and correspondence with the BBC.
37   Editorial *BMJ* 1945; **2**: 292.
38   Walshe FMR, Symonds CP. Letter to Editor. *BMJ* 1945; **2**: 364.
39   Jefferson G. Letter to Editor. *BMJ* 1945; **2**: 473.
40   Cairns H to GJ. Letter 24th September 1945.
41   Walshe FMR. Geoffrey Jefferson (1886–1961). *Biographical memoirs of the Fellows of the Royal Society of London* 1961; **7**: 127–35.

42   GJ to EHB. Letter 26th November 1945.
43   Cairns H to GJ. Letter 23rd October 1945.
44   GMJ to AJ. Letter 8th September 1945.
45   *Report of the Goodenough Committee on Medical Education* HMSO B 61 (07).
46   GJ. MS Notes for Senate of Manchester University.
47   Contract on the appointment of GJ to a new Chair, dated 29th September 1945.
48   GJ. MS Report to the Medical Research Council, 1945.
49   GJ to EHB. Letter 26th November 1945.

Chapter 19

Eminence
1946–1948

The SBNS Planning Committee did not produce its report for more than another year but, by 1946, an attempt to put together its conclusions was already under way. Jefferson had sent Rowbotham some notes for his comments and had received a number of suggestions from his former colleague concerning one or two aspects of the draft. In his acknowledgement of these Jeff replied: 'I am heartily sick of this thing, its occupied far too much of my time. You are quite right, this sort of activity is very tiring and bothersome. I greatly fear that there will be a terrific outburst of it when the Health Act comes out [creating the National Health Service in 1948] but I shall try to keep out of it. I've had too much in the last 5 yrs., its terribly bad for ones work and requires energies that one wants to spend on thinking and doing of a more congenial and scientific kind. But there's always the fear that, exasperating though it is, one is evading a responsibility that may have long lasting effects if one steps out of it. Cairns has sent in his Head Injury thing practically unaltered. Its not very good[1]. I think we had better leave Head Injuries without figures. The Insurance Cos. are the only people who could tell us what we really want to know — ie. not only numbers (and they don't have all of them) but invalidism'[2]. Despite the fact that Jeff had demanded notification of all these injuries by the EMS hospitals during the war, there were no national records of minor cases and their outcome, except among the casualties from the armed forces; and civilian injuries are very different from those due to missiles. When the report did come out, this section highlighted the problems but gave no clear recommendations for their solution. The only rehabilitation centres at that time were those run by the Services, the future of which was uncertain, yet the report did not ask for the establishment of civilian equivalents, although stating that aftercare for severe cases should be 'at a convalescent centre'. The lack of civilian rehabilitation centres became apparent in the years to come and was a serious deficiency. Jefferson's undated manuscript entitled *Notes on large scale planning for head injuries*, was probably written at about this time.

During 1946 the *British Journal of Surgery* was preparing to publish War Surgery Supplement No 1 on head injuries[3], and Cairns reminded Jeff of his promise of an article for it[4]. Jefferson's admirable contribution was entitled *Head wounds and infection in two wars*, and was accompanied by others from Joe Schorstein and Richard Johnson, his former assistants in Manchester. Jeff told Botterell: 'I don't know what the date of publication of the special No. of the BJS is. The knights are doing it — Wakeley and Cairns. If there's room I may have a brief note in it, but it may be squeezed out by the boys'[5].

Shock waves resulting from the letter by Walshe and Symonds in the *British Medical Journal*[6], concerning the responsibility of neurosurgeons for the care of potentially surgical cases, had continued to surge. In an attempt to calm the waters but also to establish the medical priority they so urgently sought, the two neurologists invited Jefferson, Cairns and one other surgeon of their own choice to dine with them. Cairns wrote to Jeff: 'I don't know who else should come — my personal preference would be for Willie [Henderson], but he doesn't say much on occasions such as this may be.... However, I have no confidence that I am seeing the light in this matter so you had better make the decision. One of the basic notions they must be made to accept is that no specialist group of doctors should ever direct another group.... I think there is some case for compromise about head injuries.... The neurologist and the psychiatrist should somehow be brought into the head injury organisation, for their usefulness in the later stages can be considerable. The problem really is how to save British medical neurology from cutting its own throat'[7]. This last was a remark with which the physicians would hardly have agreed, since their endeavour was to ensure that all neurological cases of every kind should be referred to them in the first instance. In the event the dinner was arranged for 28th March and Douglas Northfield, from the London Hospital, was asked to attend as the third surgeon.

There is, unfortunately, no record of the discussion that took place at that meeting but, on the following day, Cairns again wrote to Jefferson: 'That was a fine meeting last night and I thought your innings the best, or one of the best I have ever seen you play — straight bat, quickness of the feet, and on your toes all the time and scoring all round the wicket'[8]. Cairns shared Jeff's early love of cricket and used cricketing metaphors in more than one of his letters to him. 'It was a good thing there was no body line stuff (in spite of Northfield), and there was much less spin bowling than I had expected. In fact some really useful work was done for the future of neurology'[8]. It is difficult to say what effect the meeting may have had in the longer view but in the short term the National Hospital, Queen Square, continued to admit surgical patients under the neurologists as they had in the past, and it was left for everyone else to make their own arrangements[9].

April 10th 1946 was Geoffrey Jefferson's sixtieth birthday, and the *Manchester Medical Students' Gazette* gave him a *Festschrift*. He was honoured by an introductory *Appreciation* by Wilder Penfield, the only neurosurgeon ever to have received an Order of Merit, in which the founder of the Montreal Neurological Institute recalled Jeff's early papers in neuro-anatomy and neurophysiology and how he had progressed 'from knowledge of structure, to mechanisms of development and localisation of function'. 'This throws light on his approach to clinical surgery', he wrote, 'for, although he has since become a neurosurgeon second to none in technical skill, it is as a neurophysiologist that Geoffrey Jefferson is outstanding. All through his life he seems to have appreciated the heaven-sent opportunity that disease presents to the prepared neurologist, the opportunity to gain insight into the fundamental mechanisms of the nervous system. In this he is like Hughlings Jackson. Where other surgeons rush on from case to case in punctual unthinking rhythm, Jefferson lingers to ponder and to rationalise; and one might imagine that Jackson lingers with him at the bedside'[10]. These words, from a very thoughtful friend whom he greatly admired, must have given Jeff much satisfaction. It was a theme to be repeated by others: 'Every operation is a unique performance, fraught with opportunities for

Figure 20   *Geoffrey Jefferson and Harry Botterell.*

edifying physiological experiment, and with possibilities alike for benefit to the patient, or for his irreparable injury and death'[11]. The *Gazette* carried several more articles about Jefferson and different aspects of his career. Among them James Hardman described his Chief's attributes as a mentor, writing that he 'does not imprint a dogmatism, but fosters and encourages original thought...it is true to say that no-one has felt mentally fettered or has had his personality suppressed in his association with this truly great teacher'[13]. That article ended with the following apt quotation from Alexander Pope's *Essay on criticism*[12]: 'Let such teach others who themselves excel, And censure freely who have written well'[13].

In June 1946 Jefferson went fishing in Ripon with his great friend John Morley. Jeff wrote to Botterell: 'I'm not much good at it yet.... I must go to the Ministry meeting in London tomorrow on the layout of neurology for Britain under the new Health Act'[14]. Changing the subject once more, he said: 'You'll be glad to learn that I'm getting rid of Marshall Hall by putting him in the Singer 70th birthday *Festschrift*. But that doesn't clear him right off the field as he started too many hares in my head'[14]. The original paper on Marshall Hall's work on the grasp reflex had been given by Jeff to the Montreal Neurological Society in June 1943, during his extended war-time transatlantic journey, and had now been revised for publication[15]. A later version appeared in Jefferson's *Selected papers*[16]. The recipient of this *Festschrift* was the famous medical historian, Professor Charles Singer of the Wellcome Institute for the History of Medicine.

That letter to Botterell continued with the news that Jefferson expected to meet Penfield 'next week when he lectures at the Royal Society. I don't know about what...'[14]. Jeff then wrote: 'I have now to confess a great sin...its your paper on Tantalum repair wh. has been sitting in a folder on my desk for 15 mos. under piles of other stuff. If only it had a horn or something to draw my attention to it things would have been different, but it sat there as quiet as a mouse and I had completely forgotten that I had ever had it, then I denied the charge, and then little bits of memory began to piece themselves together till I made a search'[14]. Finally, he remarked that none of the building of the new facilities for neurosurgery at the Manchester Royal Infirmary had yet started, Norman Guthkelch had been working with him as first assistant for the past year and Richard Johnson was due to join him again on 30th June. He imagined that, 'I can sit back a bit more — or so I think, but that means that I've only got the normal overwork to do. I wonder how I survived those frightful years and got in as much as I did'[14]. In the previous year, 1945, more than 800 neurosurgical procedures had been performed in Jefferson's unit, many by Jeff himself.

September 1946 saw the award of two more honours from his colleagues, when Jeff became the president of the Manchester Pathological Society and was made an honorary member of the Scandinavian Neurosurgical Society. In the following month his mother, Mrs Cecilia Jefferson, died. He also suffered another attack of recurrent diverticulitis. Cairns was about to visit America at the beginning of October when he wrote: 'I am sorry that you have had another go of diverticulitis and I am glad you have given up the Vienna trip which was bound to be strenuous and probably dispiriting. There is no doubt that you should take care of yourself, in other people's interests as well as your own — because you can do so much good even by sitting back and just being around'[17].

An additional and perhaps unnecessary problem arose just then. Norman Dott had written to Jefferson to try to persuade him to perform a chordotomy (division of pain pathways in the spinal cord) in an endeavour to relieve the pain in his arthritic hip, rather than that he should have an arthrodesis which would have made the joint immobile and would produce great difficulty in operating when sitting down, or even in bending over patients to examine them. In fact, despite these significant limitations, fixation (arthrodesis) would have been the better choice. The arthritis was a late sequel to a motorycycle accident in Dott's youth and for years had been a source of great pain and discomfort, as well as causing difficulty in walking. Jeff had asked Cairns if he would assist at the operation, the results of which are by no means universally successful, and Cairns in his reply wrote: 'I am sorry to hear about Norman; it seems a big step to take but of course I will come up when you do the cordotomy. Preferably after the end of term — ie. after Dec 7'[17]. Jefferson had undoubtedly written ...chordotomy and Cairns was trying to point out that he spelt it with a C alone, as was usual in American practice but, incidentally, also used by those who, unlike Jeff, lacked a classical education*.

The operation on Norman Dott was performed by Jefferson in Manchester in the middle of December, with Cairns assisting. Initially it successfully relieved the pain, for Cairns told Jeff he had had 'a delightful letter from Norman today [20th December 1946] confirming your welcome telephone message of last Monday. It is simply grand and I do congratulate you. But isn't the upper limit the devil?'[18]. This remark refers to the difficulty of cutting a sufficient amount of the spino-thalamic tract in the spinal cord to produce a high enough level of pain loss without interfering with other functions. Unfortunately Dott's pain returned,

*Chordotomy The derivation is from χορη a chord, χ=Chi and not the initial κ=Kappa as in κυπρωσ, copper, for instance. However, cordotomy eventually became the universally accepted spelling. *Tempora mutantur, et nos mutamur in illis.* Times change, and we change with them.

as might have been predicted. There is a tendency for the level to fall in the days following operation but, this apart, very chronic pain is not usually relieved by this means. Jefferson must have known this and have operated against his better judgement as a result of Dott's powers of persuasion, and with some support from the argument that there would have been less disability after a successful chordotomy than after an arthrodesis. The operation must have caused Jeff considerable anxiety. That two of the three 'wise men' were performing an elective and uncertain procedure on the third was surely tempting providence. Later Dott had the hip joint fused and the leg shortened, but the fusion became insecure, and he continued to suffer pain, as he had done for most of his life.

The 17th January 1947 was the anniversary of the Jefferson's wedding, and Gertrude wrote a touching paean of affection to accompany a present to Jeff of a claret jug and a book. 'As the years go by you are more and more dear to me as you reveal progressively the depth and tenderness and beauty of your inner self. You are so patient & kind & thoughtful to me, and so truly deserve the affection and esteem of your many friends outside the family. I hope we shall be spared for many years of even closer companionship and unity of spirit—This is Heaven on earth'[19].

On 2nd March 1947 Geoffrey Jefferson became a Fellow of the Royal Society of London. This was a very singular honour for a surgeon, for there are very few medical men on the roll compared with the number that there were in the past. It was undoubtedly Jeff's knowledge and interest in neuro-anatomy and neurophysiology which made him stand out, together with his personality and ability to write and speak well; sadly clinicians are not particularly highly regarded by scientists. It was an award which he very greatly appreciated, from the oldest scientific society in Britain and one of the most prestigious in the world. It placed him among the greatest scientific academics of the nation, even if he did not claim to be one of them himself. The comitia of the Royal College of Physicians then added to Jefferson's pleasure by making him an Honorary Fellow at their meeting on 26th April. This underlined his endeavours to unite neurology and neurosurgery, setting aside the fruitless rivalries as far as he was concerned.

There were many congratulations on this double recognition, a typical example of which was a cable from Botterell: 'News of the FRS and FRCP restores our faith in virtue being rewarded. Most appropriate richly deserved honours. Felicitations. Affectionately Harry'[20]. It was acknowledged by Jeff as follows: 'My dear Harry, Thank you for your charmingly worded cable, I liked that. I've known it might come since last Nov. when Walshe and Adrian began to agitate for me.... Yes, its a pretty satisfactory beginning and the day after I got a letter from the RCP saying that if I would accept it they proposed making me an F at the comitia of Apr. 26. So that my cup is now full'[21]. He told Botterell that he was flying to Lisbon for a meeting of the SBNS hosted by Egas Moniz in a day or two and that, in the following week, he would be attending a joint meeting with the French at the Royal Society of Medicine, when they would be talking about cerebral oedema. 'Its a grand illusion that the matter will be advanced by our discussions', he commented, somewhat cynically but with justification[21].

On the same day Jefferson also wrote in acknowledgement of congratulations from GF Rowbotham: 'Something would have been missing if I had not had a letter from you, for you know how warm a place in my heart I have for you, and I think you know better than most how much the FRS means to the poor clinician. There ought to be more doctors in the R.S.'[22]. Rowbotham was not intending to travel to Lisbon for the forthcoming meeting, largely because of the expense, which drew unusually strong protests from Jeff about the cost of living: 'Its plain confiscation now by what must surely be the most boastful, noisy, stupid and incompetent Govt. we have had in 200 years'[22]. Clement Attlee's Labour government was still in office.

The Association of Surgeons, a group of senior consultants in all branches of surgery, met in Oxford in July 1947, under the presidency of Sir Hugh Cairns and, at their dinner in the hall of Christchurch College, Jefferson proposed the Association's health. He presented an address about the nature and future of surgery, which was given in the prevailing atmosphere of apprehension about what would happen to the discipline when it became a part of the forthcoming National Health Service.

In his speech Jeff said: 'The surgeon can very easily surrender the scientific side of his work by his slip slop use of the facts available to him, or by his failure to discover what the facts really are'[23]. He described the 'emotional glory' that some scientists felt on making discoveries, but 'we have to beware that this emotional feeling...does not flood over us on too slight a provocation, and [to remember] that we should mistrust reason as both Roger and Francis Bacon told us that we should. The philosopher with the most cogent message for the surgeon was...David Hume who first wrote down what is on reflection a very obvious fact, that you can only talk given a cause; you cannot tell what the result will be unless you have experience of it.... "Give me a cause and reason, and I will tell you what follows." This is untrue unless, said Hume, we had experienced the cause before and learnt from experience what followed. This is...one of the bases of scientific method'[23]. The aim of the Association, said Jefferson, was to meet for 'the perfection of our technique, of our craft and for the periodic review of the principles upon which we act. It has been fashionable these years past to beware of pity, to deny sentiment, but I am quite sure that the cynic does more harm than the sentimentalist, for the cynic eventually destroys himself. Virtues must always be mixed and we should hold them in moderation as I hope that our faults are measured also. But I remain one for whom a veneration for qualities and virtues is a faculty no less sincere than my belief in the scientific method. Neither the one nor the other will make the complete man in which individual skill is the dominant factor.... It is only because of the uncertainties that there is any interest in our craft. As soon as we have [got rid of them] completely it becomes a routine, not merely a dull one but, something that we must face, that we are not likely to come upon any new or interesting fact. Surgery, and indeed medicine, concerns itself in the end with facts, and it is that above all else which still leaves [the members of] our profession some entitlement to be, or to become scientists'[23].

In the autumn Jefferson visited Norway and Sweden before giving the Inaugural Lecture to the Faculty of Medicine of Leeds University on 14th October. This was entitled *Scepsis Scientifica** and in it he developed some of the

*Scepsis Scientifica. A title borrowed from a work by Joseph Glanville (or Glanvill) 1636–1680.

lines of thought he had explored in his recent Oxford speech. It was published in the *British Medical Journal* early in the following year and became the first of several semi-philosophical essays, 'reflections' or 'meditations' in which Jefferson sought to express various ideas that had concerned him over the years. Later, when he was choosing the material for the publication in book form of his *Selected papers*, this work was one of the first three in the volume[24].

After a few words of introduction Jefferson began: 'The habit of mind of any scientist is sceptical in so far as he is or should be unwilling to admit the truth of anything without proof. The antithesis is a habit of faith in beliefs, usually expressed in abstract ideas, that make so strong an appeal to the individual as to require no proof; to him they seem self-evident.... The habit of faith is one shared by scientists, who must accept teaching and beliefs that they have not personally inquired into. They know that they can obtain verification of the facts if they turn to the descriptions of the original experiments or calculations. Such reversion to original sources can be used equally by believers in an idea. The scientist has the advantage in that he can, if he still feels sceptical, try a rigidly identical experiment himself when it is in his power to do so or devise new ones to test the results previously given'[24].

Jeff referred to the constant changes in what are accepted as "facts", which become modified as knowledge advances. 'Science has nothing to do with truth'; "correctness" or "accuracy" is its aim. The amended definition would then run: 'that a sceptical habit of mind is proper for scientists with reference to their own as well as other people's work, that it embraces unwillingness to accept without adequate proof the correctness of a certain type of observation, usually one with limited aim; and it might be added that this proof should preferably be quantitative, should take some form of measurement. The last requirement is applicable only to some parts of the biological and clinical sciences'[24].

AN Whitehead in *Science and the modern world* [1925] speaks of 'the essential irrationality of science, by which he means its pursuit of crude and brutal fact and imperative acceptance of fact, irrespective of its having any recognisable meaning'[24]. However, Jefferson observed that even when the results of experiments are not in line with orthodox beliefs, they must still be recorded, even when they are more "irrational" than might have been expected[24]. He went on to say that personal bias presents a significant risk to the scientist, for it is not possible, as the nineteenth century physiologist François Magendie advocated, to rid the observer of all preconceptions and emotional content.

He drew attention to three important considerations: 'a) freedom to submit anything whatever to sceptical criticism, b) the danger of the scientist being deceived by his own experiments, and c) recognition that the scientific method could not expect to solve all the problems that face mankind'[24]. Jefferson considered these points in the light of the work of Joseph Glanvill and Francis Bacon in the seventeenth century. They attacked the belief that established ways of thinking were necessarily the best. They were separating 'erudition hammered out by thinking, meditation, by logic and by reason, from suppositions not subjected and often not amenable to test'[24]. Jefferson remarked how Bacon's teaching that 'speculation could lead to absurdity' had been re-expounded by Wilfred Trotter in the twentieth century. Trotter, that most philosophical of surgeons, deduced that 'ideas which aroused emotion were the most dangerous, because most violently defended'[24].

The next subject Jefferson considered under his title of *Scepsis Scientifica* was the problem of the relation of mind to brain. He reviewed the matter from Bishop Berkeley's proposition, that nothing exists save in the mind, to Hume's dismissal of that statement with the remark that such ideas 'admit of no answer and produce no conviction'. Jeff moved his own argument forwards in time from the views of Descartes, Kant, Sherrington and finally to the psychologists, who 'have shown little more interest in structure than Plato'[24]. And once again he turned to David Hume, whom he supposed to be the arch-sceptic, observing, as quoted earlier, that he came 'nearest to the scientist's ideal of a philosopher in his axiom that given a cause, we cannot foretell what the result will be unless we have previous experience of that cause acting in rigidly identical circumstances. This is pure science...we know nothing except by experience'[24].

Therefore, 'are we to infer that speculation is never permissible in science?'. Jefferson asked the question rhetorically, and replied, 'By no means. The difficulty is to get the amount right.... Every good piece of research begins as an idea coming unsought into a mind'[24]. Trains of thought arise one out of another, sometimes offering a side issue or casting doubt 'not so much on the main truth of the argument as on its being the whole truth'[24]. This happened, he observed, 'classically with Newton, and it is unlikely that Einstein's correction will stand permanently unaltered'[24]. Would not Jeff have been delighted to have known how accurate that prediction was to be? However, he went on, 'to be too great a sceptic is not a sign of greatness, for it is easier and less laborious to doubt than to discover truth.... The only sciences which have succeeded in producing immediate conviction and durable results are mathematical and those into which mathematics enters to a very great degree.... Let us not laugh too loud at our fathers lest posterity overhears us!'[24]. Trotter, he recalled, spoke of man's natural resistance to new ideas. This is 'particularly so when we are satisfied with what we already know of the subject. When one's minds are vacant of explanation we seem to be extraordinarily gullible, ready to accept any theory, however nonsensical, and then we defend it'[24]. And in Jeff's own phrase: 'Orderly scepticism is a discipline, not an intuitive possession; the proper name for the intuitive variety is prejudice'[24]. For some people, there are certain ideas which are 'so clear and so distinct that they brought instantaneous conviction and were immediately acceptable as truths. But unless they can be demonstrated, unless they can be shown to be indestructible on attack, they must remain truths only for the individual who holds them. This seems a depressing conclusion; however it may well explain man's permanent liability to disagree with his fellows'[24].

Jefferson ended his lecture by saying: 'Our task in keeping emotions in control in science is difficult, since they are so permissible in much else that occupies our thoughts, they colour our lives, they are at all times ineradicable. The rules that we live by socially have been made by experience as curbs on unfettered emotional behaviours. The rules of science have a shorter history, but are in the main of the same kind narrowed by a sharper focus to a different end. We have seen that better knowledge of the brain gives us no hope for lenses that will automatically correct the astigmatism of our minds. Let us then live our lives according to rules of historical experience, and let our scientific thinking be tempered by scepticism, but let our actions be not paralysed by it'[24].

This lecture has been quoted at some length because it gives an idea of Jefferson's style, his interest in matters that are beyond day to day consideration, his ability to stimulate thought and the logical progression of his argument. He makes many points that are as valid today as they were 50 years ago. Gertrude was at the lecture in Leeds, and then went on to London to attend a meeting in her own field. She wrote to Geoffrey from the English Speaking Union: 'I am so happy the lecture was so good & I am sure Prof Stewart is right that it will long be remembered. You know I enjoyed it & was proud for the lecturer'[25].

Jefferson had served on committees of the Medical Research Council during the war, but in 1948 he became a member of the Council itself. Later, in 1953, he was to become the first chairman of its Clinical Research Board, concerned with awarding grants, and he continued to hold that important position for the following 6 years. Also in 1948, the publication of the *SBNS Planning and training report*[1] finally took place.

In May 1948 there was another combined meeting of the Section of Neurology of the Royal Society of Medicine and the Société de Neurologie de Paris, held this time in Paris, at which Jefferson read a paper entitled *Subarachnoid bleeding from angiomas and aneurysms in the young*. This was based on a study made possible by the recently developed ability to demonstrate these lesions by angiography; examinations which, at that time, were almost all carried out by open puncture of the carotid artery and injection of thorium dioxide, a radio-active and toxic substance. Jeff drew important conclusions from a series which was large for 1948. These he summarised in a number of concise precepts some of which are still valid. They exemplify to perfection his ability to combine clarity of perception with accuracy of expression[26]. He had spent a whole week in Paris and another in Vienna. His comments were: 'Paris is delightful as ever and Vienna much less grim than it is painted. The Russians are friendly enough there. I got a thrill out of lecturing in the First Surgical Clinic in the Algemeine Krankenhaus under the bust of von Eiselsberg. He bowed to me — or so I thought'[27].

In the summer of 1948 Jeff contributed three biographical articles to the *Manchester Medical Students' Gazette*, on James Ross, Sir William Thorburn and RT Williamson, all of them pioneers in neurology who had been on the staff of the Manchester Royal Infirmary[28]. On 8th July the Council of the Royal College of Surgeons gave Geoffrey Jefferson its highest award, the Lister Medal. It was something that Jeff had always coveted, for it not only marked his great achievement in surgery but also the utmost respect of its representatives. With it came the obligation to deliver an oration, which he fulfilled in the following June when he spoke on the *Mind of mechanical man*[29], a very early comparison of the action of computers with the functions of the brain. Among the first to congratulate him on the award was Hugh Cairns, who wrote: 'I was delighted to learn at Council today that you have been awarded the Lister Medal.... This is surely the highest of your many honours to date, and it is nice to think that it carries with it some material recognition of your splendid work'[30]. Among other letters of congratulation there was one from the producer of the programmes that Jeff had broadcast in the Overseas Service of the BBC: 'I am honoured to have a Lister Medallist on the programme. I do hope you will do the Descartes piece for

Figure 21   *William and Mary Sweet with Geoffrey Jefferson.*

me next year. I am sure that it can be "sold" to the third [programme] as well'. Jefferson must have broadcast a biographical note on Sir William Macewen, the great nineteenth century Scottish surgeon, for the letter continued: 'Your Macewen piece is to be printed...in "London Calling", which is the overseas "Listener" and "Radio Times"...I will remind you of the Descartes later'[31].

Meanwhile the American neurosurgeon, William Sweet, who had worked for $3\frac{1}{2}$ years during the war at the Queen Elizabeth Hospital in Birmingham, and had subsequently maintained a correspondence with Jeff, arranged to spend September 1948 with him in Manchester. Sweet and his wife stayed at High Bank. One morning during this visit Gertrude begged him to get Jeff home in time for dinner at 7.30 pm. She said, "'Bridget has become so exasperated with these dinners at 10 pm night after night that I'm afraid she'll leave us. I'm counting on you Bill!"'. Almost inevitably, a suspected brain abscess was admitted late in the day and, although no operation was performed that night, when Jeff had finally been located he spent about 2 hours with the patient. They sat down to dinner yet again at 10 pm. That month spent by Sweet in Manchester coincided with meetings in Holland and Belgium, to which he was fortunate in being able to accompany Jeff and to take advantage of the doors that were thereby opened for him[32].

Jefferson returned again to the subject of *Sir William Macewen's contribution to neurosurgery and its sequels*, working it up to become the Macewen Memorial Lecture, which he delivered in Glasgow on 1st October 1948 on the occasion of his receipt of an Honorary LLD degree from the University[33]. It was the centenary of the birth of the great Scottish surgeon, and the choice of Jefferson to give the lecture on that occasion was very appropriate. Macewen had graduated in 1870 and during the next two decades his fame grew in several fields, but particularly in that of the surgery of the nervous system. His most important papers (1881 and 1888) on this subject were entitled *Intracranial lesions*[34] and *On the surgery of the brain and spinal cord*[35]. Jefferson observed: 'The contents of this [1881] paper affirm beyond any possibility of rejection the fact that Macewen was the first to make useful application to man of the new laboratory research on the cerebral cortex'[33]; he was referring to the work of Fristch, Hitzig, Ferrier and Hughlings Jackson. The 1888 paper had been delivered by Macewen at the annual meeting of the BMA, when, Jefferson suggested, 'The Assembly must have felt it had assisted at the birth of a new and...immediately acceptable idea, so compelling was the authority of the speaker, so convincing the demonstration'[33]. For the first time a surgeon had used the principles of cortical localisation to identify the situation of a brain lesion, and he had illustrated this principle with seven cases. The demonstration Macewen had given enabled Rickman Godlee, assisted by David Ferrier, to be the first to remove a tumour from within the brain, and others soon followed. Macewen's fame also rests on his *Pyogenic diseases of the brain and spinal cord*, published in 1893[36], in which he reported results in the treatment of these conditions that were still a challenge in Jefferson's day. 'It is only the young', Jeff observed in conclusion, 'who can be deceived into thinking that we are really cleverer than our forefathers'[33].

Gertrude Jefferson had by now been a medical officer for the Maternity and Child Welfare Services of Manchester for many years. In the course of this work she had observed how often the ailing or difficult child was the offspring of immature, neurotic or unhappy parents, and she had developed a project for the establishment of centres to provide care and advice for young people with problems after leaving school who would soon become parents themselves. As she said: 'The individual is looked after by the local authorities until school age, and by the education authority until school leaving age, after which he is nobody's care. It seemed therefore important, if home life were to be stabilised after the havoc of two world wars, to provide some means of influencing the adolescent either directly, or indirectly through the parents, towards responsible citizenship and parenthood. A Family Welfare Service in Child Welfare buildings seemed to provide a solution'[37]. She had presented the idea to the Medical Officer of Health in Manchester in 1944 when it was received with interest, but it was not until 1948 that permission to set up centres was obtained from the Ministry of Health and a grant was given by the Manchester Corporation. Such was the success of the scheme that, having been started on a voluntary basis, full responsibility was eventually taken over by the Manchester Corporation Health Services[37]. It was a unique family-based service that aimed at preventing mental ill-health in the long term.

Geoffrey Jefferson was now approaching the summit of his career. Still more honours lay ahead as also did the advent of his retirement, during which his reputation continued to soar. With the prospect of handing over his responsibilities in the University and in the Royal Infirmary in only 3 years time, Jefferson continued to worry in case he might not be able to effectively choose his successor by appointing an appropriate candidate to a consultant position in the neurosurgical unit while he yet remained in command.

REFERENCES

GJ=Geoffrey Jefferson; GMJ=Gertrude Jefferson
1   SBNS Planning Committee Report, 1945–1947. *Head injuries.* Privately published. 15–17.
2   GJ to Rowbotham F. Letter 1st January 1946.
3   Wounds of the head. *Br J Surg War Supplement No 1.* 1947. Bristol: John Wright.
4   Cairns H to GJ. Letter 23rd May 1946.
5   GJ to Botterell EH. Letter 26th June 1946.
6   Walshe FMR, Symonds CP. Letter *BMJ* 1945; **2**: 364.
7   Cairns H to GJ. Letter 6th March 1946.
8   Cairns H to GJ. Letter 29th March 1946.
9   Harries BJ. Personal communication.
10   Penfield W. Geoffrey Jefferson, an appreciation. *Manchester University Medical Students' Gazette* 1946; **25**: 43.
11   Bailey RA. Professor Jefferson, the man. *Manchester University Medical Students' Gazette* 1946; **25**: 48–50.
12   Pope A. *An Essay on criticism.* 1711.
13   Hardman J. Professor Jefferson as a teacher. *Manchester University Medical Students' Gazette* 1946; **25**: 52–5.
14   GJ to Botterell EH. Letter 13th June 1946.
15   Jefferson G. Marshall Hall. The grasp reflex and the diastaltic spinal cord. In: Underwood A, ed. *Science, medicine and history, essays written in honour of Charles Singer.* London: Oxford University Press, 1953; **2**: 303–20.
16   Jefferson G. *Selected papers.* London: Pitman Medical, 1960: 73–93.
17   Cairns H to GJ. Letter 6th October 1946.
18   Cairns H to GJ. Letter 20th December 1946.
19   GMJ to GJ. Letter 16th January 1947.
20   Botterell EH to GJ. Cable 26th March 1947.
21   GJ to Botterell EH. Letter 3rd April 1947.
22   GJ to Rowbotham GF. Letter 3rd April 1947.
23   GJ. MS of speech to the Association of Surgeons July 1947.
24   Jefferson G. Scepsis Scientifica. *BMJ* 1948; **1**: 379–82 and *Selected papers.* London: Pitman Medical, 1960: 24–34.
25   GMJ to GJ. Letter 17th October 1947.
26   Jefferson G. Les hémorrhages sous-arachnoidiennes par angiomes et anévrysmes chez les jeunes. *Revue Neurologique* 1948; **80**: 413–32.
27   GJ to Sweet WH. Letter 21st June 1947.
28   Jefferson G. James Ross, Sir William Thorburn, RT Williamson—Pioneers in neurology. *Manchester University Medical Students' Gazette* 1948; **27**: 1–12.
29   Jefferson G. The mind of mechanical man. *BMJ* 1949; **1**: 1105–1110 and *Selected papers.* London: Pitman Medical, 1960: 10–23.
30   Cairns H to GJ. Letter 8th July 1948.
31   Jellis R to GJ. Letter 18th July 1948.
32   Sweet WH. Personal communication.
33   Jefferson G. *Sir William Macewen's contribution to neurosurgery and its sequels.* Glasgow University Publications No. 81 Glasgow: Jackson & Co, 1950 and *Selected papers.* London; Pitman Medical, 1960: 132–49.
34   Macewen W. Intracranial lesions. *Lancet* 1881; **2**: 543–4.
35   Macewen W. On the surgery of the brain and spinal cord. *BMJ* 1888; **2**: 302–303.
36   Macewen W. *Pyogenic diseases of the brain and spinal cord.* Glasgow: James Maclehose, 1893.
37   Jefferson GM. The Manchester Family Welfare Service. Its origins and aims. *Medical Women's Federation Journal,* October 1952.

Chapter 20

The pre-retirement years
1949–1950

Despite the ending of the war, Jefferson's duties at the Ministry of Health were not over; he was now one of the advisers on the closure of the Emergency Medical Services as they merged with the new National Health Service. The Act, which had been passed in 1946, had come into force on 5th July 1948. Naturally enough, it required a few years for its provisions to be implemented and to gain strength and momentum, and there were still many problems to be sorted out by the beginning of 1949. As Jeff himself wrote in a manuscript assessing the hospital situation in Britain at this time, 'The first six months working of the National Health Service could hardly be expected to produce fundamental changes'[1]. The report demonstrates that, although the first half year of the Service had seen minor readjustments, mainly in the field of administration, it was not until 1949 that significant changes in organisation began to take place.

Jefferson's appraisal is comprehensive, showing again his ability to grasp the key issues. The distribution of specialists of all kinds, including neurosurgeons, was not in accordance with the needs of the population as a whole and was often uneconomic, many specialists 'having small responsibilities in several hospitals, shared with others in each, when simple redistribution could effect great economies in time and improve the availability of service'[1]. A review of the grading of individuals was also needed, and establishments had to be agreed. It is remarkable how this document covers so many aspects, from general practitioner services to the working of Regional Boards, and from specialist services within the hospitals to the medical records departments. It was for his ability to see things comprehensively that the Ministry of Health sought Jefferson's advice so eagerly, both on the setting up of new neurosurgical units throughout the country as the staff for them became available, and on the regulation of the supply of trained neurosurgeons according to the number of training posts provided; later on this became part of the brief of the Willink Committee on Medical Manpower, of which Jeff was a member. Incidentally, it was Jeff's position as adviser to the Government on neurosurgical matters and the willing support of his colleagues, that gave the Society of British Neurological Surgeons its position as the voice of neurosurgical opinion in the United Kingdom.

Warm correspondence continued between Jeff and Harry Botterell: 'Oh dear Harry, I owe you an enormous letter. I have just done the hardest thing of all— verifying all the references in the bibliography of the paper on subarachnoid haemorrhage from angiomas and aneurysms that I gave in Paris last summer, and that needless to say is a month late, and I am just off to London for a Ministry meeting and a Medical Research Council meeting, mixed up with a special lecture at Queen Square, and the second edition of my 1937 paper on

Compression of the Chiasma and Optic Nerves by Aneurysms. I have got another 10 or 11 cases of varying degrees of beauty'[2]. A fortnight later he told Botterell that he had 'two or three short of 300 meningiomas and nearly 400 pituitaries in the bag now!'[3].

February 1949 brought a request from the National Portrait Gallery for a photograph to include in the National Record of Distinguished Persons. This honour had only been extended to around 5000 individuals in the previous 30 years. The Royal Society also asked for his portrait.

During March there was a flurry of letters between Jefferson and his old friend, the radiologist AE Barclay, with whom he had been in touch as much as 36 years previously, during his work on the passage of fluid through the body of the human stomach. In brilliant research carried out with his colleague in Oxford, Barclay had, in recent years, demonstrated the existence of arterial shunts in the renal circulation and their relation to vascular hypertension and urine output. These could be opened or closed, thus controlling the blood supply to parts of the kidneys. The first of these letters was from Barclay, to thank Jeff for any rôle he might have played in the promised award of an honorary DSc degree by his old university of Manchester. Barclay was now an invalid with terminal cancer, and he remarked that if the degree had to wait until conferment at the end of the academic year, he might be 'virtually certain to miss the boat'[4]. He was unable any longer to work in the laboratory, but could 'do a bit of writing and a lot of thinking'[4]. He described in the letter how failure to switch off shunts might lead to hypersecretion, and fantasised on other possibilities if similar arterial shunts were to be found elsewhere than in the kidneys and, as he had even more recently shown, in the stomach. 'I do believe that you and John Fulton between you will drive me to taking myself and my work seriously. John Fulton writes of the micro-technique and the gastric shunt as one of the greatest milestones in medical science and he has said quite a lot of more or less comparable things. And J.F. is one of the most far-seeing and envisaging people I have ever met'[4].

In his sympathetic reply Jeff wrote: 'I am fascinated with your gastric shunt. I am only too sorry that you are laid up, and cannot have a crack at the brain, because it is pretty certain I should think, that something a bit like this does happen in the brain too'[5]. Four days later, Barclay wrote to ask Jeff when the micro-apparatus for carrying out such experiments would be delivered to Manchester, and continued: 'I have always wanted to do brain but would not do it so long as Peter Daniel was doing that for Cairns'[6]. Although instructions for carrying out experiments to demonstrate the possibility of arterial brain shunts were minutely described by Barclay in a letter to Jeff, in the hope that he, or a member of his team, might perform them, this never came to fruition, and neither did any answer come from Peter Daniel's laboratory[6]. Subsequent discoveries have shown that there are collateral vessels in the brain, which are to be found on the borders between the main areas of arterial supply, but the extent to which they can be controlled remains a matter for discussion[7].

Nevertheless, the dying thinker was given hope and rewarded by another letter from Jefferson which began: 'What a pet, and what a worker you are. I am extremely grateful to you for having told me exactly how we should set about the vascular architecture of the brain. It will be most useful to me . . . . I am obliged to you for your new philosophical statement about the biology of cells. I am filing all these notes of yours carefully together, because they will be of the greatest importance to us.... I spoke to Jock [JSB Stopford, the vice-chancellor of Manchester University] about your DSc, and he tells me that the degree will be conferred under any circumstances. I don't know quite whether I have gone a bit further than I should in saying that, but I know that that is what everybody would want to do'[8]. There is a final letter from Barclay which reads 'Why file? ...Personally, I'd love to know if my hunch is correct, as I firmly believe it is. On Friday I had my most miserable day but at 5.0'c came a wire from JSBS [Stopford] saying that the DSc had already been conferred *in absentia*. How awfully nice of him to send that wire but I guess it is to your initiation that I owe this honour from my home university. Bless you and all your works. Yours as ever, A.E.B'[9].

The lease on High Bank, Didsbury, had been for 10 years and was about to expire. The price that was being asked in 1949 was still beyond Jefferson, so he conceived the idea that the university might purchase the house and let him continue to rent it. Unfortunately they were not interested although, much later, it did become the residence of the vice-chancellor. In the previous year, Jeff had written to the owner, Mr H Bradburn: 'The price is a bit much for us. I had wondered if the University might be tempted to get it because it is the sort of situation most admirably fitted for University people'[10]. Jeff then went on to explain in this letter that Gertrude and he were very attached to the house and the idea of leaving it would be most depressing. They were still anxiously looking for a solution to the problem when Robert Holt, a surgical colleague at the Manchester Royal Infirmary, agreed to purchase High Bank and divide it in two, so that he would have the major part and the Jeffersons would occupy most of the first floor[11]. At first Jeff hoped to keep the original front entrance and the handsome sweep of the staircase, but this was impractical and would have deprived the Holts of two bedrooms. To press the point would have meant losing the sale altogether. In the end, the conversion was made quite simply. A somewhat unimpressive entrance to the Jefferson's rearranged quarters was provided by a pre-existing side door, beyond which was a lobby, occluded from the rest of the ground floor by a new wall, and the former 'back staircase' gave them access to the upstairs rooms. A further wall at the top of the stairs, blocked off about a quarter of the landing which led to the two bedrooms occupied by the Holts, and a new kitchen was made for the Jeffersons[11,12]. Later, they came to regret this arrangement[12].

For the John Mallet Purser lecture in the School of Physic at Trinity College, Dublin, given on 26th May 1949, Jefferson chose to speak on one of his favourite subjects, *René Descartes and the localization of the soul*. It was his intention for this to be one of several essays on the anatomy of the soul but it was, in fact, the only one that he wrote. It was a historical and analytical review of seventeenth century thought on the subject, a matter which had fascinated Jeff. He made a Descartes 'pilgrimage' in France later in the year, before adding to the original lecture for a further version which he delivered to the Medical Society of the London Hospital in November 1950, the tercentenary year of the philosopher's death. For Descartes, the soul was synonymous with the mind, but in the philosophy of his day the soul did have other properties as well. It was the mind that Descartes sought to locate, not the theological soul, unless it is accepted that in order to appreciate life after death a mind would clearly be necessary. His big mistake was to regard the lining of the ventricles of the brain as the chief nervous structure, following the thinking of the writers of the time. The ventricles, they believed, were filled with 'the nervous energy of the subtle, volatile, invisible, and immaterial animal spirits'[13] and, according to Descartes, control of the flow of these spirits was through the action of the pineal gland. However, the theory was not quite so simple as it at first appears, for he concluded that the pineal gland emitted its own spirits that crossed the ventricles to enter selected pores in their walls, in addition to its somewhat mechanical action as a valve. He saw the pineal 'suspended in the whirl of animal spirits dancing and jigging...like a balloon captive above a fire, or like a ball dancing in a jet of water'[13]. It was generally believed that animals did not have souls, so there was no need to extrapolate the theory beyond humanity. Jefferson outlined some of the contemporary criticisms of Descartes' ideas and followed the search for a structural location of *mind* into the eighteenth century, ending with a delightful quotation from Joseph Glanvill (1636–1680). 'How should a thought be united to a marble statue or a sunbeam to a lump of clay...to hang weights on the wings of the winde seems far more intelligible'[13]. Jeff thereby indicated his own opinion.

It is perhaps permissible to adopt a Cartesian attitude and suggest that part of an individual's soul or mind, no less Jefferson's, is to be discovered through the expression of his or her thoughts and beliefs.

On 9th June 1949 Jefferson received the Lister Medal that he had been awarded by the Royal College of Surgeons to his great delight and just pride. He also delivered the Lister oration which he entitled *The mind of mechanical man*. On the day that it was due to be given he received a letter from the well-known anatomist Professor JZ Young, to whom Jeff had sent a draft copy of the lecture for his comments. The letter began: 'I have read your oration with the greatest interest, and find that I agree very much with the general ideas. I also found many most suggestive new historical points and analogies, but there are one or two places where I think you should be careful'[14]. He then produced three pages of comment and argument, which must have been quite devastating to receive at the last minute before such a momentous occasion. It is more than likely that Jeff delivered the lecture as he had written it and then, when it was submitted for publication, incorporated, or brushed aside, the fourteen or fifteen points picked up by JZ Young.

The oration, as we know it now from publication, began with the premise that the true scientific method was to see whether some idea or other could be substantiated by experiment, for by waiting for certainty one would never get anywhere. Man's desire to understand the relationship between brain and mind pushed him gently towards accepting that there was a 'likeness between the actions of electronic machines and those of the nervous system'[15]. Jefferson was writing at the very beginning of the era of computer science, so that much of what he wrote is now of historical rather than scientific interest. Having said that, it is a delight to read and to follow Jeff's argument starting from automata, through Descartes' philosophical postulations, to the description of nervous impulses and finally to 'calculating machines', as he knew them. He concluded that although some of the simpler activities of the nervous system could be paralleled by electronic apparatus, there remained a blank wall when it came to exploring thought. He warned against being persuaded by the airy theories with which machines were anthropomorphised. In a postscript to the version of *The mind of the mechanical man* in his *Selected papers,* Jefferson pointed out that his was 'the first paper by a neurologist faced with the new electronic computing machines . . . . It was a protest against jumping to conclusions'[16]. At the time that it was written many people assumed that the intricacies of the mind-brain problem were all but solved, and there was much newspaper comment on Jeff's lecture. Indeed, there was disagreement with what he had said, but perhaps to stir up some controversy was partly his intention. As he said at the beginning: 'I am encouraged . . . to proceed in the hope that, although we shall not arrive at certainty, we may discover some illumination on the way'[15,16]. Jefferson's first pencil notes, headed 'Jottings of thoughts in composition of Lister Medal'[17] [sic], contain all the main themes of the final product, which shows that he had a Mozartian ability to envisage a whole work before attempting to write anything down. Jefferson was very aware of the importance of the oration, both for the occasion and for himself, and he must have communicated some of that anxiety to JZ Young, who added a handwritten postscript to his letter: 'P.S. How well I know the feeling of wishing to be done with it. These general things are devils to prepare. But it will be over by to-morrow. J'[14].

On 12th September a version of Jefferson's lecture was broadcast in the BBC Third programme. He had recorded it on 26th August. 'I wrote and told Alfred Webb-Johnson [President of the Royal College of Surgeons] that I had "canned" the oration as I thought he ought to know. He wrote back to say that he would ask the BBC for the records, a good idea in its way. Would that we had Hunter's and Lister's and Paget's and Huxley's voices. I'm glad they've got Sherrington's but it was 30 yrs and more too late. I had a gruelling time putting it on the air. I was very tired after doing a total extirpation of an acoustic and had a hurried lunch brought over to the surgeon's dressing room . . . and was a good 15–20 mins late for Mrs Prudence Smith the 3rd Programme science boss. I had to read the new version through, made some alterations and sat down and went at it. It took 50 mins & a few secs. Mrs P.S. came in and said it was terrible, such a dull rendering, I was tired wasn't I, quality of voice excellent (whatever that means) but oh so flat, so boring. Would I have some Whiskey, would I do it another day? I said no thanks, no whiskey, what ought I to do. Just put more expression into it and not start every sentence on the same note. Difficult this if you haven't thought about it. I said I'd have a try if she'd split it into 4 parts with a break in between. She agreed, so we did it that way, and I found it more tolerable, but I expect it was terrible. Mrs P.S. says it is so hard to get people to listen to a talk that goes on for 50 mins and that I can well believe'[18].

The theme of the physical basis of mind was taken up again by Jefferson in a speech to the meeting of the British Association for the Advancement of Science in Newcastle on 2nd September 1949. It was entitled *Body and mind relationship,* thus enlarging the scope and enabling him to produce a very different lecture, of a less philosophical but more physiological and anatomical nature than the Lister Oration. He 'mentioned the dependence of the brain on the body as the source of its life, and the uses of the body not only in supplying it with sensations but of its enormous value as a vehicle by which the brain can enlarge its experience by exploration'[19]. Finally, he recounted some of his beliefs 'about the nature of thinking and the uses of words, sounds and gestures by animals and man'[19].

Jefferson himself reported part of the discussion which followed his paper when writing his diary 2 weeks later. 'A physicist drew attention to the behaviour of neon tubes in circuit when both will never light together, he had found a mathematical formula to explain it. He thought this was what happens when we go to sleep. I said "Well it could be but its no better than an illustration, a sort of modern dress simile...". That annoyed him. He said did I know his formula? No, I didn't but had he any idea what nerve cells were like? He hadn't so O=O I thought. He was not amused. But I was more right than he'[18].

In just over a week after the meeting of the British Association, Jefferson went with Gertrude to the Fourth International Congress of Neurology in Paris, which was under the chairmanship of Professor Alajouanine. Jeff wrote in his diary that when they were descending the steep hill in Lewes on the way to catch the boat at Newhaven he 'had induced an explosion in the silencer that made a hole in it to our great chagrin; couldn't get it mended that evening and so drove to Paris with it after an alarm as to whether the exhaust was setting the floor boards on fire'[20]. And doubtless making enough noise to announce their arrival some time in advance. Jefferson gave a paper there on the invasion of the chiasma by gliomas; 'I did it as an exercise in factual reporting'[20]. This was also the subject of a special lecture that he gave at the National Hospital, Queen Square, that year, as it had been that of his Doyne Lecture in 1945[21].

From Paris he drove with Gertrude to the Loire valley to make his Descartes pilgrimage. He wrote quite copious notes and comments about the journey, during which they went from Chenonceaux to La Haye-Descartes which 'lies in the wide valley of the Creuse.... To this day it is a small town, ca 1500 inhabitants, a farming town.... Most of the postcards were of the Rue Descartes, or of the house where the philosopher was born in 1596, or the church of St. George where he was christened'[22]. The Jeffersons were unable to visit the interior of the birthplace. 'It is a plain enough house...with 4 shuttered windows, the sills of the lower windows only just above the ground, built in stone with a feathered brick balcony leading from the house proper to a sort of older defensive tower.... It was his gt. grnd. mother's home'[22]. Descartes' mother died in 1597 when he was still a very young baby, and Jeff states that the young René was probably brought up in his father's house at Châtellerault, about 10 miles away. 'The latter is much the bigger and busier and more picturesque town, full of old houses and pleasant tree-lined boulevards.... Today there was a fearful thunder storm as we went in, making it difficult to get information. Out of 4 or 5 people whom we asked none knew where the D. museum or the D. house was, and at the height of the thunder storm when one could hardly see, I backed the car, following false directions, into a telegraph pole and unshipped the rear bumper already damaged by the rough handling of the stevedores at either Newhaven or Dieppe.... But it was no day for exploration and so we turned for home'[22]. The bumper was temporarily held on by a leather strap through the handle of the boot.

Jeff was reading Proust at the time and drew attention to his 'long and very involved sentences, mere half-meanings.... His sentences are queerly constructed and the grammar is not above genuine suspicion, in fact if not wrong, his ambiguities are careless and unnecessary'[22]. He must have forgotten that he was reading a translation.

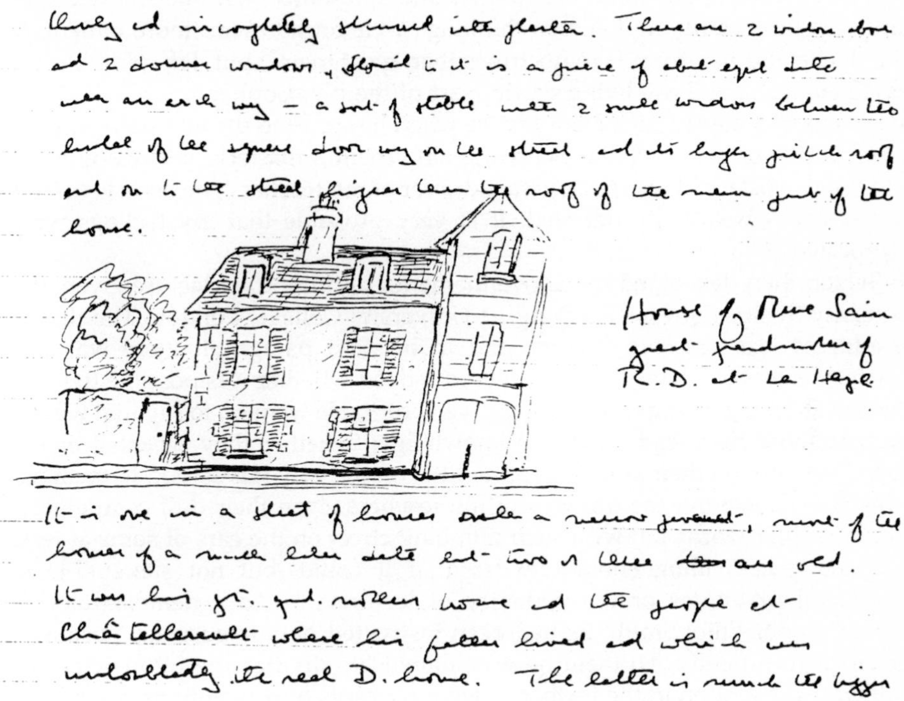

Figure 22 *The Descartes family home at Châtellerault. From Jefferson's diary of the visit.*

On 18th September the Jeffersons went back to Châtellerault and this time found the Descartes family home in the rue Bourbon. 'Not very ornate, 3 good rooms downstairs.... A yard behind with a gallery over it at one side only, the left, stables behind, not a château by any means.... The family owned a number of small properties but one would not think that their revenue was very large. Its a bit puzzling to me to assess what income he could have had...yet he had several manservants in Holland.... I wonder what the finances of his publications were'[23].

The Jeffersons returned to England on 24th September, having been to Rouen, to Trouville and also to La Fléche, where Descartes had attended the Jesuit College. Jeff thought that the district resembled the region around La Haye: 'Its a sweet little town, looking from the bridge its a picture'[24]. But there were no Descartes relics at the former college and 'the concierge didn't even know what room he had'[24]. A little later Jeff added interesting notes on Francine, Descartes' illegitimate daughter by a servant named Hélène. It seems that he took Francine's mother into his service so that he could watch the child grow up, for he was devoted to her. When she died on 7th September 1640 at the age of five 'little Francine's death caused him the greatest sadness that he had ever felt in his life. He said "I am not of those who hold that tears and sadness belong only to women and that to appear manly one should always strive to show a tranquil face"'[24]. Descartes 'was by no means averse to the company of women...he enjoyed their company and found that the questions that they asked him stimulated him, clarifying his own thinking'[24]. He found them 'more patient, & more docile and free from fake doctrines than most men'[24] but, Jeff added, there was no evidence of loose living on the part of the philosopher.

Jefferson was hardly back from France when he spoke to the Old Mancunians, former pupils of his Grammar School, giving them a masterly address entitled *Postscript to Aristotle*. 'I was not a great admirer of my teachers', he observed, 'and some of them I cordially detested. It is very probable that my feelings were reciprocated'[25].

Jefferson then developed the above theme for an important lecture given at a University Symposium on Teaching, at University College, London. The title of the address was *Teaching teachers*, and in his first paragraph there was this arresting sentence: 'I have often wondered indeed whether it is possible to teach anybody anything, using teach as an active verb'[26]. He went on to say that we can never do more than lead people to knowledge; 'whether they accept it or not depends greatly on their appetite but no little on the way it is served to them.... It was not the age but the dullness of my teachers, even their dull competence, that made their words fall with such numbing effect on the ears of some at least of an audience willing enough to learn, if it could, but not susceptible to professorial platitudes or the pedantry of lecturers'[26]. As a demonstrator in anatomy under Elliot Smith, he had been instructed only to succour those who were in real difficulty. To them he was allowed to divulge the ultimate secret, that what was written in the textbooks were concepts or conventions 'as stylised and artificial as a Restoration Comedy'[26]. In teaching 'either by the written or the spoken word we use conventions in trying to approximate ourselves to the truth'[26]. Using the teacher he admired above all others as an example, he recalled that Elliot Smith 'exercised authority without pomposity and was not afraid of admitting that descriptions can never be universally correct and, what was more important, that it was exciting that it was so'[26]. Jefferson believed that didactic teaching suggested that we knew more than we did.

He continued by reminding the symposium that the student coming fresh from chemistry and physics had been charmed by the simplicity and logic of processes that were similar to mathematics. 'A retentive memory satisfies demands...but when he comes to physiology the student is undone.... He faces something that is dynamic, on the move, coming from somewhere and going places, never finished and never still.... The greatest possible clarity is the clue to good teaching'[26] but the trouble about clarity is that it brings one very quickly to the dilemma that very often it exposes weaknesses in the argument and reveals gaps in the chain of logic. These must be admitted. The defects 'will be apparent to you before they are apparent to your hearers or readers.... I cannot deny that sometimes men of great power of mind have written in a way difficult to understand but I take this to be a defect in them. Anyone who takes the trouble to rewrite their paragraphs for them will find either that they could have been more simply expressed or, more surprisingly, that sometimes they do not mean anything'[26].

He went on to say that a teacher must seek plain speaking, avoid ambiguity and be ready to admit it when he or she did not know something. There was also an absolute need for teachers to know the history of their subjects, which illustrates the birth and growth of ideas. It is necessary, he said, to be familiar with the writings of the great clinicians of the 19th century in order really to know what had been found out to date. Another advantage was that one of the greatest virtues of our forebears was their lucidity. 'No one can write clearly unless he thinks clearly.... Conversation is different.... Lists are only popular because they help students to pass examinations'[26]; which points to the faults there are in questions that are neither unusual nor ingenious. 'Medicine is a rich and succulent material and I hate to see it filleted and only its bones offered to the student'[26]. Teachers who reduce their subjects to schemata 'damage themselves and at the end of 20 years are worthless creatures out of touch with reality, which is so untidy a thing.... The lazy man's ideal is that he should be a passive receiver, taught something painlessly without any effort on his own part. There is no escape from work and it would be a dreadful thing if there were'[26].

For Jeff, the most important quality of all in a teacher 'is a passionate enthusiasm, a real belief that what he is going to tell his listeners is fascinating, is irresistible'[26]. Ideas had to be built up simply from the bottom. If an audience was unenthusiastic, it was often because the teacher assumed it to be more familiar with the subject than was the case. 'Never assume any knowledge on the part of your audience.' There is 'a place for histrionics of a subdued kind', by timing and the avoidance of flat delivery[26].

'The essence of greatness [in a teacher] is surely that the man presents more than a surface, that he is a figure in the round, that he is excellent in more than one way.... Since we were sent into the world with minds as yet barren of any knowledge whatever...let us remember that some of our knowledge was taught to us, by which I mean that some pieces of information were so temptingly put before us that we grabbed them for our own'[26]. Jefferson then concluded by saying that '...we have a duty to put into *teachers'* minds the importance of quality rather than quantity, to suggest to them clean bright bits of knowledge for their wits to work on. Let them do the same to others in their turn'[26].

In his capacity as a pedagogue this is as clear a *credo* as Jefferson could possibly have expressed. He was not called 'the master' for nothing, and he lived up to his ideals. All over the world, medical schools and other learned institutions cried out for him to come and instruct them, which is quite apparent from the huge number of lectures that he gave. This outstanding paper was never published, which is why it has been quoted in such detail and in order, now, to pass on some of his wisdom.

There is an interesting letter from the Ministry of Health, dated 11th October 1949, concerning the *Medical Supplies Working Party, Neurosurgery Group*, of which Jefferson was the chairman. Sir Waldon Dalrymple-Champneys took Jeff to task for having slipped a recommendation into his report 'that there should eventually be a neurosurgery unit of a minimum of 50 beds for each one million of population'[27]. This was not only outside the terms of reference of the Working Party but, as Sir Waldon also pointed out, it was '...not in accordance with RHB(48)1 which gives 40 beds per million as the optimum. I am not suggesting that such a recommendation is above criticism but only that such criticism should be made through other channels than the Working Party which is concerned with supplies'[27]. Unfortunately we do not have Jeff's reply, but the fact that he kept this letter indicates that it might have been worth reading!

There was yet one more important address to deliver that year; the Inaugural Lecture to the Institute of Otolaryngology on 20th November 1949, on the subject of acoustic neuromas. The text of this has not survived, but the arguments at that time concerned the relative merits of radical removal versus 'intracapsular' enucleation, and it is likely that this lecture was a resumé of Jefferson's experience. The radical operation almost inevitably destroyed the facial nerve at that time, which intracapsular removal did not, but there was a high recurrence rate after the latter procedure. Total extirpation with preservation of the facial nerve, transaural removal and combined supra- and infra-tentorial approaches, let alone combined neurosurgical and ENT operations, were concepts for the future.

In the midst of all his thought-provoking non-medical compositions, his day to day neurosurgical work continued. He was constantly seeking to improve and enlarge its scope, by being aware of and involved in innovations, as well as by monitoring their outcome. For instance, Dr Franc Ingraham, who was a paediatric neurosurgeon in Boston and a great friend of Cairns, had been 'largely concerned with the initial use and preparation'[28] of a film made of fibrin, obtained from blood, which had been developed as a substitute for dura in cases in which that layer of the meninges was missing for one reason or another. Cairns had a small amount of this preparation which had been given to him by Ingraham, and he offered some to Jefferson who readily accepted it for trial[28]. A foamy jelly had also been prepared for stopping venous and capillary bleeding. These fibrin products were the forerunners of gelatin film and foam, which proved to be as efficient, but safer and more easily prepared than their precursors.

At the beginning of 1950 a number of letters concerning the future of British neurosurgery were exchanged between Jefferson and Cairns, who had been president of the SBNS from 1945 to 1948. Jeff had the ear of the Ministry of Health in his capacity as Adviser in Neurosurgery; he was the Éminence grise of the SBNS and Cairns wanted a channel for his views. These were a concern that 'relations with the neurologists are not improving as we had hoped after Walshe's dinner at the Mayfair. And the arrangements at the Paris Congress were from the neurosurgical point of view poor'[29]. Cairns, therefore, proposed that there should be a combined meeting every year between the British neurologists and neurosurgeons[29]. Since the SBNS endeavoured to hold one of its two annual meetings abroad, an annual arrangement was not practicable, as Jeff must have pointed out. However, these discussions did stimulate the idea of regular combined meetings which came to take place every other year from 1952 to 1959, and for some of which the venue was abroad. Subsequently, although they were to be held on a less regular basis, they proved to be popular with both parties.

Harry Botterell was delighted that Jefferson had accepted an invitation to give the Balfour Lecture in Toronto later in the year. On 12th February 1950 Jeff commented: 'Finding the subject is the real thing because if you are happy in your subject it will go well enough. I have not thought of the right one yet, nor for the Martin Lecture at Boston on Oct. 23rd. They very kindly propose to make me an FACS [Fellow of the American College of Surgeons], a gesture that I appreciate a lot.... I have just been in the PPH [Private Patients' Hospital] having my colon X-rayed again. It was because my old diverticulitis was bothering me more and more. It hasn't altered much, a bit more stenosed but it still works .... I am ready for work again or very nearly'[30].

Jefferson's indisposition, however, left him briefly with time on his hands and he wrote another letter to Botterell just three days later; he had just finished an article on the *Localization of function in the cerebral cortex* which he now sent to his Canadian friend for his comments[31]. In connection with this paper, Jeff was critical of an article Botterell had written with Denny Brown. 'I used your paper with Denny Brown for quite a bit of it, but my God, Harry, its practically impossible to understand it. I know very well how you have to chew the butt of your pen when you are writing (so do I) but Denny is much worse at expressing himself and manages to be terribly verbose in a way both clever and obscure! Golly, I hope I didn't hurt your feelings but I bet you didn't think it was a model of clarity .... It is I suspect the most important paper yet on the motor area'[32]. In fairness to Botterell it must be said that Denny Brown had probably been mainly responsible for writing it, and Jeff's remarks about his style were apt. Botterell wrote his own comments on the paper by Jeff, who thanked him 'for kind and indulgent editing of my script'[32]. He was busy writing four other articles and addresses, and said that a passage had been booked on the RMS *Mauretania* for 15th September. 'What I want is a timetable that doesn't kill me .... I feel as if my batteries need recharging! I seem to have said most of everything already! Horrid State!'[32].

Shortly after his letter of 3rd February, Cairns wrote to ask if Jefferson would allow his name to be put forward for election to the Council of the Royal College of Surgeons, the proposal having been made by the Moynihan Club — a society of senior surgeons[33]. It was a very persuasive letter but Jefferson did not immediately agree to the request, being unwell. He gave an evasive reply which caused Cairns to write: 'I hope you are better and also feeling refreshed. It was good to know that you might decide to stand for Council. You would, of course, walk in at the head of the poll. More important, you would be able to do so much for Surgery in this country'[34]. Nevertheless, it was more than Jeff felt he could undertake, for he had ahead of him the impending visit to Canada and the United States with much work to prepare for it and, in addition to his other commitments, the May meeting of the SBNS was due to be held in Manchester, with all the work which that entailed. The prospect of regular extra journeys to London if he were to be elected to the Council would be too much for him. Cairns wrote to say how sorry he was about the refusal, but congratulated Jeff on the two eponymous lectureships he had been awarded for his forthcoming visit to North America[35]. There were further letters about the Manchester meeting and a proposal for a combined investigation of the merits of two ways of treating cerebral abscesses but, more significantly, Cairns put forward the idea that Jefferson should become president of the SBNS for a second time, 'to rouse up our Society a bit' and ensure the success of the combined meetings with the neurologists[36]. This was only a tentative enquiry to see how Jeff felt about it, but the proposal went forward in due course and Jeff resumed, from 1954 to 1956, the leadership of the society. This was the only re-election of a president of the SBNS that has ever taken place.

Cairns also wrote to say that he wanted to report the results of his work with Honor Smith, on the tuberculin treatment for tuberculous meningitis, to the SBNS

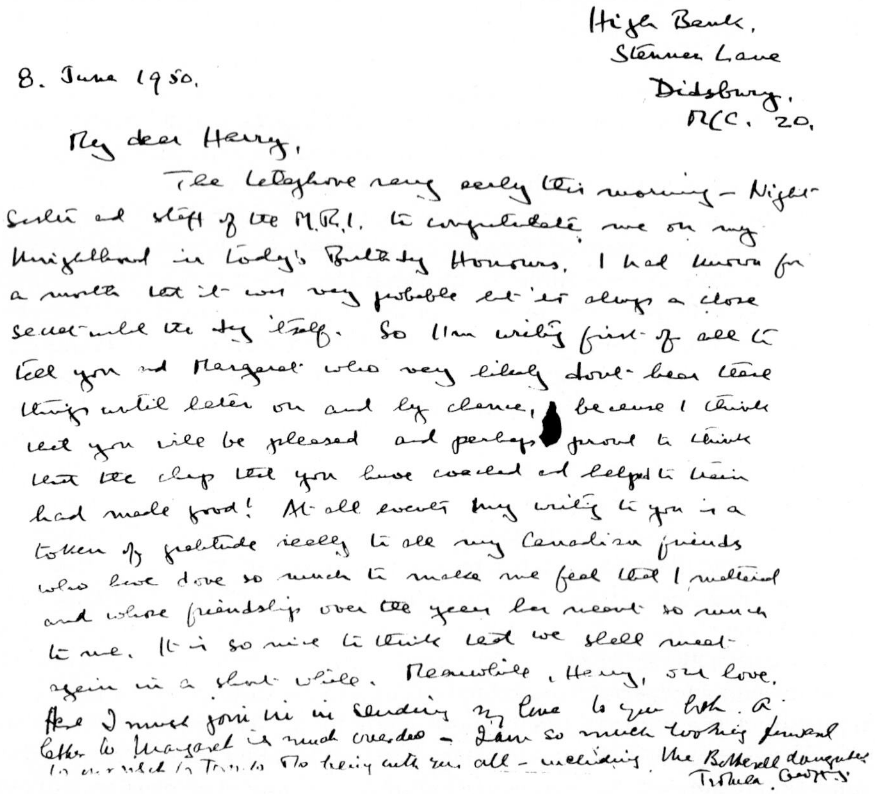

Figure 23   *Letter to Harry Botterell from Geoffrey Jefferson, informing him of Jeff's knighthood.*

at its Manchester meeting. And he commented that he accepted the proposal that combined meetings with the neurologists should be held every other year rather than annually[37]. One of his reasons for proposing them was his anxiety that neurosurgery might become too technological: 'I have great fears for our Society and specialty if it withdraws from medical neurology. The younger neurosurgeons...know less of neurology than they should'[37]. It is possible that time has justified his concern.

At last, on 3rd May 1950 during a meeting there of the SBNS, the new department of neurosurgery at the Manchester Royal Infirmary was opened by Lord Webb-Johnson, Past President of the Royal College of Surgeons, and himself a Manchester graduate. It was the culmination of much planning by Jefferson and the realisation of one of his ambitions, though an earlier dream of a Northern Neurological Institute, which he had planned with Fergus Ferguson, never materialised. The new department fulfilled needs which had become only too apparent since the war ended, and Jeff now had the latest equipment, especially in radiology, and greatly improved operating theatres. The department's creation had been helped by the Feilden bequest of £96,000, which was channelled in that direction by the Board of the Infirmary. There were refurbished wards, new research rooms and laboratories, together with offices and all the other necessary facilities which are required in a neurosurgical unit[38]. The sad aspect was that this had only been achieved in the last year before Jefferson was due to retire. Following the Manchester meeting, Cairns wrote to say how much he had enjoyed the occasion and what a success it had been. 'It was grand having you in the chair again; you gave just that wayward, unworldly, unorganised feeling of enjoying it all, and it spread through the room'[39].

During this meeting of the SBNS, Jefferson wished to demonstrate an operation in the new theatre, as was the custom on these occasions, but the Matron of the Royal Infirmary, known formally as the Lady Superintendent of Nurses, was someone over whom even Jeff did not have control. She wrote: 'I quite realise that you would like to use the new theatre for this purpose but at the moment I am afraid it is quite impossible to staff it .... I note that you say that you would like to start work in the new theatre a week after the opening. I had understood from you earlier that you thought it was unlikely that the theatre would be used for some months so was rather perturbed in view of the staff position, to learn that you were hoping that it would be available'[40]. Some form of compromise was arrived at, however, for the author himself witnessed the operation on 19th May as planned; it was for the removal of a parietal meningioma.

Now, at last, came national recognition of all that Jefferson had done for the care of civilian and military head injuries during the war, for the organisation of neurosurgery in the EMS and National Health Service, and for his personal achievements; Jeff was to be dubbed a Knight Bachelor. It was a belated honour and, if he had been in one of the Services, it might have been sooner and have been equal to that of Cairns and Symonds, who had been appointed KBE four years previously. He had been informed of the probability, but of course nothing could be said until it was publicly announced. Jeff wrote to Botterell on 8th June 1950: 'The telephone rang early this morning—Night Sister and staff of the M.R.I. to congratulate me on my Knighthood in today's Birthday Honours.... My writing to you is a token of gratitude really to all my Canadian friends who have done so much to make me feel that I mattered and whose friendship over the years has meant so much to me'[41]. Perhaps this sentence shows that not all of the lack of self-assurance that he had manifested from time to time in the earlier part of his career had completely disappeared. There was also a desire to share his pleasure with one of his best friends. A few weeks later another letter announced: 'I've got 500 letters to get through and they haven't stopped yet...everyone seems to be genuinely pleased and that is a great thing. I personally am not as thrilled as all that because I valued my F.R.S. and my Lister medal more. But I wouldn't be honest and I wouldn't be the loyal subject of H.M. that I am if I wasn't pleased at all. We go to the Palace on 4th July for the accolade. Trude and Michael are coming this time in place of Trude and E.H.B. last time for the "C" [CBE]'[42].

An American neurosurgeon named Bert Selverstone, who was working at the Massachusetts General Hospital in Boston, came to spend a short time with Jeff in Manchester during August 1950. Jefferson told Bill Sweet, who had arranged the visit, in a letter written soon after Selverstone's arrival: 'He caused fireworks over here by bringing a lot of P.32 [radioactive phosphorus] which we have buckets of in this country and the atomic folk were pretty mad with him for bringing any in, as all isotopes are watched pretty closely by the authorities.... I got excited calls from the Board of Trade and Customs folk but fortunately I knew nothing about it as your Bert hadn't told me. So I escaped a proper "rocket"'[43]. Jeff also thanked Bill Sweet for his congratulations on the knighthood. 'We haven't got used to it yet and I refer to myself as "Prof" or even "Mr" still and shall go on doing so. "Jeff" is best!'[43].

In August Jeff took a short holiday before his strenuous visit to Canada and the United States. 'I've had four days fishing this year — the first day I forgot my reel and line, remembering everything else; the next time, a three day affair, the river was in flood and the fish fighting for their lives to prevent being swept out to sea, so my fishing this year is over and totals a row of noughts'[44].

Before leaving England Jeff wrote to Bill Sweet: 'I haven't started to write my papers, God help me! This Knighthood business has played havoc with everything — I've written just under 600 letters to people who congratulated me, most of them proper letters in my own hand. It nearly finished me and I've got a horrible conjunctivitis as a result of over-work — a nice start indeed to paper writing'[43]. Not having completed his lectures when he left England, he worked on them during a somewhat stormy voyage across the Atlantic. On 16th September, which was their second day at sea, for Gertrude was travelling with him, he wrote from the *Mauretania*: '2 out of 7 lectures really written and the rest canned in the cranium, only needing an opener. If I can get some weather when I am not drugged I'll do it — at least 2 more'[45].

Bill and Mary Sweet had arranged to meet Jeff and Gertrude on their arrival in New York, as had JC White and his wife, also from Boston. Jefferson's itinerary during the next 2 months was to take him from New York to Toronto and then Rochester, Minnesota. From there to Portland, Oregon, and on to Seattle and Victoria BC, for Gertrude's sake. Next to San Francisco, back to Toronto and on to Boston before returning to New York. He delivered the 5th Franklin Martin Memorial Lecture to the Clinical Congress of the American College of Surgeons in Boston on 23rd October. It was on *The balance of life and death in cerebral lesions*[46], and was the occasion on which he received his Honorary FACS. The lecture was mostly concerned with compression of the brain stem by tentorial coning — 'a chain reaction of individual failures which leads to death'[46], and a subject on which Jeff had made original observations of great significance. He put the importance of the brain in perspective when he said: 'The rest of the body exists for one purpose only, to provide the nervous system, and especially the brain, with two things — first with energy and then with opportunity'[46]. Sweet recalled later that 'the talk was devoted mainly to a discussion of lessons learned about the management of intracranial tumours from a critical analysis of autopsies'[47] and was in considerable contrast to the usual speakers who relentlessly recounted a succession of unmitigated triumphs. In fact 'this variation in the intellectual pabulum went over well'[47]. The Balfour Lecture had to be given in Toronto, and at least five others elsewhere. It is not clear what were the subjects of all of these, but Jeff published five papers in 1950 and two in the following year, some of which were undoubtedly related to these lectures.

Shortly before sailing, Jefferson had written to Botterell to say that he would like to give his Balfour Lecture on *Injuries to the facial colliculus during operations on fourth ventricle ependymomas*. 'Why I was so cagey [about the subject] was because

I've been in such a manic state getting my slides and what not prepared that I feared to commit myself. Also I haven't felt very well and am scared stiff of getting over-tired but I look fine. Its probably psychological and reprehensible'[48].

There was no doubt, however, that Jeff was unwell, and Michael Jefferson wrote to Botterell asking him to keep a close eye on the situation while his father was away. 'In the last year he has been having chronic obstructive symptoms, which has been rather worrying for the family. He seemed to be in such a bad way just before he left for America that I was really disturbed at his going at all. However, his heart was set on it.... Its a great burden & responsibility on my mother to try to check him unaided & she herself has lately been in poor health'[49]. As it turned out, neither Jeff nor Gertrude suffered any illness during weeks of travelling.

On their return to England in November 1950, once more on the *Mauretania*, the Jeffersons had another rough crossing. While at sea, Jeff wrote to Botterell: 'After seeing you I found the American Surgical [?American College of Surgeons meeting] just short of a nightmare with never a moment when we weren't involved in something either surgical or social, the latter the most common, the former the most bearable'[50]. Shortly after his return, Jeff lectured to the Medical Society of the London Hospital on his long-espoused subject, *René Descartes (1596–1650), Philosopher, mathematician, physiologist*[13]. It must have been with some sense of relief and pleasure that he was able to speak once again in a relaxed atmosphere about his "old friend".

On 14th December 1950 the Chairman of the Board of the Manchester Royal Infirmary wrote to ask if Jeff would agree to continue his duties after his 65th birthday on 10th April 1951 until the end of the Academic Year on 29th September. After that it was hoped that he would 'honour the hospital by accepting and keeping a Consulting position on the staff'. The letter continued: 'It would really be a tragedy if all this went unrecorded and I do hope you will find it possible to see that posterity has the benefit.... It is only the feeling that the easing of the strain upon you may give you the leisure to do the work you would like to do that reconciles me and the entire Board to what is, unfortunately, to happen'[51]. His obvious expectation was that Jeff would use his retirement to continue to write papers and possibly a book, or even an autobiography.

REFERENCES

GJ=Geoffrey Jefferson; EHB=Harry Botterell; AEB=Alfred Barclay; HC=Hugh Cairns

1   GJ. MS *The hospitals in 1949.*
2   GJ to EHB. Letter 20th January 1949.
3   GJ to EHB. Letter 6th February 1949
4   AEB to GJ. Letter 1st March 1949.
5   GJ to AEB. Letter 3rd March 1949.
6   AEB to GJ. Letters 7th, 9th and 10th March 1949.
7   Kuschinsky W. Personal communication.
8   GJ to AEB. Letter 17th March 1949.
9   AEB to GJ. Letter 20th March 1949.
10   GJ to Bradburn H. Letter 22nd March 1949.
11   Jefferson M. Personal communication.

12   Jefferson A. Personal communication.
13   Jefferson G. René Descartes on the localization of the soul. *Irish J Med Sci* 1949; **285**: 691–706, and *Selected papers*. London: Pitman Medical, 1960: 45–72. Also René Descartes (1596–1650) Philosopher, mathematician, physiologist. *Lond Hosp Gazette* 1950; **53**: 69–78.
14   Young JZ to GJ. Letter 8th June 1949.
15   Jefferson G. The mind of mechanical man. *BMJ* 1949; **1**: 1105–10.
16   Jefferson G. The mind of mechanical man. In: Jefferson G. *Selected Papers*. London: Pitman Medical, 1960: 10–23.
17   GJ. MS Jottings of thoughts in composition of Lister Medal.
18   GJ. MS Notes written on 15th September 1949.
19   Jefferson G. Body and mind relationship. *Br Assoc Adv Sci* 1950; **1**: 46–56.
20   GJ. MS Notes written on 13th September 1949.
21   Jefferson G. On compression and invasion of the optic nerves and chiasma by neighbouring gliomas. *Trans Ophthalmol Soc UK* 1945; **65**: 262–303.
22   GJ. MS Notes written on 14th September 1949.
23   GJ. MS Notes written on 19th September 1949
24   GJ. MS Notes written on 23rd September 1949.
25   Jefferson G. *A postscript to Aristotle*. The Old Mancunian's Association. Manchester: Rawson, Crosskeys Press, 1949.
26   GJ. MS *Teaching Teachers*. 1949.
27   Darlymple-Champneys W to GJ. Letter 11th October 1949.
28   HC to GJ. Letter 28th June 1949.
29   HC to GJ. Letter 3rd February 1950.
30   GJ to EHB. Letter 12th February 1950.
31   Jefferson G. Localization of function in the cerebral cortex. *Brit Med Bull* 1950; **6**: 333–40.
32   GJ to EHB. Letter 17th March 1950.
33   HC to GJ. Letter 19th February 1950.
34   HC to GJ. Letter 9th March 1950.
35   HC to GJ. Letter 17th March 1950.
36   HC to GJ. Letters 16th and 27th April 1950.
37   HC to GJ. Letter 5th April 1950.
38   New neurosurgical theatre and neuroradiological department at the Manchester Royal Infirmary. *BMJ* 1950; **1**: 1134–5 and The neurosurgical clinic and the neurological laboratories at the Royal Infirmary, Manchester. *Br J Surg* 1955; **43**: 317–23.
39   HC to GJ. Letter 28th May 1950.
40   Duff Grant LG to GJ. Letter 21st April 1950.
41   GJ to EHB. Letter 8th June 1950.
42   GJ to EHB. Letter 19th June 1950.
43   GJ to Sweet WH. Letter 25th July 1950.
44   GJ to EHB. Letter 30th August 1950.
45   GJ to Sweet WH. Letter 16th September 1950.
46   Jefferson G. The balance of life and death in cerebral lesions. *Surg Gynecol Obstet* 1951; **93**: 444–58 and in *Selected papers*. London: Pitman Medical, 1960: 466–85.
47   Sweet WH. Personal communication.
48   GJ to EHB. Letter 11th September 1950.
49   Jefferson M to EHB. Letter 28th September 1950.
50   GJ to EHB. Letter November 1950, undated from *RMS Mauretania*.
51   Skinner C to GJ. Letter 14th December 1950.

Chapter 21

Retirement, or metamorphosis
1951–1953

The year 1951 began with illness for Jefferson; once again it was related to his diverticulitis, this time manifested by both abdominal pain and bleeding. He put himself under the care of his friend John Morley.

X-rays of the large bowel showed that the whole colon was involved, and that it seemed likely that Jeff might develop acute intestinal obstruction. This was a threat of which he was very conscious, and he had for a long time taken such precautions as were possible by way of diet and medication. A further opinion was sought from Sir James Paterson Ross of St Bartholomew's Hospital, London, who saw the recent x-ray films. Despite his awareness that it is always unwise to give an opinion about treatment on x-ray evidence alone without seeing the patient, Sir James was sufficiently convinced to advise against operation. Surgery would have called for a very difficult excision of most of the colon, and he considered that it should be deferred unless or until signs of obstruction actually did develop. Once again the recommendation was for rest, which Jeff found hard to accept or, at least, to comply with. Other causes having been excluded, it was assumed that the bleeding was a result of inflammation. The letter in which Paterson Ross explained his views to his patient ended with apologies for its length, but he added that he 'would also like, at the risk of making it even longer, to say that having seen the pictures of your colon, I admire you even more than I did before for what you have achieved in the course of the past twenty years'[1].

Sir James in his turn asked for another opinion, this one from his colleague Clifford Naunton Morgan, who was internationally known for his expertise in the field of large bowel disease. He too was against operating unless it became imperative[2]. This consultation produced a further letter to Jefferson from Sir James, who pointed out that although the disease had only progressed slowly during the previous 10 years it had nevertheless advanced. But there was general agreement that conservative management with chloramphenicol, diet and rest was indicated[3]. It was a decision which time was to prove to have been correct.

Jeff's 65th birthday on 10th April 1951 came and went without any dramatic event, since he had been asked to retain his appointments until the end of September, but his health continued to be a source of anxiety. Cairns wrote: 'I am sorry you have had to go under doctor's orders, but am not surprised for you have been driven very hard this last year or so'[4]. The SBNS memorandum on the supply of neurosurgeons had now been drafted, and it made clear the fact that there would be a limited number of training posts, geared to the expected number of consultant vacancies. In order to monitor this, annual reports of their establishments were to be required from all the neurosurgical centres. Within a year or two, several new neurosurgical units were opened. As a consequence of an underestimation of the needs, there were insufficient candidates to fill the vacant posts, in addition to those created by retirement and death, and the choice of candidates was inevitably inadequate. The situation was saved to some extent by those trainees from abroad who returned home on completion of their registrar appointments, and more senior registrar posts were eventually provided. This was, of course, many years before programmed specialty training and the certification now required by a Specialist Advisory Committee. Cairns' letter continued: 'I hope you will be able to polish the draft before it is sent to the Min. of Health and to the medical press. I hope also that you will be all right for the Assoc. of Surgeons meeting; don't try to do too much at it'[4] — for Jefferson had been elected President of the Association of Surgeons of Great Britain and Ireland, and the next meeting was to be held in Manchester in July.

Another honour had been added to Jefferson's growing list when the Spanish Academy of Medicine made him an honorary member on 28th April 1951. There had, unfortunately, been no possibility of his going to the meeting in Madrid at which it was to be conferred, since throughout the spring and early summer he was still on sick leave. He did not break his convalescence until July.

The toast to the Association of Surgeons and its President was given by none other than Sir James Paterson Ross, to which Jefferson spoke in acknowledgement and reply. His speech was not particularly memorable, though in it he marked the passing of three of his former colleagues; Arthur Burgess whose house surgeon he had been, Garnett Wright who had operated on him and diagnosed his diverticulitis, and his colleague Robert Ollerenshaw a well-known orthopaedic surgeon from the Salford Royal Hospital. In his concluding sentence Jeff said: 'Would that it had been possible to have three Presidents for John Morley and Harry Platt would have filled the Chair as worthily as I. But here am I saying "Thank you all"'[5]. This was followed by a surprising footnote to the manuscript: 'Note to myself — I deliberately did not say better than I because it would have been insincere even though it would have been perfect manners'[5].

Hugh Cairns had been a guest of the Jeffersons during the meeting and, on his return to Oxford, he wrote a letter of thanks to Gertrude: 'I enjoyed it all, and was so happy that Geoffrey had such an unqualified success, and that he seemed none the worse for it. I hope that you both will now have a really good holiday, during which Geoffrey can complete his convalescence'[6]. There is no record of where this holiday was spent, if indeed it happened at all. On the following day Cairns flew to Kenya and on to South Africa in connection with his work on tuberculous meningitis. On his return he told Jeff that he had been very impressed by the training programme and the hemispherectomy operations that he had seen at Rowland Krynauw's unit in Johannesburg[7].

Meanwhile, Jefferson had still not found a successor to the chair of neurosurgery at Manchester and, in July 1951, with the agreement of the University, Bill Sweet from Boston had been invited to occupy it. It was known that Sweet, having spent several years working in England, first at Queen Square and then in Birmingham, had found it a very congenial part of his career. He and Jeff knew each other well and he was familiar with the Manchester scene. Furthermore, he was involved in exciting new research in Boston on proton emission as a means of tumour diagnosis, and his exceptional surgical skills had already been demonstrated. It seemed that he was an ideal candidate for the post.

A complication, from Sweet's point of view, was that he had also been offered 'a similar position at Western Reserve University and the Lakeside Hospital in Cleveland, Ohio'[8]. His plans were to concentrate on research and to reduce his clinical commitment. However, he wrote to Jefferson that, with Richard Johnson as his colleague, 'a superlatively capable neurosurgeon,... this was an ideal situation to permit a person with my research interests to concentrate on them'[8]. It seemed to him that the new department and facilities at Manchester 'added up to a neurosurgeon's paradise'[8]. In July, he was invited to come to England for an interview and to meet the Vice-Chancellor of the University, Sir John Stopford.

There was no doubt about the enthusiasm with which Bill Sweet viewed the prospect of coming to Britain. Comparison with the Western Reserve appointment was strongly in favour of Manchester for several reasons, the chief being that in Ohio he would have been responsible for developing the university's clinical service at the Lakeside Hospital, which would unavoidably have limited the amount of time available for research. The prestige of the Manchester appointment was undoubted, but there remained a problem of obtaining the necessary funds, for the stipend of the professor, although sufficient for normal expenses, did not include money for carrying out costly research projects such as those on which Sweet was then engaged. At first he thought that there would be little difficulty in obtaining support from various American sources, but these proved not to be forthcoming and, after a month or two, Sir John Stopford wrote to Jefferson: 'I have been pursuing a number of enquiries with regard to the possibility of getting additional grants for Sweet,... [but] it became perfectly clear to all of us that we could not approach the figure required and furthermore we had to think in these austere times of priorities and the position of other medical departments. We were all very disappointed and discouraged but we felt bound to come to the conclusion that we should have to give up all hope of getting Sweet and with that went also the prospect of procuring a Professor of Neuro-Surgery in the immediate future.... I have had to tell Sweet of our disappointment and inability to meet his needs'[9].

In the meantime Sweet had been negotiating in Cleveland with Western Reserve University; but, on 16th December, they too finally failed to reach an agreement and the matter of going there was also closed. On the following day he telephoned the Vice-Chancellor in Manchester to say that he would be prepared to accept the chair on terms that had been outlined at an earlier stage, but this would only be practicable if one other possible source of funding, that had still not been tried, was supportive of his work. He hoped that the Atomic Energy Commission, who were backing his research in Boston, might transfer their funds to allow him to continue that project in the United Kingdom. But he wrote to Jefferson, 'it sent a cold chill down my spine this morning when the Vice-Chancellor seemed mighty dubious about being able to re-extend the invitation'[10]. January 1952 brought the final closure of the episode, for neither in Manchester nor in the United States could Sweet find the resources that would have been needed to meet his proposals for a predominantly research-orientated appointment. So he remained a member of the staff of the Massachusetts General Hospital and Harvard University in Boston.

In the October of 1951 Jefferson was made an Honorary member of the American Academy of Neurosurgeons[11]. When he received the news he thanked

Botterell for the cable in which he had announced it and, in his reply, Jeff told his friend of his retirement, which had now taken place. 'I gave up my chair 2 weeks ago having reached the limit and am not entitled to the "Prof" on this notepaper, but the Senate will make an honest man of me at their next meeting so I get it back again as Emeritus — an old goat's beard of a name! . . . . What I have never published and should have done is my work that I did in Victoria [British Columbia] on the muscle layers of the lumen of the stomach. I spent a great deal of time on that and still have photographs of the dissections I made. It was part of the natural curiosity that I was born with, wouldn't let me be!'[12]. In fact two papers related to work on the stomach had come out in 1914/15, but clearly he envisaged a further publication based on its musculature.

As if he had not had enough illness during 1951, Jefferson also suffered from an ischio-rectal abscess in that year, though it is not exactly clear when this took place. Botterell wrote in September to say how sorry he was to hear about it. As there had been some correspondence between them in February and March, this suggests that the abscess was not associated with that earlier episode of diverticulitis in the spring, and it seems likely that there was another recurrence late in the summer. According to Jeff, writing in October, it 'would not have been so bad if I hadn't had a nasty do with the diverticula at the same time, but its all over and I'm as good as ever unless, as is quite possible, I wholly deceive myself'[12]. Incidentally, Botterell also told Jefferson that he had come across the original report of a muscle in the penis, which Jeff had described in a very early paper as contributory to the mechanism of phimosis[13], adding that he felt that this report was insufficiently appreciated and that its illustrious discoverer deserved some belated credit for the description![14] On 21st November 1951 Jefferson's expected appointment as Emeritus Professor of Neurosurgery was announced by the Victoria University of Manchester, thus restoring his title.

There are some manuscript notes from the latter part of 1951 that are worth a mention. These were prepared for an address to the English Speaking Union, and expressed thoughts about Jeff's journey to the United States and Canada in the previous year'[15]. Among his remarks were a few observations on the changes that take place in the faces of some of those who are in public life. For example President Roosevelt, whose face was 'soft and dandified in his youth' had 'been strengthened and enobled' after his attack of poliomyelitis[15]. Whether one agrees with this statement or not, it might have been interesting to have had other examples if Jeff had been able to develop the theme further. In a Skinner Lecture, addressing an audience of radiologists in Manchester, Jeff discussed his own large series of 405 meningiomas, and the progress of knowledge about these tumours up to that time. This work does not appear to have been published[16]. On the 25th January of the new year, 1952, Jefferson gave a London University Lecture in the series of *Fundamentals of physiology*. The title was *The organization of cortical mechanisms*, and it was largely of a review nature[17].

The shadow of tragedy now fell on British neurosurgery. Sir Hugh Cairns had been taken ill on 27th December 1951 with abdominal symptoms, which recurred on 17th January and he was admitted to the Radcliffe Infirmary, Oxford, where he was found to have a lymphosarcoma of the caecum. A resection of the ascending colon was carried out on the following day by Arthur Elliot Smith, the son of Jeff's idol and mentor in Manchester before World War I. This was followed by a course of radiotherapy[18]. Jefferson wrote on 3rd February to say how sorry he was to hear the news and to wish him well[19]. Just over 2 weeks later, Hugh Cairns sent a cheerful letter back to Jefferson: 'I am nearly through my x-ray treatment now, without any unpleasant symptoms, and next week go to Sussex for a more strenuous phase of convalescence'[20]. He regretted that he would miss the imminent joint meeting with the neurologists, due to take place at the National Hospital, Queen Square[20]. There is a double burn marking the top edge of this letter. One can imagine Jefferson pondering over the situation, careless of the ash which fell from the cigarette that was seldom absent when he was at his desk. What did the future hold? Cairns was only 56 years of age, ten years younger than Jeff, but would he be able to maintain his immense drive if he survived this awful thing? And if he did not . . . ?

Jefferson wrote again to Cairns to give him the news of a successful meeting with the neurologists[21]. The SBNS had suggested that Cairns should take over the position of secretary of the society from Joe Pennybacker, who had held it for many years, and he had replied with a promise to think it over. He was now convalescing at South Stoke, his country home near Arundel, and he wrote to Jeff: 'I am rapidly gaining strength here. I am pigeon shooting much of the day, and Barbara [his wife] reads aloud the Osbert Sitwell biographies in the evening'[22]. Cairns then declined the offer of becoming the secretary of the SBNS and, in a letter to Jeff, suggested that the position should be held by Douglas Northfield. However, he offered himself as Assistant Secretary 'for a few years to help with foreign contacts, and also to see that the society doesn't break with its old easy-going traditions and become very constitutional and active about things which don't really have much to do with neurosurgery. It will be difficult enough to preserve the flavour which you have imparted to the Society'[23]. It may be recalled that Geoffrey Jefferson was not due to return to his presidential role until October 1954.

Despite a recurrence of pain, Cairns went on a holiday to Portugal at the end of March with his daughter, Elizabeth. But he had to be readmitted to hospital shortly after he returned home only 2 weeks later. He was clearly very unwell, and a second exploratory operation was performed on 26th April. The situation that was found could hardly have been worse, for the tumour was now widely spread and, although a further course of radiotherapy was begun on 7th May, it was not completed[18]. Jefferson visited Cairns at the Churchill Hospital, Oxford, in June[24].

Sir Hugh Cairns died in hospital on 18th July 1952, and Jefferson attended his friend's funeral service in Oxford 4 days later. He contributed obituaries or 'appreciations' for the British Medical Journal[25] and the Lancet[26], and for The Times and Manchester Guardian; also, later on, for the Journal of Neurosurgery[27]. John Fulton and a number of others wrote to say how moved they had been by what Jeff had written. It is not easy to abstract a sentence or two to convey the emotions which Jefferson had expressed, but the following may afford an idea: 'It is difficult to keep private grief out of a public message', he wrote. 'But I and all of us cannot but most bitterly lament the departure of a character of such integrity, such power, such courage, and such charm. The next 10 years or so, his lost years, would have seen the real flowering of all that he had striven for so hard and so long . . . . Hugh Cairns's sun has gone down and it is dusk for more than him'[25].

Jefferson had known Cairns throughout his career as a neurosurgeon, from his youthful beginnings to his final achievements. He had been his adviser, his colleague at the beginning of World War II, and from then on had been his partner in shaping the future of British neurosurgery. With Norman Dott in Edinburgh, and Hugh Cairns, at first in London and then in Oxford, Jefferson had refounded the specialty in the United Kingdom and created and nurtured the SBNS.

During the passage of these events Jefferson had delivered the Cavendish Lecture to the West London Medical Society on 22nd May at the Royal Society of Medicine. It was on *The brain as an integrated mechanism*[28]. He had been abroad again in June when he travelled to Zurich for a meeting of the SBNS, at which he spoke of what was then the sad plight of Hugh Cairns. From there he went on to Strasbourg. Shortly after his return he visited Dublin to receive an Honorary Fellowship of the Royal College of Surgeons of Ireland and, in his after-dinner speech at the Shelburne Hotel, paid just tribute to his friend Adams McConnell, the founder of Irish neurosurgery. He also recalled the pleasure he had experienced when in Dublin in his youth[29].

In the autumn, the editors of the *British Medical Students' Journal* requested Jeff to write an article about himself. This prompted a delightful essay from his pen, entitled *On being happy and liking it*. It began: 'There have been those, like Bernard Shaw, who have held that the most fascinating subject in the world is oneself.... I think, however, that the real joys of talking like this cannot be tasted except by the young or the mad and if the former then in groups of two or three or four of the same sex. I say of the same sex because in mixed company all males and all females engaged in this sort of autobiographical gossip are in a kind of courtship parade or display and however hard they try are no more sincere than the emotional strains of the moment permit them to be. To be quite sincere would be to be dumb..."the pursuit of happiness" which was laid down by Thomas Jefferson in the American Declaration of Independence proves to be no more than a nice sounding set of words but quite unreal. Happiness is a by-product.... But let me ask myself "Have I been happy?" and it is easy. I answer without hesitation, "Oh yes, immensely so", neglecting the many occasions when I was not, for it is the total effect that matters.... And what most made me happy? Why of course, having work to do which for me has no equal, and besides that, perhaps having been born with a temperament that made me like nearly everybody instinctively'[30]. It is tempting to continue to quote this analysis by Jefferson of himself, but it can be summed up in his assessment that life 'has been the greatest fun. Material rewards do not enter into this picture.... A very wise and dear friend of mine, the late Dr. EW Twining, once said to me: "You know, Jeff, it's remarkably easy to get on in life. You don't have to do much really because there's such a powerful suction that pulls you forward. All you have to do is to steer and kick your legs a bit at times to get past something, but the current will take you forward". There is a lot of truth in that. I suppose that there was a deal of suction in front of me. I hope you will be equally fortunate'[30]. At this time Jeff was the Honorary President of the British Medical Students' Union.

Jefferson retired from the chairmanship of the Research Committee of the Medical Research Council in September and received a very appreciative letter from Lord Woolton, thanking him for his services during the previous 4 years[31]. However, his association with the Ministry of Health continued, although without the considerable responsibilities that there had been during the war.

There was to be yet more trouble from diverticulitis in September and Jefferson had to miss a meeting of the Council of the SBNS at which the membership categories of the society were discussed, but he recovered in time to deliver the Godlee Lecture at University College, London, on 23rd October 1952, to which he gave the interesting title, *Prodromes to cortical localization*. It was 'a journey back into the past' such as Trotter had taken in discovering what sort of knowledge Rickman Godlee could have possessed when he removed the first cerebral glioma at the National Hospital, Queen Square, in 1884. Jeff traced the early beliefs about brain function through to the doubts which arose in the middle of the 19th century. These were to culminate in the tremendous discoveries that took place during Godlee's lifetime, which eventually produced sufficient knowledge about the functional anatomy and physiology of the brain to allow the birth of neurosurgery, though this could not have taken place if the fruits of the work of Lister had not also been available to diminish the risk of infection. This combination of events allowed Macewen in Glasgow in the 1870s, to take advantage of 'the new physiology in the practical treatment of brain abscess, injury, and dural tumours'[32]. This was a superb piece of neurophysiological history writing. The nervous system has more personal names attached to it than any other part of the body; in this study the eponymists have been brought to life and their work placed in its chronological context.

Another appreciative letter was sent to Jeff. This time it was from the Royal Society, to thank him for his services on their Physiology and Medical Sciences Sectional Committee, from which he had retired[33].

And what of Lady Jefferson? Gertrude's busy life as a psychotherapist continued at High Bank, the Royal Infirmary, at Lorne Street and at the Manchester Family Welfare Services and Maternity and Child Welfare Clinics. Her own secretary, Elizabeth Bridge, helped to organise her activities, which included administrative responsibilities for the Centres that she had set up in the city. But this was not all. She gave talks, from 1952 and for the next 3 years, in the Bishop of Manchester's series of post-ordination classes for the clergy, under the title of *The priest and psychological disorders*. Writing later about the class, she said: 'The group is composed of all ages and they seem to be chiefly interested in learning how to distinguish mental from moral disease'[34].

Gertrude Jefferson had by now opened and staffed three Family Welfare Centres in Manchester. She described this service in the *Medical Women's Federation Journal* to which, in the same issue, she also contributed an obituary for a colleague, Dr Catherine Chisholm[35]. Gertrude declared open the Alice Kenyon Industrial Centre in Oldham in 1952, and lectured to the Royal Infirmary nurses on *The approach and management of a neurotic patient*. During the year she was asked to become a member of the Commission on the Church's Ministry of Healing, set up by Archbishops Fisher and Ramsey, to which she was appointed in 1953. She put in a lot of time on this work since there was a vast amount of written evidence to consider. The Commission emphasised the need to find a basis for co-operation between the clergy and the medical profession in the physical and spiritual care of patients. They also considered many other matters which were more exclusively the concern of the church's ministry. Their findings were published in 1958[36]. Among the other matters on which they deliberated was the subject of spiritual healing. Gertrude herself was not directly associated with this topic, though she appears to have accepted it and, indeed, one of her sons described her as practising 'Theo-psychiatry'. However, her real gift was for encouraging people to talk to her, even though she herself was not especially communicative. In view of her strong religious feelings, it is worth noting that, despite what some have thought, she was not a Jungian psycho-analyst or, indeed, an analyst of any sort. Peter Ascroft, a neurosurgeon who had done some of his training in Manchester, described her in a letter to her husband, as having 'an aura of blessedness'[37].

Jefferson himself, freed at last from clinical, administrative and teaching responsibilities, found he was still very much in demand, not only for private consultations but more especially as a speaker of repute and an acknowledged attractor of audiences. He enjoyed lecturing, travelling and being in the position of ambassador for British neurosurgery, and he also enjoyed the adulation that went with this. Lecturing gave him the opportunity to discourse on a wide range of subjects, medical, historical and philosophical, both at home and abroad.

In 1953 he became the chairman of the newly created and important Clinical Research Board of the Medical Research Council, which had the task of recommending the projects that should be supported by funds distributed by the Council. He held this prestigious position for the next 4 years. He also delivered a considerable number of important lectures. The first of these had been occupying his mind when he wrote to Harry Botterell in March: 'I have just finished writing up a paper given to the R.S.M. on the Differential Diagnosis of Posterior Fossa Lesions[38]. I concluded that you were lucky if you could (apart from cerebello-pontine angle lesions)! I had to decline Wilder Penfield's invitation to come to Montreal in May to give the Hughlings Jackson Lecture as I had no time to work up a subject, having committed myself to too many already.... I have agreed to come to New Orleans in November.... I'm up to my ears with my Bowman Lecture now on lesions of the cavernous sinus, which will be mainly aneurysms and a few tumours, most of them naso-pharyngeal growths'[39]. This last lecture was delivered to the annual congress of the Ophthalmological Society of the United Kingdom on 23rd April[40]. He also gave the William Sheen Lecture in Cardiff that year on a rather similar subject, that of *Cavernous aneurysms, saccular and fistulous*.

Jefferson's presidential address to the Manchester Literary and Philosophical Society was entitled *The search for the mechanisms involved in thinking and talking*. It was, naturally, a historical review for a mainly lay audience. He mentioned the problems that there were in converting thoughts into such language as was adequate to communicate meaning and emotion, and how this was supplemented by gesture and changes in tone and expression. He also pondered that: 'If, when the last thing is known about the brain, then there is still something left over which can in no way be accounted for, that remaining part could be the Soul.... Science has nothing to say about the Soul—nothing for or against it'[41]. The year 1953 was also notable for Jefferson's Sherrington Lecture to Liverpool University on *The invasive adenomas of the pituitary*[42]. He described certain pituitary adenomas which appeared to pass through neighbouring structures rather than to push them aside, but yet did not appear to him to be malignant. It represented an important step in our knowledge of pituitary pathology, even though not everything that he said is still accepted. Jeff also contributed a general review of recent advances in neurosurgery to *The Practitioner*[43].

On 25th August Jeff addressed the First World Congress on Medical Education and took *Teaching surgery at the bedside and in the theatre* as his theme[44]. On the following day the *Manchester Evening News* picked up the "bombshell" that, in relation to medical students, he had said that it was a shocking waste of time for them to be hanging about in the theatre, when they would be much better employed in the wards. This statement was apparently not supported by others, who pointed out that only those were present in the theatre who were personally concerned with a particular operation and, while agreeing that seeing too many operations was a waste of time, it was essential for students to watch experienced surgeons at work. The newspaper made a final comment that Jeff was noted at the Manchester Royal Infirmary 'for his informality in touring the wards, without the customary white coat—and without a retinue'[45]. The last remark undoubtedly referred to his way of dropping into the wards at odd times when it was convenient for him; but his message to the conference was clearly concerned with the importance of teaching at the bedside, and he can be seen doing just this, with retinue and without a white coat, in a photograph of him engaged on a "round"[46].

September found Jefferson in Lisbon and Madrid. He wrote to Botterell: 'It was too far to learn so little. And then of course the heat was too much (102°F & humid) and of course a lot of us got our insides upset to make the whole thing unpleasant.... Norman Dott had brought his family by car and drove me from Lisbon to Madrid, after which experience I was glad that I had excused myself from accompanying them the whole way from home. The heat was unendurable, the countryside burnt and brown and very sparsely populated. How on earth our troops survived to fight all over the peninsula 150 years ago I can't think, especially in the uniforms of those days. We stayed the night in Badajoz and sweat ran off us in streams, its said to be the hottest town in Spain. Drinking didn't seem to be much good, though we drank a great deal; I expect it was salt we needed. My respect for Wellington's army was great after seeing some of that country'[47]. Jeff said he was looking forward to seeing Harry Botterell in 'a couple of month's time. I haven't really completed the papers I've said I'd give. One never does—not till long after the event'[47]. On at least one occasion during a lecture he is known to have admitted that his audience would have to wait for the published version in order to have his complete thoughts on the subject! In view of the above description of his discomforts in the Iberian peninsula, it is hardly surprising that he suffered 'the most abominable of abdominal pains' during the congress[48].

By the autumn, plans had been finalised for the tour of the United States and Canada. Gertrude and Geoffrey Jefferson sailed yet again across the Atlantic from Liverpool, aboard the RMS *Media* on 31st October 1953, and arrived in New York on 7th November. As on previous occasions, the crossing had been stormy and Sweet, who met them in New York before travelling south, very kindly wrote to Jeff's next host that he needed a recuperative day of rest in his schedule[49].

Figure 24 *Geoffrey Jefferson, Jefferson Penfield (named after GJ), Wilder Penfield and Francis McNaughten at the Penfield home in Montreal.*

From New York Jefferson travelled by train to New Orleans, where he spent almost a week, Gertrude remaining for the time being in Boston with Dr and Mrs James White. The visit to New Orleans was undertaken in order to participate in the meeting of the American Congress of Neurological Surgeons; on this occasion Jefferson was their Honoured Guest, of whom there is one at each annual congress. In fact he was the second of their Honoured Guests, the first having been Herbert Olivecrona from Stockholm, but Jeff's visit was the first to be published, and was reported soon afterwards in the initial number of a series of annual records of their proceedings, this one having Jefferson's portrait as a frontispiece[50]. An introductory talk was given by him on *Changing views on the integration of the brain*: 'We now know accurately something that has been a burning question in clinical medicine for generations. Namely, the anatomical levels where lesions most easily produce coma, unconsciousness, parasomnia, or lack of the expected responses to happenings in the environment'[50]. These levels, he pointed out, were located in the brain stem and some parts of the thalami, but the problem of memory was still unsolved. The position of Honoured Guest was indeed an honour, but no sinecure. The recipient has to deliver a series of lectures. Jeff gave no less than four, including the one just mentioned, and another in which he gathered together the current knowledge about trigeminal neuromas, with some remarks about malignant invasion of the gasserian ganglion[50,51]. In this he drew mainly from his own experience, but also from published work. It was an extremely valuable contribution to the recognition and management of these tumours before the advent of scanning techniques. The third lecture was on *Compression of the optic pathways by intracranial aneurysms*[50], being an extension of his Elsberg Lecture due to be given in New York in December, in which he also drew on his Doyne lecture of 1945 and the Bowman lecture he had given that spring. The fourth address, though delivered, was not included in the volume because the topic was that of the Sherrington Lecture which he had delivered earlier in the year, and that was being published by Liverpool University[42,50]. While in New Orleans, he also spoke at Tulane University on the now familiar topic of *The localization of the soul*.

The success of the lectures to the Congress of Neurological Surgeons may be judged by a letter from Dr Frederick Rehfeldt. 'My heart is so full of gratitude for what you did for our group of younger neurosurgeons that I believe it would be fully impossible to express those feelings,' he wrote. 'Let me put it this way, that in some magic way you made almost everyone present feel as if one knew you personally and had known you for a long time. Your remarks, particularly at the end of your third paper, set up vibrations which will continue throughout the life-time of those who heard you .... There is no way in which you can ever know how many young minds and young hearts you enriched during those three days'[52].

Jefferson next spent 3 days in Galveston, Texas, where he delivered the Greenwood lecture to the medical school on *The neurology of the trigeminal nerve and its clinical significance*. This was before going to Montreal for yet another 3-day stint. There he attended the opening of Wilder Penfield's new wing of the Montreal Neurological Institute on 20th November. On that occasion he gave an address in which, among other things, he reviewed the particular fascinations of neurology: 'I spoke of it as enchanting, a very proper term, since it casts a spell over its chosen subjects that makes them willing slaves'[53]. Jeff then considered various discoveries in the neurological field and continued: 'He would be a foolish man who believed in recognisable mental brilliance. Our geniuses are all biological sports, they are not men or women standing on the tip of a pyramid of betterment.... Some odd observation is made that may be more use in a sister field than its own enclosure. And then someone almost intuitively sees a special use for it.... One would need the mantle of Elijah to prophesy what the future of neuro-surgery will be'[53]. It was the neurologists who were working on 'the overiding Master System, the thing that makes us men and women rather than units in a herbaceous border.... We still have before us that limitless field for exploration—the nature of man's mental processes, and who but us will get as near the truth as those who have worked here and others like them in the years to come.... It has been well said that theory is the poetry of science. It is a necessary part of it, for without a theory no idea can be tested'[53].

Without a pause, Jeff travelled on from Montreal to Toronto for a further 3 days, and to stay with the Botterells. Here he gave another lecture on *The pituitary adenomas* and enjoyed a very short spell of relaxation. Boston was his next stop, where he arrived on 27th November. During the 3 days he spent there he spoke to the New England Neurosurgical Society on *The invasive adenomas of the pituitary* and to the Boston Neurological Society on *Trigeminal neurinomas*. Jefferson's next engagement was to give the 13th James M Anders Memorial Lecture to the

Philadelphia Academy of Medicine on 2nd December; it was on the topic of *Pituitary infantilism*[54]. He also addressed the Philadelphia Neurologic Society.

From Philadelphia Jefferson journeyed to Baltimore and, on 7th December after a weekend break, he gave a lecture under the title of *The spinal cord in 1837*. He left on the following day to return to New York for 2 more days, during which he lectured to the New York Neurological Institute, once again on the *Invasive pituitary adenomas*, and he gave the 3rd Elsberg Lecture to the New York Society of Neurological Surgeons. This was on *Chiasmal lesions caused by aneurysms*[50]. He also spoke at the New York Academy of Medicine on *Chiasmal aneurysms*. This completed a tour that would have been exhausting for a fit young man. Inevitably, there was some repetition among the subjects of his lectures, though familiarity with the topics lightened the burden but slightly. At every stop there were social activities at which he was lionised, and these could be as tiring as the academic demands, not to mention the strain of travelling huge distances by rail and air. It must have been with some relief that, on Friday 11th December, Jeff and Gertrude sailed once more from New York, bound for Liverpool, again on the *Media*.

REFERENCES

GJ=Geoffrey Jefferson; HC=Hugh Cairns; GMJ=Gertrude Jefferson
1   Paterson Ross J to GJ. Letter 28th February 1951.
2   Naunton Morgan C to Paterson Ross J. Letter 2nd March 1951.
3   Paterson Ross J to GJ. Letter 5th March 1951.
4   HC to GJ. Letter 11th May 1951.
5   GJ. MS Reply to Toast at the Association of Surgeons dinner, July 1951.
6   HC to GMJ. Letter 22nd July 1951.
7   HC to GJ. Letter 27th August 1951.
8   Sweet WH. Personal communication.
9   Stopford JSB to GJ. Letter 19th October 1951.
10 Sweet WH to GJ. Letter 17th December 1951.
11 Botterell EH to GJ. Letter 12th October 1951.
12 GJ to Botterell EH. Letter 14th October 1951.
13 Jefferson G. The peripenic muscle; some observations on the anatomy of phimosis. *Surg Gynecol Obstet* 1916; **23**: 177–81.
14 Botterell EH to GJ. Letter 28th September 1951.
15 GJ. MS Address to the English Speaking Union. September 1951.
16 GJ. MS *Meningiomas*. Skinner Lecture 1951.
17 Jefferson G. The organization of cortical mechanisms. In: *The scientific basis of medicine*. Vol. 1. London: London University Press, 1952: 61–78.
18 Fraenkel GJ. *Hugh Cairns*. Oxford: Oxford University Press, 1991: 217–21.
19 GJ to HC. Letter 3rd February 1952.
20 HC to GJ. Letter 19th February 1952.
21 GJ to HC. Letter 24th February 1952.
22 HC to GJ. Letter 3rd March 1952.
23 HC to GJ. Letter 20th March 1952.
24 Pennybacker, Winifred to GJ. Letter 22nd June 1952.
25 Jefferson G. Sir Hugh Cairns. *BMJ* 1952; **2**: 233–5.
26 Jefferson G. Hugh William Bell Cairns. *Lancet* 1952; **2**: 202–203
27 Jefferson G. Sir Hugh Cairns. *J Neurosurg* 1953; **10**: 87–9.
28 Jefferson G. The brain as an integrated mechanism. *West Lond Med J* 1952; **57**: 78–92.
29 GJ. MS After-dinner speech, Dublin, 11th July 1952.
30 Jefferson G. On being happy and liking it. *Br Med Students' J* 1952; **6**: 2–4 and *Selected papers*. London: Pitman Medical, 1960: 550–3.

31   Woolton, Lord to GJ. Letter 26th September 1952.
32   Jefferson G. Prodromes to cortical localization. *J Neurol Neurosurg Psychiat* 1953; **16**: 59–72 and *Selected papers*. London: Pitman Medical, 1960: 113–31.
33   Royal Society, Secretary to GJ. Letter 17th December 1952.
34   GMJ to Wilde JF. Letter 8th October 1956.
35   Jefferson GM. The Manchester Family Welfare Service; its origins and aims. *Medical Women's Federation Journal* October 1952.
36   *Report of the Commission on the Church's Ministry of Healing*. London: The Church Information Board, 1958.
37   Ascroft P to GJ. Letter 4th November 1954.
38   Jefferson G. Discussion of the differential diagnosis of lesions of the posterior fossa. *Proc Roy Soc Med* 1953; **46**: 719–38.
39   GJ to Botterell EH. Letter 17th March 1953.
40   Jefferson G. Concerning injuries, aneurysms and tumours involving the cavernous sinus. *Trans Ophthalmol Soc UK* 1953; **73**: 117–52.
41   Jefferson G. The search for the mechanisms involved in thinking and talking. *Memoirs of the Proceedings of the Manchester Literary and Philosophical Society 1953–1954* 1954; **95**: 1–16.
42   Jefferson G. *The invasive adenomas of the pituitary*. Liverpool: Liverpool University Press, 1953.
43   Jefferson G. Advances in neurosurgery. *The Practitioner* 1953; **171**: 413–23.
44   Jefferson G. Teaching surgery at the bedside and in the theatre. *Proceedings of the 1st World Conference on Medical Education*. London: Oxford University Press, 1953: 405–413.
45   *Manchester Evening News*. 26th August 1953.
46   Visits to clinics. *Br J Surg* 1955; **43**: 319.
47   GJ to Botterell EH. Letter 22nd September 1953.
48   GJ to Rowbotham GF. Letter 20th October 1953.
49   Sweet WH to Jackson I. Letter 13th November 1953.
50   Jefferson G. *Changing views on the integration of the brain*, pp. 1–10 *Trigeminal neuromas*, pp. 11–54. *Compression of the optic pathways by intracranial aneurysms*, pp. 55–103. In: *Clinical Neurosurgery*. Baltimore: Williams Wilkins, 1955: 1–103.
51   Jefferson G. The trigeminal neuromas. In *Selected papers*. London: Pitman Medical, 1960: 500–25.
52   Rehfeldt F to GJ. Letter 15th December 1953.
53   GJ. MS Address at the Opening of the Montreal Neurological Institute. 20th November 1953.
54   Jefferson G. Reflections on pituitary infantilism. *Transactions and Studies of the College of Physicians of Philadelphia* 1954; **22**: 1–9.

Chapter 22

More lectures and a return to Russia
1954–1956

After his retirement from the National Health Service, Jefferson maintained a continuing presence in the Manchester Royal Infirmary, treating patients in the private wing. He used the facilities of the new neurosurgical department very much as before, and retained his consulting room in Lorne Street. He also continued to enjoy chats with members of the staff over a cup of tea. Such occasions may have been the source of a companionship, at first based on and associated with shared responsibilities, which gradually developed into a significant relationship that became one of long standing. Always a man who delighted in the company of women, this was a close friendship, observed and understood by many and tolerated by Gertrude Jefferson.

Books too, always a further source of delight for Jeff, still meant a great deal to him. His collection had been discerningly amassed over the years and included first editions, both of recent literature and of many medical classics. He sorely missed the spacious library that he formerly had at High Bank. In January 1954 he made a contribution to a discussion at the Royal Society of Medicine in which he spoke on *Harvey Cushing and his books*[1], incidentally giving us an insight into his own motives for collecting. 'The most accurate method of knowing about a library is that, as it were, of accountancy where the provenance of each volume is known, its date of purchase, and (an unending source of enjoyment) the amount paid for it. That is the surest way, but the more illuminating is to enquire why the books were bought. As an unrepentant book buyer it would, I know well, tax my memory, my powers of invention maybe, had I to give reasons for all my purchases. I have no doubt that anyone looking over another's books must frequently exclaim: "Good gracious, what on earth did he buy that for! I had no idea he had any interest either in that subject or that author". And maybe there has been none; the book just made its way into the company. But this is a universal frailty to which all book lovers are subject. How often do we resolve that we shall limit our purchases to this subject or that, to such and such a period, or to a few writers in whom we are particularly interested. And how vainly! There is among books a sort of "bibliotaxis", as Cushing remarked.... Did Dr Cushing read his books? There is among bibliophiles a gentleman's agreement not to ask that question. Of course he did not read all of them, none of us do, or can, or ever have done so. Marcus Antoninus as long ago as AD 121* advised his readers to cherish no illusions of that kind. We read selectively, we pursue what we require, we read what attracts us... we can often be fascinated by the form, shape, colour and feel of books in which we don't read even fifty lines'[1].

*__Marcus Antoninus.__ Marcus Aurelius Antoninus, Roman Emperor and Stoic philosopher was born in AD 121. It is therefore likely that this advice was given somewhat later! He died in AD 180.

Jefferson went on to say that 'a more interesting study is to see how much use a collector who is also a writer makes of his books, to discover who were his favourites, and especially what trends of thought, what climates of opinion, made particular appeal'[1]. While pursuing this approach, Jeff found that the majority of the names of authors which emerged from his analysis of Cushing's library were those of doctors, savants, or scientists, and that 'few, a very few, were of purely literary men'[1]. This was certainly not true of Jeff's library which, unfortunately, has not been preserved in this country, for most of the volumes are believed to be in America at Austin University in Texas. However, we can still glance at the catalogue of its eventual sale by auction at Sotheby's[2].

Not unexpectedly there were some exceptional medical and scientific works. These included first editions of Harvey's *De Motu Cordis*, Marshall Hall's Lectures, Hilton's *Rest and pain*, Morgagni (1769), Pavlov's first English edition, Percival Pott's *Chirurgical works* (1775), and no less than 30 volumes by or about William Osler, including first editions of his work. There was Descartes' (1644) *Principia* in its first edition as well as the first English edition of 1650; also 'firsts' of Astley Cooper, Charles Bell and many other stars from the medical firmament. This is not to mention Sir Isaac Newton's copy of Homer, Hughlings Jackson's copy of Bell's *Nervous system*, and similar delights. Of course he possessed Sir Thomas Browne's *Religio medici*, but only in the seventh edition of 1672! There were first editions of Richard Bright's *Reports*, Thomas Willis's *Pharmaceutica rationalis* and Priestley's *Disquisitions*. Among the many other valuable acquisitions that were not, however, in their first edition were the works of Plutarch (1676), Galileo (1656), Paré (1649), Kenelm Digby (1645) and John Hunter (1835).

But Jeff's tastes were catholic and wide-ranging; in the sale there were many books of a more literary nature that had been on his shelves. Again, there were first editions of many authors, including Charlotte Brontë's (Currer Bell) *The Professor*, three works by Rupert Brooke, also three by Virginia Woolf and three by JB Yeats. There were no less than eight books by his better known brother WB Yeats, all first editions. There were signed copies of Masefield's works, and many of the publications by the Nonsuch Press. The early letters between Gertrude and Geoffrey contained frequent references to poetry, and this was reflected in the library to a large degree, including fine editions from the Kelmscott and Golden Cockerel Presses[2].

As we have seen, in their earlier years together, poetry and literature were a constant source of stimulation, discussion, comparison and criticism for Geoffrey and Gertude Jefferson but, as the demands of neurosurgery and psychiatry increased out of all proportion to their other interests, it was natural that their more esoteric pastimes became submerged. It was all that Jeff could do to keep up with the medical journals and the study required for his considerable output of lectures and papers, while Gertrude's later reading was mainly either psychiatric or devotional[3]. She even preferred newspapers that were two or three days old — was that because she could feel the events, disasters and crises were no longer in an acute state, and whatever worrying things she read about had moved a stage further on by the time she became aware of them? However, latterly, Jeff always listened to the evening news on the radio, so she must have had some idea of what was going on. Music did not feature in the library, but it remained an abiding interest.

On 30th January 1954, Jefferson gave the Pearson Lecture of the Rochdale
Literary and Scientific Society, on *The mechanisms of mental processes*. It was
delivered to a 'capacity audience' in the local Art Gallery and was reported at
length in the next issue of the *Rochdale Observer*[4]. He remarked, in his
introductory paragraph, that the real beauty of Science was the choice of the
question to be asked, 'because there were a lot of questions that...did not allow
an answer.... Those who had made the greatest advances in science had always
done so because they had been able to put clever questions'[5]. A discerning
observation.

The SBNS had commissioned an oil painting of Sir Geoffrey Jefferson by Sir
Gerald Kelly, the famous portraitist and president of the Royal Academy from
1949 to 1954. During February Jefferson had passed on the message to the artist
that his family did not want him to be painted in academic robes but in his
ordinary clothes, since they would convey more of an impression of his true
character. This produced the following reply from Sir Gerald: 'I've painted many
pictures of men in waistcoats and coats and I don't mind painting one more. I try
and get the portrait like, and as I go on getting employment, presumably I
succeed. So I will waive the academic robe if your family are against it. I only
suggested it because when I'm painting anybody of academic distinction it is the
only legitimate excuse for making a coloured picture, and I find coloured pictures
better to live with than *sub fusc* ones'[6]. He then suggested a first appointment on
19th March.

Figure 25   *Sir Gerald Kelly painting Sir Geoffrey Jefferson.*

Figure 26 *Drawing of Jefferson asleep, by Wilder Penfield at the end of a letter from Helen Penfield. 4302 Montrose was the Penfield's address.*

It was to be more than 2 years before the painting was completely finished, but it is certainly extremely 'like'; in fact, a brilliant portrait. The presentation, before the last touches had been made, was to take place in 1955; it now hangs on the staircase of the Royal College of Surgeons of England, to whom it is on loan from the family. A friendship grew up between the artist and his sitter, and when Jeff congratulated Sir Gerald not only on the portrait but also on an appearance he had recently made on television, it drew the remark: 'I'm glad you liked the T.V. stuff. I can do better than that'[7].

The summer months of 1954 were taken up by travelling. In a letter to Sir Harold Himsworth, the secretary of the Medical Research Council, written in response to an invitation to meet for a discussion, Jeff remarked: 'I am all billed up by the American College of Surgeons and preparations for Italy before that. I leave on Wednesday afternoon, May 19th at 3.30'[8]. The SBNS met in May that year, in Belgium, so attendance at its meeting cannot have been the reason for travelling to Italy. Unfortunately, we do not have any details of this journey, or of that visit to Canada and the United States. On the American trip he was probably accompanied by Gertrude, for Mrs Penfield wrote later (giving the day and month but not the year) about a dressing-gown belt and camera that she and

Geoffrey had lost or left behind in Montreal. Helen Penfield continued: 'Of course we are busy having a plaque made to go on the outside of the house — a replica of the sign found on the wall in the little room next yours! It should make the re-sale of this house much more profitable when the time comes'[9]. As a joke, Jeff had fixed up a card on which was written 'Geoffrey Jefferson slept here'. The letter ended with a drawing of Jeff asleep, the artist being none other than Wilder Penfield himself.

Jefferson had been much concerned in previous months with the establishment of a new Midland Centre for Neurosurgery and Neurology at Smethwick, in Birmingham. It has since been closed and absorbed by the unit at the Queen Elizabeth Hospital. In September 1954, he opened it himself in his official capacity as president of the SBNS for the second time. In the following week he wrote to Bill Sweet: 'I went to Birmingham last Tuesday to open the new "Midland Neurosurgical Centre".... It has 50 beds, to be expanded to 75, and is in a disused Isolation Hospital at Smethwick. It is a very pleasant set-up and they'll do good work'[10]. In sadder vein he continued, 'My only brother, Jack, two years younger than I, is just about dying, poor lad, of acute leukaemia. Total history about 2 months. It's a ghastly thing to get since there is no answer, nothing known to have caused the leucopenia and appearance of "blasts" in the blood. The Borough of Rochdale decided a couple of months or so ago to give him the "Freedom of the Borough", a very rare honour, there are only 3 others, Gracie Fields is one! They are going to do it in absentia to-morrow', which was, in fact, to be the day on which he died. Jeff continued the letter: 'I've at last finished the Sherrington Lecture on invasive adenomas of the pituitary and feel rather proud of it (for once).... Trotula joins me in love to you and Mary. It was such fun seeing you this summer, since you left it became the worst summer in most folks' memories, a real stinker, cold and wet, wet, wet. It's still horrible, no Indian summer even'[10].

On 4th November Jeff gave the Stephen Paget Lecture to the Research Defence Society, on *Man as an experimental animal*[11]. In it he pointed out that for much of the research on the nervous system, man is the only possible subject, especially when sensation, pain or thought is being studied. However, he also related some of the discoveries that had transformed neurological medicine and surgery, but which had depended upon initial work that had been done on animals, simply because it could not have been done on man. For instance, the mapping of the functions of different parts of the brain had depended on animal work and the result was, to quote a riposte by John Ruskin to the Bishop of Oxford in 1884, that 'the gateway to cerebral surgery had been opened'[11,12]. He also gave the Rutherford Morrison Lecture in Newcastle on *The variable behaviour of pituitary adenomas*, which was based on his own experience of 285 operated cases.

A draft agreement to write a book for Hodder and Stoughton entitled *The brain and its working*, had been drawn up in February 1954, but was never signed. The publishers asked for not less than 65,000 words within 2 years, and a letter from Nesta Pain makes it clear that discussions about it had been held. 'We're all having sleepless nights worrying about when you're going to sign the contract for the book. Please! I can't wait to read it'[13]. However, Jeff very wisely decided not to undertake the project, which would have greatly interfered with his other writing and could have caused him much anxiety.

The Thomas Young Lecture, given by Jefferson on 25th March 1955 at St George's Hospital, London, on sleep and coma, seems not to have been published. A number of papers appeared in print during that year, some of which have been quoted, but the most important was certainly the Third Sherrington Lecture, on *The invasive adenomas of the pituitary*, which he had delivered to the University of Liverpool in 1953, and which had also formed the basis of one of his lectures to the Congress of Neurosurgeons[14]. It was published by the university in the form of a monograph.

On 29th March Jefferson gave the Ludwig Mond Lecture at Manchester University, on *The contemporary reaction to phrenology*. The title is slightly ambiguous, for he referred both to the time at which he was writing, and to the views of the contemporaries of proponents of phrenology in the eighteenth and nineteenth centuries. It is an informative and widely researched address of some length, which is most interesting to read. He concluded by giving 'posthumous thanks' to those who had 'produced evidence and stimulated others to find much more of the inequalities of man's mental endowments and skills and the distribution of those personal characteristics to which we give the value judgements of "good" or "bad", inequalities which education can only partly repair and punishment not always correct'[15]. The *Manchester Guardian*'s reporter thought that Jeff's interpretation of science's views on phrenology was 'kindlier than many people would have suspected'[16].

The correspondence with Harry Botterell in Toronto picked up again in April 1955 with a letter from Jeff outlining his plans for a further visit to North America, in the coming June, and asking if he would arrange for them to go fishing together somewhere or other. He also expressed his disappointment that he would be unable to accept an honorary LLD from Queen's University, Kingston, Ontario, because he would be leaving England only on the previous day, and could not get to Kingston in time for the ceremony. This was the second honorary degree he had had to refuse, and for the same reason: 'I missed an "Hon" at Brown in 1943 by very stupidly keeping an engagement at the Mayo Clinic. So I shall return again undecorated. Oh well!'[17].

In his capacity as President of the Manchester Royal Infirmary Old Residents' Club, Jeff wrote to Lord Webb-Johnson in April to ask if he would become Vice-president of the club; this, in view of his ineligibility for the Presidency, the holder of which office had to be a member of the Consultant Staff. In his letter of acceptance Lord Webb-Johnson, who was a Manchester graduate and had been a Surgical Registrar when Jeff was 'on the house', asked to be spared from making a speech at the dinner due to be held on 1st October[18]. Disappointed, Jeff replied: 'I very much hope that you will decide to speak because a Dinner that you attend and are not heard at does not seem right somehow, not in this town certainly'[19]. He also congratulated Webb-Johnson on a recent speech that he had given at the Middlesex Hospital and said: 'I was so sorry that I could not go to that but I had to go to an M.R.C. Council Meeting that afternoon, and as the H bomb and the polio vaccine were on the agenda I felt it my duty to attend, but I should much sooner have been at the Middlesex'[19].

Gertrude was unwell and could not accompany her husband on his next visit to Canada and the USA. So Jeff wrote to Botterell: 'I am only too sorry that Trude won't be there with me, its a great pity. Your proposal that we should go off to

Muskoka Lake sounds to me like the best part of the whole trip — a pity its for so short a time. Couldn't we break away on Sunday. I am going to Holland to-morrow to the Netherlands Neurosurgical, a nuisance really since I haven't written my Canadian things yet and, what is worse, don't find them composing themselves in my head. I have been so occupied with the Clinical Research Board lately that I have not had any leisure whatever. And now I am on this Government enquiry into Medical Manpower, the future predictable needs of the population in relation to intake in Medical Schools. My Godfathers!'[20]. This was the Willink committee.

On 2nd June Jeff flew from Prestwick to Boston, where he spent a week at the Massachusetts General Hospital as a Visiting Professor at the invitation of JC White. He was there for a big party given to mark Dr White's 21 years in neurosurgery and his elevation to full professorship in the Harvard Medical School. Shortly afterwards Jeff received a letter from his Boston host, in which he was thanked for his work in the hospital during that visit. James White remarked on the tremendous impression that Jeff had made on 'the residents, who had never encountered a teacher of your quality, and various secretaries who had never had their legs pulled by a V.I.P.'[21].

From there, on 14th June 1955, Jeff flew on to Toronto where he lectured at a combined meeting of the British, Canadian and Ontario Medical Associations then being held in that city. His subject was *Cortical localization*, and in his review of its history he returned to his interest in phrenology and suggested that it had played an unrecognised part in the mapping of brain functions. 'We see the powers that reside in human minds called into being along the ancient pathways which man shares with animals — but with a final result so different because of the immense potential cellular wealth of the cortex and the vast richness of its relays and communications systems.... This is the crux of the new play of integration in which cortical localization has its proper place. [Even] if we no longer believe that such things as love and loyalty, tenderness and friendship and happiness, have special abodes in the brain, yet we know that some such attributes exist, fictitious as definite entitities though they may be, and that they are the by-products of the harmony of body and brain'[22]. In addition to speaking on that occasion, Jeff also attended a combined meeting of the SBNS with the Canadian Neurosurgical Association in Toronto. However, he managed to find time to spend the promised week-end fishing with Harry Botterell at Bala on Lake Muskoka, about 100 miles north of the city. This transatlantic visit was considerably shorter than any of his previous journeys, made so by the increasingly available option of long distance flying.

On returning to Manchester in July, Jeff wrote to Botterell: 'I left an envelope on the bed in my room that had some things in it that I wanted ... if you have not thrown it away I would be glad to have that'[23]. He then thanked his friend for his kindness 'not only now but in the years past. I hope that you get as much pleasure out of talking to me as I do out of listening to you. I never seem to say anything much that I can remember, but I do remember what other people say to me. I wonder though whether that isn't the way the mind works and that none of us recollect saying anything but a disjointed sentence here and there in a torrent of other people's talk. I must stop and go to bed'[23].

Another introspective letter was written to Botterell a month later. In it Jeff said: 'Those few days that I had up at the lakes were superb. But I liked it all, only that more'[24]. He had been re-reading some of the notes he had made in 1940, and continued: '... about my early days in neurosurgery I said this: "Those who started later will not know, will not be able of course to remember the early days that were often so heart-breaking, will not know the papers that were written and no one (unless I tell them) will ever know the papers I meant to write, what I meant to do, to teach, to create, those aspirations that came to nothing through lack of energy or assiduous application, through lack (to use my favourite word) of industry". Well, I did a lot to remedy that in the last 15 years.... I showed a certain amount of insight into myself but I must have been feeling that I'd never get done what I hoped and wished to do so much. Now I know I can't do all of it and I no longer mind. I suppose age has blunted me — and the realization that we all must die with so much undone'[24]. He went on to regret that a paper he had written on concussion did not contribute enough towards treatment: 'The need to have a wide and deep understanding employs my thoughts and I have always assumed that treatment springs from it necessarily. But in that I think I have erred by not thinking out deeply enough what treatment is possible. I could, and do, claim that the more important things are the fundamentals of causation, of nature, of progress, of valuable result and that, given that, others can think up treatment'[24].

Harry Botterell replied: 'Your thought that you had erred by not thinking deeply enough what treatment is possible is, I am sure, a minor matter. It strikes me that what has held neurosurgery back is the inability of most of us to develop a wide and deep understanding. Surely the complexities of human thought and cerebral function can only be unravelled by profound thinking and the development of hypotheses. Without human endeavour of this type, the study of electrical potentials, the use of calculating machines and the electron microscope, constitute a mass of material without strategic overall significance'[25].

On 20th June 1955 Jefferson gave a paper to the Section of Neurology of the Royal Society of Medicine, in conjunction with Richard Johnson, on the *Disintegration of consciousness in posterior fossa lesions*. On the following day he was handed the diploma of Honorary Fellowship of the Society by its President, an award which Jeff valued very much. Several distinguished neurologists were there when Jeff was formally presented by Sir Francis Walshe. In his speech Walshe drew attention to the 'impulse of Harvey Cushing, a man of dominating personality who impressed himself so strongly upon the numbers of his distinguished pupils and successors over more than a generation, that many of them never achieved intellectual or emotional emancipation, and, returning to their mother countries, filled with apostolic zeal and the foibles of the prima donna, personified him in their various degrees and were happy in doing so, whether wittingly or unwittingly. Yet to whatever Cushing vintage they belonged, their bouquet was unmistakeable. There is only one Jefferson vintage.... It is unique and must be so, it is wholly of native provenance, and achieves its brilliant best'. The typically Walshian phrases rolled on, with their occasional barbed remarks, mostly with some basis in truth, but often unkind in their generalisations. However, he was generous to Jeff, despite the altercations that had taken place between them a few years earlier over the place of surgery in the National Hospital to which, unrepentantly, he could not refrain from making a reference, even at this event: 'In the occasional skirmishes that take place on the frontier between neurological medicine and surgery, Sir Geoffrey and I have not always found ourselves on the same side, and I recall an occasion when he felt impelled to tell me that my remarks were not all sweetness and light. I hope he will find no hardness in what I have had to say to-day in humble tribute to him, though I am sure he knows that this is not because I have run out of that commodity. And if the sweetness of my regard for him is not apparent, it is only because I lack words to express it'[26]. This strangely ambivalent relationship between neurologist and neurosurgeon was finally sealed, with the irony that has been mentioned, when it was to be Walshe who wrote Jefferson's obituary for the Royal Society. In this he placed Jefferson outside the scarcely veiled contempt in which he held most surgeons.

As if all these honours were not enough, Jeff was also awarded the Hughlings Jackson Medal of the Royal Society of Medicine and gave the eponymous lecture on the *Neurology of the trigeminal nerve*. The vote of thanks for this was proposed by Sir Charles Symonds, who remarked on Jeff's ability to throw new light on a subject which might generally be regarded as having been played out, and still make it sparkle. 'The danger for most of us', Sir Charles said, 'is that experience crystalises too soon, so that we go on making the same mistakes over and over again and arrive at the same wrong conclusions. Sir Geoffrey Jefferson is not like that. For him experience is never static.... It is not only for what he says that we are his grateful listeners but for the way he says it. He takes us quietly into his confidence and tells his story, so easily and so well that the hour seems scarcely begun before it is ended'[27]. A vote of thanks from 'CPS', as most people called him, added to the honour of the occasion. The Chairman of the Medical Board of the Manchester Royal Infirmary also wrote to congratulate Jeff, and to appreciate the honour reflected on that institution by these awards[28].

At the end of July the Jeffersons went on holiday. Elizabeth Armistead sent some documents on to him, adding that she hoped that Lady Jefferson, who was still under the weather, was better. She wrote, 'I wish I knew when you were going to Brussels.... You are very booked up next week, even on Saturday. You won't like it a bit I know'[29]. Inevitably, Jefferson did go to the meeting in Brussels to which she had referred. This was the International Neurological Congress, during which there were private discussions about the formation of a separate international organisation for neurosurgery. Afterwards Jeff wrote a three page letter to Douglas Northfield about the matter. As always, he had been anxious for neurosurgeons to retain close links with the neurologists, and argued tenaciously for this despite some severe opposition from surgeons representing several countries. 'All that I could do against that weight of unanimity was to make it a condition for the British consent that we should be interlocked with the Neurologists for some of our meetings'[30]. It had also been mooted that all the various congresses of the neurosciences should be included under one name. 'We proposed "Federation of the Neurological Sciences" but as there were objections from the French and some other medical neurologists to the word "Federation" as having some undesirable significance not clear to me, it was concluded...to call it provisionally "Congresses of the Neurological Sciences" as a blanket title for the whole lot'[30]. A year or two later the World Federations of both Neurological and Neurosurgical Societies were formed! Such is the way with committees, especially those of an international nature. In due course, Jefferson was elected to the Presidency of the First International Neurosurgical Congress, which was to be held in Brussels in the autumn of 1957.

The very idea of forming an International Neurosurgical Federation, however, drew a typically dramatic response from Sir Francis Walshe. 'More in sorrow than in anger!', he wrote, 'Why have you got to tear the seamless garment of neurology still further. The neuropathologists started it, and now I read in the *Bulletin of the Canadian Neurological Society* that the decision to form an International Organisation of Neurosurgeons to hold its separate International Congress "was greatly influenced by the wise and ponderous [*sic*] advice so generously given in a very tactful manner by Sir Geoffrey Jefferson". It seems to me dreadful that that hypomanic creature S– should be able to push all this under your aegis, or is he really entitled to do so. Oh! Oh! Jefferson!'[31]. We unfortunately do not know how Jeff may have replied; but it would surely have been with both firmness and tact.

On 19th September 1955 Jefferson gave an address at the recently opened Midland Centre for Neurosurgery and Neurology in Smethwick. He styled the lecture *Remarks on the future of neurosurgery*, and recalled some of the advances that had taken place during his own experience. He reminded his audience that the only drug which used to be recommended for meningeal infections was hexamine, since it had a molecule capable of passing the blood-brain barrier. 'But how feeble, how useless a weapon that was!'[32]. Post-operative infections then were sure to be fatal. On another topic, although Francis Grant had said that brain tumours were no longer interesting because all that could be known or done about them had been achieved, Jeff disagreed. He called for more neurosurgical beds, operating facilities and consulting staff, for there were but approximately 50 neurosurgeons in the UK and Ireland at that time. And he pointed out that there were plenty of opportunities for research if neurosurgeons were given sufficient time for reflection and the practical development of ideas. The large number of neurosurgeons in America enabled them to have the time to 'chance their arm at the more experimental breakables of the neurological sciences', such as the use of radioactive isotopes, stereotactic surgery and the treatment of epilepsy. Jeff did not attempt to forecast the future of British neurosurgery, but he made a plea for the facilities that were necessary to secure it, of which finance was not the least[32]. In many respects his remarks were eventually heeded, at least for a certain period of time. Nor did Jefferson distance himself from new developments after he had retired, and we find him attending the Atkinson Morley's Hospital unit in 1956 in order to see Kenneth Till perform the recently introduced stereotactic chemopallidectomy for Parkinson's disease.

Jeff took an opportunity for another brief holiday which was spent in Wales, using the time to polish up the *Cortical localization* paper for its publication. Then he was back in Manchester ready to preside at the dinner of the past residents of the Manchester Royal Infirmary, to which he had invited Lord Webb-Johnson, and which was attended by no less than 250 guests[33]. On the following day, he gave the opening address for the new session at University College Hospital Medical School, London, in which he related his reflective *Meditations on the sources of knowledge*. One of the questions he asked himself concerned 'the why or how of the natural inequalities among men'[34], but without finding any clear answer. This was followed by a lecture to the Midland Medical Society on 2nd

November, on *Sleep and stupor*, to which he attracted a record attendance for that forum of 200[35]. A few days later he was to give the Wood Jones Lecture to the students of his old medical school in Manchester.

A letter from the editor of the *British Journal of Surgery* in 1949, before Jefferson's retirement, had warned him that the editorial committee planned to publish an article, in the *Visits to clinics* series, about the neurosurgical unit at the Manchester Royal Infirmary and its illustrious chief. This was not published until December 1955 and, when it appeared, the article was really about Jeff rather than the unit, although he was no longer the head of the department which he had founded and directed for so many years. It was a biography in brief and a tribute to a great surgeon, which had the unusual merit of having been published during his lifetime[36].

The portrait by Sir Gerald Kelly was now officially presented to Sir Geoffrey Jefferson at a special gathering of the SBNS associated with a joint meeting with the neurologists on 11th November 1955. In his presentation speech, Norman Dott said that it had been given to Jeff 'as founder of this Society, as its leader and guardian since that day and unto this day and hour'[37]. No other portrait had ever been presented to anyone by the Society. Dott could not resist a jibe at Jeff's inability to keep to a schedule: 'We might have selected a fine timepiece—a friendly and practical assistance to your appreciation of chronometry—but that would not express our stronger sentiments'. After some remarks on Celestial and Terrestrial immortality, Dott paid worthy compliments to Lady Jefferson as well as those to her husband[37]. Jeff replied that few occasions could be more embarrassing than one of the present nature. 'As I look at this face I wonder what sort of a man really hides behind it.... I wonder as I look what this man is thinking...no doubt "Its damned cold in his studio to-day. Its funny that he starts off painting my skin grey or black isn't it? ...My leg has gone to sleep, I'd like to walk around..." I can assure you that during the, to me, countless sittings that we have had there have passed some of the most delightful and interesting hours that I can remember'[38]. Later he turned to the subject of the SBNS itself. 'I feel proud of the Society because it has been the motivating force in the creation of neurosurgery as a lively and now rapidly growing body of enlightened opinion.' And he concluded with his 'warmest, my most cordial, my most grateful thanks' to the council and members of the Society[38]. A letter from Douglas Northfield in May 1956 to say that the portrait had eventually been completed, confirms that some final touches were still needed, even at the time of its presentation[38].

The painting was then shown in the 1956 Summer Exhibition of the Royal Academy. Jeff told Botterell: 'A couple of weeks ago when I got back from London at lunch time, I found that someone was calling up from London at 2.30. At 2.30 the bell rang, the conversation went like this:— Me: "Hello". Voice: "Is that you Geoffrey—number 87—wonderful, absolutely wonderful—I've been twice—its a marvellous picture—who is Gerald Kelly?" Me, recovering my wits: "Oh. Hello John, when did you arrive?" It was John Fulton talking about my portrait in the Royal Academy. The upshot is that John is having himself painted right now by Gerald. He'll do him very well, he's a picturesquely good subject'[40]. However, the artist himself was apprehensive and commented: 'He is extremely nice but will be difficult to paint because he is very changeable and does move around a lot'[41].

With his finger, as ever, on the pulse of surgical events, Jeff had written to Sir James Learmonth to beg him to stay on as Professor of Surgery in the University of Edinburgh, rather than take early retirement. Learmonth wrote a delightful, if rather regretful, reply which began: 'I have been greatly moved by your letter. I don't keep many, but I shall keep your one—for young James'[42]. He was not alone in having such a resolve. It is a measure of Jefferson's ability to express himself pleasingly and to put his thoughts so well into words, that so many of his letters have come to light with the writing of this biography. However, in spite of Jeff's plea, Sir James maintained his resolution and resigned.

November in Britain has always had a notorious reputation for fogs, which were much worse before the Clean Air Act of 1956. On 30th November 1955 Jeff was due to go to London to thank Lord Adrian of Cambridge for his term as president of the Royal Society, but fog prevented him from making the journey and his speech was read for him by Sir Rudolph Peters. It was an honour to be asked to give the vote of thanks to one who was both a friend and one of the foremost neurophysiologists in the world, whose Order of Merit and peerage were 'not only a reward for great services in the advancement of knowledge but for the manner of their demonstration, a reward not only for the integrity of his thinking—for that scientists expect, and have a right to expect—but for those personal qualities, particularly his own, which have ensured so much and so often right guidance to others'[43]. Lord Adrian wrote a day or two later to say how sorry he had been that Jeff had not been able to give the speech himself and thanked him for all that he had written; 'The whole proceedings made me depart in a glow of shocking self-satisfaction!'[44].

Egas Moniz, the Portuguese physician, psychiatrist and politician (he had led the Portuguese delegation to the Peace Conference after World War I), died at the end of 1955. He had been responsible for the introduction of cerebral angiography and pre-frontal leucotomy, for which he was awarded a Nobel prize. In tribute to him, Jeff wrote a letter to the *Lancet*[45]. John Fulton wished to reprint this in the *Journal of Neurophysiology*, of which he was then the editor, and he asked Jefferson for permission. 'It is much the best appreciation that has appeared; I have just had a group [of tributes] from Spain and Portugal, but none of them are as felicitous as is yours'[46]. Almeida Lima, the Lisbon neurosurgeon with whom Moniz had worked and who had trained under Cairns at Oxford, then wrote to invite Jefferson to represent World Neurology at a Memorial Commemoration of their hero. 'Everyone immediately thought of you as the most distinguished and considered among the neurologists and neurosurgeons of our time, and that no one could better than you be the representative of all the neurologists'[47]. The occasion was planned to take place in Lisbon in March or early April 1956. Jeff accepted on condition that Gertrude might come too, since they had both known Professor and Madame Moniz well. Later he was informed that the Portuguese Society of Neurology and Psychiatry 'decided by unanimity to elect you Eminent Member, not only as an acknowledgement of the great service you have done, but also as an homage to one whom it considers as the most prominent neurosurgeon of our days. Egas Moniz was our only Eminent Member and we shall continue to have only one'[48].

Jefferson was to write another appreciation a few weeks later, this time for the *British Medical Journal* and *The Times*. It concerned the death of Diana Beck, consultant neurosurgeon to the Middlesex Hospital, London, who was highly regarded by her colleagues, and who had been one of the very few women in the specialty at that time, apart from those in the Soviet Union[49]. Following its publication, Professor Dorothy Russell, the famous neuropathologist at the London Hospital, wrote to Jeff: '...we all know and love your turn of phrase, with its strong individual touch that seems to come straight from the heart as well as the head.... Your faith in her [Diana Beck] and your support saved her soul at a most critical point and gave her courage to go on'[50]. The individual kindnesses of people so often remain secret or quite unknown, even by the recipients.

In February 1956, on the occasion of the centenary of the *Rochdale Observer*, Jefferson was asked to contribute an article. He chose to write about a few memories of his life in the town between 1895 and 1910. After recounting the stories of his boyhood that have already been mentioned, he ended with an undoubted twinkle in his eye: 'But you will see dear "observer", that my memories of Rochdale, limited in scope as they necessarily are, are mainly happy ones. Were we boys constant readers of the "Observer"? Sure to have been. I don't really remember'[51].

Then, quite unexpectedly, on 7th May 1956, Jeff received a letter from Dr A Macrae, the Secretary of the British Medical Association, which must have caused him considerable excitement and pleasure. In it Dr Macrae passed on an invitation from the Minister of Health of the USSR and the President of the Soviet Academy of Medical Sciences, for him to join an official party of six doctors on a visit to Russia in the coming August[52]. One can imagine that he accepted with alacrity for, despite his abhorrence of communism, Jeff had always retained a warmth of feeling for Russia and its people. He had risked his life for them on the Eastern Front when he was a young man, and had felt himself to be one with the people and their cause, at least until their capitulation and the revolutions that came in 1917. There was now a chance to renew his acquaintance with the country, and to help to improve relationships between Russia and Britain during the tense period of the Cold War which followed World War II, just as the staff of the Anglo-Russian Hospital had done 40 years earlier.

The delegation arrived in Moscow on 4th August 1956. Other members of the party, in addition to Jefferson, included Sir George Pickering, (later Sir) Ian Fraser, Sir James Paterson Ross, a radiotherapist and a woman doctor. The first week was spent in Moscow where the party was entertained with much generosity accompanied by the inevitable formalities. Jeff was very impressed by a performance at the puppet theatre, among other leisure entertainments with which the visits to various institutions were interspersed. They were received at the First Institute of Medicine and, on 7th August, spent the whole morning at the Burdenko Neurosurgical Institute. There was a free discussion with the Russians about various neurosurgical problems. It is of interest that aneurysms appeared to them to be of no importance since, apparently, few were seen, or perhaps few were being diagnosed at that time. On 11th August the delegation departed by train for Leningrad (once Petrograd, and now, once more, St Petersburg) and, with great civility, one of the Muscovite professors bade them farewell at the station, even at the early hour of 4 am[53]. This must have been the part of the journey which Jeff would have anticipated with the greatest pleasure.

After arriving in Leningrad at 10 am, on the same day and without respite after the overnight train journey from Moscow, some of the party, including Jeff, were taken straight to the Peterhof palace, several miles outside the city. There he found the fountains and the gilded statues from Greek mythology most impressive: 'Its the gold gleaming in the sun that makes the magic.... The fountains are arranged in steps, yet the height of the water is the same in all except the centre piece.... The palace was closed, having been destroyed by the Germans, but is rebuilt just as it was.... The view from the terrace is remarkable, 500 metres or so to the sea between woods on either side and a canal in the centre'[53]. On the way back to their hotel they made a tour of the city by car, and then went on to 'the Astoria Hotel, where Trude had stayed just before Michael was born, to pick up a guide who had gone after waiting 3 hours for us!'[53]. So they went by themselves round the old part of the city on foot. Jeff remembered many places that he wanted to see again and he seemed to have had no difficulty in finding them; the Winter Palace, the Fortress of St Peter and St Paul, the Field of Mars, the Mariinski Palace, Mariinski Theatre and so forth, all of which were within easy walking distance of the Astoria. He could have had no access to the former Dmitri palace which was, at that time, the headquarters of the local Soviet.

'It is easy enough to recapture the graciousness of this lovely city', he wrote in his diary of the visit, and 'the distinction conferred on [it] by the buildings of the nobles and the Imperial Court. The view from the opposite side of the river is surely the loveliest in Europe'[53]. The view of the Thames from Lambeth Bridge looking towards St Paul's on a summer evening, he observed, 'is superb — but the view of St Petersburg is I am sure more durable because of the beauty and concord of its buildings — the harmony of the picture which will always be lovely whatever the light'[53].

Jeff spent the next day in bed on account of 'violent hay-fever+fatigue', and slept on and off all day, reading *Anna Karenina* intermittently. On the 14th August he visited the old and new Pavlov laboratories. A woman, who accompanied another from the Ministry of Health, asked Jeff for his impressions of Leningrad. With his slightly wicked sense of humour, he replied that it appeared that the plumbing system in the hotel had not been attended to since the liberation of the serfs. 'This was translated, the lady smiled and went away. I found then to my dismay that this woman was not one of the Ministry staff but a reporter from the Russian Television and the radio service of Tass agency'[53]. Needless to say, as he himself observed, his gaffe was not reported.

Jeff described his second visit to the city in a memorable lecture given to the SBNS, and in an 'Envoi' to his *Selected papers* which he called *Return to Russia*[54]. It began: 'Time which changes so much had brought no difference to the glint of the sun on the tall slender golden spire of the Admiralty building at the north end of the Nevsky Prospekt.... Come to that, remarkably little was different either in the buildings or in the always shabby looking shops that dot the length of this superb street.... Nor on the banks of the Neva was the Winter Palace changed.... Only the colour of the walls had been altered from the deep red of old days to green.... The coloured walls, though still there, look more undistinguished now that the Court is dead and the cultured people that lent it such vivacity and dignity are no more.... For me the great City was a city of ghosts, a city I suppose of my departed youth and of my dead friends. For here I had met some of the most intelligent and informed people the like of whom scarcely entered my life again. They had a vivacity and charm that was unsurpassed[54]. He recalled how, in 1916, he saw Nijinski and Karsavina dance and remembered attending performances of the operas of Rimski-Korsakov and Tchaikovsky, especially 'Eugeny Onyegin'. There had even been a choice between three operas in one evening[54].

Jefferson told his audience of the Easter scene outside the Kazan Cathedral, and the splendour of the Dmitri Palace (now called the Beloselsky-Belozersky Palace) where the Anglo-Russian Hospital had been accommodated, and from the windows of which he had watched the beginning of the Revolution in the spring of 1917. His description of those scenes is vivid and of historical importance, for it is a primary source that had been locked up within his memory, unaffected by subsequent political considerations which gave a different interpretation to some of the events of 1917. He spoke of the place where the detachment he commanded was first established at Rozhische, towards the front, but still not near enough to the fighting to be effective, and painted a word-picture of the Russian countryside, its flowers and trees, particularly the silver birches and wild cherries which are so characteristic of that part of Russia, and which had impressed him so much. He told of their next move to the railhead at Lutsk, where they were able to receive and treat the casualties more effectively. 'There were memorable snatches — such as watching in the evening groups of soldiers around a wood fire under September skies — soldiers singing traditional songs, or the then very popular song of the Volga pirate Stienka Razin and his beautiful prisoner, whom he has to throw overboard to appease the complaints of his crew that he is losing ferocity...or those wonderfully taut marching songs'[54]. None of the doctors whom Jeff had known before were alive in Leningrad in 1956. Of four whom he specifically mentioned, all were, 'like Alexei Khomiakov, dead, but all save him, in the natural course of age'[54].

On 17th August they travelled south to Kiev and visited the University, where the group was most kindly received by the Rector and various other dignitaries, with whom they discussed how the management of that University compared with Manchester and Oxford. The conclusion seems to have been that they were much the same, except for the larger number of professors at Kiev[53].

The party returned briefly to Moscow before setting off for home on 20th August. They flew via Riga to Copenhagen, where Professor Busch met them and invited Jeff to his home, a visit which must have been short, even when a time change of one hour is allowed for, since they were back at London Airport by 6.30 pm, where Gertrude and Dr Macrae were waiting to greet them[53]. Gertrude's concern for Jeff's health on this arduous journey was such that Dr Macrae, after 10 days, had seen fit to write her a reassuring letter to say that he had heard from the medical officer of the British Embassy in Moscow that Jeff was fit and enjoying his trip[55].

After the group had returned to England, Ian Fraser wrote to Jefferson: 'One of the most pleasant parts of our holiday was that we had you for our guide, philosopher and friend. Your ready wit, your history of the background of Russia, and your friendship, which I am proud to have had for 30 years, added very greatly to our holiday'[56]. In his autobiography, Sir Ian Fraser related how one of their hosts in Moscow, came of an evening to announce that he was preparing four operations for them to see on the following day, and that he would expect them at his hospital at 9 am. This was probably the occasion on which they visited the Burdenko Institute. Knowing Jeff's inability to keep an appointment on time, Ian Fraser suggested that they might be there by 10 am. In fact they arrived at the hospital at 11 am, which was very awkward since the four cases were brain operations, one taking place in each corner of a large operating theatre in which four women surgeons had begun their preparations at 7.30 am, so that the professor could move from one patient to another and be seen performing the vital part of each procedure. Regardless of the fact that the patients were under local anaesthesia, and despite the delay, the operations were apparently all carried out with skill and efficiency. He also described an operation they had witnessed, which was to correct a stricture of the oesophagus caused by swallowing corrosive fluid; this was apparently a not uncommon event in Russia at that time[57]. Swallowing corrosive fluids was used as a means of suicide, but is also known to have been used elsewhere during World War II as a means of torture.

Sir Ian Fraser came from Belfast, and he mentions in his autobiography how Jefferson had set out to attend a meeting there on some occasion or other, but had succeeded in taking a plane to Dublin instead. Finding himself in the wrong place, Jeff decided to take a taxi to Belfast, a distance of 101 miles. Naturally, he was long overdue at the luncheon party he should have attended, and when he arrived he had not got enough cash with him to pay the taxi. As Sir Ian said: 'I fully understood what Lady Jefferson meant when, as we boarded the plane in London for Russia, she whispered in my ear, "Do please keep an eye on Geoff"'[57]. No doubt her thoughts were primarily concerned with his health, but the responsibility extended well beyond this. Jeff was very often late but always turned up smiling, and he was usually forgiven for it. His secretary used to book spare rooms in hotels for patients that he might fail to see during an afternoon list. Also, on occasion, she would telephone the station master at Manchester to hold up the London train for him. He would then arrive smiling and have a nonchalant conversation with the station master while the train continued to wait. One day he was visiting a relative in Northern Ireland and announced that he would arrive on a train from Belfast. His hostess was amazed when he not only turned up early by car, but with three companions. The train he had selected apparently did not exist; and his companions had unexpectedly to be accommodated. When he finally left to go to the airport, he arrived there just before take-off and announced that he could not find his ticket. He was asked what he had been wearing when he originally landed in Northern Ireland, and declared that it had been a suit that was now in his case. Thereupon his hostess unpacked the bag on the airport floor and produced the ticket from a pocket in the suit[58]. He was genuinely absent-minded, but could also be very perverse and did, on occasion, cause a great deal of inconvenience through lack of consideration for others.

In September 1956, Jefferson received an invitation to give the Tenth Victor Horsley Memorial Lecture in the April of the coming year, which was to be the centenary of the birth of this pioneer neurosurgeon. It is possible that Jeff spent more time and energy preparing this lecture than almost any other of the numerous ones that he gave. He obtained copies of Horsley's notes and case records, and entered into a voluminous correspondence with everyone he could think of who might have known his subject, or would be able to give him useful information.

Amongst this Horsley correspondence is a copy of a letter which Jeff wrote to Sir Gerald Kelly concerning Horsley's father, who was a well-known Victorian painter. In the concluding paragraph Jeff makes a revealing remark: 'I'm very bothered about this lecture — its a very important one and after I'd been to Russia last August I got very disturbed somehow — not afraid, I don't mean that, far from it. Memories of the past I suppose'[59]. Jefferson's return to Russia had moved him to happiness, to sadness and, more deeply, to a fatalistic sense of frailty and defencelessness in the face of over-powering events.

REFERENCES

GJ=Geoffrey Jefferson; EHB=Harry Botterell; GMJ=Gertrude Jefferson
1   Jefferson G. Harvey Cushing and his books. *J Hist Med* 1946; **1**: 246–53 and *Selected papers*. London: Pitman Medical, 1960: 188–94.
2   Sotherby's Catalogue, 18th and 24th July 1961, available in the Jefferson Memorial Library, Manchester Royal Infirmary.
3   Jefferson M. Personal communication.
4   *Rochdale Observer*, 3rd February 1954.
5   GJ. MS *The mechanisms of mental processes*.
6   Kelly G to GJ. Letter 2nd March 1954.
7   Kelly G to GJ. Letter 21st June 1956.
8   GJ to Himsworth H. Letter 4th May 1954.
9   Penfield H to GMJ. Letter 28th November.
10   GJ to Sweet WH. Letter 20th September 1954.
11   Jefferson G. Man as an experimental animal. *Conquest* 1955; **43**: 2–13 and *Lancet* 1955; **1**: 59–61.
12   Ruskin J. Quoted in *The Times* 27th December 1884.
13   Pain N to GJ. Letter 17th March 1954.
14   Jefferson G. *The invasive adenomas of the pituitary*. Liverpool: Liverpool University Press, 1955.
15   Jefferson G. The contemporary reaction to phrenology. In *Selected papers*. London: Pitman Medical, 1960: 94–112.
16   *Manchester Guardian*. 30th March 1955.
17   GJ to EHB. Letter 18th April 1955.
18   Webb-Johnson A to GJ. Letter 19th April 1955.
19   GJ to Webb-Johnson A. Letter 28th April 1955.
20   GJ to EHB. Letter 16th May 1955.
21   White JC to GJ. Letter 27th June 1955.
22   Jefferson G. Variations on a neurological theme — cortical localization. *BMJ* 1955; **2**: 1405–1408 and *Selected papers*. London: Pitman Medical, 1960: 35–44.
23   GJ to EHB. Letter 8th July 1955.
24   GJ to EHB, Letter 11th August 1955.
25   EHB to GJ. Letter 11th December 1955.
26   Walshe FMR. MS Presentation of GJ for Honorary Fellowship of the Royal Society of Medicine. 21st June 1955.
27   Symonds CP. MS Vote of thanks following the Hughlings Jackson lecture given by GJ in 1955.
28   Chairman of the Medical Board of the Manchester Royal Infirmary to GJ. Letter 21st October 1955.

29 Armistead E to GJ. Letter 2nd August 1955.
30 GJ to Northfield DWC. Letter 16th September 1955.
31 Walshe FMR to GJ. Letter 1st February 1956.
32 GJ MS *Remarks on the future of neurosurgery*. 19th September 1955.
33 GJ to EHB. Letter 4th October 1955.
34 Jefferson G. Meditations on the sources of knowledge. *Lancet* 1955; **2**: 935–7 and in *Selected papers*. London: Pitman Medical, 1960: 3–9.
35 Hawkins CF to GJ. Letter 11th November 1955.
36 The neurosurgical clinic and the neurological laboratories at the Royal Infirmary, Manchester. *Br J Surg* 1955; **43**: 317–23.
37 Dott N. MS Speech at the presentation to GJ of his portrait. 11th November 1955.
38 GJ. MS Speech in reply to Norman Dott. 11th November 1955.
39 Northfield DWC to GJ. Letter 12th May 1956.
40 GJ to EHB. Letter 4th July 1956.
41 Kelly G to GJ. Letter 21st June 1956.
42 Learmonth J to GJ. Letter 20th November 1955.
43 GJ. MS Speech to Lord Adrian at the Royal Society. 30th November 1955.
44 Adrian ED to GJ. Letter 3rd December 1955.
45 Jefferson G. Letter *Lancet* 1955; **2**: 197 and *J Neurophysiol* 1956; **19**: 196.
46 Fulton J to GJ. Letter 5th January 1956.
47 Lima A to GJ. Letter 23rd April 1956 and correspondence with the British Council.
48 Secretary of Academia des Ciências to GJ. Letter. 16th March 1956.
49 Jefferson G. *Diana Beck* Obituary. *BMJ* 1956; **1**: 634.
50 Russell D to GJ. Letter 6th March 1956.
51 Sir Geoffrey Jefferson CBE FRS MS. *Rochdale Observer* 18th February 1956.
52 Macrae A to GJ. Letter 7th May 1956.
53 GJ. MS Diary of his visit to Russia in 1956.
54 Jefferson G. Return to Russia in *Selected papers*. London: Pitman Medical, 1960: 541–9.
55 Macrae A to GMJ. Letter 14th August 1956.
56 Fraser I to GJ. Letter 8th September 1956.
57 Fraser I. *Blood sweat and cheers*. London: BMA Publishing, 1989: 133–4.
58 Jefferson E. Personal communication.
59 GJ to Kelly G. Letter 22nd January 1957.

Chapter 23

Further lectures and travel
1957–1959

Jefferson visited Sir George Pickering, the Regius Professor of Medicine, in Oxford in January 1957, and wrote to William Sweet that he had spent 'a couple of days in 13 Norham Gardens, Oxford the old Osler House'[1]. During February he was unwell, for there is a letter from Sir Henry Willink, the chairman of the Medical Manpower Committee, concerning the drafting of that Committee's report, in which he mentions that, as a consequence, Jeff had been unable to attend the last meeting[2]. In his reply to this letter Jeff concluded by saying: 'What a week it has been for me. Cambridge D.Sc., Manchester proposing Hon. LL.D., Edinburgh Royal College of Surgeons Hon. Fellowship, and this morning a telephone call from Sydney asking if I would go for two months in the autumn to give some lectures at their expense (that was the point!). I feel quite dizzy'[3].

The forthcoming Horsley Lecture, meanwhile, was causing Jeff concern, and it continued to be the subject of much correspondence. One of these letters was that to William Sweet at the end of January: 'The Horsley Centenary Lecture in April has been killing me. I am now impressed by this chap. He was a wonder. Harvey Cushing did not even try to understand him*. When I say that, I have to admit that I didn't either until this compulsory survey was forced on me'[4]. Another Horsley letter was from Charles Phillips, the Oxford neurophysiologist, who answered certain questions posed by Jeff and also mentioned: 'I am glad you are working on a lecture on the reticular formation'. He went on to give his views on some aspects of the physiology of that part of the brain stem[5]. This was on 20th February. A week later Jeff wrote to Ernest Sachs, the senior and very well-known American neurosurgeon who was formerly at Washington University, St. Louis: 'I am sorry that I did not tell you, as I realise that I didn't, that I am coming to the States the week after next.... The occasion is a symposium on the reticular formation in the Henry Ford Hospital at Detroit. This isn't a tour, it is a plain visit'[6]. And so one major demand on Jeff's somewhat frail constitution was followed by yet another.

Jefferson set off for Detroit on 12th March 1957, on a British Overseas Airways DC7; the flight took nearly 15 hours. He arrived in Detroit at 4.00 am, having already had three breakfasts en route. The meeting lasted 3 days of 'the most concentrated and intensely neuro-phys. that I have ever listened to'[7]. Jeff chaired the final session and summarised the proceedings, after which he was greatly

---

*Cushing. In 1900 WS Halsted sent Harvey Cushing from the Johns Hopkins Hospital in Baltimore to Europe, to learn about neurological surgery before setting up a department in that hospital. Cushing planned to begin his study with Horsley. However, having seen Horsley operate just once, he decided that he had nothing to learn from him and went to visit Osler, who gave him many introductions. After travelling around Europe, he spent some time working with Sherrington in Liverpool before returning to the United States.

congratulated for his grasp of the subject[8]. There were few neurosurgeons then, as now, who were also distinguished in the rôles of both anatomist and neurophysiologist. While in Detroit he did manage to fit in a visit to the art gallery, which he enjoyed, especially the beautiful Italian courtyard in which a Brahms trio was being played[7].

After this very brief visit to Detroit he made a detour on his return home, going by way of Toronto in order to visit his friends there, and making the journey by train on 17th March. 'The courtesy of the train crew was impressive'[7]. On arrival he was met by Harry and Margaret Botterell, and spent the first afternoon resting and listening to Tchaikovsky on the gramophone. He noted in his diary: 'My right leg was swollen and my dermatitis worrying me'[7]. The swollen leg could be attributed to the train journey, but this is the first and only mention of dermatitis. He showed the Botterells the slides of photos that he had taken in Russia and, on the next day, led a discussion about the Detroit Symposium and watched Harry Botterell operate. From Toronto Jeff continued his journey by air to Boston. He was met by William Sweet on arrival and gave a lecture on Sir Victor Horsley at the Massachusetts General Hospital that same evening, thus providing himself with a dress rehearsal for the major event scheduled for April[7].

Jefferson finally embarked from New York on 27th March and returned home on the RMS *Queen Mary* in 'a handsome cabin on B deck...[and] seated at the Captain's table'[7] but, before leaving, he attended a clinical conference at the Bellevue Hospital with Tom Hoen who, a year or two later, was to show him exceptional kindness. The *Queen Mary* had been declared 'black' in England for having used naval tugs to bring her out of Southampton Water during a strike at the beginning of her previous voyage. In consequence, she tied up in Cherbourg after crossing the Atlantic, and the passengers were transferred to another ship, the *Ivernia*, to take them to Plymouth, from whence they arrived in London the following evening[7]. His 'plain visit' had, after all, turned into quite a 'tour'.

Friday 12th April arrived and Jefferson delivered his Victor Horsley Memorial Lecture in the Great Hall of British Medical Association House in London[9]. It was entitled *Sir Victor Horsley—his life and work*. The centenary had given Jeff an opportunity to treat the occasion biographically; however, this inevitably gave him less scope to express his own philosophical ideas. He was at pains to show that Cushing had been mistaken in his judgement of Horsley, and to pay tribute to this seemingly tireless individual who worked as a surgeon in the mornings, and in his laboratories at University College and at his house in Cavendish Square every afternoon and evening. He had achieved the distinction of Fellowship of the Royal Society when he was only 29 years old. The extent and originality of Horsley's research was profound, helped latterly by collaboration with RH Clarke, who invented the first stereotactic apparatus. Horsley's approach to surgery through physiology appealed very much to Jefferson's own contentions and aspirations. This carefully documented and researched lecture ends with a remark about Horsley's character. Jeff wrote that he had a 'kaleidoscopically colourful personality and makes us feel pale and desiccated beside him. Violent in expression Victor Horsley might at times have been, but he was a fastidious man as well as generous and humorous too. Well might he say now "Praise me for my virtues, excuse me for my faults, which were never mean"'[9].

On 15th May 1957 Jefferson attended the Congregation for the Conferment of Honorary Degrees in the Whitworth Hall of his own University of Manchester, where he was made an Honorary Doctor of Laws (LLD). Shortly after this he went to the SBNS meeting then being held in Dublin, where he was able to see his old friend Adams McConnell once more. Here he received an Honorary degree of Master of Surgery (MCh) from the University. On 13th June he was in Cambridge, where he became a Doctor of Science (DSc *Honoris causa*). During this last ceremony the Deputy Orator of the University delivered a eulogy in Latin saying, among other things, that Jeff 'used the scalpel with wonderful skill and not violently, as did Ennius the poet who "crushed the brain", but expertly and discriminately...'[10]*. Jefferson's next obligation was to deliver the 1957 Linacre Oration of the Royal College of Physicians in London, on *Thomas Grainger and the spinal cord in 1837*. Then, on 10th July he was in Edinburgh receiving an Honorary Fellowship from the Royal College of Surgeons, on which occasion he was formally presented to the President by Norman Dott. His carefully chosen phrases, this time in English, were slowly savoured by Dott as he spoke in his somewhat high-pitched voice and Edinburgh accent. They had a classical grandeur but, in contrast to Cambridge, could be understood by all those present. Congratulations flowed in from all quarters.

The First International Congress of Neurosurgery was held in Brussels at the end of July 1957 with Geoffrey Jefferson, who had been its prime mover, as its president. On 28th of that month he gave an address at Louvain University in homage to Arthur van Gehuchten (1861–1915) who, with Ramón y Cajal, had established neurone theory. Van Gehuchten was also the teacher of many of those who were responsible for working out 'the bare facts of the nerve-cell and fibre'[11]. Jeff also received an invitation, as the natural choice, to give the first Sir Hugh Cairns Memorial Lecture in the following spring. With modesty and some tact, he wrote to Lady Cairns to ask if this had her approval, which she most heartily gave. She had felt bitter at, seemingly, being left out in the cold after the death of her husband, and wrote: 'I am most truly touched by you writing to tell me. I am not used to this sort of consideration — of remembrance'[12]. There was to be much further correspondence with her and with others in preparation for that lecture but, for the moment, Jeff had other things on his mind: he was bound for Australia in fulfilment of the invitation he had received in March..

Accordingly, on 23rd August 1957 Gertrude and Geoffrey Jefferson set sail, this time from Tilbury, on the P&O liner RMS *Himalaya*. Gertrude had flatly refused to let Jeff go on his own. This was to be a much greater undertaking than had been the familiar visits to Canada and the United States; they would be going to a land where they did not have close friends wherever they went, and much time would be spent travelling while they were there, as well as on the voyages to and from Australia. Both of them had misgivings about undertaking so long a journey, which was to last almost 4 months. Jeff even recorded, in the diary that he kept during the entire visit: 'So to bed feeling very homesick and sorry we were going too far we thought at our age, and knowing nobody. We were tired

---

*Public Orator: 'Mira etiam cum arte scalpello utitur, neque violenter, ut Ennius poeta, "cere comminuit cerebrum", sed scienter et subtiliter insectum sanat.' (Translated by Mair Andrade). Ennius Quintus, 239–169 BC., was a renowned Roman poet.

too'[13]. Furthermore, the schedule arranged by the Royal Australian College of Surgeons promised to be extremely taxing.

Right at the start, they encountered a severe gale in the English Channel: 'it was rough off Ushant, but the Bay of Biscay behaved very well'[13]. Gibraltar did not impress Jeff, 'a flash, unexpectedly, and gone again'[13]. They slipped into the Mediterranean, which was 'smooth and extremely blue', but missed seeing Malta[13]. After reaching Port Said early on the morning of 30th August they entered the Suez Canal at noon. Jeff had not visited the East before and was fascinated by all that he saw. He took photographs whenever the opportunity presented and wrote long descriptions in his diary. The sand and heat were, to him, remarkable and made him comment sympathetically: 'What a horrid place the Canal Zone must have been for military service'[13]. After leaving the canal 'the next three days were all the same — smooth as Windermere'[13]. Gertrude gave out the prizes for a fancy dress competition, and the shade temperature on deck reached 116 °F. In the Indian Ocean he recorded: 'We have been sailing through a monsoon the last 36 hours and got into it properly last evening — it may be tailing off a little but we're still rolling a lot — sea rough, a strong <u>warm</u> wind which is rather a new experience'[13]. When they reached Bombay on 4th September they were, unexpectedly, fêted and taken on a lightning tour of the city and some of its hospitals by Dr Ginde and a group of neurologists and neurosurgeons. The visit ended in the Malabar Hills, from where fine views were to be seen of Back Bay and the city, but Jeff did not go to the caves there which played so important a part in EM Forster's *A passage to India*. Instead, he was entranced by a snake charmer with a cobra and a mongoose that he watched and photographed. A similar reception greeted them in Colombo, Sri Lanka, where they arrived 2 days later. This happened to be a Sunday, and was marked by drinks with the Captain of the *Himalaya* in his cabin after he had taken the Morning Service[13].

They crossed the Indian Ocean without incident and arrived at Perth, Western Australia, on 15th September, where they were met by the professor of surgery and a representative of the Australian Broadcasting Corporation. Jeff was immediately interviewed by reporters and, during their brief stay there, was entertained at the hospital, where he took part in a clinical discussion. He was delighted by the city, and they only returned to the ship just in time to rejoin it before departing for Sydney by way of Adelaide and Melbourne[13].

When, on 23rd September, they arrived in Sydney they were again besieged by reporters, but were also met by some of Jeff's slightly distant relatives and Sir Douglas Miller, who was the president of the Royal Australasian College of Surgeons and doyen of Australian neurosurgeons[13]. It had come as something of a surprise and delight to Jefferson that he was made so welcome at every port of call in his journey, and regarded as an important visiting dignitary.

On the day after their arrival Jeff and Gertrude made the 190 mile journey inland by car to Canberra for the opening ceremony of the university and then returned to their hotel in Sydney. However, their activities during their first week there were mainly social. Among those whom they met was a member of the staff of the British High Commissioner, with whom Jeff took the opportunity to discuss their plans for revisiting India on their return journey; a tour of various Indian neurosurgical centres had been suggested by the British Council[13].

But Jefferson was back at work, in Sydney, on 1st October beginning with a visit to the Prince Alfred Hospital, then to St. Vincent's Hospital where he spoke on headache, and continuing steadily in a similar way throughout the next 6 weeks in various cities in Australia. On 6th October, after church, he attended a luncheon party at which he met Sir Stewart Duke-Elder, the London ophthalmologist who had earlier examined Gertrude's eyes when her vision had begun to cause her concern. Undoubtedly Jeff used the occasion to mention that there had been some further deterioration in her sight, and they invited Sir Stewart to tea a day or two later, thus giving him the opportunity to re-examine her. Duke-Elder gave a report to Jeff in which he prescribed nicotinamide and said: 'There are definite changes in the left eye of vaso-obliteration in the choroid in the central area, and there are also some fresh changes in the right eye. All that can be done is to try to delay the process. I would suggest that you make the dose of nicotinamide 100 mg t.i.d. for 3 weeks and then slip back to 50 mg b.d. I don't think Commonwealth relations are important enough to risk accelerating the loss of central vision in the left eye by tackling India'[14]. The vision in the right eye was already seriously impaired and Sir Stewart wrote a further note on the same lines: 'As you know, the central vision in the right eye has gone. There is evidence that similar changes are beginning to appear in the left eye. It is possible that she may retain vision in this eye provided that she rests and relaxes over the next four months.... I must advise you to cut down your obligations in Australia and without any question cancel your projected Indian tour.... I would suggest that you should take her home slowly by sea — I don't think she should make any long journey by air'[15].

The Jefferson's time in Sydney was filled by more engagements of an academic, neurosurgical and social nature. During that week Jeff visited the Royal North Shore Hospital and the Prince Alfred Hospital again. He lectured as well, but there were moments when he had time for reflection and one such arose during the preparation of a response to the award of an Honorary Fellowship of the Royal Australasian College of Surgeons which he was due to receive on 18th October. As on many other occasions, he wrote down his thoughts, and he let them wander well beyond what he might have said in his speech: 'I believe it is impossible for any man to know how important he is by introspection'[13], he wrote in the diary, and this was to be almost the only sentence from these particular reflections that he included in his remarks when the ceremony actually took place. He continued writing, pondering: 'Importance in the world's sense is given him by the World and must be expressed by it before he can tell how he stands. It is impudent to pretend to know it without being told, and being told why, it is dishonest to pretend not to be gratified if the verdict is favourable, delicious if it is very favourable! For well, may I or anyone say "What have I done"? and find it very difficult to answer in a manner encouraging to oneself. All that meditation tells you is that you are just another chap who did a job well enough but might have done it better if more attention and more effort had been directed in another one or two directions, if one had been less sensitive to opinion, no, less sensitive not to opinion but to the drag of what was demanded by one's immediate environment — routine hospital work & family ties and yet — and yet was I as sensitive to the latter at least, and too sensitive to the other — I think I was, so that what I mean is that I should at one or two vital times in my life [have] absented myself from the hospital work (not the family)—but how could I with no financial backing, living as I did in a period when there was no money to be got for any projects and nowhere to do the animal work that my soul craved for, for M/C [Manchester] was dreadfully behind in that, even nothing at all, nowhere to do recovery experiments, a defect not remedied until I was at the end of my time and hopelessly bogged down in National and Hospital work—Ministry, Health Act, then MRC and RS Council.... But it was too late, for my bright ideas and yearnings had antedated that time by 20 years'[13].

Jeff entertained Duke-Elder once more during this stay in Sydney, on 13th October, and he was a fellow guest on 16th. On the day before, Jeff had spoken at the University on *Integration in the brain*, and taken part in a clinical conference at St Vincent's Hospital. He also gave papers at a meeting of Australian neurologists[13].

On 18th October the Jeffersons left in the morning for the two-hour flight to Melbourne where, on the same day, the main purpose of the visit was fulfilled when Jeff was made an Honorary Fellow of the Royal Australasian College of Surgeons. He was 'presented by Leonard Lindon in a gracious speech, in which he mentioned the encouragement I'd given Hugh Cairns and my 6 Fellowships.... I listened with as much detachment as I could muster, concluding that the man of whom he spoke was rather a good sort of chap—I wished that I knew him'[13].

On the next day they flew to Adelaide, where they were entertained by Trevor Dinning, a neurosurgeon who had trained in England. He took them, the following morning, to the old home of the Cairns family at Riverton. Then he visited Adelaide High School, Cairns' *alma mater*, and met his friend's old head master. Jeff spoke to about 60 boys of the 'Honour Forms', before going on to see a number of patients at the Royal Adelaide Hospital, to give 'a pep talk to surgical staff on research in hospitals' and a talk on Sleep and Stupor 'to a good sized audience. Good, I did it well', he noted in his diary[13]. The scenery and the brilliant Australian sunshine had delighted him.

He was taken by the Dean of the Medical School of Adelaide University to see the new Queen Elizabeth Hospital at Woodville, and they were accompanied by a reporter on the relatively short journey there by car. There was 'much talk about the Committee of Management that consists of 3 people—a business man, a nursing sister and a Gov't official'[13]. It is clear that the Dean felt that the clinicians and the University were inadequately represented on the committee. He asked for Jeff's opinion, which seems to have been given with a degree of frankness that suggests he did not realise that the reporter would record his remarks in the Press. The diary continues, referring to the committee members: 'They haven't done such a bad job but it is quite wrong if the Univ. and the staff are not represented. I said so rather vigorously—see Press cuttings'[13]. The newspaper gave a factual report of Jeff's comments and accompanied it by an editorial which was firmly in support of them. This drew an indignant reply from one of the Committee members who, in a letter to the same paper a few days later, told Jeff, in so many words, to mind his own business. 'I wrote a more or less conciliatory letter from Melbourne with a sting in its tail'[13], he commented in the diary.

The Jeffersons returned to Melbourne on 22nd October, where it had begun to rain heavily after a long dry spell. They spent a whole week there in a state of semi-exhaustion. Jeff wrote on the day after their arrival: 'So tired I stayed in bed and slept till afternoon—no lunch—Got lecture ready, 'Headache' at BMA building. Trude in bed tired'[13]. Even this uncharacteristic shorthand manner of diary writing tells of their need for a rest. However, Jeff visited the University on the following morning, and attended a clinical conference at the hospital in the afternoon. At dinner 'afterwards I yarned about Sherrington and many other neurologists until 11 pm'[13]. He was back at the University again the next day to admire their new electron microscope; then he saw a patient in the Melbourne Hospital and lectured again at the BMA on *The seat of the soul*, with Graeme Robertson, a well-known neurologist, in the chair. The rest of the week he spent visiting hospitals and talking informally; but Gertrude and Jeff also managed to find time to go together to the new art gallery in the city. Somewhat typically, the Jeffersons returned to their hotel late in the afternoon, to find that they had forgotten that they had invited a couple to tea, who had been waiting patiently for them to arrive[13].

On 29th October they flew back to Sydney, still feeling very tired. On the following day, with a cousin of Jeff's, they visited a famous beauty spot known as Sublime Point, which was about 40 miles away; but the attractions of a scenic drive through a nature reserve had been spoilt by a recent bush fire. Jeff was very impressed by the rather skeletal and 'almost anatomical' shapes of some of the burnt eucalyptus trees. He commented that these are 'rightly called bush rather than forest fires—fact is that gums carry very little foliage and that high in tufts at the end of their branches—there is a lot of branch and not much leaf. I liked the gums a great deal, they are often delightful shapes'[13].

Jefferson was back at St Vincent's Hospital on 1st November, and on the next day saw various cases and spoke again in the evening. A day later they went to see part of the New South Wales golf championship and, the next day being a Sunday, was again spent with Jeff's relatives; after which he saw more patients at St Vincent's and 'talked to the boys'[13].

On 5th November they travelled in the company of Sir Douglas Miller by train to Newcastle, a large city about 30 miles away. It was a very hot and humid journey in a carriage which had no air-conditioning. Jeff was impressed by the state-supported hospital there: 'It was a relief to come across a hospital with a pattern of staffing like ours', he said[13]. He found that medical practice was less lucrative away from the State capital than it was in Sydney itself, and wrote: 'It reminded me of my own struggle to make a living, I only reached the upper money bracket when it was hardly worth making it because of the taxation. No wonder we have managed to save so little'[13]. Jeff lectured in Newcastle in the evening on *The anatomical search for the seat of the soul*, which 'went down v. well—a surprising choice it had seemed to me but I found McCaffrey a great admirer of my more philosophical writings & esp. "Meditations"'[13]. They returned to Sydney by road passing the Hawkesbury River and Broken Hill on the way. Jeff slept throughout the journey.

On 8th November Jefferson spoke at the Royal Australasian College of Physicians on *The influence of phrenology on neurology*. There was a 'mediocre attendance'[13]. He talked at a weekend meeting for general practitioners and lectured on the *Pituitary gland and growth* before the time came for a farewell cocktail party given during 'a warm evening' in his cousin's garden[13].

The Jeffersons left Australia on 13th November, having been there for just over 6 weeks. In addition to many hospital visits, Jeff had given ten lectures, four speeches and six interviews with the Press and others. The social entertainment and the welcome they had received had been most generous, but they were both exhausted, and it may have been with some relief that they embarked on the liner RMS *Oronsay*. The plan to visit India had been abandoned on the advice of Duke-Elder, and they were now about to return home by way of the United States and Canada.

While crossing the South Pacific Ocean the *Oronsay* called at Suva, Fiji, where they were entertained by Dr Cohen and Jeff saw some patients. Honolulu was the next port of call, and there they dined with the neurosurgeon Ralph Cloward with whom there was a discussion about the surgery of the neck and Cloward's operation for fusion of the vertebrae in particular. Jeff frequently commented in his diary on the food they had been given, and on this occasion he remarked that they had 'a singularly fine juicy fat turkey'[13]. They reached Seattle on 1st December, where the weather was 'horrid, wet and cloudy'[13]. Here they visited Norma Ritchie, Gertrude's sister, and her violinist husband with whom she was now reunited. He also went to the University laboratories where Warren McCulloch worked—the 'most brilliant & most kindly, most fertile imaginatively. He will throw up 10 ideas, 9 of which will probably be wrong, the 10th brilliant'[13].

From Seattle they flew to Victoria, where they called on old friends, particularly Aggie Renny who was now bedridden, and they saw again the greatly changed places that had been familiar to Gertrude in her youth. 'We were tired—I ought to put that statement down for every day.... We went back to see 835 Pemberton Road where at last after 25 yrs the site is being built upon. 4 small ranch houses are nearly finished'[13]. It was with sadness that they boarded 'the night boat, *Princess Joan*, to Vancouver—we had a de luxe cabin on this old-fashioned boat'[13].

As their train climbed through the Rocky Mountains en route to Halifax, Nova Scotia, Jeff noted that: 'There have been much heavier falls of snow here and its a fairyland of tree trunks we are going through, thickly dusted or coated with snow, such different colours...just marvellous to look at mile after mile'[13]. They broke the journey at Toronto, in order to visit the Botterells, but an attack of abdominal pain put Jeff to bed for a day or so before they could continue on their way to Montreal. From there they travelled by train to Halifax, from whence they embarked on 13th December in the RMS *Carinthia* reaching Liverpool 7 days later, to be met by Michael and his wife Margaret. They had intended to return 'via Boston and New York, but had we done so we should have missed Christmas with the children, and that seemed a pity'[16].

Whereas the records that Jeff kept of some of his visits to America, and even of his return to Russia, are on loose sheets of paper, the diary of his visit to Australia is different[13]. It was written in a University note book with board covers. Also, unlike the others, it was illustrated by postcards and those folded strips of coloured illustrations of cities and places recently visited, which are the ready-made mementoes that mystify those who have not been there and are seldom looked at by those that have been. For whom did he write the diary? It may have been a sense of adventure that made him want to record everything, for his notes on leaving Tilbury make it clear that the journey was for him nothing less; or perhaps he wanted to recall it in tranquility later on, or show it to his friends. It contains not only a daily, or near daily, record of events, but also many of the introspective notes that Jeff could seldom refrain from making. There are also lists of the names of those whom he met, those to whom he owed 'thank-you' letters, and of the many letters sent home and to friends; his children each received a card or letter about once a week, written by one parent or the other. Miss Armistead, holding the fort at home, received no less than seventeen letters and postcards, all but one from Jeff.

We can imagine the satisfaction with which Jeff glued the First Class ticket from the *Oronsay* on one of the pages of his diary, and also the many adulatory cuttings from newspapers; he did not leave out the criticism by the press of the controversial remarks he made in Adelaide. There are notes of the names of books that he read, with brief comments on some of them, such as 'Justin — Lawrence Durrell — pretentious — no good'[13]. There were a few days when he was either too tired or too busy to write; then there would be a summary of the events on several of them, followed by a retrospective daily record. The book tells one much about Jeff, apart from being a very detailed chronicle. It is a concentrate of the characteristics that marked his life. His work, of course, takes pride of place and is happily supported by his enjoyment of travel and his constant willingness to communicate his thoughts and knowledge; his pleasure when things went well shows through, and his delight on being acclaimed wherever he went; even his absent-mindedness is revealed, as well as his poor idea of time; but apparent above all is the desire to record everything, of which the diary is itself a product.

For her part, during the Australian tour and in her rôle as a psychiatrist with an abiding interest in family welfare, Gertrude had discussed her work with doctors and social workers and with members of the press on four or five occasions. She had also talked, mainly to women, on the family problems that she had encountered in Manchester, particularly those concerned with young mothers and adolescents. She had been interviewed on the radio in *Woman's Hour*, had spoken to a group of psychiatrists in Sydney and had discussed the rôle of psychiatry in religious teaching with the Primate of Australia[13]. But Gertrude had not enjoyed the trip at all. Apparently, the only thing that made it worthwhile for her had been the opportunity to see her sister in Seattle and to have had a last glimpse of Victoria which, though much changed, was still beautiful. The journey had, for the most part, been very hot and extremely tiring, and she had been constantly worried about Jeff's heavy programme of engagements. She had also been rather upset by the attentions of the Australian journalists[17]. On arrival home she developed a bad cough and a fever[16].

John Fulton wrote a delightful letter to Jeff at the beginning of December 1957, which accompanied the long essay in which he annually reviewed the year's events with a view to circulating it to his friends at Christmas time. It began: 'Dear Ancient Mariner, Your Cheerful letter of 12th August has gone unanswered because as usual you had gone off on your travels, but I had not quite appreciated that you were on your way round the world. Of course nothing that you do would ever surprise me. I am glad to know that before leaving you took part in the Van Gehuchten Celebrations and that you met that remarkable fellow, the Rector Magnificus, who, as you say, is indeed "an amiable sort of chap". I hope you discovered that he has one of the best private cellars in all of Europe.... Whoever appointed you the first Hugh Cairns Memorial Lecturer had a stroke of genius; I know your tribute will be generous.... Victor Horsley was difficult, but you dealt with this cantankerous fellow as you did with Walshe after he had torn Wilder Penfield to bits'[18]. The last remark refers to a polemical argument between Walshe and Penfield that occupied the medical press for several weeks. This did the reputation of neither of them much good, least of all that of Walshe, who regularly wrote criticisms of papers he had read, and perhaps saw himself as a righter of wrong thinking, the *malleus malefactorum*, as he has been described[19]. However, Walshe's remarks to Penfield had overstepped the bounds of courtesy. The controversy concerned Penfield's map of the localisation of function in the pre-Rolandic gyrus of the cerebral cortex, which he had drawn in the form of an inverted homunculus, with disproportionate features that were magnified according to the extent of the cortical representation of that part. Jeff's letter, to which Fulton referred has, unfortunately, not been identified, for it would have made revealing reading.

With the arrival of another New Year, Jefferson now began the task of editing and sorting certain of his lectures and articles, which he had been planning for some time to republish under the title of *Selected papers*. He told William Sweet: 'I have been having fun reading through, and making some small amendments where necessary, to a bunch of my old papers that are going to be reprinted in book form[20]. I have been more than a little dilatory about this and rather lukewarm, but I became so entranced by some of these old things that I got quite excited! I did not complete the re-read and I am cooling off fast now'[16]. In correspondence with Harry Botterell, Jeff thanked him for sending the *Atlantic Monthly* magazine, which he greatly enjoyed reading, and then turned to the subject of poetry. 'I never disguised its fascination for me from an early age. I still can recite "Little Miss Muffet" as well as bits of Milton and scraps of Keats—"What are Keats?" some Cambridge Rugger Rough is supposed to have said'[21]. He then apologised for the episode of abdominal pain that had disturbed his recent visit to Toronto on the way back from Australia: 'I am fine. So disappointing my Toronto breakdown, but I had, thanks to you, a charming room to have a belly-ache in and that matters'[21].

Occasionally Jeff's letters to Botterell showed evidence of 'letting off steam'. One such occasion followed his reading of the periodical news record of the American Academy of Neurological Surgeons, to whom he had been invited to speak later in the year. 'I have probably for the first time read right through your Academy's "Neurosurgeon" and of all the tripe! All this babble about Hi and Ly and Mom and Dave and Kitty. You personally came out of it well. Nobody but Yanks could indulge in this sort of Gal's gossip and keep a straight face. This is the Visiting Fireman indeed. The impression left on anybody foolhardy enough to overdose himself by reading it right through is one of perfectly horrifying smugness. There is clearly only one world, the American. Such unperceptive dolts! Yet I know that these chaps in the Academy are really intelligent fine chaps. It's this blasted feminine invasion of scientific occasions which I think must be responsible for making this seem to be so mushy, so soft-centred, so exhibitionist. Of course women are marvellous in their right place and you know as well as I where, in detail, that is. Perhaps I have got it all wrong and the "Neurosurgeon" is really a "House Journal" as of United Steel or General Motors — all the slush about Mom and Pop and "our fine kids". Who gives a d... anyway! Lets not talk about it any more. Do you suppose something is wrong with me — could be I suppose? I am feeling fine, its a frosty morning, the sun is streaming in, all is well with the world. I hope that by tomorrow I don't go back on all the foregoing and decide not to send it for fear of hurting your feelings. Today I don't think you would be hurt. Please let me think so tomorrow'[22]. The letter concludes by saying that, unless some financial help was forthcoming, he would not be able to accept Botterell's invitation to the opening of his new department in Toronto in November[22]. Botterell replied, calmly, just over a week later, that 'fair femininity does not encroach upon the scientific or business meeting' of the Academy, and he would see what finances he could find[23].

With the Cairns Memorial Lecture no doubt in mind, Jeff and Gertrude had arranged to visit Lady Cairns at South Stoke. She wrote to invite them to come on 22nd February 1958, but this was not to be[24]. A letter from Gertrude to Harry Botterell explains: 'You will be sorry to hear that Geoffrey had a heart attack on the 14th February and is still in the P.P.H. [Private wing of the hospital]. His condition was complicated by the fact that he had a coincident haemorrhage ?silent duodenal or due to his old diverticulitis. This has made treatment for both conditions very difficult, especially as his haemoglobin has fallen to below 50%. We are all naturally very anxious, but after a blood transfusion on Saturday he definitely improved and everything is better except for the temperature, which we hope will respond to another antibiotic, which I think is now to be streptomycin'[25]. There were some diagnostic misinterpretations at this stage of the illness, as we shall see; Jefferson was now almost seventy-two years old.

The history was that, over a period of 3 or 4 days, Jeff had developed a curious upper abdominal pain which he could not explain, and had felt unwell. He had been used to having attacks of angina for several years, but realised that this was unlike the earlier ones and that therefore there must be some other cause. He had been due to travel to Preston on 14th February on a pastoral visit to the new neurosurgical unit there, but realised while he was dressing that morning that he was not well enough to undertake the journey[17,25].

Jeff's physician colleague, Sir Robert Platt (later Lord Platt, and unrelated to Sir Harry), was away that day, so Gertrude arranged for the Manchester cardiologist Dr Morgan Jones to come to see him. He was immediately admitted to the Private Patients' Hospital at the Royal Infirmary, where he was found to be having a severe gastro-intestinal haemorrhage with melaena. He was grossly anaemic, with a red cell count of 'about two million' (per cubic millimetre) or less than a half the normal amount, and a haemoglobin at the dangerous level of 'less than 6 grams' (per litre). There was a consultation between Sir Robert Platt and Dr Morgan Jones, who were now joined by Dr Henry Taylor, a gastro-enterologist. They concluded that Jeff's heart was in too poor a state to allow him to be transfused with the volume of whole blood that would be necessary to replace the amount he had lost, for fear of overloading the circulation and putting further strain on the heart. So he was given small quantities of packed red cells over a period of 10 days. During the early part of this treatment his haemoglobin level dropped even further, and there were real fears that he might not recover. However, the bleeding gradually stopped and, very slowly, Jeff's condition began to improve. He was not given a barium x-ray of the stomach, which was almost certainly the source of the blood loss, for fear of starting another haemorrhage[17,25]. All this of course took place when there were no flexible gastroscopes, all the appropriate instruments at that time being rigid and large in diameter, and it was long before the days when gastro-endoscopy was to become a relatively minor, and much more informative procedure.

Jefferson wrote to Botterell: 'Scarcely had I put down my pen from writing that last letter to you when I followed it with something acute that turned out to be a bad duodenal haemorrhage [sic] with a consequential heart attack. I have been in the P.P.H. now under the physicians these last $2\frac{1}{4}$ weeks, having packed cell transfusions. Whether I shall ever be any good again remains to be seen, but I seem to be alright today.... I must say I'm getting better fast Hb 78 now'. This last part of the letter was in very unsteady writing. There followed a postscript from Gertrude, explaining there had been a delay in posting the letter because Jeff had not been supposed to write or dictate[26].

Jefferson's colleague, William Brockbank, wrote that 'Sir Robert Platt has recorded that he was a wonderful patient, not because he was ever likely to do as he was told, or because he would ever give a wholly truthful account of his symptoms, but because to visit him and steer him through a serious illness was a great experience'[27]. For example, he recalled that they were once discussing ageing, and Sir Robert had said 'that the realisation of ageing was liable to come upon one quite suddenly'. Jeff replied, '"Yes Robert, all the things you are going to do which are important, and then, quite suddenly, you realise that the time has gone, and you say to yourself, 'So that was it, was it, this thing we call life. Is that all it was?'"[27,28]*.

Jefferson was in hospital for a month, and it took him another 4 or 5 weeks to achieve a reasonable degree of recovery. Later, he described how, following that illness, he had become severely depressed. Indeed several months were to pass before he had completely regained his normal equilibrium.

The Cairns Memorial Lecture was to have been given by Jeff at the London Hospital on 14th March 1958 but, inevitably, it had to be postponed. In due course, Botterell wrote to say how delighted he was to hear of the progress that Jeff was making[28], and by 20th May Elizabeth Armistead was able to report that he was very much better and now working again. He had lost some weight but looked his old self once more[29]. The University of Toronto had agreed to fund his visit to the opening of the new unit there, due to take place on 8th November, and there might also be funds to allow him to go to Boston and Philadelphia. Jeff was never very willing to give up a chance to travel.

Looking back, it seems certain that the cause of the haemorrhage was aspirin. That it could produce devastating gastric bleeding was not recognised at that

---

*Is that all it was? Elsewhere Lord Platt records a slightly different version of the conversation, although the sense is the same: 'All the time life is in front of you, leading you on. It is the things you are going to do which matter. Then, quite suddenly, you realize that the time has gone, and you can say to yourself "so that was it, was it? This thing we call life. Is that all it was?"'. (Platt R. Annual address as President of the Royal College of Physicians London: Royal College of Physicians, 1961 and Private and controversial. London: Casell, 1972: 174.).

time, and there is good supporting evidence for the diagnosis. Jeff had used aspirin to control his attacks of angina and also to moderate the pain of intermittent claudication caused by arterial insufficiency in his left leg, the one which had previously swollen during a long journey. He himself had noticed for some time that the peripheral pulses in that limb had vanished, and he had also told his son Michael, in the early 1950s, that he had found an aspirin at bedtime was an excellent way of avoiding having to get up at night to pass water, presumably because his sleep was then undisturbed by pain. There can be no doubt that he had been consuming a fair amount of the drug for one reason or another[17].

By July, Jefferson had decided that he was well enough to undertake the journey to North America, and he wrote to various people in connection with the visit. First among these was Harry Botterell, the opening of whose new unit in Toronto had initiated the plan, an event that would, to Jeff, have been the greatest possible incentive. He accepted an invitation to stay with the Botterells from November 5th to 8th but, although finance was offered for Gertrude to come too, her eye condition would not allow her to do so. As Jeff wrote: 'I am not sure whether Duke-Elder will let her fly across'[30]. Jeff and Gertrude had attended a garden party at Buckingham Palace during the second week of July, after lunching at the American Embassy with Betsey Whitney, who was Cushing's daughter, and her husband John Hey Whitney the United States Ambassador. To conclude an eventful day, they had tea at the Ritz Hotel and 'drove away with Charles Laughton and Elsa Lanchester in their Bentley'[30]. Jeff then spent $2\frac{1}{2}$ days fishing in Wales, '2 of them too wet to be of the least use'[30].

Another letter to Botterell explained that he would be accompanied by his daughter Monica on his visit to Toronto. Having married, she was now Mrs Bruce-Gardner. They would sail from Liverpool on the Canadian Pacific liner *Empress of England* on 24th October. 'I'm up to the eyebrows in Hugh Cairns. I have to give his Memorial Lecture.... I'll have to write my Toronto paper in the ship'[31].

In his acknowledgement of that letter, Harry Botterell unfortunately left out the hyphen and inserted an "i" in Gardner. The following riposte was hardly merited by the unintentional mistake: 'Thanks for bringing me up to date in the <u>Vaguest</u> way about the meeting. I've no idea what time the Function is on the Wed. & I suppose it is in the Hospital, how long is the opener and how long any others speak, on these important things I have no information at all.... And look here, Major Bottlewell, my daughter's name is Monica Bruce-Gardner—note hyphen and no i in Gardner—please Bottlewell'[32].* In his reply, Botterell gave as good as he had received: 'My dear Professor:- Father of Michael, Father of Antony and Father of MONICA BRUCE-GARDNER and, as Damon Runyon would quote in the contemporary soda-fountain jargon, heavy on the hyphen and skip the "i". Margaret and I and Miss Garrow are most depressed, but you must never say anything bad about my writing again, bad as it is...'[33].

---

*Bottlewell. This was what the Jefferson's cook, Bridget, called Botterell. She thought he was 'a very nice man'. The rank of major given to him by Jefferson was a demotion from Botterell's previously held status of Lieutenant Colonel.

Concerning daughters, the Botterells had a daughter named Jocelyn who was an accomplished ballet dancer, known to Jeff as Olga Petrovna. They had met on several occasions and, with obvious affection, he frequently asked to be remembered to her. With the possibility in mind of meeting Jocelyn again in Toronto on this next visit, he wrote to the famous prima ballerina, Tamara Karsavina, telling her of the ballets in which he had seen her dance during the dramatic years of 1916 and 1917. He, apparently, had asked her one or two questions in this letter, which produced a delightful hand-written reply: 'Your letter rang so many bells in my memory. How well you remember Petersburgh [sic] (I will call it so) and I can see you loved its beauty. To me of course it is still so. I am only too glad if I can help you remember the dancers you want'[34]. There followed a list which included Nijinsky, Fokine, and the names of the ballets danced by Karsavina herself. 'Thank you for remembering those years you spent in Petersburgh with affection'[34]. Jeff enjoyed giving a copy of this letter to Jocelyn.

During October he addressed the nurses of the Manchester Royal Infirmary at their annual Prize Giving Ceremony. His message was a model for a talk of this kind. After the more expected remarks, he thanked the nurses for choosing to go to that hospital to learn their profession, and for the quality of the service that they had given. This was a timely reminder that nurses in training are the essential core of the nursing staff, to whom patients and the medical profession owe their gratitude. He ended, 'You must have many memories of much happiness and of some frustrations perhaps, but joy in some degree is never far away when a lot of young people are together.... Learn to endure with courage what you can't mend but bring honour to your profession'[35].

On 22nd October 1958, the day before he was due to sail across the Atlantic yet again, Jefferson gave the postponed first Sir Hugh Cairns Memorial Lecture at the London Hospital[36]. Speaking about his friend and colleague was not a very difficult task, but there had been problems concerning the extent to which Cairns had been responsible for influencing Lord Nuffield in the founding of the Oxford Medical School, and the degree to which others had designed the form which it finally took. Jefferson had a lengthy correspondence with several of the important people who had been involved, but it was left to him to draw his own conclusions from slightly conflicting evidence. Lady Cairns also put her point of view quite strongly in several letters. In the end he left the matter open. There was no doubt of the vital role that Cairns had played. But, he said, '... it is extremely difficult to apportion credit fairly when looking back over these happenings. Although I think... that Hugh Cairns was the real begetter of the final scheme, it would be very odd indeed if it were quite so virtuoso a solo performance as it probably appears to those who did not know who was who in those days'[36]. Jeff's tribute was heartfelt, and therefore very much in sympathy with the feelings of all those who knew and admired the good-looking, ambitious and hard-driving Australian, who had become one of the three pillars on which British neurosurgery was to stand. Cairns' perceptive organisation of the neurosurgical services in the army, the development of crash helmets and Mobile Neurosurgical Units in particular, and also his work with penicillin and on tuberculous meningitis — these Jefferson saw as his memorial, now that those whom he had trained in the manner that Cushing had taught him, were handing on his influence to another generation. The success of the lecture may be judged by the remarks of Lady Cairns, no easy critic, who wrote to Gertrude about 'the splendid and most moving lecture—most moving. He gave it the perfect personal touch…, we were unanimous & deeply grateful'[37]. A very warm letter was also received from Sir Charles Symonds, in which he ended by saying: 'It was good to see and hear you in your very best form. Curb your indomitable spirit on this next tour and take care of yourself for the sake of your friends for whom there is no one who could replace you'[38].

On 23rd October 1958 Miss Armistead reported to Harry Botterell: 'I have just seen Sir Geoffrey off at the train. He was in excellent spirits, and very disgusted because he was five minutes too soon for the train! The last I saw of him he was waving his hat furiously out of the carriage window. Do take care of him and don't let him work too hard'[39]. Jeff had not been able to let his frustration lie quiet for, before leaving Manchester, he had written yet another letter to Botterell: 'I need hardly tell you, with real American laziboneness, no programme has arrived here, nor will until I am on the ocean—if then. I have no idea who the officers of the Academy are nor who the President is—Jess Harriman [Herrmann] I daresay. I suppose I should know what he is famous for. I think I threw away the "House Magazine" of the Academy so I don't know who its members are…. I am very sorry that we shall miss The Party, it is a bit of a perisher travelling overnight and arriving Toronto so early. If there is anything on Thursday evening I shall not go. You have no idea how tiresome I can be. It was, as I think I told you, those transfusions of female blood that have made me moody, easily hurt above all, jealous and unloved without constant assurances to the contrary—certainly needing constant attention and flattery. It will be lovely to see you. Monica is in a state of vertiginous delight. We sail to-morrow afternoon. Trudie joins in sending her love, its been an act of the most stupendous self-denial for her to stay at home…'[40].

Bridget, the invaluable friend of the family, their cook and general manager of the household, had suffered a stroke. After so many years of selfless support she was no longer there for the family to lean on. In order to keep things running, for she could not have managed to do it herself, Gertrude asked a doctor's widow named V– to come as housekeeper, companion and cook; the Jeffersons still retained a 'cleaning lady' at this time. Gertrude's separation from Jeff by the visit to Toronto and onwards, meant that letters passed between them once more. She wrote: 'Today V. has started with me on clearing up the sewing-room. We have already done something and I am sure she is going to be a tremendous help to me. I have been trying to remember what you asked me to do about your manuscripts'[41]. Jeff had left some which needed to be typed and to have slides made. Gertrude had little more than routine news to pass on: 'I stayed in bed this morning until lunch time—egged on to do this by V. and found it very pleasant. This afternoon has been tiring as I had a couple of patients after the Centres and am now waiting for dinner'[42]. Jeff had written a most loving letter to her, which she greatly appreciated: 'All that you say to & about me I reciprocate & multiply'[43]. Events in the following months would make these few communications between them very poignant. Her need to rest and her unfamiliar exhaustion may have been the earliest signs of a worsening illness, presaged by her impaired vision. 'I am having a nice rest from getting up in the morning, putting out the milk bottle at night & being responsible for the telephone. Neither you nor Monica need worry about me'[43]. As Jeff said at that time, 'I think it is really true, that she does not worry about herself. She's always been very nervous and worried greatly over anything happening to me, but for herself she's as brave as a lion'[17]. Harry Botterell reassured her about Jeff: 'I am really quite determined that he shall do things gently in Toronto for a few days and, I hope, enjoy himself even without you'[44]. He had cancelled an arrangement for Jeff to visit Chicago.

The meeting of the American Academy of Neurological Surgeons was held from the 6th to 8th November in Toronto, and had been arranged to coincide with the opening of the new Neurosurgical Unit at the Toronto General Hospital on the last day, when Jefferson spoke on neurosurgery *Then and now* and, later, repeated the Cairns Memorial lecture at a staff meeting. While he was there he went to see the spinal unit at Sunnybrook Hospital and called at another hospital as well. The visit was much appreciated by Harry Botterell, who wrote later: 'You must know how much you have done for the Botterell's this last week and that without you our celebration would have been a poor thing. In fact, under Ken McKenzie's banner [the most senior neurosurgeon in Canada at the time] and your leadership, with Dr Penfield's support, I believe great things have been achieved for the General Hospital and the University, not just in Neurosurgery but for the clinical departments at large'[45]. It is not clear where else Jeff went before returning home, but as he travelled via Montreal, he would certainly have visited the Penfields. He did not go on to Boston and Philadelphia. A future visit, to Los Angeles, was already being planned.

Monica had returned ahead of Jeff, who now was consequently unaccompanied, much to Gertrude's distress. Furthermore, she wrote in a letter to him: 'I am very upset today because Miss A rang up to say, also you never mentioned it to me yourself, that you are planning to go to Liverpool on Thursday next week. I feel after all my anxiety for $5\frac{1}{2}$ weeks that I couldn't bear this.... Then there is Sheffield I hear the following Monday. Do please have pity and don't go to Liverpool. Miss A says to tell me [sic, you] I shall have to go to London alone on Friday 5th Dec. This too I can't face.... A frightful moan this I know but Thursday for Liverpool is the last straw. Please forgive me for this misery'[46]. The tone of that letter must be regarded as a sign of unusual distress on Gertrude's part. She seldom expressed her feelings so strongly and their separation while Jeff was abroad may not have been the only reason for it. The earlier references to staying in bed, her dependence on V— and the loss of Bridget may all have pointed to a degree of recognition by her of her own increasing disability and new signs of further problems ahead. One wonders whether or not Jeff did actually go to Liverpool that Thursday after he returned home from Canada; we do not know.

On 23rd January 1959 Jeff wrote a note to Harry Botterell, saying he was sending him a copy of *Autumn gleaning*, an autobiography by Sir Henry Dale. 'After last Friday's MRC meeting...I went to Sadler's Wells to hear *Eugene Onyegin*. It was a first rate production and a joy to me to hear after so very many years. It is my favourite, there are so many lovely airs in it, like Lenski's aria before the duel in which he is killed.... I wonder whether...you have to be deeply and hopelessly in love, as I was, to have it seep into your tissues? News on the home front—nothing good. Poor old Bridget died two weeks ago and was buried, bless her, on a brilliant frosty day...the helper and friend for nearly 20 years of ourselves. You will be sorry. Trudie has got a nice woman living with us as a sort of companion because her (Trudie's) legs have gone funny, loss of power and unsteadiness.... She can get about fairly well with a stick for confidence but if she sinks to the floor it takes her ages to get up again. This, Harry, is secret, at least the cause is. She takes it with the greatest good humour, pointing out the difference between facing a difficulty that may get worse and worrying about it. So she says she is not worrying. I don't think she is either. She is still doing her work, but what with her defective vision (she can still read easily) and her poor legs, she is on the verge of retiring from driving a car, even in daylight. I am telling you this because you are one of my closest friends.... Better not to refer to it except lightly in reply'[47].

A week later Jeff told Antony: 'Your Mum has been seen by Ferguson [neurologist] who advises her entry to MRI preferably to his ward for tests.... Walshe, who is coming here for a lecture on Friday 13th. will have a look at her that day or next. She is fine generally and in high spirits. She is scarcely appreciably wobblier on her feet than she was a month ago'[48]. No firm diagnosis was made.

Gertrude was also seen, a month or two later, by Sir Charles Symonds, who commented particularly on the vascular changes in her eyes and felt that other similar cerebrovascular deficiencies were responsible for her condition. He wrote: 'I have been thinking about Trude and Los Angeles and how I would feel about it myself. I don't believe the journey would do her any harm. But where would you be staying? And who would be with her when you are out and about?... We have got to face the fact that she is at risk of a stroke. I don't myself think its at all a large one. My impression is that when there is generalised cerebral atheroma, strokes don't usually happen. Only if it did happen you'd be in a bit of a fix. There is not only the problem of delay in your return home but the appalling expense of illness in the U.S.A..... Trude obviously wants to go, knowing that these excursions are the breath of life to you.... Wouldn't it perhaps be best if you were to take Monica with you? Of course what Los Angeles should do is to ask me to come too with Peggy [Lady Symonds] to look after us both! It would be fun to strike sparks out of one another'[49].

Jefferson passed the sad news of Gertrude's incapacity on to William Sweet in a letter at the end of March: 'I haven't told you, although it has been on my mind for weeks to do so that poor Lady J has so much difficulty she is unsafe by herself. Sir Charles Symonds thinks that it is an apraxia of vascular origin because both legs are affected with no pyramidal signs. The use of her hands is little diminished though her hand-writing has altered a lot and her memory is a bit affected.... It started just after I got home last December, maybe a trifle before. I can't tell you how worrying it is and how profoundly it has already affected my life and, oddly, my thinking and desire to do things.... It looks most horribly as if her travelling days are over'[50].

Working on his book could have been of help to Jefferson during these anxious months. His *Selected papers* were in fact published in the following year, 1960[20]. It is the best and most accessible record of his written work. On 11th June 1959, he spoke to the Merseyside Epileptic Association in Liverpool, when he gave an explanation of the nature of epilepsy and its implications; the talk was aimed at a lay audience[51].

On 1st July Jeff was able to tell Botterell that 'Monica's Mum has been a bit better on her legs this last few days', but that 'this only means that she steps out a bit better from room to room with still a great deal of support. Left standing she would fall over in no time.... Her conversation is minimal, she replies to questions or remarks, she reads very little, memory very patchy. Still she enjoyed greatly a visit from Betsey Cushing [Whitney]'[52]. Six weeks later, he wrote further that Gertrude was going to a Convalescent Home, accompanied by V—, while he himself went to Copenhagen by sea and train for a meeting and then on to Stockholm, where the occasion of Olivecrona's retirement was to be marked. After that he intended to take the opportunity, whilst Gertrude was being cared for away from home, for a brief visit to Grange-over-Sands for a short break at the seaside. He continued: 'I had what the physicians thought might have been a coronary, a very little one, and they told me not to go nowhere for a month. I did not believe them and do not, but I admit that I was very tired and I have taken no special notice of this advice. However, I don't go into full action again until October'[53]. He was 'carrying on with the MRC' until December. 'I feel very lost with Trudie so disabled'[53], he added. Jeff had suffered that heart attack about the middle of June, and had mentioned it to his friend Botterell in his letter of 1st July, when he had written that he had 'a queer pain behind the sternum during a MRC meeting, lasted for hours, 2 weeks ago and again next day. ECG shows something apparently—advice, stay home a month, but that's rubbish. Please don't refer to this writing home'[52]. He hoped that they would be able to meet in Copenhagen, and this was confirmed when Botterell wrote to say that he would arrive there with his daughter Jocelyn on 30th August[54]. They did manage to see each other and Jeff then continued his journey to Sweden, though it was noticed that he did not look well. Botterell wrote: 'Petrovna [Jocelyn] and I had such a delightful time in Copenhagen with you. We both hope you survived Stockholm'[55].

But this was not a happy time for Geoffrey and Gertrude. They spent part of the winter of 1959 with Antony and Eirlys, his wife, in Sheffield, and Christmas with Michael and his wife Margaret in Birmingham. There was now even further deterioration in Gertrude's ability to walk, she lacked spontaneous conversation and was clearly also failing in other respects, a process which was to continue during the following months. The diagnosis of a multifocal vascular encephalopathy seemed more and more likely, with a prognosis that gave no hope of any improvement. It was the beginning of a terminal illness.

REFERENCES

GJ=Geoffrey Jefferson; EHB=Harry Botterell; GMJ=Gertrude Jefferson
1   GJ to Sweet WH. Letter 29th January 1957.
2   Willink H to GJ. Letter 28th February 1957.
3   GJ to Willink H. Letter 4th March 1957.
4   GJ to Sweet WH. Letter 29th January 1957.
5   Phillips C to GJ. Letter 20th February 1957.
6   GJ to Sachs E. Letter 28th February 1957.

7   GJ. MS Diary notes March 1957.
8   *The reticular formation of the brain. Henry Ford Hospital, Detroit, International Symposium 1957.* London: Churchill, 1958.
9   Jefferson G. Sir Victor Horsley — his life and work. *BMJ* 1957; **1**: 903–910 and *Selected papers.* London: Pitman Medical, 1960: 150–69.
10 Speech by the Deputy Orator of Cambridge University, 13th June 1957.
11 GJ. MS Speech, *Homage to Arthur van Gehuchten,* 28th July 1957.
12 Cairns B to GJ. Letter 15th July 1957.
13 GJ. MS *Diary of Australian tour,* 1957.
14 Duke-Elder S to GJ. Note undated October 1957.
15 Duke-Elder S to GJ. Note undated October 1957.
16 GJ to Sweet WH. Letter 10th January 1958.
17 Jefferson M. Personal communication.
18 Fulton J to GJ. Letter 4th December 1957.
19 Critchley M. *The ventricles of the brain.* New York: Raven Press, 1993: 198.
20 Jefferson G. *Selected papers.* London: Pitman Medical, 1960.
21 GJ to EHB. Letter 17th January 1958.
22 GJ to EHB. Letter 10th February 1958.
23 EHB to GJ. Letter 19th February 1958.
24 Cairns B to GJ. Letter 10th February 1958.
25 GMJ to EHB. Letter 25th February 1958.
26 GJ to EHB. Letter 3rd March 1958.
27 Brockbank W. *The honorary Medical Staff of the Manchester Royal Infirmary (1830–1948).* Manchester: Manchester University Press, 1965.
28 EHB to GJ. Letters 15th and 29th March 1958.
29 Armistead E to EHB. Letter. 20th May 1958.
30 GJ to EHB. Letter 17th July 1958.
31 GJ to EHB. Letter 23rd September 1958.
32 GJ to EHB. Letter 11th October 1958.
33 EHB to GJ. Letter 20th October 1958.
34 Karsavina T to GJ. Letter 31st October 1958.
35 GJ. MS Speech for the Nurses' Prize-giving, 1958.
36 Jefferson G. Memories of Hugh Cairns. *J Neurol Neurosurg Psychiat* 1959; **22**: 155–66.
37 Cairns B to GMJ. Letter 23rd October 1958.
38 Symonds CP to GJ. Letter 23rd October 1958.
39 Armistead E to EHB. Letter 23rd October 1958.
40 GJ to EHB. Letter 23rd October 1958.
41 GMJ to GJ. Letter 26th October 1958.
42 GMJ to GJ. Letter 28th October 1958.
43 GMJ to GJ. Letter 29th October 1958.
44 EHB to GMJ. Letter 28th October 1958.
45 EHB to GJ. Letter 17th November 1958.
46 GMJ to GJ. Letter 24th November 1958.
47 GJ to EHB. Letter 23rd January 1959.
48 GJ to Jefferson A. Letter 31st January 1959.
49 Symonds CP to GJ. Letter 7th March 1959.
50 GJ to Sweet WH. Letter 31st March 1959.
51 Jefferson G. *The nature of epilepsy.* Abridged in the Bulletin of the Merseyside Epileptic Association of Liverpool. January 1960.
52 GJ to EHB. Letter 1st July 1959.
53 GJ to EHB. Letter 15th August 1959.
54 EHB to GJ. Letter 20th August 1959.
55 EHB to GJ. Letter 31st September 1959.

Chapter 24

A clouded sunset
1960–1961

Sweet, in an endeavour to offer some hope, had written to Jefferson suggesting that the condition of normal pressure hydrocephalus might be the source of Gertrude's symptoms, but the opinions of those who were treating her were against a surgical diagnosis, a vascular explanation of the condition being thought to be the more likely. Jeff replied on 2nd January 1960 to thank him for his suggestion and to say that there had been no further deterioration and 'though she is no better, she can be got up and down stairs with two people helping and along the flat with my assistance. She is her old charming self except that she does not initiate conversation'[1].

At the same time, it would seem that an irresistible force drove Geoffrey Jefferson to ignore the signs and warnings of his own illness; perhaps it was just a determination to use the life he had been given to the very last quantum. Above all, he would not have been able to face an existence that was not filled by the demands made upon him for lectures and discussion, a life in which his pre-eminence in the sphere of British and international neurosurgery might have diminished. That he was well aware of the transitoriness of human endeavour is clear from various letters that have been quoted, but he may have felt that there was always one more thing to be done, even though he could not achieve everything that he wished to accomplish, and his ability to survive extraordinary hazards had already been demonstrated to his own satisfaction.

Whatever may have been his reasons or excuses, and despite advice and pressure from the family, Jeff accepted the invitation to visit the University of Los Angeles in California, which had been proposed in the previous year. There was no longer any question of being accompanied by Gertrude, and uninhibited by her anxiety, he set forth alone at the beginning of January 1960. In a letter to Sweet he explained that: 'Trude and V., the doctor's widow who looks after her (+daily help) are going to Antony and Eirlys in Sheffield for the $2\frac{1}{2}$ months that I shall be away. That invitation comes as a relief to me, though at the moment there are no alarming signs or symptoms or else I should not be traipsing off to Los Angeles'[1].

Jefferson sailed 'on the slow ship *Brittania*' via Halifax to New York: 'I'm indulging for once in this leisurely travel because there is no deadline at the L.A. end. I arrive when I like.... They expect me to give 3 lectures on Descartes and write a lengthy foreword to a translation of his *Traité de l'Homme*'[1]. When the ship was within sight of the Statue of Liberty, on 20th January 1960, Jefferson realised that he was in the grip of a severe coronary infarction and that he was having no ordinary anginal attack. Fortunately, he was due to be met at the quayside by the New York neurosurgeon, Tom Hoen, and a kinder or more generous person he could not have found. Dr Hoen arranged for Jeff to be admitted immediately to the private pavilion of the Lenox Hill Hospital, where he came under first class cardiological care[2].

For once, Jeff did not describe his symptoms and the events surrounding them to Harry Botterell; he was too ill to do so. When he was able to write, 12 days after the coronary occlusion happened, it was to tell his friend that he was about to move from the hospital into the Hoen's apartment. 'My convalescence is so far advanced...that it is a bit of a bore alone in here. I've no pain and no symptoms so that, unless Zeus is grinning behind a cloud all over his fat face, holding a rock he plans to throw at me, I am in the clear. This can be the optimism of ignorance but by Friday I expect the cards will have been laid face upwards by my Doc'[3]. Then there followed the extraordinary news, which serves to emphasise the kindness of the Hoen family: 'Tom Hoen will be having a gastrectomy next week but in spite of that they seem to like to have me around—I can scarcely credit it, but the statement has stood up to some powerful criticism by me'[3]. Jeff named a few visitors he had had, one of whom had brought him soups and desserts. 'Of course I'm on the B. diet, the no salt and anti-cholesterol, but if I find that I continue to dislike it I shall discard it—what's the point in living for ever! Also I'm on a no cigarette diet—or so they think, but you can of course lock yourself in a very small room now and then'[3]. Jeff certainly fell into the category of a 'difficult' patient.

Harry Botterell must have travelled all the way from Toronto to New York to visit Jefferson for, a week after that letter, he wrote to Antony: 'Just a note to tell you that, while your Dad looks really a good deal better than when I saw him in Copenhagen in September, nevertheless I feel sure that he should fly home first class as soon as he has completed his immediate convalescence with the Hoens and Echlins'[4]. This is the first mention of a plan to continue the convalescence with Dr Francis Echlin, another New York neurosurgeon, and his family, to whom Jeff went for 10 days before flying home on 18th February. He was well entertained while he was there. It had been his intention to visit his sister-in-law in Seattle on the way back from California, so he wrote to her to explain that he could not come. In answer, Norma Ritchie said that she and her husband expected that he would visit them in 1961, and also hoped that Gertrude was better, to whom she passed on messages from several of their Canadian friends. Her letter also confirms that Jeff's colleagues had, very generously, taken care of all the medical expenses in New York[5].

Showing, once again, his tenaciousness, Jeff had even offered to continue his journey to the University of California as soon as he was better, but this was refused by JD French, the neurosurgical friend there who would have been his host: 'Your letter to me arrived and all of us here are touched and filled with admiration by your gallant willingness to carry on in spite of your recent illness. Eager as we are to encourage the revised plan for you to come to UCLA at this time, we are unanimous in the conviction that you must not be permitted to do so.... Sir Robert Platt cautioned us about over-taxing a Professor Jefferson convalescent from a bout of diverticulitis, he would incinerate us now if we connived to do anything but encourage Professor Jefferson's complete rest and recovery. And so you see, we have no choice but to await a more propitious time for a visit from you for we are determined to have one'[6].

On his arrival back in England about the 18th of February, Jefferson was met by Michael and planned to stay with him and his wife Margaret in Birmingham for a few weeks in order to complete his convalescence. Miss Armistead greeted Jeff by letter: 'Just a note to welcome you home, a bit earlier than expected, but never mind you are just as welcome.... Your idea of convalescing is very funny, you sound to have been having a wonderful time, what with sculptresses, dinners, ladies taking you out.... Well, Lorne Street furniture has gone to H.B. to-day [from the consulting rooms to High Bank]. I thought I had better get my new office at H.B. fixed up first. There are a few things which haven't gone yet, like pictures.... You are not going to do any work until I get the O.K. from your medical adviser'[7]. It is clear from this letter that Jeff had decided to have fewer consultations on his return home and had given up his Lorne Street rooms; another letter from Miss Armistead refers to the future prospects of patients being seen at High Bank[8].

Gertrude was too ill for her to have any need for a consulting room of her own. Two undated letters that she wrote to Jeff at this time are in pitifully poor hand-writing which wanders all over the paper. They are almost indecipherable, but show clearly that she was well aware of the events that were taking place[9]. She had returned with V— to High Bank by the beginning of March 1960, where she was visited by Miss Armistead, who reported to Jeff that 'Lady J. is very bright, bless her'[10].

However, as soon as Jefferson had returned to England he developed a bad cold. He had travelled from Heathrow airport to London, then spent a night at Maidenhead and, on the following day, reached Birmingham. Very shortly after his arrival there he again suffered from cardiac pain, in consequence of which he was admitted to the Queen Elizabeth Hospital in that city. His sister, Madge, wrote to say that she was glad to hear that they had 'laid on V.I.P. service' for him[11]. Once again, the symptoms abated and he left hospital to continue his stay with Michael on or about the 18th March. He told Botterell that he was 'still getting 3–4 min. attacks, stopped by amyl nitrate [sic]', and reported that Trude was 'quite happy and generally well'[12]. Also that Birmingham University was giving him an Honorary D.Sc in July, 'if he isn't where Massa was'[12]. Fortunately, when the day came, he wasn't 'in de cold cold ground', and the degree was able to be awarded in due course.

A specimen copy of the *Selected papers* had been sent to Jeff while he was in New York, and he had presented it to Tom Hoen. In thanking him, Dr Hoen wrote: 'The first section was sheer delight on first reading, and I found myself tumbling through page after page like a child sating himself with candy on Christmas morning'[13]. There was some delay in producing the full edition, but it was hoped that it would be ready for distribution by the middle of March[14].

In a letter to Sir Harold Himsworth of the Medical Research Council, written at the beginning of May, Jeff mentions that he was able to go out for a quarter of an hour; this remark was intended to show how he had progressed, but it was in truth a measure of the degree of his continuing disability at that time. He remained ever hopeful and told Sir Harold: 'Now I think I can see an end to this blasted coronary business of mine.... I cannot relate these attacks of pain that I get to exercise in particular. A very favourite time for them is when I wake in the morning and then variably during the day. One thing is certain and that is, that they are much less severe than they were and also less frequent.... I can easily stop the pain with a tablet of amyl nitrate [sic].... I should be able to come to

London and sit through a meeting. I am so mad at missing your committee meetings'[15]. Jeff had been awarded the Fedor Krause medal by the Deutsche Gesellschaft für Neurochirurgie, but by 20th May, when he was due to receive it, he was still not fit enough to travel to Groningen, in Holland, for it to be presented at a joint meeting between the German and Dutch neurosurgeons. It was therefore received on his behalf by Michael, who read his father's speech for him. However, Jeff was able to receive his Hon DSc in person at Birmingham University.

Jeff was in correspondence with William Sweet again in August and began by thanking him for his comments on the *Selected papers,* and for telling him 'about the creation of these Research Professorships with a great deal of money attached. I have forgotten how much, but it was enough, enough for anything at all, including mink suspenders...'[16]. Sweet himself may have felt disappointment that such schemes had not been in place earlier on. Jeff also commented on the Royal Society Exhibition in London, which he had apparently been well enough to attend, and at which it had seemed to him that the greatest advances in the medical field had been in immunology and genetics. He had enjoyed a remark by the President (Professor Hinshelwood) who, surrounded by all sorts of chemical analyses, said that the really important research tool wasn't any of that stuff but the human brain. 'Yes, the brain is the thing...'[16]. Using those vast sums of money, Jeff went on to say, would be an experiment in itself, and he pontificated: 'I can't see anything worth the money in clinical medicine'[16]. The Royal Society tercentenary 'made the rather pretentious Queen Sq. centenary seem rather trivial, not historically but in its modern apologists. I think now more than ever I did before that I ought to have gone there and stayed but perhaps I would not have done as much general good as I did. I can't tell. I was happy and the 6 years that I spent part time there were perhaps enough to polish my wits by rubbing against the great neurologists of my time — Kinnier Wilson, Holmes, Charles Symonds, Geo. Riddoch and Greenfield [No mention of Walshe!]. I don't know, William, how the subject came up! I heard ... that you and Mary are going to Japan for a month — "for the land's sake, Massa William where will be next!". I'm very well, my pain has stopped but this cure is very recent. However, I can do all I want. I am not an invalid'[16]. The desire to have been a London consultant was never quite extinguished in him, and it should be remembered, as Michael Jefferson has observed, that 'the lack of competition in his field in Manchester, as opposed to London, allowed his personality to expand and his thoughts to blossom, to make in the last twenty years of his life many valuable contributions, valuable not only medically but in a philosophical and literary sense'[2].

Harry Botterell had returned from a holiday in Greece. In reply to an enthusiastic letter, Jeff wrote: 'Your stimulation by Greece is exciting, you'll know much more about it than I, who was unfortunately never set alight by my 6 years of Greek grammar and Greek history at school. I must have been very badly taught or very resistant to that particular sort of knowledge at that pubertal age'[17]. He recalled that he had met Sir Maurice Bowra at the Royal Society. 'He is regarded as the most exciting mind in Oxford, a big, stout vital creature who scintillates with witty sayings and wisdom in general'[17]. At that time Botterell was considering making a new career outside neurosurgery, and Jeff continued: 'I would not object to you accepting a deanship. [He did in fact become Dean at Queen's University, Kingston, Ontario.] I wonder if you'd be really satisfied — the intractability of human nature that you have to deal with, the impossibility of getting rid of some useless, some tiresome people might drive you dotty. You would be excellent in our House of Lords, the debates of which are so good — Yes, a life-peerage would be just the thing.... Trudie is the same — no worse no better, been in this satisfactory R.C. Hospital [St. Joseph's at Chorlton-cum-Hardy] for nearly 3 mos. as she needs 2 people to get her up, bath her, and so on — she is up in a chair all day and sits in the garden'[17]. At this time Gertrude was having frequent attacks of coughing, and the control of her arms was so poor that she could no longer use her hands for eating or drinking. Though her legs were not spastic, she had no movement in them. She was hardly responsive at all to conversation, disregarded the presence of her family or the television, and made no spontaneous remarks. Yet she looked well in a general sense, well nourished and facially 'just like her normal self as we'd known her for years past'[2].

Jefferson's life at High Bank must have been very depressing. In October he gave an address to the nurses of Cheadle Royal Hospital, which was very much on the same lines as the one he had given at the Manchester Royal Infirmary in the previous year. He also spoke to the Southport Medical Society on *Changing interests in neurosurgery*.

Then, in November 1960, he went to Blackpool for a convalescent holiday, with V— as his 'minder-housekeeper'. Her services had no longer been needed to look after Gertrude since her admission to hospital in May, but there was still High Bank to run and Jeff to care for, so she had stayed on. Michael and Margaret Jefferson received a long letter from Blackpool. Jeff had greatly appreciated the meals which Margaret had prepared while he was staying in Birmingham after his return from the United States, hence the reference in the letter to cooking and eating, for she enjoyed making dishes from *Larousse Gastronomique* and other sources of inspiration. The letter was addressed to Margaret, though he had told V— that he was writing to Michael. 'I thought it would be more fun to write it to the little woman', he remarked in a postscript[18].

The letter began by describing how the hotel in which he was staying in Blackpool had been recommended by a colleague who had been at school with the proprietress: 'He used to sit next to her and crib from her at school. As he laid the ground bait for us we have VIP treatment, 2 rooms and a nice private sitting room thrown in. The food here is excellent and I get greedier and greedier every day. Do tell me what you are cooking and eating, and I expect you have already read all the new novels that are available, sitting in that lovely flagged kitchen of yours. We have been lucky with the weather so far, apart from one day when there was the worst storm since 1933, but that was gone in no time. The weather is breezy and the air bracing. I get out for health giving little walks of a few hundred yards and rest in strategically placed concrete nooks. Otherwise I mostly sit and think, or just sit. Its a wonderful place, a real Xanadu laid out flat. I've been to one movie only — *Inherit the Wind* — about the heresy trial [concerning the rejection of Darwinism in an American country town] superbly done with Spencer Tracy as a marvellous defence lawyer.... Of course I remember the real thing very well but I forget the date and where it was except the South, but not the deep South. V. says I look extraordinarly well, not a day over $72\frac{1}{2}$ or 73, but she may be exaggerating [he was actually $74\frac{1}{2}$]. Its doing me so much good I'm going to stay on till Sunday week'[18].

In this letter Jeff also gave some details of his various occupations in Blackpool, other than reading and going for little walks. One day he had managed to make the journey to Manchester by train to see Gertrude, and had finally tinkered with an unpublished lecture from 3 or 4 years earlier, entitled *The applied physiology of sleep*, which he sent as a promised contribution to a book edited by Hugh Garland[19]. One wonders what his thoughts may have been when he prefaced that paper by a quotation from Shakespeare's *Antony and Cleopatra*: 'Unarm, Eros; the long day's task is done, and we must sleep'[20]. Despite this possibly introspective prefix, the paper is scientific and not philosophical. It is concerned with theories of the mechanism of sleep and what Magoun called the 'waking brain'[21]. Jeff was thinking about accepting an invitation from the CIBA Foundation to visit Switzerland in January 1961, though, wisely, it seems that he did not in fact do so.

When Jefferson returned to Manchester he wrote to Paul Bucy, a very well-known neurosurgeon working in Chicago: 'At long last I seem to be stabilised and able to do much more. I am seeing the odd patient and writing letters'[22]. He had officiated in his capacity as chairman of the Manchester Branch of the English Speaking Union, and even remarked that he intended to go to a meeting in Washington later in the year, no doubt with the idea of continuing the journey to Los Angeles, Seattle and Toronto.

High Bank continued to be a lonely place. There is a touching letter from Jefferson to Botterell, written on 13th January 1961: 'We were ourselves able to have Trudie home for 3 days from St. Joseph's at the New Year.... She seemed to perk up a lot, or perhaps it was just chance that her limbs were in a good phase. Her limbs are stiffer than they were.... The condition remains quite painless. This week she was home this Monday but had a cold and that has got worse so that she cannot come this Friday. We were having her home two days a week for a treat.... Thanks for telling me about Petrovna. She is a real companion now isn't she? I bet you enjoyed her birthday party as much as she did. I do not remember a 21st birthday party for myself. We probably had a dance around about that time, but not a trace remains.... I have just reviewed Russell Brain's book on "Genius" for the Daily Herald. It is very interesting really with 5 studies, of the great Dr Johnson, Jonathan Swift and others'[23]. He asked if Harry Botterell had seen any reviews of the *Selected papers*, and continued: 'I had a bad attack of pain in my chest, with vomiting, one evening a week ago and that has upset everything badly. I am to be confined to one floor of the house for 3 weeks. Although I don't feel any different they say there is slight extension of myocardial damage. There is still no evidence of thrombosis of a vessel of major importance, so I do not despair of coming across in October. The M.R.C. is giving a Complimentary Dinner to the Earl of Limerick and me for our work as Chairmen. It was to have been held next week but because of this recent attack of mine they have had to put it off until May, a very great pity because as time passes it rather loses its point. I am very depressed about that. It would have been a remarkable collection of medical FRSs raising their glasses. Miss Armistead is getting sick of doing this letter although she is as you know, very interested in all that both you and I do. My love Harry boy and the same to Maggie'[23]. It was Jeff's last letter to Harry Botterell, it was also the last letter that Elizabeth Armistead typed for him. The sands were running out of a long partnership and Jeff did not realise, when dictating this letter, that she too was unwell.

A fortnight later, during the evening of Saturday 28th January 1961, Geoffrey Jefferson was admitted, after a serious heart attack, to the Manchester Royal Infirmary under the care of Sir Robert Platt. Miss JW Charleton remembers that the nursing report that night quoted Jeff as having said to him: 'No heroics, Robert'[24]. On the following morning he was seen again by his doctor, after a night of cardiac pain. Jeff greeted him with the words: 'I always feel I ought to think up something to cheer up my physician, but this morning I must confess I find it pretty difficult'[25]. When doing her round of the medical wards a little later, Miss Charleton came to Jefferson's bedside. 'After a few words about his condition and anything that he needed, he said, "I think I'm a little short of air; could you lift me a little higher up the bed?" '[24]. With the assistance of a nurse she then lifted him to a more upright position. She remembered that 'he smiled and thanked us, then taking hold of my hand, he closed his eyes & within minutes he passed peacefully away. During many years of nursing I do not think I have ever witnessed a patient who passed away so calmly & peacefully'[24].

Miss Armistead herself had been admitted to the Infirmary with bronchopneumonia, and she recalled in a letter: 'I had been in a week when the Sister told me Sir G. had been admitted to the next ward. He had got over so many serious illnesses I thought he would get over this, but it was not to be. He came in at 5pm. Saturday & died at 10 o'clock Sunday morning [29th January 1961]. I was heart broken as you can imagine. He died in the hospital he had done so much for.... I went 3 half days a week to High Bank & I could see him slowly failing, but he put up such a brave fight.... I am proud to have worked for him for nearly 34 years'[26]. She herself was to die in the following year.

On 30th January, the day after Geoffrey Jefferson's death, Michael and his wife went to visit Gertrude at St. Joseph's Hospital. They told her of the events of the weekend. Her clinical state at this point was not noticeably different and she did not in any way signal that she had received or grasped the message. Antony and his wife went to see her shortly afterwards and they had the same experience. Yet it is clear that at some level of consciousness, there was an understanding which did not require formulation in words; she did realise what had happened, and that her life's work helping, advising, stimulating and loving her husband was now over. She stopped eating, would hardly take anything to drink, and then slipped quietly into a coma which faded into death. Gertrude Jefferson passed away just 12 days after her Geoffrey, on 10th February 1961. Their funeral services were held in Didsbury Parish Church, almost opposite their home, High Bank, where a commemorative plaque has been placed on one of the walls of the church. Each, in their turn, was cremated, and their ashes were scattered in the churchyard, where they lay together on the receptive earth.

And it was as they both would have wished. On 17th February, the Memorial Service at St Ann's Church, Manchester, was for Sir Geoffrey Jefferson and his Lady, Gertrude. The lesson was read by Douglas Northfield, the Secretary of the SBNS, and the address was given by Sir George Pickering, the Regius Professor of Medicine at Oxford University. In it he outlined the career of one of the most outstanding of British surgeons and, in tribute to the excellence of Jeff's writing, almost a third of what he said was by way of quotation from Jefferson's own words. He said he had never known anyone so deeply respected or so widely loved, and we can believe this to be true. Sir George also paid tribute to Gertrude who, as a result of her work in social psychiatry, had established a unique position of her own in Manchester and whose devotion to her husband had survived many anxieties and had remained undiminished by time.

REFERENCES

GJ=Geoffrey Jefferson; EHB=Harry Botterell; GMJ=Gertrude Jefferson

1　GJ to Sweet WH. Letter 2nd January 1960.
2　Jefferson M. Personal communication.
3　GJ to EHB. Letter 1st February 1960.
4　EHB to Jefferson A. Letter 9th February 1960.
5　Ritchie N to GJ. Letter 19th February 1960.
6　French JD to GJ. Letter 2nd February 1960.
7　Armistead E to GJ. Letter 18th February 1960.
8　Armistead E to GJ. Letter 4th March 1960.
9　GMJ to GJ. Letter undated March 1960.
10　Armistead E to GJ. Letter 8th March 1960.
11　Collins M to GJ. Letter 23rd February 1960.
12　GJ to EHB. Letter 25th March 1960.
13　Hoen T to GJ. Letter 25th February 1960.
14　Pitman Medical to GJ. Letter 3rd March 1960.
15　GJ to Himsworth H. Letter 3rd May 1960.
16　GJ to Sweet WH. Letter 8th August 1960.
17　GJ to EHB. Letter 9th August 1960.
18　GJ to Jefferson, Margaret. Letter 10th November 1960.
19　Garland H, Ed. *The scientific aspects of neurology*. Edinburgh: E & S Livingstone, 1961.
20　Shakespeare W. *Antony and Cleopatra*. Act IV. Scene 14.
21　Magoun HW. *The waking brain*. Springfield Ill: Charles C. Thomas, 1959.
22　GJ to Bucy P. Letter 30th November 1960.
23　GJ to EHB. Letter 13th January 1961.
24　Charleton JW. Personal communication. Letter 9th March 1993.
25　Brockbank W. *The honorary Medical Staff of the Manchester Royal Infirmary (1830–1948)*. Manchester: Manchester University Press, 1965: 223.
26　Armistead E to EHB. Letter 8th March 1961.

Chapter 25

Epilogue

The tale is told. Jefferson's comment lingers in the memory — 'so that was it, was it? This thing we call life. Is that all it was'. The words are either an enigma, an understatement or an unconsidered remark. They cannot possibly have been the last, for that would have been completely out of character. They cannot have implied that life had somehow failed to live up to his expectations, for that would have been manifestly untrue; and Jeff was not given to understatement. Nor can he have meant to be dismissive of the considerable pleasure he had in living, as witness his talk *On being happy and liking it*. Furthermore, his achievements were not made without effort. An enigma is what it must remain. An observer, displaced in space and time can, nevertheless, say 'but what a life!'.

Obituaries for Sir Geoffrey Jefferson were written in the specialist and general medical journals of many countries, in addition to those in the daily press, and in the records of the Royal Society and Royal Colleges of Physicians and Surgeons. Such writings usually have the disadvantage of nearness in time, occasionally of reticence, but more often of too much eulogy or even hyperbole. In the case of Jefferson, however, the writers all knew their subject intimately, and knew also that he would never tolerate misrepresentation, a point specifically made by Sir Francis Walshe. Honesty was certainly their endeavour. Yet, even within this bond, each essay, without exception, would have given Jeff pleasure and justifiable pride. The strength and quality of the life they described was apparent in them all. In his own words, written in his maturity: 'So long as a man has accomplished something, it is enough'[1]. He more than fulfilled that modest requirement.

The many lectures and papers written by Jefferson, appear in an almost complete bibliography at the end of Walshe's obituary in the *Biographical memoirs of Fellows of the Royal Society*[2]. As many as possible of those that are missing have been mentioned in this text. Rowbotham summed up this aspect of his many-faceted career very succinctly: 'That he occasionally took himself to the borderlands of revelation and nibbled there must be accepted. That he did not cross the boundary and stay there was equally obvious.... [However, his last major product], the *Selected Papers*, will become more important as time passes. In that he created a masterpiece'[3].

The panorama of Jefferson's clinical interests was outlined by his son Antony, also a neurosurgeon, in a tribute written shortly before the centenary of his father's birth[4]. Though by no means comprehensive, the list is as follows:-

1. Intracranial aneurysms, with special reference to optic nerve compression and compression of nerves in the wall of the cavernous sinus.
2. Pituitary tumours, with particular note of his Sherrington lecture on invasive adenomas.

3. The Tentorial pressure cone, concerning which his papers are a basis of current thought on this important topic.
4. Disturbance of consciousness of brain stem and posterior fossa origin.
5. Compression and/or invasion of the optic nerves and chiasm by gliomas.
6. Radiology, initially of the stomach and then of the nervous system; particularly the paper with EW Twining on the radiology of the third and fourth ventricles.
7. Frontal lobectomy for invasive brain tumours, which he pioneered.
8. Injuries of the head and spinal column, particularly in war.
9. Trigeminal and glossopharyngeal neuralgia and trigeminal neuromas.

Then there are the biographical and contemplative writings, which he referred to as his 'meditations'. They may be read and enjoyed now with as much pleasure as when they were first heard or published. As Tom Morley, the son of

Figure 27 *The Jefferson Memorial Room and Library, Manchester Royal Infirmary, when it was opened in 1971.*

Jeff's friend, wrote: 'With his unerring eye for humbug he knew he was no philosopher in the sense reserved for professional academic thinkers of that title, but with his consuming interest in the tangible and intangible aspects of brain function, his wide reading, and his never ending interest in the lives, experiences and opinions of people from all walks of life, he was unusually well-informed and an ardent lover of wisdom'[5]. Added to this, one has to remember his very personal and lucid literary style, his economy with words and his remarkably logical sequences of thought. There was also a sensitive side to his nature, which showed itself not only in his love of poetry. An example was quoted by a daily newspaper, which mentioned a tall ash tree that grew in the grounds of the Royal Infirmary and was known as 'Sir Geoffrey's tree'. 'He loved it. Every spring he awaited its budding among the bricks and mortar. Every time he visited patients in the ward he would look at it with a pleasure that was almost childlike'[6]. Perhaps it reminded him that away from the grime of the busy city there were trees and moors and the Sussex Downs. Perhaps he was also reminded of the hours he had enjoyed on river banks dreaming of the fish he might have caught but which, for one reason or another, he failed to do so. He had watched that tree in the hospital grounds for half a century.

In January 1964, three years after his death, a public appeal for £50,000 was launched in order to provide a memorial to Sir Geoffrey Jefferson. To quote from the appeal brochure: 'Looking back on Sir Geoffrey's work in the hospital, one great want tormented him, and that was a room where he could think, where he could detach himself from the daily routine of patient care and surrounded by a few books enjoy some undisturbed moments of deep reflection; for this is how new ideas which may change the whole aspect of disease are born'[7]. Thus was the form of his memorial determined. On 30th January the *Daily Mail* newspaper carried a call for support occupying almost a whole page, and headed by the photograph of Jeff's portrait being painted by Sir Gerald Kelly.

A further 7 years later, on 9th June 1971, the Jefferson Memorial Library was opened at the Manchester Royal Infirmary by Sir Harry Platt, Jeff's friend from student days. As many members of the Jefferson family as possible were present among the other honoured guests. In declaring the library open Sir Harry called it 'a symbol of those intellectual values to which Geoffrey was faithful throughout his life of outstanding distinction'; and at the end he said, 'I accept this task with humility, but with deep thankfulness as the last thing I can do for him'[8]. Words which we can but echo.

REFERENCES

1   Jefferson G to Fulton J. Letter 14th August 1942.
2   *Biographical Memoirs of the Fellows of the Royal Society* 1961; **7**: 127–35.
3   Rowbotham GF. In Memoriam, Geoffrey Jefferson, an appreciation. *Br J Surg* 1961; **48**: 586–8.
4   Jefferson A. Sir Geoffrey Jefferson, 1886–1961. *Surgical Neurol* 1984; **22**: 1–4. See also Guthkelch, N. *J Neurosurg* 1987; **66**: 642–7.
5   Morley TP. Sir Geoffrey Jefferson. *Acta Neurochirurgica* 1961; **9**: 718–21.
6   *Daily Mail.* 30th January 1964. p 6.
7   Brochure of the Jefferson Memorial Trust.
8   Platt H. MS Speech at the opening of the Jefferson Memorial Library on 9th January 1971.

My wife asked me not to write the familiar dedication in which the author acknowledges the assistance he has received from his spouse. However, this book would be incomplete without mentioning the invaluable help and criticism given by Susan as each chapter was written and rewritten many times. For this and for her tolerance, I thank her with all my heart.

P H S

Index